FOOD ENGINEERING OPERATIONS

Third Edition

FOOD ENGINEERING OPERATIONS

Third Edition

J. G. BRENNAN, J. R. BUTTERS, N. D. COWELL

Department of Food Science and Technology,
University of Reading, Reading, UK

and

A. E. V. LILLEY

Formerly of the Department of Food Science and Technology,
University of Reading, Reading, UK

ELSEVIER APPLIED SCIENCE

LONDON and NEW YORK

ELSEVIER SCIENCE PUBLISHERS LTD
Crown House, Linton Road, Barking, Essex IG11 8JU, England

Sole Distributor in the USA and Canada
ELSEVIER SCIENCE PUBLISHING CO., INC.
655 Avenue of the Americas, New York, NY 10010, USA

First edition 1969
Second edition 1976
Third edition 1990

WITH 28 TABLES AND 270 ILLUSTRATIONS

© 1990 ELSEVIER SCIENCE PUBLISHERS LTD

British Library Cataloguing in Publication Data

Food engineering operations. —3rd ed.
  1. Food technology
  I. Brennan, J. G.
  664

  ISBN 1-85166-444-0

Library of Congress Cataloguing-in-Publication Data

Food engineering operations / J. G. Brennan... [et al.]. —3rd ed.
  p. cm.
  Includes bibliographical references.
  ISBN 1-85166-444-0
  1. Food industry and trade. I. Brennan, J. G.
  TP370.F62   1990
  664—dc20
                                90-3028
                                CIP

Printed in Great Britain by Galliard (Printers) Ltd, Great Yarmouth

FOREWORD TO THE THIRD EDITION

I am honoured and delighted to be able to welcome the new third edition of this standard textbook on the principles of food engineering. The National College of Food Technology has become well-known and respected, largely through those who have used this textbook, either as students at Weybridge or in other courses taught in countries around the world.

Since the last edition appeared, the National College has merged with the Department of Food Science at the University of Reading and now, as the Department of Food Science and Technology, occupies an excellent, well-equipped modern building on the attractive Whiteknights campus in Reading. This facility, including a versatile modern food processing plant, was largely provided by the generosity of the British food industry, recognising the contribution which has already been made, and will be increasingly needed, to meet the exacting standards of the modern food industry.

The modern consumer wants food to be convenient to use, to be as 'natural' as possible, only minimally preserved and, of course, to be safe. The increasingly international and competitive food industry can only fulfil these needs by employing food scientists, technologists and process engineers who understand and can apply optimal food processing methods, meeting the twin needs of process efficiency and product safety. This third edition of *Food Engineering Operations* will be an essential text for present and future undergraduate students. Today's students will need to purchase their own copies of this book to help establish their personal reference libraries in the demanding years ahead.

Geoffrey Campbell-Platt
National College Professor of Food Technology and
Head of the Department of Food Science and Technology,
University of Reading, UK

PREFACE TO THE THIRD EDITION

In preparing this third edition, the authors have endeavoured to take account of significant changes in processing techniques, equipment design and applications which have occurred since the second edition was published in 1976. Examples of changes made for this edition are: new membrane materials and configurations in Chapter 6; extraction with supercritical CO_2 in Chapter 8; extrusion cooking in Chapter 10; developments in irradiation in Chapter 15 and extension of the discussion of aerobic and anaerobic treatments for waste materials in Chapter 18. The reference lists at the end of each chapter have been updated but some early key references have been retained. In Appendix II the section on unsteady state heat transfer by conduction has been enlarged. A new chapter on 'Pumping in the Food Industry' has been added to complement the chapter on 'Materials Handling'. The importance of packaging in maintaining quality and extending the shelf life of foods has been acknowledged by the inclusion of a new chapter on that topic.

J.G.B.
J.R.B.
N.D.C.
A.E.V.L.

PREFACE TO THE SECOND EDITION

In preparing the second edition, the whole work has been revised and more extended treatments given in some places. New sections have been added, e.g. on membrane separation and thawing, and one new chapter on solid–liquid extraction and expression. However, the guiding principle in this edition has been the same as in the first: to produce an undergraduate textbook giving a basic coverage of the subject and, through selected references, directing the reader's attention to more extensive or detailed treatments of specific topics.

The SI system of units has been used throughout, but in certain circumstances, particularly when discussing topics where these units are not yet extensively used, quantities expressed in SI units are accompanied by their equivalents in more conventional terms.

The authors acknowledge with gratitude the assistance given by Mr I. F. Davison in the preparation of this second edition.

J.G.B.
J.R.B.
N.D.C.
A.E.V.L.

CONTENTS

Contents

APPENDICES

Contents

PART I

PRELIMINARY OPERATIONS

CHAPTER 1

THE RAW MATERIAL AND THE PROCESS

1.1. INTRODUCTION

Food processing is seasonal in nature, both in the demand for its output and in the availability of its raw materials, many of which have to be imported. In common with any other manufacturer the food processor would prefer his raw materials: to be continuously available in sufficient quantity and quality to enable him to operate on a planned year-round basis; to be stable in storage; to be of uniform characteristics and to be of predictable price. In practice few, if any, of these criteria are satisfied and it is the purpose of this chapter to identify the particular raw material requirements of the food industry, to indicate some of the problems of supply and to show how the industry and its suppliers respond to these.

In general, the process suitability (S) of a food raw material is determined by a balanced assessment of its properties such as: its availability (a); its geometric (g), physical (p), functional (f), growth (gr) and mechanical (m) properties and its thermal (t) and electrical characteristics (e), etc. Thus:

$$S = \phi(a + g + p + f + gr + m + t + e + \cdots) \tag{1.1}$$

The relative importance of these factors in their contribution to the suitability index will, of course, vary depending on the raw material, the process applied to it and the end product made from it.

Properties of major importance in the selection of food raw materials are:

(i) *Geometric properties*—shape, shape uniformity, freedom from surface irregularities, unit size, unit weight.

(ii) *Other physical properties*—colour, texture, aero- and hydrodynamic characteristics, frictional and surface properties.

3

(iii) *Functional properties*—flavour, stress resistance, defect level, processability.
(iv) *Growth properties*—growth and maturation characteristics.

1.2. GEOMETRIC PROPERTIES OF THE FOOD

Foods of regular geometry are best suited to high speed mechanised processes. Potato varieties of smooth shape and with shallow eyes are preferred for mechanical peeling and washing. Again, smooth-skinned tomato varieties are more easily washed than ribbed varieties (which also tend to harbour insects such as *Drosophila*). Other examples of shape selection are pigs with long lean backs for bacon and straight runner beans for mechanical snipping (i.e. topping and tailing) and slicing. Thus, shape, uniformity of shape, freedom from surface irregularities and size are important processing indices.

1.2.1. SHAPE
The dimensional relationships of a food unit are important: in packaging; in controlling fill-in weight; in freezing; in canning and other heat processes; and in determining the way in which materials behave during pneumatic conveying and bulk storage.

Measurement of a set of specimens enables the magnitude of the contribution of each dimensional variable to the overall process suitability to be estimated. Griffiths and Smith[1] found that the volume of quartzite pebbles could be estimated simply from the relationship:

$$\log(\text{volume}) = b_1 . \log(\text{major axis}) + b_2 . \log(\text{minor axis})$$

Using this measurement of maximum and minimum dimensions of a representative sample of fruits and vegetables permits estimation of the number or weight of these which will fit into a given container or vessel. Mohsenin[2] describes the application of this technique to the measurement of the volumes of irregularly shaped maize kernels and other foods.

1.2.2. UNIFORMITY OF SHAPE
This is of importance during: filling into containers; conveying; heat treatment; freezing; dehydration; and during sorting and grading operations.

The roundness of biscuits and hamburgers; the sphericity of apples or potatoes; pears which are of uniform pyriform shape and cucumbers of regular fusiform shape are examples of desirable shape-uniformity characteristics. Shape classifications for UK varieties of fruits and vegetables are discussed by Arthey,[3] and Mohsenin[2] describes procedures whereby roundness and sphericity may be measured and lists data for US varieties of apples and other fruits. Information of this type enables the processor to select cultivars for particular purposes.

1.2.3. FREEDOM FROM SURFACE IRREGULARITIES

Clearly, surface projections and depressions occurring in a food unit present cleaning and processing problems. The food industry is relatively labour and energy intensive and raw materials account for a large proportion of the cost of processed foods. Surface imperfections removed either intentionally or during processing contribute significantly to these costs. Specific varieties must be selected or developed to minimise these defects.

1.2.4. SIZE AND WEIGHT OF FOOD UNITS

Optimum dimensions exist for each process and raw materials complying with these specifications must be provided. Whilst sorting (see Chapter 3) can assist in size and weight control, raw materials containing oversize and undersize materials present the processor with economic and disposal problems. Determination of unit weight may be carried out by the use of automatic weighing machines (see Chapter 19) or assessed by manual weighing of representative samples.

Raw materials of uniform size or weight are mandatory in ensuring uniform processing (e.g. heating, cooling, sterilising, etc.) and uniform fill-in weights in containers. Size is important in waste control (e.g. peel- and stone-to-fruit ratios are size dependent), whilst with processes handling individual food units (e.g. peeling or skinning machines) throughput is dependent on unit size.

Sampling and testing of raw materials for size and weight uniformity is essential.

1.3. OTHER PHYSICAL PROPERTIES OF THE RAW MATERIAL

Many physical properties, in addition to geometric properties (Section 1.2) warrant consideration when selecting food raw materials. These include: colour; texture; resistance to mechanical stress; aero- and hydrodynamic properties; frictional characteristics and surface properties.

1.3.1. COLOUR PROPERTIES

In low temperature processes (e.g. freezing or freeze drying), colour changes during processing are minimal, so the colour of the raw material is a reasonable index of its suitability for these processes. In heat processes (e.g. canning and dehydration), the fresh-food colour is not a reliable index of suitability. Thus, some varieties of apples and pears develop a pink tinge on canning, whilst rhubarb and some cherry varieties become bleached due to migration of colour into canning syrups. Again, chlorophyll is converted into brown-green phaeophytin during the heat processing of green vegetables. Potatoes pose special problems; varieties exhibiting minimum browning are necessary for canning or dehydration whereas for potato chip processing, some degree of browning is necessary.

Colour control is best exercised by selecting varieties of known processing performance, by using the correct pretreatment procedures such as blanching (see Chapter 10) and by using process conditions designed to retain the natural food colour. The use of added colourings, preferably those of natural origin, or in the limit, artificial colours in the permitted list[4] may be necessary. Methods of colour sorting are discussed in Chapter 3.

1.3.2. TEXTURAL PROPERTIES

The textural characteristics of the raw material are of great importance. The first requirement is that the raw material must be sufficiently robust to withstand the mechanical stresses to which it is subjected during preparative operations. Secondly, the raw material must withstand the processing conditions so as to yield a final product of the desired texture. Fruit and vegetable varieties with improved mechanical strength have been developed, such as tough-skinned peaches and tomatoes suited to mechanised washing, peeling and sorting. Other examples include the selection of blackcurrant varieties suitable for mechanical strigging (i.e. stalk removal) and pea and bean varieties which will withstand mechanical podding.

The evaluation of textural characteristics is based either on sensory testing using trained panels or on instrumental procedures.[3] The well known Tenderometer, and other machines such as the Maturometer, the General Foods Texturometer (General Foods Corp., N.Y., USA) and the Instron Food Texture Tester (Instron Ltd, High Wycombe, Bucks., England) are typical instruments used in this field. Whilst the correlation between that perceived and that measured is not easy, instrumental procedures are of considerable assistance in the prediction of the behaviour of raw materials during processing.

1.3.3. AERO- AND HYDRODYNAMIC PROPERTIES

Differences in these properties between the desired and undesired parts of a raw material may be used to clean, sort and grade the raw material (see Chapters 2 and 3). In addition, air and water are frequently used to convey, mix and process materials. Thus, aerodynamic and hydrodynamic properties are important raw material characteristics.

Reference to Appendix I relating to fluid flow will indicate that many of the physical properties discussed in this chapter, such as size, shape, uniformity of shape and surface properties are operative in determining how particulate foods behave in fluid flow. Additional material properties involved include density and porosity.

Data regarding these material properties are reported in the literature[5] and the subject of pneumatic conveying is discussed in Chapter 19.

1.3.4. FRICTIONAL PROPERTIES

Before grain can slide down a chute or discharge from a bulk bin the forces of static friction due to interparticle action and particle–wall friction must be overcome. Once the material begins to flow, the coefficient of dynamic friction must be exceeded in order that flow should continue. The friction properties of food materials thus play an important part: in gravity and pneumatic conveying; in flow into and discharge from bulk storage vessels and in mixing operations.

Differences in frictional properties may be used to effect separation of contaminants in cleaning processes (Chapter 2) and to sort out blemished or damaged units from sound material (Chapter 3).

Knowledge and understanding of frictional characteristics of food ingredients are essential for effective processing. Friction theory is discussed briefly in Chapter 19. Detailed treatment is reported elsewhere.[6]

1.3.5. SPECIFIC SURFACE OF FOOD UNITS

This raw material property is important in processes involving gas/solid and liquid/solid reactions such as respiration, extraction, smoking, brining and oxidation. It is also an important economic factor in determining peel and core to fruit or vegetable ratios and washing losses. The specific surface properties of particulate foods are also of importance in fluidised processing and movement (see Appendix I) and in other surface-sensitive phenomena such as: contaminant retention; cleaning; radiant energy transfer (infra-red, dielectric and microwave heating) and in aero- and hydrodynamic transfer.

Surface areas may be determined by peeling followed by measurement of

the peel area using a planimeter. Simple relationships between the surface
area (A) and the weight (W), of the form $A = K_1 + K_2 W$ (where K_1 and K_2
are constants) are available in the literature for varieties of apples, pears
and plums.[2] The specific surface of powders (important in staling and
storage behaviour) may be determined from gas adsorption measurements
using nitrogen or helium.

1.4. FUNCTIONAL PROPERTIES OF FOOD RAW MATERIALS

A raw material of ideal functionality is one which may be processed to give
a first quality product whilst permitting maximum process effectiveness.
Clearly, the functional properties required of a material will vary
depending upon the process to which it is to be subjected.

Many examples of varieties developed for special purposes are common
knowledge, e.g. sheep bred for wool or meat and cattle for meat or milk.
Special wheat varieties yield soft, low protein flour suitable for biscuits and
cakes whilst other, high protein wheats are used for bread flours. Similarly,
the dry solids content of potatoes, which may vary between 16 and 22% is
of great importance to the potato processor and the development of
suitable, high solids content varieties has received much attention.[7]

Selection of raw materials on a functional basis usually involves process-
testing of varieties. In some cases it is possible to assess function by
chemical or physical testing or combinations of these. An example of this is
the evaluation of cereal flours for bread, cake or biscuit manufacture using
specially designed apparatus such as the 'Research' Dough Testing
Equipment (Henry Simons Ltd, Stockport, England) and the Brabender
Farinograph (C. W. Brabender Instruments Inc., N.J., USA). Cultivar
testing is carried out by trade research associations on a regular basis.[8,9,10]

1.4.1. FLAVOUR PROPERTIES

Flavour, perhaps more than any other property, is a matter of personal
preference. In serving a mass market, extremes of flavour must be avoided.
In some cases, the flavour of the processed food is more a function of
additives than of the raw material. Examples of this are the use of strongly
flavoured syrups in some canned fruits and of protein hydrolysates and
yeast extracts in meat soups.

In general, therefore, varieties selected for processing should impart only
flavours which are characteristic of the food and these flavours should be
neither too powerful nor too weak. For these reasons, flavour is of less

importance than other factors (e.g. colour and texture), in determining the suitability of a variety for processing.

1.4.2. RESISTANCE TO PROCESSING STRESSES

Apple varieties vary widely in suitability for processing. Some dessert varieties lose their rigidity on processing and are, therefore, unsuitable. Firm, white-fleshed, acid varieties are preferred for canning and freezing. Again, clingstone peaches have excellent texture when canned. For this reason this variety is used almost exclusively, in preference to the better flavoured but more delicate freestone and white peach varieties. Similarly, the relatively tough Marrowfat pea varieties are used for canned, processed peas whilst the more tender pea varieties are used for canned and frozen garden peas.

Bartlett pears of high acidity and tannin content are reported to give a pink colour when canned. The growing conditions and soil types were shown to be of importance in controlling this defect and pink colour formation could be eliminated by using high pH fruit.[11]

These examples are typical and illustrate the importance of adequate pilot-testing before approving raw materials for processing purposes.

1.4.3. FREEDOM FROM DEFECTS

Food manufacture, unfortunately, is a low profit activity, and based as it is on raw materials of natural origin, these representing a major cost factor, it is vital to procure low defect-level input materials. Cleaning, sorting and grading generate labour and plant costs and may cause product damage, producing material defects. These preparatory procedures are essential steps in processing but the plant used must be carefully designed and the operators thoroughly trained if defect levels are to be controlled. The literature contains numerous references to defects produced in the field or orchard, to the sowing of varieties which are insufficiently disease resistant and to harvesting and handling damage. The combined effect of these defect-producing activities is evidenced by the large output of waste from most food factories. Clearly, the plan must be to start with the best and then to treat it with loving care.

Defects which affect processing suitability include the following:

(i)   Geometric deformities and unequalities.
(ii) Mechanical damage due to impact, puncture or abrasion.
(iii) Colour defects.
(iv) Insect, animal, fungal and microbial damage.

(v) Extraneous matter contamination.
(vi) Textural and functional defects.
(vii) Immaturity or over-maturity.

1.5. GROWTH PROPERTIES OF THE RAW MATERIAL

It will be apparent from the foregoing that the food manufacturer is vitally concerned with the characteristics of natural or nature-derived raw materials. It is not surprising, therefore, that the modern processor regards his factory as extending back to the growing area. Thus the processor becomes involved in many aspects formerly the concern of the supplier, such as contract buying, growth programming, transportation and storage.

1.5.1. CONTRACT PURCHASING OF RAW MATERIALS
Purchasing of raw material produce in the open market is substantially outmoded. These days the food processor contracts ahead with the farmer or grower for a definite acreage of produce. Under this system the processor may do any or all of the following:

(i) Agree the sowing plan.
(ii) Supply seed of selected varieties, fertiliser and sprays.
(iii) Indicate expected harvest date.
(iv) Provide technical advice via his field men.
(v) Provide harvesting or vining equipment and, sometimes, labour.
(vi) Arrange or provide transport keyed to his production and handling systems.

This system is applied to an ever growing list of food raw materials from wheat, barley and rye, to vegetables such as potatoes, peas and beans. It is a most effective method of assuring supplies of the required materials at the required time and in the required quantity.

1.5.2. SELECTIVE BREEDING OF RAW MATERIALS
Any improvement in the suitability of the raw material for its intended purpose, or in the spreading of the season over which the raw material may be harvested, results in improved processing efficiency and plant utilisation. The development of varieties for food processing involves consideration of all those attributes of the raw material which are reflected in the quality of the finished product (Chapter 3). The development of suitable varieties for

processing requires close cooperation between breeders, research stations and processors and considerable progress has been made.

Selective breeding of processing raw materials is now commonplace. Typical examples include: high dry-matter content potatoes, tomatoes and onions; tomatoes giving puree of improved colour and flavour; brussels sprouts of improved freezing properties; and bitter-free cucumber varieties.

The widespread adoption of mechanical harvesting has stimulated the breeding of varieties with suitable growth habits. For example, pea varieties are now available which have a low, upright, firm growth bearing tangle-free pods. Again, fruit varieties which may be easily plucked or shaken free by mechanical harvesters have been developed.

1.5.3. MATURATION PROPERTIES

The maturity of the raw material is important in controlling both the quality of the final product and the effectiveness of processing. Processing varieties are required to mature both uniformly (to facilitate mechanical harvesting) and predictably, to permit adequate planning.

Over-maturity results in a high proportion of reject material, excessive product damage and spoilage during storage. Sterilisation efficiency may be reduced due to the high microbiological loads often encountered with over-mature materials. Under-maturity implies a reduced yield and the final product is liable to have substandard colour, flavour and texture.

In some foods (e.g. meat, cheese, wines), a period of maturing is essential whilst, in others (e.g. eggs), maturing is undesirable. Fruits and vegetables may be harvested over a range of maturities, depending on their destined end-use. Peas are a particular example and much work has been carried out relating canning and freezing properties to maturity.[9] As a result of this work, it is possible to harvest peas at their optimum maturity for any desired purpose. Since, in many cases, the optimum is reached and passed in a matter of a few hours, this is a matter of great importance to the processor. Similar work has been carried out with broad beans.[9]

1.5.4. PREDICTION OF MATURITY

Forecasting of harvest dates is of great value to the planner. In many commodities (e.g. meat, milk, eggs), harvest patterns are well established. For peas and beans, the Heat Unit System[12] has proved to be useful in predicting maturity. This system is based on the fact that attainment of maturity is a function of growth temperature. Armed with specific growth data on the variety of crop and a knowledge of the average meterological records of the growing area, it is possible to make a long-range forecast of the probable harvest date for any sowing. Corrections can then be made, during the growing period, for the actual weather conditions and the long range forecast may be adjusted accordingly. For example, peas are assumed not to grow at all below 40°F (4·5°C). In any one day of growth, the difference between 40°F (4·5°C) and the average temperature throughout that day is known as the number of 'degree days' or accumulated heat units (AHUs). The AHU measurements of many pea and bean varieties are now available from the seed supplier so that reasonably reliable harvest forecasts may be made using this method.

1.5.5. EXTENSION OF HARVEST SEASON

The use of early, middle and late varieties has done much to spread the season over which food raw materials become available for processing. The widespread adoption of the broiler and battery systems has extended the availability of chicken meat and eggs. The broiler system is now being used in the production of beef and promising results are being obtained. Pea varieties have been the subject of much investigation regarding the spread of harvest season.

Availability may be extended by using preserved raw materials such as brined, dried or pulped crops or by storing part-processed or raw foods. Usually, increased costs are incurred with these procedures and their economic feasibility must be considered carefully before adoption.

Fish pose special problems as a result of the steeply rising harvesting costs, the depletion of fish stocks and the consequent political problems. Fish farming would appear to offer an attractive prospect.[13] Currently, rainbow trout weighing around 5 kg at very competitive prices are being farmed in the UK. Investigatory work involving salt water fish is proceeding apace.[14]

Hydroponics, i.e. soilless culture, also presents interesting future possibilities for spreading harvests. This system, using solar-actuated climatic control, permits simplified disease control, water economies and concentrated planting. Soilless culture is now an established commercial practice in many countries.[15]

1.6. MECHANISATION AND THE RAW MATERIAL

The food industry, faced with soaring labour costs and low profitability has mechanised its operations wherever practicable. Mechanisation, whilst offering undoubted advantages, unless carefully engineered, can cause excessive product damage.

1.6.1. PRODUCT DAMAGE

The main causes of damage during food preparation are: operator damage caused by careless manipulation; unsuitable mechanical handling procedures; poor equipment design and incorrect containerisation.

Damage occurs at every stage of the manufacturing chain starting with the grower or breeder and extending through processing to packaging and distribution.

Damage manifests itself in many ways: the appearance of the food is affected; mould and rot infections invade bruised and punctured areas; infestation by insects and vermin occurs and enzymatic and chemical spoilage is accelerated. Damage spoilage spreads to adjacent material causing financial loss and impairment or invalidation of process effectiveness. In the extreme this represents a positive health hazard.

Produce is damaged: by impact with other produce or hard surfaces; by excessive pressure caused by overlying food; by puncturing by sharp projections and by abrasion caused by movement and vibration.

A detailed discussion of the mechanics of damage is inappropriate here but the reader is referred to the literature on the subject.[2]

1.6.2. MECHANICAL HARVESTING

The change from selective to mechanical harvesting of the 'once-over' or destructive type has produced substantial reductions in labour costs but has many disadvantages. Amongst the more important of these are excessive damage and consequent quality reduction and increased capital investment and maintenance costs. Additionally, this system requires careful coordination between the field and the factory. Frequently, this involves the manufacturer in process alterations and in changes in his handling, containerisation and storage arrangements.

In the UK the combine harvester, the pea viner, the bean harvester and various harvesters for root crops are familiar. In the USA there has been considerable development of harvesters for many other crops (e.g. berry fruits, asparagus, sprouts, cucumbers, cabbage, spinach and tomatoes). Apples and citrus fruits may be harvested using tree shakers and blowers.[16,17]

Currently, mechanical harvesting machines utilise one or more of the following seven principles:

(i)   Shaking of trees or bushes carrying crops (sometimes used in conjunction with abscission promoting sprays).

(ii) Combing of berry fruits such as blueberries and strawberries.

(iii) Cutting of cabbages, lettuces, cauliflowers, etc., the plant being severed at ground level.

(iv) Pulling of carrots, radishes and celery in which the stems are gripped by opposing, driven belts.

(v) Stripping of cucumbers and maize ears using differentially driven soft rubber rollers.

(vi) Vining of peas and beans involving either stripping, pulling or cutting of the vines followed by podding.

(vii) Mechanical digging of root crops such as potatoes or onions.

Frequently, harvesting machines carry out other preparative operations such as aspiration, screening, destoning and colour sorting (see Chapter 3).

Mechanical harvesting, therefore, requires a multi-disciplinary approach with breeders, farmers, food technologists, engineers and economists working in close cooperation.[18]

1.6.3. DESIGN OF TRANSIT CONTAINERS FOR RAW MATERIALS

In-transit damage due to impact, abrasion and pressure, frequently is the result of incorrect containerisation. In tomato handling studies, some workers have reported reduced damage when the fruit is harvested into shallow lug-boxes compared with collection in bulk bins, whereas other studies have shown the reverse to be true. The former finding suggests that fruit-to-container surface impacts were less damaging than fruit-to-fruit contacts whilst the latter finding suggests the opposite.

Evidently, consideration must be given to other factors such as: the type and variety of fruit; its maturity; its shape; its size (as affecting its kinetic energy when falling) and the nature of the container surface (e.g. its hardness and texture). The warning is clear, each situation calls for its own investigation and of interest in this respect is the work of O'Brien and Guillou[19] who have developed an in-transit vibration simulator for fruit handling studies and Hammerle's[20] work on the evaluation of abrasion resistance in fruit and vegetables.

Pressure damage caused by overlying material in containers which are too deep or by overfilling of open top containers which are then stacked is all too common. Some apples will not withstand an overlying static weight in excess of 4 kg whilst peaches are even more fragile. Pressure damage is cumulative, a pyramid of damage emanating from the original pressure point. Damage of this latter type is likely to be more extensive in shallow containers with a high exposed-surface-to-fruit ratio than when deep containers are used.

1.6.4. TRANSPORTATION OF RAW MATERIALS

Arranging to have available raw materials of the proper quality in the required amounts and at the correct time is mandatory to any process. In the food industry particular problems of supply exist. Raw foods sensitive to microbiological, insect and chemical spoilage and, in many cases, still continuing to respire, become available over a relatively short period at harvest. Delivery delays disorganise production and impair raw material quality. Proper scheduling is vital and the processor should either specify delivery procedures in the buying contract (including a penalty clause in the event of default) or, alternatively, exclude delivery from the supplier's liability and accept responsibility for transport himself.

Particular care must be exercised in the correct choice of container (Section 1.6.3) and in maintaining these in a sound and clean condition so as to avoid contamination of the raw material with wood fragments, nails, etc. Where transportation takes place in bags or sacks, careful sack cleaning and examination is necessary. Second-hand sacks which may have contained fertilisers or spray materials are sometimes pressed into service in an emergency, occasionally with dire consequences.

Transportation vehicles require special attention. They should be properly maintained so as to avoid tainting or discolouration of the food by exhaust gases or fuel. Vehicles should give a smooth, uninterrupted ride to their contents and be well-ventilated to allow product heat to dissipate during the journey. Above all, vehicles should be thoroughly clean and insect free. Contract transport is notoriously difficult to control in these respects and, all too frequently, outbreaks of insect infestation are traceable to foods being transported in a vehicle which has been incompletely cleaned after carrying infested material for another customer.

Finally, it is important to ensure, as far as possible, that the transportation operation, as a whole, is integrated with the handling system in use in the factory. Rehandling is expensive and, inevitably, causes raw material damage.

1.6.5. RAW MATERIAL STORAGE

Ideally, all raw materials are processed immediately on arrival at the factory. In practice this situation seldom exists so that some provision must be made for on-site storage of raw materials and part-processed products. In this way, delivery delays, plant breakdowns and bumper harvests may be accommodated and, occasionally, the store can be an asset allowing forward-buying when advantageous market conditions exist.

Reference to Chapter 16 will indicate that, for most food materials, storage conditions are highly specific with respect to temperature, humidity and surrounding atmosphere. Storage of any type ties up capital and is costly to provide and operate. With the demanding conditions imposed by many foodstuffs these factors warrant the most careful consideration when planning the provision of storage facilities. More often than not emergency situations may be resolved by overtime working or by temporary hiring of storage space. Provision of emergency storage capacity should therefore be on a minimal basis.

REFERENCES

1. Griffiths, J. C. and Smith, C. M., Relationships between volume and axes of some quartzite pebbles. *Amer. J. of Sci.*, **262**(4) (1964) 497–512.
2. Mohsenin, N. N., *Physical Properties of Plant and Animal Materials. Vol. 1.* Gordon & Breach Science Publishers, New York, 1980.
3. Arthey, V. D., *Quality of Horticultural Products.* Butterworths, London, 1975.
4. Anon., The Colouring Matter in Foods Regulations. Report No. 1340, HMSO, London, 1973. Amended: Report No. 1488 (1975); No. 2086 (1976); No. 1787 (1978), No. 1987 (1987).
5. Kraus, M. N., *Pneumatic Conveying of Bulk Materials.* McGraw-Hill, New York, 1980.
6. Roscoe, B., Friction fact and fiction. *Chemy Ind.*, **14** (1982) 467–74.
7. Talburt, W. F. and Smith, O., *Potato Processing.* AVI, Westport, Conn., USA, 1975.
8. Anon., *Varieties for Processing—Vegetables.* Campden Food Preservation Research Association, Chipping Campden, England, 1984.
9. Anon., *Varieties for Processing—Legumes.* Campden Food Preservation Research Association, Chipping Campden, England, 1984.
10. Anon., *Varieties for Processing—Fruit.* Campden Food Preservation Research Association, Chipping Campden, England, 1984.
11. Luh, B. S., Leonard, S. and Patel, D. S., Pink discolouration in canned Bartlett pears. *Food Technol.*, **14**(1) (1960) 53–6.
12. Seaton, H. L., Scheduling plantings and predicting harvest maturities for processing vegetables. *Food Technol.*, **9**(3) (1955) 202–9.
13. Brown, E. E., Mariculture and aquaculture. *Food Technol.*, **27**(12) (1973) 60–6.
14. Anon., Fish Farming. *British Food J.*, **86**(9/9) (1984) 50–2.
15. Rahman, A. R., Hydroponic culture—Past, present, future. Paper presented at Session 01, 1st International Congress on Engineering and Food, Boston, Mass., USA, 1976.
16. O'Brien, M., *Principles and Practices for Harvesting and Handling Fruits and Nuts.* AVI, Westport, Conn., USA, 1983.
17. Ryall, A. L. and Pentzer, W. T., *Handling, Transportation and Storage of Fruits and Vegetables.* AVI, Westport, Conn., USA, 1974.
18. Zahara, M. B. and Johnson, S. S., Cost comparison of hand and mechanical harvesting of mature green tomatoes. *Calif. Agric.*, **35**(7/8) (1981) 7–9.
19. O'Brien, M. and Guillou, H., An in-transit vibration simulator for fruit handling studies. *Trans. Amer. Soc. Agric. Engng*, **12**(1) (1969) 94–7.
20. Hammerle, J. R., A technique for evaluating fruit and vegetable abrasion resistance. *Trans. Amer. Soc. Agric. Engng*, **13**(5) (1970) 672–5.

CHAPTER 2

CLEANING OF RAW MATERIALS

The preliminary preparative operation of cleaning, together with the operations of sorting and grading dealt with in Chapter 3, are conveniently regarded as separation operations.

Cleaning   Separates contaminants from the raw materials.

Sorting   Separates the raw material into categories of different physical characteristics such as size, shape and colour.

Grading   Separates the raw material into categories of different quality.

This classification is useful but not rigid, since cleaning and sorting operations result in up-grading of quality, and grading always involves sorting of some kind. However, the terms are meaningful, providing they are applied to the primary purpose of the activity.

2.1. THE FUNCTIONS OF CLEANING

In cleaning his raw material, the processor has two main objectives: (i) the removal of contaminants which constitute a health hazard or which are aesthetically unacceptable; (ii) the control of microbiological loads and chemical and biochemical reactions which impair subsequent process effectiveness and product quality.

An acceptable cleaning process must satisfy the following requirements:

(i)   The separation efficiency of the process must be as high as possible consistent with minimum wastage of good material.

(ii)   The contaminant must be removed completely after separation so as to avoid recontamination of the cleaned food.

(iii) The process and equipment should be so designed as to limit recontamination of the cleaned food, e.g. by flying dust or by contaminated wash water from previous batches.

(iv)   The cleaning process must leave the cleaned surface in an acceptable condition.

(v)   Product damage must be avoided.

(vi)   Volumes and strengths of liquid effluents must be kept to a minimum.

Completely clean raw materials are an unattainable ideal. In practice a balance has to be struck between cleaning costs (as reflected in reject material and labour and process charges) and the need to produce good quality food. Thus, 'acceptable' standards of raw material cleanliness must be specified for each end-use, taking into account the extent to which raw material contamination will be reflected in the final product.

Inefficient removal and disposal of the contaminant, once it is separated, results in product recontamination. Occasionally, gross recontamination occurs when some, or all, of the contaminant from a large quantity of cleaned material is redeposited in a small quantity of following material, resulting in a localised concentration of the contaminant. Examples of such gross recontamination include that caused by sudden failure of a continuous electromagnetic separator or by holing of a continuous screen.

The prevention of recontamination of the cleaned food is a vital consideration which is often neglected both in the design and operation of food cleaning plant. Reliable removal of the contaminants both from the cleaned food raw material and from the processing area is an important step controlling the effectiveness of subsequent processing and preservation operations. Thus, in canning, sterilisation heat processes are designed assuming a standard initial microbiological load. If, due to a cleaning failure, this initial load is exceeded then a product of unacceptable microbiological quality will result. Similarly, low temperature processes, such as freezing, freeze drying and spray drying, require raw materials of high microbiological quality since such processes result in relatively small decreases in initial bacteriological contamination.

The condition in which the cleaning operation leaves the surface of the material is a matter of great importance to the food processor. Roughened surfaces are unattractive in appearance and, in fruits and vegetables, the damaged outer cells lead to rapid browning. Again wet, bruised or damaged surfaces provide excellent breeding grounds for micro-organisms and insect pests such as vinegar flies and weevils.

The problems of product damage are discussed in Chapters 1 and 3 and, unfortunately, many cleaning processes result in unacceptably high damage rates. Common cleaning damage factors include: puncture from sharp projections on chutes, screens, etc.; impact with hard, unpadded surfaces and excessive abrasion due to contact with moving surfaces of cleaners.

Effluents (particularly liquids) are generated in large volumes during cleaning. Restriction of effluent production and efficient collection and disposal of wastes are vital factors controlling cleaning effectiveness and costs.

Some of the defects of ineffective cleaning operations may be screened out during the subsequent process of sorting and grading but, inevitably, many of these defects will be transmitted to the finished product. Cleaning plant must be: carefully designed and properly constructed from smooth, non-contaminating materials; carefully finished; amenable to easy sanitation and be sufficiently flexible to cope with the wide variation in extent and type of contaminants encountered in natural raw materials.

Regrettably, many cleaning plants do not satisfy the foregoing criteria. Until they do so, wastage and spoilage will continue to represent a large (and avoidable) cost factor in food processing.

2.2. CONTAMINANTS IN FOOD RAW MATERIALS

In the UK, contamination of foods is regulated by the Food Act 1984, which prohibits the sale of food which is not of the nature, substance and quality demanded and/or which is unfit for human consumption. Contaminated food accounts for nearly 50% of all UK prosecutions under this act.[1]

Contaminants range from those of molecular size, such as trace toxic metals, spray residues, taints, etc., through microorganisms to inclusions such as tractor and machinery parts. The growth of mechanisation in the harvesting, processing, handling and storage of foods has increased, rather than reduced, the occurrence of mineral, plant and animal contaminants in foodstuff raw materials. Similarly, the rapid extension in the use of agricultural sprays provides an added hazard in food processing.

The importance of microbiological cleanliness has been stressed already and it is important to appreciate that practically all the ingredients used in

TABLE 2.1

Methods of detection and/or removal of food contaminants

Property	Principle	Examples of application	Disadvantages
1. Appearance.	Manual sorting.	General for blemishes and overall assessment (R, D).	Fatigue and loss of effectiveness.
2. Size.	Sieving.	General size classification (R, D).	Contaminants of same size remain.
3. Shape.	Disc sorter.	Weed seeds, husks, bird and animal droppings in cereals (R).	Size also operative.
4. Colour.	Reflectance photometry + reject mechanism.	Discoloured or wormholed peas, beans, rice and so on (R, D).	Costly machinery, rather slow.
5. Density or buoyancy.	(a) Sedimentation in liquids.	Stones in peas, gross 'filth' in herbs (D).	Effluent problems.
	(b) Sedimentation in air (aspiration).	Husks, stones and sand in cereals (R).	Dusty—potentially explosive and recontaminating
	(c) Flotation.	Bran in flour. Overmature peas in young peas using brines of different densities (R, D).	Take up of liquid by food.
6. Solubility.	Filtration.	Clarifying oils, brines and syrups (R).	Few foodstuffs wholly liquid.
7. Magnetic properties.	Magnetic separators.	Ferromagnetic materials in food raw materials and products (R, D)	Only ferromagnetic metals removed.

8. Opacity to X-rays.	X-ray cabinet.	Solder ex cans, plastic, glass or wood inclusions in confectionery (R).	Operator fatigue. Health hazards.
9. Electrical properties.	Metal detectors + reject gear.	Removal of ferrous and non-ferrous metals, some stones, graphited grease (R).	Conducting foods affect sensitivity.
10. Surface properties.	Wettability. Froth flotation.	Insect fragments and eggs in flour and herbs (D). Deadly nightshade berries in peas (R).	Contamination by frothing agents and detergents.
11. Combination (surface props and solubility).	Washing with or without detergents.	Adhering soil, spray residues and pesticides, rodent urine, mould and mould mycelium in fruits, vegetables and cereals (R).	Effluent problems. Water costly. Food left in wet condition. Detergent contamination.
12. Microscopic appearance.	Configuration under poly- and monochromatic light.	Insect parts, hairs and excreta. Contaminating starches. Fibres like string and jute, plastics, etc. (D).	Restricted sample size. Considerable expertise in recognition necessary.
13. Optical properties.	Refractive index. Visible light transmission.	Categorisation of glasses. Ripeness and core blemishes in apples. (D).	As 12 above.
14. Chemical properties.	Toxic and other metals tests. Dyestuffs analysis, etc.	Identification and segregation of contaminated batches or bulks (D).	As 12 above.

D, method of detection.
R, method of removal.

the food industry—water, sugar, starches, spices, colouring matter and even containers—are capable of causing microbiological contamination of food products.[2,3]

The types of contamination most frequently encountered are:

(i)   *Mineral*   —soil, sand, stones, grease, glass fragments, metallic particles and oil.
(ii) *Plant*   —twigs, foliage, stalks, pits, skins, husks, wood pieces, rope and string.
(iii) *Animal*   —excreta, hairs, feathers, insect eggs, body parts.
(iv) *Chemical*   —spray residues and fertilisers.
(v)   *Microbial* —micro-organisms and their by-products.

The food industry exercises extreme vigilance in detecting and removing contaminants, paying particular attention to raw materials which are high risk ingredients. The major entry points of contamination are listed below in decreasing order of risk:

(i)   Raw materials delivered to the factory.
(ii) Raw materials stored in the factory.
(iii) Factory processing area.
(iv) Finished product store.
(v)   Wholesale and retail storage.

Effective cleaning depends, firstly, on effective detection of the contaminant and secondly on its effective removal. Both of these components exploit differences in physical or chemical properties for their prosecution. The more important properties used for contaminant recognition and removal are set out in Table 2.1.

A discussion covering methods of detecting contaminants in foods is inappropriate here but readers are referred to the excellent publications of Gorham,[3] Smith[4] and to the official USA methods described in AOAC.[5]

The more general industrial procedures for cleaning of food raw materials are discussed in Section 2.3.

2.3.   CLEANING METHODS

The wide variety of contaminant encountered in raw food materials and the low tolerances permitted for these contaminants calls for a variety of cleaning methods to be adopted. The methods in use fall into two groups:

(i)   *Dry cleaning methods*—Screening, brushing, aspiration, abrasion, magnetic separation.

(ii) *Wet cleaning methods*—Soaking, spraying, fluming, flotation, ultrasonic cleaning, filtration, settling.

These processes are used, almost invariably, in combination—the methods employed depending on the nature of the raw material, the contaminants to be removed and the desired condition of the cleaned material. It is impracticable, within the narrow confines of this chapter, to deal fully with this wide range of equipment. However, the following examples should serve to indicate the more important features of these two groups of cleaning equipment.

2.3.1. DRY CLEANING METHODS

These methods have the advantages of relative cheapness and convenience whilst the cleaned surface is left in a dry condition. However, unless considerable care is taken to minimise the spread of dust, recontamination can occur. Further, the dusty conditions encountered during dry cleaning can give rise to fire and explosion hazards. Dust explosions are a real and continuous hazard in food processing. H.M. Factory Inspectorate lists no fewer than 64 food materials which either have initiated or are capable of initiating a dust explosion.[6] Fortunately, the dust concentration which has to be achieved before a dust explosion can occur is $\sim 30\,\mathrm{mg\,litre^{-1}}$ which is above that usually regarded as tolerable in a working environment ($\sim 10\,\mathrm{mg\,litre^{-1}}$). However, dislodgement of dust from rafters, tops of doors and window sills by a small primary explosion or disturbance may create a situation which then needs only a spark of around 100 mJ intensity (e.g. from a falling tool or a faulty electrical connection) to cause a major explosion.

Careful control of dust is important in the food industry generally[7] (in milling, high-speed conveying, etc.) but especially so in dry cleaning where dusty conditions are present in conjunction with potential spark generators such as stones, and tramp metal occurring as extraneous matter in the raw material. Remedial measures include: dust-proofing of equipment; dust extraction; rigorous housekeeping and, with high-risk equipment, spark-proofing and the fitting of special relief systems which, instantaneously, vent the primary-explosion shock waves outside the building.

2.3.1.1. Screening

Primarily, screens are size separators which fall into the class of sorting machines (Chapter 3). However, screens may be used as cleaning equipment, removing contaminants of different size from that of the raw material.

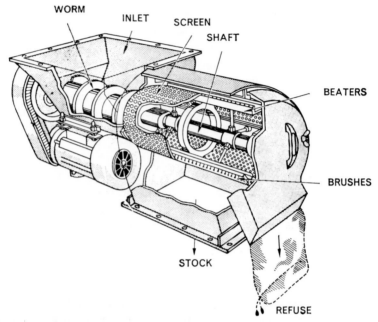

WORM
INLET
SCREEN
SHAFT
BEATERS
BRUSHES
STOCK
REFUSE

FIG. 2.1. Diagram of the Le Coq Sifter. (By courtesy of Simon Barron Ltd.)

In its simplest form a screen is a perforated bed supported on a frame and screens of this elementary pattern are still in use in the food industry. Such discontinuous screens have now been largely replaced by continuous types of which the drum screen (Fig. 2.1) and the flat-bed screen (Fig. 2.2) are typical.

Rotary drum screens, variously referred to as trommels, centrifugal screens or reels, are continuous units which find numerous applications in the food industry. Cleaning may be carried out so as to retain undesired oversize material such as string bag-hairs, etc., from flour, salt or sugar, whilst discharging a cleaned product. Alternatively, the screen may be arranged to retain the cleaned material as oversize whilst discharging undesired material, e.g. in the removal of weed-seeds, grit and small stones from cereals.

Screens of this type have good capacity and they are relatively inexpensive to install, maintain and operate. Disadvantageously, unless carefully designed, they are difficult to clean and recontamination may occur. Rotary drum screens exhibit speed criticality (see Chapter 4).

Flat-bed screens, in general, consist of one or more flat screen-decks fixed

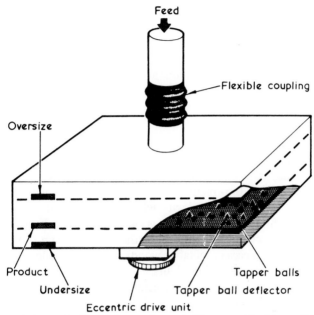

Feed

Flexible coupling

Oversize

Product

Undersize

Eccentric drive unit

Tapper ball deflector

Tapper balls

FIG. 2.2.   Diagram of a flat-bed screening unit. The eccentric drive unit imparts a gyratory motion to the box containing the screens.

together in a dust-tight casing, the assembly being shaken by a variety of devices. It is usual to include hard rubber tapper-balls between the decks to minimise blinding of the screen apertures with fine materials. Flat-bed screens are excellent for cleaning fine materials such as flour and ground spices, since they are not easily blinded. They must be easily accessible for frequent cleaning. Large pieces of foreign matter trapped in the screen may be pulverised by abrasion, this resulting in the spreading of contamination.

The abrasion and impact caused by moving bed screens, although useful in loosening adherent soil, may damage sensitive foods. Often it is found that the small, repetitive impacts encountered in equipment of this type cause greater damage than one or two heavier collisions. The extent of injury is dependent on the total energy transferred.

Screening effectiveness is a function of the shape-regularity of the working substance (Chapter 1). Spherical materials may be sorted accurately on screens whereas other shapes are sorted, usually, on a minimum-dimension basis. Screening, therefore, tends to give incomplete separation although it is of wide application in the preliminary stages of cleaning and sorting chains.

2.3.1.2. Abrasion cleaning

Abrasion between food particles or between the food and moving parts of cleaning machinery is used to loosen and to remove adhering contaminants. Trommels, tumblers, vibrators, abrasive discs and rotating brushes are used for this purpose. Scrupulous attention to dust removal is necessary in order to limit recontamination, to protect operators and to prevent dust explosions.

2.3.1.3. Aspiration cleaning

Aspiration (or winnowing) finds wide application in removing debris differing in buoyancy, i.e. in aerodynamic properties (see Chapter 1), from the desired material. In principle, the material to be cleaned is fed into a stream of air at controlled velocity when separation into two or more streams (e.g. light, middle and heavy) is effected. It is usually arranged for the cleaned product to be discharged as the middle stream leaving heavy debris (e.g. stones, pieces of metal or wood) behind whilst floating off light debris such as stalks, husks and hairs.

One machine which uses this principle is shown in Fig. 2.3. This is suitable for two- or three-stream separation of cereals, nuts and similar foods.

Aspiration, as a cleaning stage, is used extensively in combine-harvesters, in pea-viners, in bean-harvesters and in similar machines.

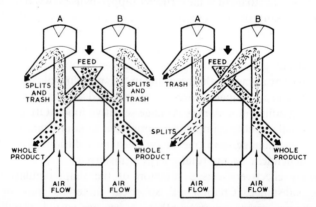

FIG. 2.3. The Sortex Air Separator. A and B are two separators in which the solid material is removed from the air stream. Separator B has a swivelling discharge to allow the plant to be used as a two- or three-way separator, as shown. (By courtesy of Gunson's Sortex Ltd, London.)

The aspiration principle is used to clean onions, melons, eggs and other foods which are not amenable to wetting. The soil is loosened by abrasion, using brushing or by contacting with rotating rubber fingers (pintles), and the debris is then removed, selectively, by air streams.[8]
Aspirators are capable of very precise adjustment. They may be used to remove bran particles from flour and even to discriminate between protein and starch fragments in the production of protein enriched flours. One such machine claims to separate within the range of 3–60 μm.[9] Aspirators use large quantities of low-pressure air and, hence, consume much energy. Careful dust-control is necessary for safety and health reasons and to prevent the spread of contaminants. The method should not be used with oxidation-sensitive materials.

2.3.1.4. Magnetic cleaning
This involves, at its simplest, cascading the contaminated product stream over one or more magnets which are usually located in the conveyor trunking. Magnetic separators may also take the form of rotating or stationary magnetic drums, magnetised belts, magnets located over belts carrying the food or staggered magnetised grids through which the food is passed.
Both permanent magnets and electromagnets are used. The latter are more suitable for foodstuff cleaning, the adhering metallic particles being removed easily by switching off the current. The frequent removal of the screenings is vital since, if a build-up occurs, then the particles may be swept off by the product stream, causing gross recontamination. Electromagnets are considerably more expensive than permanent magnets and are subject to power failure.
Separators of this type may be followed by an electronic metal-detector which monitors the product for both ferrous and non-ferrous particles. Such detectors generate a powerful electromagnetic field through which the food is passed. The presence of a metallic inclusion distorts this field; the disturbance is amplified and the resulting signal is utilised to sound an alarm or activate an automatic reject device.[10] Electronic detectors can also detect certain other inclusions such as clinker, some stones, carbonised grease and metal-impregnated grease.

2.3.1.5. Miscellaneous dry-cleaning principles
Theoretically, any procedure which can detect a property difference can be used to effect separation and, hence, clean, sort, and, possibly, grade materials. Increasing labour costs in the food industry have encouraged

research into the field of mechanised separation. Interesting developments in this direction include the following.

Electrostatic cleaning takes advantage of differences in electrostatic charging of materials under controlled humidity conditions, charged particles being removed by oppositely-charged or earthed rollers, grids, etc. This procedure is used in dust extraction and in other processes such as the cleaning of tea. In this application, tea-fannings are cleaned of dust, stalks, etc., by flowing the material over a roller charged to a potential of 5–20 kV and rotating at 70–350 rpm. The tea is adjusted to a moisture content of 3–4% and the separated matter is removed from the roller, continuously, by rotating brushes.[11]

Radio-isotope separation of clods of earth and stones from potatoes using low-energy gamma radiation, is being investigated by The Scottish Institute of Agricultural Engineering. The potatoes are distinguished from rubbish by differences in opacity to gamma rays emitted by ^{241}Am. The differences are sensed by a Geiger–Muller detector, the signals from this being used to actuate a mechanism which rejects the rubbish. The prototype machine is reported to remove 90% of the contaminants.[12]

X-ray separation of stones, glass and metal fragments in foods such as confectionery is well established. The food is conveyed through an X-ray scanner and the image is viewed on a fluorescent screen by an operator who stops the conveyor when an inclusion is seen.

Mechanisation of this process has proved difficult but a machine capable of detecting inclusions in pickles has been reported. In this machine, a difference in contrast between the optical and X-ray images of jars of pickles is used to generate an electrical signal which triggers an ejection device.[13]

Application of this principle to bulk-food cleaning is still awaited but the ability to remove non-metallic inclusions from food presents an attractive prospect.

2.3.2. WET CLEANING METHODS

Wet cleaning is effective in removing firmly-adherent soils and in allowing the use of detergents and sanitisers. Unfortunately, the method has a number of disadvantageous features. First, it uses large amounts of high-quality water, which is becoming increasingly costly, and regenerates this as troublesome effluent at high rates (~ 15 000 litres of effluent per tonne of food processed). Such effluent is highly polluting and requires expensive treatment before disposal. Second, wet surfaces spoil more rapidly, thus wet cleaning often involves final de-watering to provide cleaned material suitable for processing or storage. When wet processes are used, careful attention must be paid to water conservation and management,[14] to plant sanitation and to water quality (Chapters 17 and 18). The theory of wet cleaning is discussed by Krochta and Bellows.[15]

2.3.2.1. Soaking

This is the simplest method of wet cleaning and is often used as a preliminary stage in the cleaning of root vegetables and other foods which are heavily contaminated. Adhering soil is softened and some is removed, together with stones, sand and other abrasive materials which would damage the machinery used in the later stages of cleaning. Soak tanks are made of metal, smooth concrete or other materials of construction suitable for regular cleaning and disinfection. Absorbent materials such as wood should not be used. Gridded bottom outlets are provided for the removal of heavy soil and side outlets should be fitted to allow the removal of light debris which would otherwise be drained back into the cleaned material.

The efficiency of soaking is improved: (i) by moving the water relative to the product by means of caged propeller-stirrers built into the tank; (ii) by moving the product relative to the water either by means of slow-moving paddles or by feeding the raw material into a horizontal perforated drum which rotates whilst partially submerged in the soak tank. These procedures tend to cause damaging of delicate materials. Agitation may also be produced by sparging compressed air through the tank. This procedure can be used for delicate materials, e.g. strawberries and asparagus, or for materials like spinach or celery which trap dirt internally.

Warm water improves the efficiency of soaking but the rate of spoilage of foods may be increased thereby. The use of detergents is increasing, especially in foods contaminated by spray residues and mineral oil. Care is necessary, however, in the selection and use of such agents, since the appearance and texture of the food may be affected. Examples of this are the softening effects of sodium hexametaphosphate on peas and the toughening effect of some metal ions on peas and peaches destined for canning.

Frequently, soak tanks are supplied with lightly contaminated water from subsequent washing stages. In this way, water economies are effected and effluent volumes are reduced. With such counter-current re-use of water it becomes especially important to exercise careful microbiological control and for regular changing of soak water to be carried out.

Chlorination is used to decrease bacterial loadings in soak tank water but its high chemical oxygen demand (COD) rapidly removes active chlorine so that high concentrations of this are necessary. At high levels of chlorine the food may be affected, e.g. potatoes may develop blackened flesh. Nevertheless, used with a full understanding of its advantages and limitations, chlorine is a valuable cleaning aid.[15]

2.3.2.2. Spray washing

This is probably the most widely used method of wet cleaning, the surfaces of the food being subjected to water sprays.

The efficiency of spray washing depends on: the water pressure employed; the volume of water used; the water temperature; the distance of the food from the spray origin; the time of exposure of the food to the sprays and the number of spray-jets used. A small volume of water, at high pressure, is the most effective general combination. However, damage may be caused to ripe soft-fruits such as strawberries and to delicate vegetables like asparagus. Sometimes high pressure sprays are used to cut out damaged parts in peaches and tomatoes and to remove adherent soil, e.g. black moulds on citrus fruits.

Spray drum washers. The spray drum washer consists of a reel constructed of metal slats or rods, spaced so as to retain the food whilst allowing debris to be washed through. The drum, which rotates slowly, is inclined to the horizontal. The speed of rotation and angle of inclination control both the movement of the food within the drum and the duration of the washing cycle. The washer is equipped with a central spray-rod which is fitted with jets or slots through which water is sprayed (Fig. 2.4). Whilst the abrasion which occurs in this washer is useful in loosening dirt, it may cause damage to some foods.

Spray belt washers. This type of spray washer is simply a conveyor (e.g. a perforated belt) which carries the food beneath banks of water sprays. With roughly spherical foods such as apples, contact is improved by using roller conveyors which cause the fruit to spin beneath the sprays (Fig. 2.4). For smaller foods, movement under the sprays may be produced by using a vibratory conveyor.

The problems of water conservation and effluent generation, already referred to, have spurred research into many aspects of food processing. Examples include the development of reduced-water blanching (Section 10.5) and peeling processes. A development in the field of wet cleaning is the USDA Rubber-Disc Cleaner.[17] In this process, tomatoes are first freed of gross contamination in a soak tank and are then conveyed mechanically into a shallow channel, 10 m long by 0·3 m wide, in which adherent soil is removed in 15–25 s by exposing the fruit to the brushing action of soft

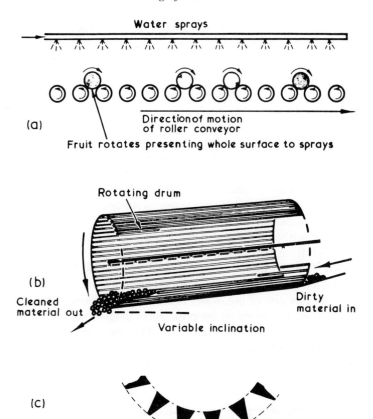

Water sprays

(a)

Direction of motion
of roller conveyor

Fruit rotates presenting whole surface to sprays

Rotating drum

(b)

Cleaned
material out

Dirty
material in

Variable inclination

(c)

FIG. 2.4. Spray washers. (a) Diagram of a belt-type spray washer. (b) Diagram of a spray drum washer, partly cut away to show the spray-rod. The drum may be made of perforated metal or from slats. Alternatively, non-blocking wedge-wire drums may be used (shown diagrammatically at (c)).

rubber discs spinning axially at 450 rpm. The specially profiled discs, which are ~ 11 cm in diameter, are mounted at 8 cm spacing on driven shafts which taper inwards from inlet to outlet end. The discs are staggered and overlap slightly. Thus, the wet fruit is brushed as it is conveyed along the channel, the soil being flung off as a mud into the base of the channel where it is removed. The residual soil is removed by spraying briefly with water into which detergents or detergent foams may be incorporated. Substantial reduction in water consumption and effluent volume are claimed, the disc-cleaner using around 20 litres of water per tonne of fruit compared with

1500–5000 litre tonne^{-1} for conventional cleaning processes. Average removals of soil, bacteria and spores were 99%, 94% and 97% respectively.

2.3.2.3. Flotation washing

This method depends on a difference in buoyancy between the desired and undesired parts of the food to be cleaned. Thus bruised or rotten apples, which sink in water, may be removed by fluming the fruit into a tank and collecting the overflow of sound fruit.

Heavy debris can be removed by fluming dirty produce over a series of adjustable weirs arranged in series. The less buoyant contaminants are trapped by and remain behind the weirs. The product, now contaminated by material of the same or higher buoyancy, is further purified by passage over a vibrated screen where water sprays remove the fine contaminants.

The flotation washer illustrated in Fig. 2.5 effectively removes stones, dirt and plant debris from peas, beans, dried fruits and similar materials at rates of 3 tonnes h^{-1}. Water flow rates in the range of 200–500 litres min^{-1} are necessary, i.e. a consumption of 4000–10 000 litres of water for each tonne of product. At this rate of use, water recirculation is necessary.

Froth flotation, depending on the principle of differential wetting of the food and its contaminants, is an elaboration of the flotation procedure. In a typical froth flotation process, peas were freed from seeds by immersion in a dilute mineral oil emulsion through which air was blown. The contami-

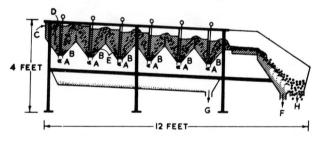

KEY

A. Quick release valve

B. Plunger

C. Water entry

D. Product entry

E. Dirt and stones collected in base cones

F. Water and refuse outlet

G. Trough outlet

H. Product outlet

FIG. 2.5.   A flotation separation system. (By courtesy of Chisholm-Ryder International Manufacturing Ltd., Middlesex, England.)

nants floated on the foam and were skimmed off whilst the peas sank and were separated and washed to remove adhering emulsion.

2.3.2.4. Ultrasonic cleaning

Ultrasonic waves are sound waves of frequencies above those detectable by the human ear, i.e. frequencies above 16 kHz. Insonation of a fluid with ultrasonic waves at frequencies of 20–100 kHz produces a rapidly alternating pressure in the path of the waves and this leads to the rapid formation and collapse of bubbles in the fluid. Cavitation and decavitation, as these effects are called, result in the release of energy in the system and this energy causes violent agitation of particles immersed in the fluid (see Chapter 5).

TABLE 2.2
Comparison of dry and wet methods of cleaning food raw materials

Cleaning method	Advantages	Disadvantages
Dry cleaning	(i) Low plant cost. (ii) Cleaned surface dry. (iii) Concentrated effluent, easily disposed of. (iv) Plant easily cleaned. (v) Chemical and microbiological activity minimised.	(i) Dusty—personnel hazard; explosion hazard; recontamination hazard. (ii) Adherent soil inefficiently removed. (iii) Product damage often high.
Wet cleaning	(i) Adherent soil efficiently removed. (ii) Flexible cleaning—use of heat, sanitisers, detergents, sterilants. (iii) Dustless. (iv) Product damage minimised.	(i) Chemical and microbiological activity accelerated. (ii) High water cost. (iii) Dilute, voluminous highly polluting effluent generated. (iv) Cleaned surface wet, costly after-processing, e.g. drying, dewatering necessary. (v) Equipment cleaning and sanitation difficult— may cause product recontamination.

This phenomenon may be utilised to effect the loosening of contaminants, e.g. grit in vegetables, grease or wax on fruits or dirt on eggs.[18] The contaminants after loosening are removed by conventional methods. Ultrasonic cleaning, using water or detergent solutions, finds many applications in the engineering industry, but application in the food industry at present appears to be limited to experimental development. The method would appear to have much to commend it to the attention of food technologists.[19]

2.3.2.5. Dewatering

Wet cleaning, more often than not, leaves the cleaned product contaminated with excess water. Dewatering may be affected by passage of the food over vibrated screens, or by the use of dewatering reels, i.e. specially designed rotary screens. In some cases, e.g. cleaned peas for freezing or

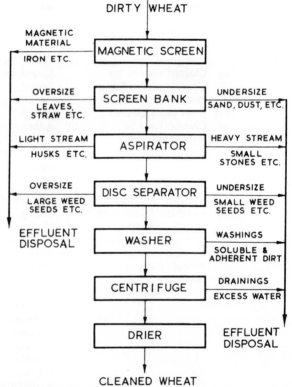

FIG. 2.6.   A typical cleaning combination for wheat prior to milling.

washed wheat for milling, dewatering centrifuges may be used (see Chapter 7). Occasionally it is necessary to resort to drying procedures, for instance with washed cereals or with wet-cleaned fruit which is to be stored or is to be sold as a finished foodstuff.

2.3.3. DRY VERSUS WET CLEANING METHODS
The characteristics of these two types of cleaning procedure are summarised in Table 2.2.

2.3.4. COMBINATION CLEANING PROCEDURES
As remarked earlier, cleaning methods are generally used in combination. Many cleaning machines involve several stages combined as a single unit. Thus, bean- or pea-washers often consist of a soak tank linked to a spray drum washer followed by a dewatering screen. Again, cleaning screens are often associated with an aspiration device and with a magnetic separator. A typical example of a combination procedure is the cleaning process used for producing cleaned wheat for milling into flour. The stages involved in this process are illustrated in Fig. 2.6. In cleaning chains, such as this, inter-stage handling methods require careful design and selection in order to control material damage, effluent volumes (e.g. in hydraulic transfer) and handling costs (Chapter 19).

REFERENCES

1. Anon., Food prosecutions. *British Food J.*, **88**(931) (1985) 37–9.
2. Hersom, A. C. and Hulland, E. D., *Canned Foods*, 7th edn. Livingstone, Edinburgh, Scotland, 1980.
3. Gorham, J. R. (ed.), *Principles of Food Analysis for Filth, Decomposition, and Foreign Matter*, FDA Tech. Bull. No. 1, 2nd edn. US Food and Drug Administration, Washington, D.C., USA, 1981.
4. Smith, P. R., Scheme for the examination of foreign material contaminants in foods. Leatherhead Food RA Report, Leatherhead Food RA, Surrey, England, 1983.
5. Williams, E. (ed.), *Official Methods of Analysis*. Association of Official Analytical Chemists, Arlington, USA, 1984.
6. Anon., Dust explosions in factories. SHW 830, HMSO, London, 1968.
7. Anon., Dust as deadly as dynamite. *Materials Handling News*, No. 318 (1984) 57–9.
8. Ryall, A. L. and Lipton, D. J., *Handling, Transportation and Storage of Fruits and Vegetables*. AVI, Westport, Conn., USA, 1972.
9. Vose, J. R., Separating grain components by air classification. *Separation and Purification Methods*, **7**(1) (1978) 1–29.

10. Lock, A. P., Metal detection. *Food Proc. Ind.*, **49**(582) (1980) 31–6.
11. Anon., Improving tea quality and stalk extraction by electrostatic means. *Food Trade Rev.*, **38**(2) (1968) 58.
12. Anon., Clods and spuds. *Bull. Inst. Phys.*, **26** (1975) 523.
13. Anon., X-Ray unit detects minute glass particles, metal, stone. *Food Proc. (Chicago)*, **34**(6) (1973) 47–8.
14. Montgomery, J. M., *Water Recycling in the Fruit and Vegetable Processing Industry*. Consulting Engineers Inc., Calif., USA, 1981.
15. Krochta, J. M. and Bellows, R. J., Cleaning of food. *Food Technol.*, **28**(2) (1974) 34–7, 47.
16. Irving, G. W. and Hoover, S. R., Food quality. Publication No. 77, American Association for the Advancement of Science, Washington, D.C., USA, 1965.
17. Krochta, J. M., Graham, R. P. and Rose, W. W., Cleaning of tomatoes using rotating rubber discs. *Food Technol.*, **28**(12) (1974) 26–34.
18. Johnson, A. H. and Peterson, M. S., *Encyclopedia of Food Technology*. AVI, Westport, Conn., USA, 1974.
19. Chamberlain, C. J., Opportunities for ultrasonics. *Food Process.*, **52**(10) (1983) 35–7.

CHAPTER 3

THE SORTING AND GRADING OF FOODS

As stated in Chapter 2, sorting and grading may be regarded as separation operations; sorting being separation into groups with differing physical properties and grading being separation into groups with differing quality characteristics.

3.1. SORTING AND GRADING—GENERAL CONSIDERATIONS

3.1.1. PRODUCT DAMAGE
The causes and effects of product damage are referred to in Chapter 1 (Section 1.6). The control of damage is important at all times but is particularly so during sorting and grading. First, the food, having been grown, harvested, transported to the factory and cleaned, has accumulated appreciable labour and process charges. Damage during sorting and grading, where the material has a relatively high value, therefore results in a substantial economic loss to the processor. Secondly, sorting and grading are the last separation stages before processing. Damage and its consequent spoilage, therefore, are likely to be transmitted to the finished product, affecting its quality and the effectiveness of the process to which it is submitted.

3.1.1.1. Drop damage
The emptying of containers (dumping) on to sorting belts and falls from sorters can cause extensive product damage. Many devices are used for minimising damage of this type, ranging from simple padded collecting chutes to more complex arrangements such as that illustrated in Fig. 3.1. In

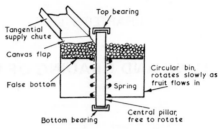

FIG. 3.1. A pivoted bin-discharge arrangement for a sorting machine.

this machine, the size-sorted fruit is fed via a canvas chute into a spring-loaded tray which is free to rotate within the bin. The influx of the fruit causes the tray to rotate slowly and, as the loading increases, the tray sinks, limiting the drop distance to a minimum.

Damage caused by emptying containers on to conveyors may be controlled by simple devices such as that depicted in Fig. 3.2. This consists of a frame in which the full container is placed. The frame is fitted with a padded, spring-loaded hinged lid and is pivoted above the conveyor so as to limit the drop to a minimum. Tipping the loaded frame is assisted by a coil spring, the flow of food being controlled by the hinged lid.

Dumping into water reduces drop damage but the product must be conveyed away immediately, either mechanically or by water-fluming, otherwise damage as a result of material to material impacts may occur.

Studies aimed at controlling drop damage aerodynamically showed typical values for the terminal velocities of fruits as given in Table 3.1. Since falls of only a few centimetres are sufficient to damage many raw materials,

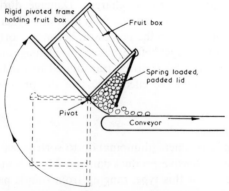

FIG. 3.2. A dumper for crated fruit.

TABLE 3.1
Typical values for terminal velocities of various
fruits

	Terminal velocity (m s^{-1})
Apples	44
Apricots	35
Blackberries	19
Cherries	25
Peaches	44
Plums	35

After Quackenbush *et al.*[1]

these figures suggest that air-cushioning, to be fully effective, would require upward air streams of similar magnitudes to the terminal velocities. The conclusion was that the provision of this would probably be too costly but this interesting concept would, possibly, repay further investigation.

3.1.1.2. Operator damage
The operation of sorting machinery and the grading of food require much human intervention and are monotonous occupations. Inattention reduces effectiveness of grading and causes malfunctioning of sorting equipment. Careful study of the ergonomics involved, i.e. the relationship between the operator, his machine and the surroundings, is important in controlling this variable. Thus the correct working height and location of machinery, the lighting and colour scheme of the work area and the relief of tedium by the use of background music are often useful in improving efficiency.

Efficient training of operators is also of great importance. For instance, considerable damage can be caused by picking up several fruits at a time instead of singly, each contact point being a potential damage area. Again, overlong finger nails can cause puncture damage and produce infection.

3.1.2. REASONS FOR SORTING
Sorting plays an important part in controlling the effectiveness of many food processes. Sorted foods have the following desirable attributes:

(i)　They are better suited to mechanised operations such as peeling, blanching, pitting and coring.

(ii)　They are necessary in processes in which uniformity of heat transfer is critical (e.g. sterilisation and pasteurisation) and they are advantageous in processes in which uniformity of heat transfer is desirable (e.g. dehydration and freezing).

(iii) They give better control over the weights filled into standard sale containers.

(iv) In consumer use, sorted products are more attractive to the eye and allow the serving of uniformly sized portions. This latter point is of particular importance in catering packs.

3.1.3. SORTING MACHINE PRINCIPLES

Sorting machines exploit property differences in order to separate the food into desired and undesired streams. The more important property differences used in food sorting are listed below:

(i) *Weight*, as used in sorting of eggs, fruits and vegetables.

(ii) *Size*, as applied in screening and in length and diameter separators.

(iii) *Shape*, as used in disc and cylinder sorters.

(iv) *Photometric characteristics*, as used in colour and transmission sorters.

(v) *Aero- and hydrodynamic behaviour*, as used in aspirators and buoyancy separators.

(vi) *Surface nature*, as used in dodder and needle sorters.

Although machines based on these principles are, primarily, single property separators (i.e. sorters), they may, in some applications, function as multiple property separators (i.e. graders). These latter applications are discussed in Section 3.6.

Automatic property discrimination has received much study[2,3] in attempts to replace costly manual methods by mechanical procedures.

3.2. WEIGHT SORTING

Concurrent with increasing raw material costs is the demand for sorting equipment of improved efficiency. Since the weight of a food unit is proportional to the cube of its characteristic dimension, weight sorting is capable of more precise separation than is dimensional sorting. For this reason weight sorting devices are replacing size sorters increasingly. Meat cuts, fish fillets and similar materials which are to be sold by weight may be weighed manually or, more generally, weighed on a computing-type scale. This automatically records the piece-weight, computes the price and delivers a printed, adhesive ticket which is affixed to the pack.

In another system, manufactured by Precision Engineering Products

Ltd, Suffolk, England, food units are weighed on a computer-controlled weighing head. The computer selects the best combination of items to make up a required weight and groups these together on a conveyor for processing or packaging. The machine assembles about 30 groups of items each minute and substantial reduction in over-weighting losses are claimed.

Many fruits (e.g. apples, pears and citrus fruits) and vegetables (e.g. potatoes, carrots and onions) are sorted by weight. Typical weight-sorting machines carry fruits in tared canvas pockets attached to pivoted beams fitted with counterbalance weights. As the beams pass along the sorter, the beam fulcrum is moved towards the counterbalance weight until such time as the weight of the fruit causes the beam to tip, discharging the fruit into padded chutes in weight categories.

In the UK, eggs, almost invariably, are sorted by weight. Weighings are carried out on a 6–12 station beam balance. Each balance has a counterweight which is pre-set to deliver eggs of a predetermined weight. Unsorted eggs are carried on a conveyor synchronised with the weighing assembly, the eggs being picked up in fingers attached to the weighers. The beam is raised with the conveyor stopped, heavy eggs are discharged into collecting chutes whilst light eggs are lowered back on to the conveyor for passage to the next weigher and the operation is repeated. Machines of this type are capable of weighing to considerable accuracy (0·5 g) at high speeds ($10\,000$ eggs h^{-1}).

Recent developments in weight-sorting machines involve the use of electro-mechanical and hydrostatic transducers to sense weight differences and improved devices, often computer-controlled, for directing the weighed units into collection chutes.

A novel approach to the problems of high-speed weighing is represented by a machine which measures, electronically, the cross-section dimensions of potatoes at $\frac{1}{4}$ in intervals along their length axes.[4] These dimensions are converted into weights by a computer which then sorts the potatoes into four weight categories at rates up to 4500 kg h^{-1}.

Weight-sorting using a catapult principle[5] is claimed to sort apples, accurately and without damage, at rates of 6000 fruits an hour into 12 weight categories. The fruits are fed, singly, into adjustable spring-loaded catapult arms which hurl the fruit into one of 12 padded collection-chutes carried on a momentum-absorbing frame. The height of the trajectory of the fruit and hence the position of the chute which collects it is related to the weight of the fruit.

The design and operation of automatic weighing machines is discussed in Section 19.8.2.

3.3. SIZE SORTING

Screens of various designs are widely used to effect size separation of foods. The engineering considerations relating generally to screens are dealt with in Chapter 4, whilst reference is made to the use of screens for cleaning in Chapter 2. The screen designs most commonly encountered in food sorting are classified in Fig. 3.3.

3.3.1. FIXED APERTURE SCREENS
Screens of this type are permanently clad with screen beds having apertures of fixed size and shape. Various types of bed material may be used depending on the application. Metal sheets perforated with holes, slots or other shapes, mesh-wire, wedge-wire, cloth and silk of various weaves are used. Movement of the food on the screen bed may be produced by rotary, vibratory or gyratory movement of the frame carrying the screen bed. Fixed aperture screens in general use for food sorting fall into two groups—flat-bed and drum types.

3.3.1.1. Flat-bed screens
This type of screen in its simplest form, as a pitched, stationary frame clad with a screen bed, still finds application for preliminary sorting of potatoes, carrots and turnips on the farm. Multideck flat screens (described in Section 2.3.1.1) find extensive use in the size sorting of raw materials (e.g. cereals and nuts) and of part-processed and finished foods, such as flour, sugar, salt, herbs and ground spices.

3.3.1.2. Drum screens
One type of drum screen has been described in Section 2.3.1.1 as a cleaning screen, but drum screens are used extensively as size sorters for peas, beans and similar foods which will withstand the tumbling action produced by the drum rotation. Drum sorters are usually required to separate the feedstock into more than two streams, so that two or more screening stages are

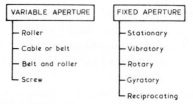

FIG. 3.3. Types of screen used in food sorting.

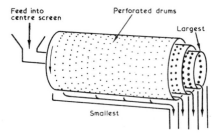

FIG. 3.4.   Diagram of a concentric drum screen.

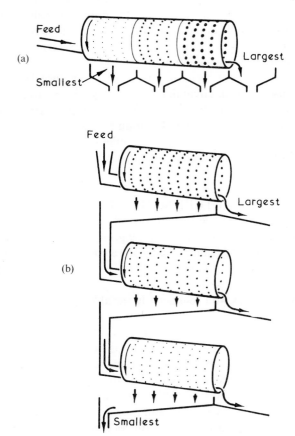

FIG. 3.5.   Consecutive drum screens. (a) Series type. (b) Parallel type.

required. This may be effected by arranging the screens to function concentrically or consecutively.

The concentric drum screen (Fig. 3.4) has the advantage of compactness but, since the feed enters at the centre, this results in the highest product loading on the smallest screen area. *The series-consecutive drum screen* (Fig. 3.5(a)) has the disadvantage of requiring a large floor area. More seriously, since the feed enters at the end which has the smallest aperture screen, the screen tends to become overloaded at the inlet end and inefficient sorting results.

The parallel-consecutive drum screen (Fig. 3.5(b)) overcomes this disadvantage by first contacting the inlet material with the large-aperture screen, leaving the following, smaller-aperture screens to deal with a reduced quantity of near and undersize material. This procedure is repeated at each stage and results in more accurate sorting than is possible with a similarly sized, series screen. Conveying between the screens in the parallel system is usually by water-fluming.

Another type of drum screen which is reported to reduce damage during pea sorting, uses spaced, circumferential, wedge-section rods instead of perforated-screen drums (manufactured by Mather and Platt Ltd, Radcliffe, Manchester, England. Publication No. QP 2697). The spacing of these rods increases in steps from inlet to outlet giving a series-consecutive system. Built-in flights ensure smooth transfer of the peas through the sorter.

3.3.2. VARIABLE APERTURE SCREENS

Size sorters of this type have apertures which may be either continuously variable or stepwise variable. In the former group are included roller, cable and belt sorters, the food being passed along a continuously diverging slot. The latter group includes some types of roller sorters and screw sorters.

3.3.2.1. Sorting screens with continuously variable apertures

The simplest design is that of a pair of inclined driven rollers with an adjustable fall from inlet to outlet. The aperture between the rolls is adjustable and a continuously variable slot is thus presented to the food. The rotation of the rollers orients the food in the position of most regular shape. For example, apples are aligned with the stem–calyx axis parallel to the rolls (Fig. 3.6(a)). Padded collection chutes, located at intervals below the rollers, collect the size-sorted food.

Roller sorting using variable pitch rollers (Fig. 3.6(b)) is the principle involved in the patented Grovesend Grader (Mather and Platt Ltd,

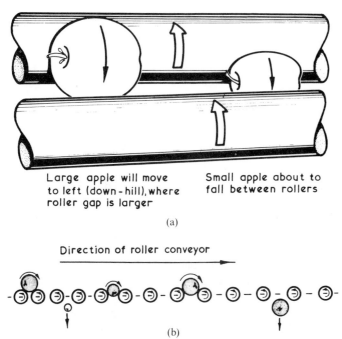

Large apple will move
to left (down-hill), where
roller gap is larger

Small apple about to
fall between rollers

(a)

Direction of roller conveyor

(b)

FIG. 3.6. Roller sorters. (a) Inclined roller type showing the position of apples during sorting. (b) Operating principle of a Mather and Platt 'Grovesend' Grader.

Radcliffe, Manchester, England. Publication No. QP 2697). This consists of a roller conveyor in which the gap between the rollers is arranged to increase regularly from inlet to outlet end of the conveyor. The food (e.g. fruit or root vegetables) remains on the conveyor until it encounters a gap in the rollers through which it falls into a padded collection chute. The roller pitch may be adjusted as required.

In *rope or cable sorters* a diverging aperture is produced by two driven inclined cables or ropes. The cables can be driven at the same or different speeds. Separation takes place on the basis of most stable position, e.g. in the case of pears as illustrated in Fig. 3.7. Sorting is, therefore, on a minimum-dimension basis.

Belt sorters (Fig. 3.8) function similarly, the food being carried along a continuously diverging slot produced by driven inclined belts. There is a tendency for the food to slip through sideways, leading to uneven sorting. This can be corrected, partially, by driving the belts at different speeds. Belt sorters of these types are gentle with the food compared with drums and moving screen sorters and, providing drop damage is minimised, little

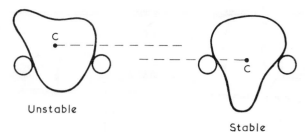

Unstable

Stable

FIG. 3.7.   The position of pears on a rope sorter. C—the centre of gravity of the fruit.

bruising of fruits is caused. They are widely used in fruit-packing houses where ripe fruits are handled in quantity.

Belt sorting efficiency has been improved substantially by the patented system used in the Jansen Fruitsizer (Jansen Patents Ltd, Reading, Berks., England). Here, the fruit is carried on endless felt belts which travel along either side of a 'vee'-shaped channel. The base of the 'vee' is cut away at an incline which slopes upwards from the inlet end of the sorter. Thus an inclined slot of a width which increases continuously from inlet to outlet is produced. The belts are driven at different speeds to produce correct orientation of the units. The fruits, after passing through a short stabilising

INPUT

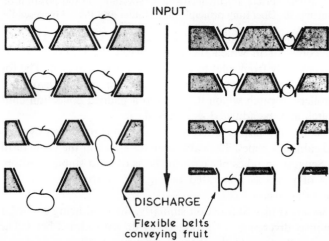

DISCHARGE

Flexible belts
conveying fruit

FIG. 3.8.   The behaviour of fruit during belt sorting. (Left) The diverging belt system where the fruit sinks in the channel throughout the process, producing a tendency for it to slip sideways. (Right) The Jansen 'Fruitsizer' where the fruit remains at a constant depth until sorted.

section, move along the sorter at constant depth in the 'vee', depending on their size. The fruit thus retains its correct orientation until it meets a position in the channel which permits it to fall through to a receiving chute. With diverging belt-sorters, in which the fruit sinks as it moves along, differences in friction between the fruit and the belt produce a tendency for the fruit to slip through sideways (Fig. 3.8).

3.3.2.2. Sorters with stepwise-variable apertures

This group includes some special types of roller sorters, belt and roller sorters, and screw sorters.

Stepwise variation of apertures in roller conveyor type sorters may be arranged by having two banks of driven rollers located one above the other. The top bank of rollers have a fixed spacing which is greater than the diameter of the largest item to be sorted. The bottom rolls are arranged to give a stepwise-variable gap between the two roller banks (Fig. 3.9). The food is both conveyed and rotated by the friction-driven rollers. Cucumbers, gherkins and similar foods with one long dimension may be width-sized on this type of sorter.

The *belt and roller sorter* (Fig. 3.10) consists of a belt conveyor inclined across its width towards driven rollers. The gap between each roller and the belt is adjusted to give the required size categories. The driven rolls cause the fruit to rotate in the position of most uniform shape, e.g. apples with their cores parallel to the rollers. This is an effective high-speed sorting machine but some bruising of delicate fruit is encountered.

The *screw sorter* (Fig. 3.11) carries the food on two partially-intermeshing helices, one of which is continuous whilst the other is divided into sections. The sorting gap between the sections and the continuous helix may be adjusted to give a stepwise increase in aperture. The rotation of the spirals both conveys the food and orients it in the position of most regular dimensions. The helices, which are usually felt covered, rotate relatively slowly and gentle handling of the fruit results.

Sorters such as those described above where a tumbling action is involved tend to damage the product. This is minimised by the use of felt-covered or soft rubber rollers.

Fig. 3.9.   The operating principle of a stepped roller sorter.

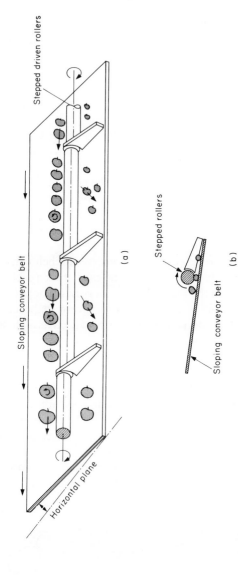

FIG. 3.10. The operating principle of a belt and roller sorter. (a) Oblique view. (b) Section across conveyor belt.

FIG. 3.11. A diagrammatic plan view of a screw sorter.

Length and width sorting may be carried out by conveying the food along slotted channels arranged in cascade. The gaps between the channel-ends increase in steps so that food units unable to bridge these gaps fall through and are thereby sorted on a length basis (Fig. 3.12). Vibration is a convenient method of conveying in these sorters.

Photoelectric size sorting on length or width bases may be effected by electronic measurement of the time required by an object, travelling at constant speed, to pass a sensing device. In a typical example of this system, a narrow, intense beam of light is projected onto the surface of the food piece carried on a constant-speed conveyor. The diffusely reflected beam is focussed onto a 128-photodiode array which generates a signal which varies linearly with the displacement of the food piece. Measurements of

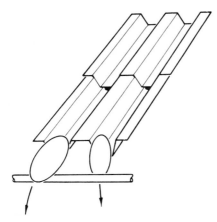

FIG. 3.12. Method of operation of a Sortex 'Polygrada' length sorter. Food pieces pass down the channels in a vibratory feeding table. The step in the table helps break clusters and ensure that the pieces reach the sorting bar in a single stream, one after the other. Short pieces are unable to bridge the gap between the table and the bar while longer pieces can pass over the bar. (By courtesy of Gunson's Sortex Ltd, London.)

length, width and thickness of biscuits, chocolate, etc., may be made at high speed (up to $500 \, s^{-1}$) using such a device.[6]

3.4. SHAPE SORTERS

In some foods, cleaning, followed by size sorting or weight sorting, may still leave the food containing undesirable constituents. For example, cleaned and sorted wheat may still contain weed-seeds of similar size and weight to the wheat. In these circumstances it may be possible to separate on the basis of shape, e.g. the combination of length and diameter.

The disc sorter (Fig. 3.13) is an example of shape sorting. It functions by collecting materials of desired shape in indentations on both sides of rotating, vertical discs. Banks of such discs are mounted on a driven, horizontal shaft and the lower ends of the discs run in a trough of the unsorted food. Foods of the correct shape are held in the indentations until the disc reaches the top of its rotation when the collected material is discharged into troughs. The material in the feed-trough is moved down the machine and, eventually, is discharged. Standard discs are available for wheat, oats, rice and barley and specially indented discs can be made for specific purposes. Standard disc sorters are available with capacities of between $\frac{1}{2}$ and $6 \, tonnes \, h^{-1}$.

The cylinder sorter functions on the same principle as the disc sorter but in this case the internal surface of a rotating, horizontal cylinder is machined with shaped indentations. Foods of the desired shape are picked up by these pockets and are discharged at about top dead-centre into a centrally located channel inside the drum whence the separated material is conveyed away. Thus the material remaining in the drum becomes enriched, progressively, with food-pieces which are unable to enter the shaped indentations.

Shape sorting may also be effected by taking advantage of the propensity of spherical particles to travel down an inclined surface. Thus, spherical seeds may be separated by feeding the food on to an inclined driven belt when spherical units run down against the belt travel, the separated material being carried upwards by the belt and discharged upstream of the feed. This principle has been used to separate snails from blackcurrants and spherical weed-seeds from wheat, barley and other cereals. Similarly, peas may be separated from vine dross and pea viners are often fitted with separators of this type which is generally called a *draper separator*. Other shape-sorters which use sphericity differences to effect separation include:

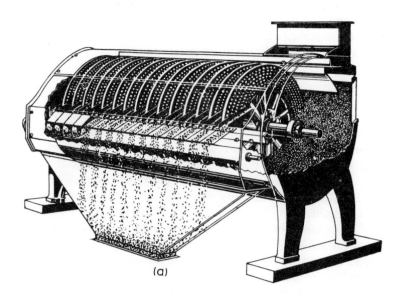

(a)

(b)

FIG. 3.13. A disc separator by Henry Simon Ltd, Stockport, England. (a) A cut-away drawing of the machine. (b) Cross-sections of a wheat disc (left) and a seed disc (right).

machines in which the material is fed, at a controlled rate, onto a horizontal rotating disc, the more spherical particles being ejected peripherally; equipment comprising a horizontal plate which is shaken or bumped at low frequency and which retains non-spherical components of a material fed onto it.

3.5. PHOTOMETRIC SORTING

The reflectance and transmittance characteristics of foods are important indicators of their processing suitability. Reflectance properties are used to indicate: raw material maturity (e.g. the colours of fruit, vegetables, meat, etc.); the presence of surface defects (e.g. worm-holed cereals or bruised fruits); the extent of processing (e.g. of biscuits, bread and potato crisps) and so on. Transmittance measurements of foods are used to determine their internal properties such as ripeness or core defects in fruits, extraneous matter inclusions and blood spots in eggs. When these measurements are used to actuate separation mechanisms then photometric sorting is effected and, if multiple-property assessment is carried out, quality separation, i.e. grading (Section 3.8) may be achieved. Photometric sorting embraces most of the electromagnetic spectrum, ranging from gamma- and X-rays through ultra-violet, visible light, infra-red, microwaves and radio frequencies to measurements (e.g. of resistance) at mains frequency.

3.5.1. REFLECTANCE SORTING

When a material is scanned, that which is seen may range from simple specular reflectance to a complex combination of radiation, scattering and reflection, depending upon the nature of the scanned surface. Thus, a glossy apple provides a different stimulus from that generated by a matt-surfaced apple of the same basic colour. This situation makes colour comparison, in practice, a matter of some difficulty.[7] In many respects, the eye, backed by the discriminatory ability of the brain, is superior to machines but unless provided with a set of comparison standards it is unable to make reliable quantitative assessments. The provision of permanent, truly representative standards represents a major problem in this type of sorting.

Visual colour-sorting is used extensively in the food industry in spite of its limitations. Permanent comparison standards in the form of coloured plastic strips, colour photographs, etc., are used, the food being sorted manually on a conveyor belt. The advantages and limitations of this procedure are discussed more fully in Section 3.8.

Mechanised colour-sorting functions on the basis of photometric scanning of the surface of each food unit as it falls past, or is rotated before

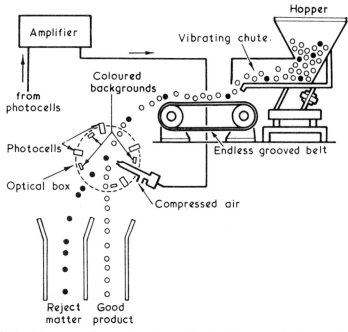

FIG. 3.14. The mode of operation of a pneumatically operated colour sorter. (By courtesy of Gunson's Sortex Ltd, London.)

a photocell. The signal generated by this photocell is compared, automatically, with an adjustable, pre-set standard signal. Imbalance between these two signals is then amplified and used to actuate sorting gear.[8] A typical sorter of this type is shown diagrammatically in Fig. 3.14. Mechanised colour-sorters are widely used to sort, clean and grade foods such as: nuts, cereals and coffee beans containing worm-holes or other defects; diced vegetables, whole potatoes, onions or fruits which are incompletely peeled; citrus fruits and tomatoes exhibiting maturity differences and finished products like jams, peanut butter, butter, crisps, etc., which may have been incorrectly processed. Mechanisation has conferred many advantages compared with manual colour-sorting, notably in reducing labour costs, in increasing throughput and in improving sorting efficiency by eliminating the boredom which impairs the performance of human sorters.

Rejection systems of various types are used. For small, particulate foods, pneumatic procedures as shown in Fig. 3.14 are employed, the signal from the discriminator being used to operate an air jet which deflects substandard material into the reject chute. With larger food units, such as diced vegetables or whole fruits which are presented for scanning individually carried on a vacuumised pick-up wheel, mechanical displacement is used. In the case of foods composed of small particles in which individual treatment would be impractical, a mechanical gate is used to deflect a small amount of the material containing substandard matter. Electrostatic separation may be used, also, the reject material being charged by an electrode and then withdrawn from the bulk of the product by an oppositely-charged electrode or deflector.

3.5.2. TRANSMITTANCE SORTING

Non-destructive internal examination of solid foods and monitoring of opaque, liquid foods by transmitted electromagnetic radiation offer attractive prospects to food processors. Application is complicated by the fact that relatively small amounts of the incident energy are transmitted by other than thin sections of many food materials. The transmitted energy may amount to as little as 0·1% of the incident energy so that very sensitive detection systems are necessary, e.g. in the examination of fruit or vegetable tissue.[7]

Manual procedures using this principle are exemplified by the candling of eggs which is described in Section 3.8. A further example is the use of a fluorescent screen to visualise X-ray transmission through solid foods followed by manual operation of reject devices. A study aimed at using this concept for automatic in-line sorting[9] reports satisfactory discrimination with thin or low-density products, such as foil sachets of dried soups or packets of potato crisps, but poor performance with thick food sections or dense products like fruit cake or canned meat. However, successful machine-sorting using this principle to sort grain, apples, lettuces and nuts have been reported.[2,10]

Transmission of light through apples, tomatoes, peaches, etc., may be related to the presence of internal defects such as core and stone rots and to chlorophyll levels in the flesh and hence to produce ripeness. Spectrophotometers using fibre-optic illuminators may be used to detect internal characteristics and to use the information to effect sorting when linked to appropriate rejection devices.[11]

3.6. BUOYANCY AND/OR DENSITY SORTING

Sorting machines which exploit differences in aero- and hydrodynamic behaviour find wide application in food processing.

Pneumatic classification or aspiration has been described in Section

2.3.1.3 as a cleaning procedure, but multi-stage aspiration also functions as an effective and efficient sorting system for cereals, peas, beans, groundnuts and walnuts.[2] Pneumatic principles are discussed in Section 19.6.

Hydrodynamic sorting is based on the theory discussed in Section 19.7 and buoyancy separation and froth flotation are described in Section 2.3.2.3. This method may be used to separate bruised and sound fruit such as apples, whilst peas of differing maturity (and hence size and density) may be separated in brines of differing density (see Section 3.8.3.3). In-line density-sensing devices and density-sorting equipment for fruits and vegetables are described in the literature.[2]

Combination aerodynamic and shape sorting is employed in a sorting machine in which material is fed to the upper end of an inclined, porous deck through which air at controlled velocity is passed; this provides an inclined air-slide. Separation then takes place on the basis of the combination sphericity and aerodynamic properties of the mixture components.[12]

3.7. MISCELLANEOUS SORTING METHODS

Electrostatic separations using differences in response to an electric field have received considerable attention.[7] Spherical non-conducting particles (e.g. seeds) exposed to an electric field accumulate smaller charges than those particles which have sharp corners. These charge differences may be used to sort materials of different shape by passing the charged material onto a rotating, earthed roller—when the more highly charged, irregularly shaped, components are more firmly attached to the roller (or 'pinned') than the more spherical components of the mixture. Thus these latter are discharged from the roller earlier in its travel than the particles which are more firmly pinned. This principle is used widely in seed cleaning (grasses, alfalfa, clover, etc.) and has been successfully employed for tea sorting. In this application, tea at 3–4% moisture is metered onto an earthed roller rotating at 70–350 rpm under a transverse bar electrode connected to a 5–20 kV electrical source. Tea fragments, stalk and fibre are collected at adjustable positions in the roller travel.

Electrostatic discrimination along similar lines to the above is also used in a modification of the colour sorter described in Section 3.5.1.

Surface property differences, such as surface roughness or stickiness or the presence of surface punctures (e.g. worm holes), are used in sorting peas, beans and cereals. Thus dodder-mills may be used to separate seeds with rough skin-coats which are preferentially retained when passed through an inclined rotating cylinder lined with muslin, velvet or flannel.[12] Again, certain weed seeds, e.g. buckthorn become sticky when damp and may be removed, as agglomerates, by screening.

Also of interest is the principle involved in a sorter designed to remove worm-holed or cracked peas from sound material. This is done by feeding the raw material into a slowly-rotating, inclined drum which is lined with fine needles which project inwards. Damaged peas are picked up by the needles and are then discharged into a collecting trough located inside the drum below top dead-centre. The whole peas are swept aside by the needles and travel slowly down the base of the drum under the influence of gravity to the discharge point located at the lower end of the drum.

3.8. GRADING OF FOODS

Grading, or quality separation, depends on an overall assessment of those properties of the food which affect its acceptance as a food or as a working substance for the food processor.

3.8.1. THE GRADING OPERATION

The term 'quality' has different connotations for different commodities and the relative importance of the component material properties which contribute to the overall suitability index (see Chapter 1) of a food ingredient depend on its destined end-use. Grading, therefore, involves overall, balanced assessment of all those properties of a material which affect its acceptance as a food and as a working substance for the processor. More often than not, grading involves simultaneous evaluation of multiple properties so that mechanical grading is a matter of some complexity. For this reason, grading is frequently carried out manually.

Whilst separations based on size, shape, colour, etc., discussed under sorting (Section 3.1.3), up-grade the material it is seldom that any one of these is sufficient, by itself, to determine quality. It is for this reason that it is considered worthwhile to differentiate between separation on the basis of single properties and to call this sorting and separation on multiple properties (i.e. quality) and to call this grading.

3.8.2. GRADING FACTORS

In general terms, the properties of a food which determine its quality fall conveniently into four groups. These are properties controlling: (i) process suitability; (ii) consumer safety; (iii) conformity with legal requirements and (iv) consumer acceptance.

There are at least as many grading standards as there are materials to be graded but grading statements commonly specify the following:

(i) *Size and shape:* as functional and acceptability factors.

(ii) *Maturity:* freshness of eggs; ripeness in fruit; ageing in meat.

(iii) *Texture:* crumb structure in bread and cakes; crispness in celery and apples; viscosity of cream.

(iv) *Flavour and aroma.*

(v) *Function,* i.e. the suitability of the food for its end use, e.g. the milling and baking properties of flour; the canning and freezing properties of fruits and vegetables.

(vi) *Freedom from blemish:* cloudy yolks, blood spots or shell cracks in eggs; bruises in fruits; insect holes in coffee beans.

(vii) *Colour:* as affecting process and consumer acceptance.

(viii) *Freedom from contaminants:* rodent hairs and insect parts in flour; soil and spray residues on fruit; micro-organisms and their by-products in meat; toxic metals in shellfish, etc.

(ix) *Freedom from undesired parts of the raw material:* bone fragments in meat products; leaf or pod residues in peas and beans; stalks or stones in fruit.

(x) Conformity with legal standards or codes of practice.

Quality standards are the responsibility of a number of regulatory bodies at national, continental and world-wide levels.[13] National standards are imposed: by statutory regulations; by codes of practice (e.g. The Fruit and Vegetable Canners Code, 1965, in the UK) and by independent bodies such as The British Standards Institution (BSI). Continental regulations may also be effective, e.g. those set up by the UN Economic Commission for Europe (ECE) or by the European Economic Community (EEC). These latter provisions apply to both international and domestic trading and although national standards may still apply, in all cases, these must either comply with, or be improvements upon, the EEC standards. Thus, with the entry of the UK into the Common Market in 1973, Britain is required to comply with EEC standards established up to that date and with all subsequent regulations (over which the UK will exercise some control). World-wide standards are being established for many processed foods. This is the responsibility of the Codex Alimentarius Commission which represents 89 member-countries. The aims of this body are to harmonise national and international standards and to facilitate international trade.

3.8.3. GRADING METHODS

These fall into two groups: (i) procedures in which the quality is determined by laboratory tests on samples drawn statistically from a batch of food, (ii) procedures which result in the physical separation of the total quantity of the food into quality categories. The first group is, properly, the province of quality control and is outside the province of this book.

The second type of grading may be carried out manually or, in a few cases, by specialised machines. In either case, the food units must be presented singly to the grader for assessment.

3.8.3.1. Presentation for grading

At its simplest, presentation may be arranged by aligning the food on an inspection belt which is often located at the end of a sorting machine. More sophisticated presentation devices are represented by the roller-table, operating on the principle illustrated in Fig. 2.4, and by the spiral-roller table.[14] The latter comprises pairs of longitudinal, driven rollers fitted with helical grooves. The pairs of rollers provide pockets in which the food-pieces are rotated whilst being conveyed along the inspection table. It is usual to divide tables of these types into lanes by fitting longitudinal rods or partitions. Other inspection procedures include the use of vibratory tables or channels and rotating wheels equipped, peripherally, with vacuum

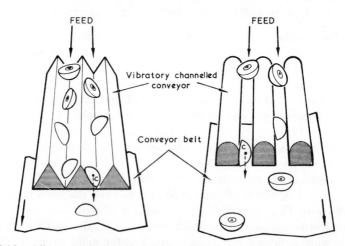

Fig. 3.15. Alignment devices for bringing halved, pitted fruit to the 'cup-up' or 'cup-down' positions. The devices ensure that on discharge from the vibratory conveyor the centre of gravity (C) of the piece lies to the appropriate side of the point of contact of the fruit-half and the conveyor belt.

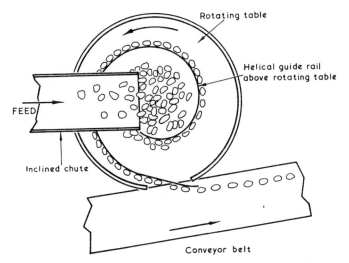

FIG. 3.16. Diagrammatic plan view of an unscrambling table.

ferrules which pick up food-pieces, rotate them for viewing and then release them at a given signal. Specialised alignment gear may be employed such as that used to inspect peeled peach-halves for defects like peel and pit residues, colour defects and blemishes. The peach-halves are fed on to an inclined vibrating table at the end of which are located comb-like projections with either rectangular or 'vee'-shaped cross sections. In passing through these projections, the fruit-halves are aligned, first cup-up and then cup-down, allowing all-round inspection of the food (Fig. 3.15). Another alignment device in common use is the unscrambling table, as used in some types of colour sorter. The food is fed, at a controlled rate, to the centre of a slowly rotating horizontal disc. Above, and just clear of the disc, is fitted a helical guide-rail. Friction between the food, the disc and the guide-rail results in the food being transformed from a pile in the centre of the disc to a single row of food units at the edge of the disc. Deflection on to an inspection band or through a mechanical scanner then permits individual inspection (Fig. 3.16).

3.8.3.2. Manual grading
Much grading is carried out by trained human operators who are able to assess a number of grading factors simultaneously. The grader forms a balanced judgement of the overall quality and physically separates the food into quality categories. Comparison is made using permanent colour

standards in the form of plastic strips or models or coloured represent-
ations either printed or photographed onto cards. Apples may be graded
using colour cards depicting various grades in terms of: proportion of the
surface showing characteristic fruit colour; extent of russeting; variation in
discolouration; surface imperfections and shape conformity. Cherries grown
in Canada are compared against models made from spheres of plastic, fitted
with nylon stems, which are dipped into specially formulated lacquers
coloured to reproduce the appearances of fruits at different stages of
maturity. Permanent standards are available for a wide variety of raw and
processed foods but although these are useful and sometimes indispensable
they have limitations. Differences in colour sensation as a result of the
different surfaces provided by the food and the standard (resulting in
different degrees of reflectance and scattering) and shape variations (e.g. a
spherical fruit surface as against a flat comparison surface), introduce
inaccuracies.

Eggs are graded manually by '*candling*'. This is a non-destructive
examination of the egg contents through the translucent shell when the egg
is spun in front of a powerful light in a darkened booth. The presentation of
each egg is automatic and a candling operator can separate several
thousand eggs an hour into 3–4 grades, taking into account up to 20
grading factors. In certain cases, light at specific wavelengths may be used.
Thus, blood spots in eggs are best detected when light at 577 and 597 nm is
used whilst green rot is revealed by fluorescence at 490 and 510 nm[7]

Meat carcases are graded by inspectors whose training enables them,
almost at a glance, to assess quality in terms of maturity, the likely eating
qualities of the meat and the bone to flesh ratio of the carcase.

Manual grading has many disadvantages, the most important being the
high cost of labour and its availability, particularly in the case of seasonal
foods, when manpower is in high demand elsewhere. Additionally,
boredom and fatigue, even though offset by the means indicated in Section
3.1.1.2, lead to reduced grading efficiency and corresponding financial loss.

Improvements in manual grading effectiveness often result from simple
adjustment of the working environment such as ensuring that station-
spacing, working height and conveyor speed are optimised. Again, the
provision of suitable humidity, temperature, lighting and seating should
receive attention. More elaborate aids include the provision of illumination
and grading belts of suitable colour, i.e. Hall[12] recommends illumination at
400–490 nm as being suitable for grading red cherries. Recently closed
circuit television cameras have been used to scan foods in the visible and
X-ray parts of the spectrum.[6] Graders 'mark' substandard components

using a light-pen and thus separate inclusions, misshapen and bruised, immature and damaged materials.

3.8.3.3. Machine grading

In some cases it is possible to combine a group of sorting operations so as to separate foods on a quality basis. Thus wheat of a particular variety (which determines its 'function', as defined in Section 3.8.2) may be graded by a combination procedure such as that set out in Fig. 2.6 (Chapter 2).

In other cases, it is possible to take advantage of the fact that a single property of the food is an index of its quality. Thus, small peas are recognised to be the most tender and of highest quality,[13] so that size sorting of cleaned peas results in quality grading. Again, there is good correlation between the density of peas and their tenderness so that they may be graded by flotation in brines of varying densities. A continuous brine-grader using this principle has been marketed (The Key Brine Grader, Key Manufacturing Co., USA).

In potatoes, high solids content (which is reflected in high density) is desirable in the manufacture of dehydrated mashed potato, potato crisps and french fries so that brine separation may be used to quality grade potatoes.

Optical property differences may be used to sort foods, but when used as multiple property indicators, can operate as grading principles.[15] In one example of the application of the above concept, sizing of peeled potatoes and separation of blemished product and extraneous matter is carried out using a video camera which scans the potatoes as they are spun beneath the camera by a driven roller conveyor. A computer, linked to the camera, interprets its signals, computes the magnitude of the measured quantity, comparing this with a preset standard and actuating a pneumatic ejector if this is exceeded. This machine is claimed to grade potatoes at rates of up to $10 \, \text{tonnes} \, \text{h}^{-1}$ and application to grading citrus fruits, peppers and avocados is planned.[16]

In another, similar, application, an important quality criterion—the lean-to-fat ratio in meat—is determined using video image processing. Block-frozen boneless meat is carried on a black conveyor belt beneath a video camera operating at $50 \, \text{frames} \, \text{s}^{-1}$. Each block takes $4 \, \text{s}$ to pass the camera and is thus scanned 200 times. A microprocessor calculates a statistical average visual lean/fat ratio.[17]

Considerable research effort is being devoted to the search for single material properties which reflect overall quality. One notable development is the correlation of the ultrasonic characteristics of animal tissues to the eventual yield and quality of the carcase. Instruments using this principle are now available which provide reliable prediction of carcase quality.[18] Current studies concerning single property quality indicators include:

(i) *Optical property discrimination* using reflectance, transmission, holography, delayed light emission and fluorescence measurements.[2,7]

(ii) *Spectrophotometric procedures* using infra-red, near infra-red, gamma-ray and X-ray radiation.[2,7]

(iii) *Electrical methods* exploiting differences in dielectric, microwave, nuclear magnetic resonance and resistance properties.[2,7]

(iv) *Mechanical property grading* using differences in resonance, vibrational, density and buoyancy behaviour.[2,3]

Clearly, mechanised grading has many advantages compared with manual grading, such as speed, reliability and low labour costs. It is to be expected that efforts will continue to develop mechanised grading principles similar to those indicated, in order to replace manual methods.

REFERENCES

1. Quackenbush, H. E., Stout, B. A. and Reis, S. K., Pneumatic tree fruit harvesting. *Agric. Engng*, **43** (1962) 385–93.
2. Gaffney, J. J. (ed.), *Quality Detection in Foods*. American Society of Agricultural Engineers, Mich., USA, 1976.
3. Mohsenin, N. N., *Physical Properties of Plant and Animal Materials*. Gordon and Breach Science Publishers, New York, 1980.
4. Anon., Tubers measured in 3D. *Amer. Veget. Grower*, **23**(1) (1975) 30.
5. Maggs, D. H., Catapult fruit grading. *Food Technol. Aust.*, **25**(11) (1973) 554–61.
6. McFarlane, I., *Automatic Control of Food Manufacturing Processes*. Applied Science Publishers, London, 1983.
7. Mohsenin, N. N., *Electromagnetic Radiation Properties of Foods and Agricultural Products*. Gordon and Breach Science Publishers, New York, 1984.
8. Anon., Gunson's Sortex nutcracker sweet. *Confection. Product.*, **51**(6) (1985) 311–12.
9. Preece, K., Detection of foreign bodies. *Food Manuf.*, **47**(9), (1972) 21–2, 51.
10. Williams, D., Sawyer, C., Conklin, W. C. and Robe, K., X-ray scanner removes stones from almonds on conveyor belt. *Food Process.*, **44**(11) (1983) 56–7.
11. Rosenthal, R. D. and Webster, D. R., On-line system sorts fruit on basis of internal quality, *Food Technol.*, **27**(7) (1973) 52–60.
12. Hall, C. W., *Processing Equipment for Agricultural Products*. AVI, Westport, Conn., USA, 1963.

13. Arthey, V. D., *Quality of Horticultural Products.* Butterworths, London, 1975.
14. Allshouse, G. W. and Stephenson, K. Q., Development of a handling and sorting system for certain fruits and vegetables. *Trans. Amer. Soc. Agric. Eng.,* **12**(3) (1969) 290–4.
15. Deshpande, S. S., Cherayan, M., Gunasekaran, S., Paulson, M. R. and Salunke, D. K., Non-destructive optical methods of food quality evaluation. *CRC Crit. Rev. in Food Sci. and Nutr.,* **21**(4) (1984) 323–79.
16. Cowlin, R., TV cameras focus on quality. *Food Process.,* **55**(7) (1986) 21–3.
17. Anon., Ultrasonic grading. *Food Engng Int.,* **6**(9) (1981) 53–5.
18. Winstanley, M., Bristol-AFRC Institute of Food Research. *Food Sci. and Technol. Today,* **1**(1) (1987) 28–31.

PART II

CONVERSION OPERATIONS

CHAPTER 4

SIZE REDUCTION AND SCREENING OF SOLIDS

4.1. GENERAL PRINCIPLES

4.1.1. INTRODUCTION

Comminution, the breakdown of solid material through the application of mechanical forces, is a frequent requirement in many food processing operations. The reasons for size reduction are varied.

(a) Size reduction may aid the extraction of a desired constituent from a composite structure, e.g. flour from wheat grains or juice from sugar cane.

(b) Reduction to a definite size range may be a specific product requirement, e.g. as in the manufacture of icing sugar, in the preparation of spices and in chocolate refining.

(c) A decrease in particle size of a material leads to an increase in surface of the solid. This increase in surface is of assistance in many rate processes, e.g.

(i)   the drying time for moist solids is much reduced by increasing the surface area of the solid.

(ii) the rate of extraction of a desired solute is increased by increasing the contact area between solid and solvent.

(iii) process time required for certain operations—cooking, blanching, etc.—can be reduced by cutting, shredding or dicing the process material.

(d) Intimate mixing or blending is usually easier with smaller size ranges of particles, an important consideration in the production of formulated, packaged soups, cake mixes, etc.

4.1.2. NATURE OF FORCES USED IN SIZE REDUCTION

Three types of force are generally recognised. In a comminution operation more than one type is usually present.

The types of force predominating in some of the mills in common use in the food industry are summarised as follows.

Force	*Principle*	*Machine*
Compressive	Compression (nutcracker)	Crushing rolls
Impact	Impact (hammer)	Hammer mill
Shear (attrition)	Attrition (grindstone)	Disc attrition mill

Compressive forces are used for the coarse crushing of hard materials. Impact forces can be regarded as general purpose forces and are used for coarse, medium and fine grinding of a variety of food materials. Attrition or shear forces are extensively used in machines for the comminution of softer, non-abrasive, materials in the smaller size ranges, i.e. in fine grinding.

The term crushing is often applied to the reduction of coarse material down to a size of about 3 mm. Grinding is the term commonly used for the production of powdered material. Crushing is more often associated with the application of compressive forces and grinding with attrition forces.

4.1.3. NUMBER OF REDUCTION STAGES FOR A GIVEN PROCESS

In a comminution process the product particles from a mill will often vary widely in size. It is often necessary to classify these particles into particular ranges of sizes. A product specification will commonly require a finished product not to contain particles greater than (or less than, depending on the process) some specified size. In comminution studies particle size is frequently referred to as screen aperture size (Section 4.7.1).

The complexity of a size reduction plant, that is, the number of individual units and intermediate size separation stages required, varies with the feed and desired product size ranges. For the reduction of relatively large, solid lumps to finely divided powder, several stages will be required, each stage capable of handling a given size reduction. Figure 4.1 shows a flow sheet for a typical size reduction plant employing three reduction stages.

4.1.4. REDUCTION RATIO (R.R.)

The ratio,

$$\frac{\text{Average size of feed}}{\text{Average size of product}}$$

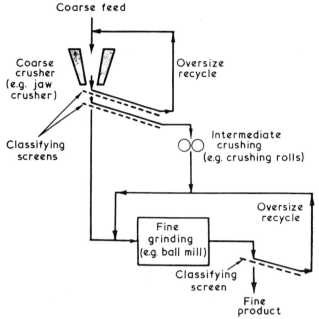

FIG. 4.1.   A typical size reduction flow sheet.

is known as the reduction ratio and can be of use in predicting the likely performance of a particular machine. Coarse crushers have size reduction ratios of below 8:1, but for fine grinding, ratios as high as 100:1 can be realised. Much depends on the particular machine and feed material. The values for average size of feed and product depend on the method of measurement. Several different average diameters are in use, depending on the methods used for the determination of particle size distribution and statistical interpretation of the results obtained. In the food industry, because of its simplicity as well as applicability over a wide range of particle sizes, sieving is the favoured method (Section 4.7.4).

4.2.   CONSIDERATIONS GOVERNING EQUIPMENT SELECTION

The aim of an economic size reduction process is to achieve the desired reduction at minimum cost. Capital, operating and maintenance costs all play a part in determining the profitability of a process and these charges, for the various possible alternatives available, must be carefully considered before selecting a particular comminution line. Consideration of the alternative machines, when working to the particular process requirement, is imperative. In general, a knowledge of the characteristics of the feed material, possible machines and of the product material will be necessary.

One of the first steps in specifying size reduction equipment is to find out as much as possible about the characteristics of the feed material.[1] North lists a number of characteristics which may require to be considered.[2] These include: hardness; toughness; abrasiveness; stickiness; softening or melting temperature; structure; specific gravity; free moisture content; chemical stability; homogeneity; and purity. Those properties of importance in any particular process vary widely. Some properties likely to be important in food processing are discussed below.

4.2.1. HARDNESS AND ABRASIVENESS OF FEED

Although not normally a primary consideration in food processing operations, a knowledge of the hardness of the feed material can be important in selecting comminution equipment. Hardness is related to the modulus of elasticity for the material;[3] a hard material may be brittle and fracture rapidly after exceeding the elastic limit or it may be ductile and deform extensively before breakdown. This influences the ease of breakdown and the energy required to bring it about (Section 4.6—see also Loncin and Merson).[4] In general, harder materials are more difficult to comminute. More energy is required and residence times in the 'action zone' must be longer. This may necessitate either (a) a slower throughput for a given mill or (b) a larger capacity mill to satisfy a particular duty. Hard materials are usually abrasive so wear of working surfaces can be pronounced. These surfaces should be fabricated in hard wearing materials of construction, such as manganese steel, and should be easily replaceable. To reduce wear, a mill for reducing the size of a hard material is relatively slow moving. It will also be of robust construction to withstand the mechanical stresses developed. For these reasons maintenance on these machines is sometimes overlooked.

4.2.2. MECHANICAL STRUCTURE OF FEED

A knowledge of the mechanical structure of the feed material can indicate the type of force most likely to effect disintegration. If the material is friable, or has a crystalline structure, fracture may occur easily along cleavage planes, larger particles fracturing more readily than smaller ones. In these cases, crushing, using compressive forces is employed.

If few cleavage planes are present and new crack tips have to be formed, impact and shear forces may be better. Many food materials have a fibrous structure and are not easily disintegrated by compressive or impact forces so shredding or cutting is required.

4.2.3. MOISTURE

The presence of water can both aid and hinder a comminution process. With many materials, moisture content in excess of 2–3% can lead to clogging of the mill. Throughput and grinding efficiency may suffer. Agglomeration or 'balling' can also occur in the presence of moisture. This is undesirable if a free flowing, finely powdered food material is required. Dust formation, arising during the dry milling of many solids, can cause problems.

(a) Prolonged inhalation of otherwise non-toxic dusts can lead to dangerous respiratory diseases and operatives must be protected against such possibilities.

(b) Many solid food materials are, in a finely divided condition, extremely inflammable and dust explosions are not unknown in the food industry.

The presence of small quantities of water helps suppress dust and, in applications where the presence of water is acceptable, water sprays are often used for this purpose. In the food industry it is frequently necessary to strictly control the moisture content of the feed, e.g. in the milling of wheat,[5] so dust control by other methods must be used.

In some food processing applications, a water stream is used to transport feed particles through the action zone of a mill in the form of a free flowing slurry. Wet milling (Section 4.4.5) is widely used in corn milling.

4.2.4. TEMPERATURE SENSITIVITY OF FEED

In the action zone of a mill, inter-particle friction arises. Particles can also be stressed within their elastic limits without fracture, the strain energy absorbed being released as heat when the stress is removed. Heat arising from both these sources can lead to a considerable rise in temperature of the material being processed and degradation could occur.

Besides a knowledge of the chemical stability of heat sensitive materials their softening or melting temperatures are also of importance. If heat generated leads to the development of a sticky charge, clogging of the mill and a reduction in the efficiency of the process may well result. Cooling facilities—jackets, coils, etc.—may be required round the action zone if heat sensitive materials are being handled.

Cryogenic comminution, using solid carbon dioxide or liquid nitrogen mixed with the food, can be used to prevent the loss of heat labile components during size reduction. The method is also useful for the production of finely divided products from fibrous materials, meats, etc., which tend to deform rather than break under an applied stress.

4.3. SIZE REDUCTION EQUIPMENT

Machines of various types and sizes are available for the comminution of food materials.[6]

Larger types of coarse crushers such as jaw crushers and gyratory crushers are not normally encountered in the food industry.

The more common types of machines used are discussed below.

4.3.1. CRUSHING ROLLS

In this machine, two or more heavy steel cylinders revolve towards each other (see Fig. 4.2). Particles of feed are nipped and pulled through the rolls, experiencing a compressive force which crushes them. In some machines a differential speed is maintained between the rolls and shearing forces also arise.

The throughput of these units is governed by roller length and diameter and by the speed of rotation. With larger diameters, speeds of 50–300 rpm

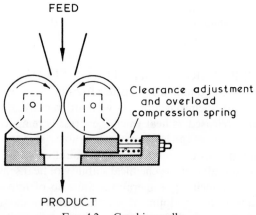

FIG. 4.2.   Crushing rolls.

are usual. Size reduction ratios are low—usually below 5. The diameter of the rolls, differential speed of the rolls and the 'nip', the spacing between the rolls, can be varied to suit the feed size and throughput rate required. An overload compression spring protects the roller surface from damage, but hard foreign bodies should be removed before crushing.

4.3.1.1. Angle of nip

The angle formed by the tangents to the roll faces at the point of contact between a particle and the rolls, the 'angle of nip', is of importance in specifying the size of a pair of crushing rolls for a given duty.

If A is the angle of nip, D_f the average diameter of the feed particles, D_p the average diameter of the product particles, D_r the diameter of the rolls, it can be shown[9] that

$$\cos\frac{A}{2} = \frac{D_r + D_p}{D_r + D_f} \qquad (4.1)$$

For the limiting case when the particle is just pulled into the rolls by friction:

$$\tan\frac{A}{2} = \mu \qquad (4.2)$$

where μ is the coefficient of friction between the particle and the rolls.

4.3.1.2. Capacity of crushing rolls

The theoretical capacity of these units is the volume of the continuous ribbon of product discharged from the rolls.

For a machine with roll diameter D_r m, and length of face l m, when the nip is D_p m and the roll speed is N rpm, the volumetric capacity (Q) is given by

$$Q = \frac{\pi D_r N D_p l}{60} \text{ m}^3 \text{ s}^{-1} \qquad (4.3)$$

Knowing the bulk density of the discharge stream the approximate mass flow rate may be estimated. In practice the actual capacity is found to lie between 0·1 and 0·3 of the theoretical capacity.

Crushing rolls are used for intermediate crushing and find wide application in the milling of wheat and in the refining of chocolate. In other modifications the roll surfaces may be studded or fluted to aid friction and nip. The orientation of the roll flutes can influence mill performance and the quality of semolinas produced.[7] Single roll crushers which compress the feed between the roll and a stationary breaker plate find use in the crushing of more friable materials.

4.3.2. HAMMER MILL

This type of impact, or percussion, grinder is common in the food industry (Fig. 4.3).

A high speed rotor carries a collar bearing a number of hammers around its periphery. When the rotor turns, the hammer heads swing through a circular path inside a close fitting casing containing a toughened breaker plate. Feed passes into the action zone where the hammers drive the material against the breaker plate. Reduction is mainly due to impact forces, although under choke feeding conditions (Section 4.4.3) attrition forces can also play a part in the size reduction. The hammers are often replaced by cutters, or by bars as in the beater bar mill. The hammer mill may be regarded as a general purpose mill, handling crystalline solids,

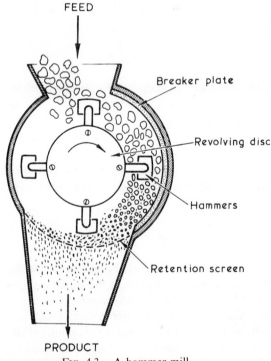

FIG. 4.3.   A hammer mill.

fibrous materials, vegetable matter, sticky materials, etc. In the food industry it is extensively used for grinding peppers and spices, dried milk, sugars, etc. Due to excessive wear, impact mills are not recommended for the fine grinding of very hard materials.[8]

4.3.3. DISC ATTRITION MILLS

Mills utilising attrition or shear forces for size reduction play a major part in fine grinding. Since much of the milling carried out in the food industry is for the production of very small particle sizes, this type of mill finds extensive application. Two types of disc mill are shown in Fig. 4.4.

4.3.3.1. Single disc mill

In this device the feed stock passes into a narrow gap between a high speed, rotating grooved disc and the stationary casing of the mill. Intense shearing action results in comminution of the feed. The gap is adjustable, depending on feed size and product requirements.

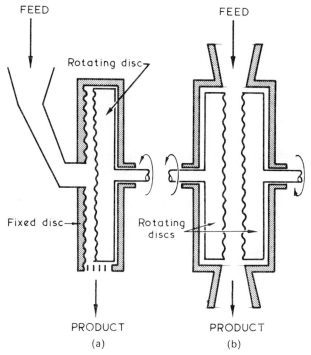

FIG. 4.4.   Disc mills. (a) A single disc mill. (b) A double disc mill.

4.3.3.2. Double disc mill

In this modification the casing contains two rotating discs. The discs rotate in opposite directions giving a greater degree of shear than that attainable in the single disc mill. In yet another modification to this basic principle, the Foos mill, the discs carry studs which aid disintegration. This type of disc attrition mill is widely used in cereal preparation, corn and rice milling.

The pin-disc mill, popular in the food industry, carries pins or pegs on the rotating elements. In this case impact forces also play a significant part in the breakdown of particulate matter.

4.3.3.3. Buhr mill

This is an older type of disc attrition mill, originally used in flour milling.

Two circular stones are mounted on a vertical axis. The upper stone, which is often fixed, has a feed entry port (Fig. 4.5). The lower stone rotates.

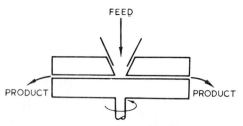

Fig. 4.5.   A Buhr mill.

Feed material passes to the gap between the upper and lower stones. The material, after subjection to the shearing force developed between the stones, is discharged over the edge of the lower stone. In some models both stones rotate, in opposite directions. In modern machines, toughened steel stones are replacing the traditional 'natural' or 'composition' stones.

This type of mill is still being used in the wet milling of corn for the separation of starch gluten from the hulls.

Other variations of this type of grinding mill are extensively used in chocolate manufacture. For example, cacao nibs are crushed in horizontal triple stone grinding machines, although here again more modern processes are utilising hardened steel, toothed discs in place of stones.

4.3.4. TUMBLING MILLS

A mill extensively used in many process industries for fine grinding is the tumbling mill.

Two basic types, the Ball mill and the Rod mill, are available.

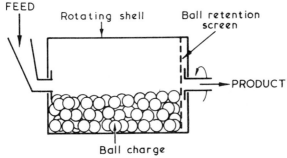

FIG. 4.6. A ball mill.

4.3.4.1. Ball mills

In the ball mill (Fig. 4.6) both shearing and impact forces are utilised in the size reduction.

The unit consists of a horizontal slow speed rotating cylinder containing a charge of steel balls or flint stones. As the cylinder rotates balls are lifted up the sides of the cylinder and drop on to the material being comminuted, which fills the void spaces between the balls. The balls also tumble over each other, exerting a shearing action on the feed material. This combination of impact and shearing forces brings about a very effective size reduction. Ball sizes are usually in the range 25–150 mm (1–6 in). Small balls give more point contacts but larger balls give greater impact. As with all grinding mills, working surfaces gradually wear, so product contamination must be guarded against.

At low speeds of rotation the balls are not lifted very far up the walls of the cylinder. The balls tumble over each other and shear forces predominate. At faster speeds the balls are lifted further and the impact forces increase. Attrition and impact forces play a part in reduction. At high speeds the balls can be carried round at the wall of the mill under the influence of centrifugal force. Under these conditions grinding ceases. For efficient milling the critical speed should not be exceeded. This is defined as the speed at which a small sphere inside the mill just begins to centrifuge.[9] It can be shown that the critical speed N_c, in rpm, is given by

$$N_c = \frac{42 \cdot 3}{(D)^{1/2}} \qquad (4.4)$$

where D is the diameter of the mill, in metres.

In practice, the optimum operating speed is about 75% of the critical speed and should be determined under the plant operating conditions.

A variation of the conventional ball mill finding increasing use for very fine grinding is the vibration ball mill. In this device the chamber containing the grinding media is caused to vibrate by means of out of balance weights attached to each end of the shaft of a double-ended electric motor. The energy imparted by the walls of the grinding chamber is transmitted to the media and the material to be ground. The latter fills the interstices between the grinding media. The void space in these mills can be varied by using different shaped media. In the Vibro Energy mill[10] using spheres the void space is about 37% whereas with cylinders it falls to 25%. At lower voidages the layers of trapped material become thinner and conditions for ultrafine grinding improve. The media vibrate without appreciable relative movement so shearing forces are minimal, the force developed being essentially that of impact. Vibration mills are also finding use in mixing and dispersing applications.

4.3.4.2. Rod mills
In the rod mill, the balls are replaced by high carbon steel rods. Impact and attrition forces still play a part but the effect of impact forces is less pronounced. Rod mills are recommended for use with sticky charges where balls can be trapped in the mass of the charge and become ineffective. The rods run the full length of the mill and, as with a ball charge, occupy about 50% of the mill volume.

4.4.   MODES OF OPERATION OF SIZE REDUCTION PLANT

Several operating methods can be considered. Not all will be applicable for a given feedstock and process requirement. Ideally, the object is to achieve the desired size reduction at minimum cost.

4.4.1.   OPEN CIRCUIT GRINDING
This is the simplest method of operating a mill (Fig. 4.7). No ancillary classifying systems (vibrating screens, etc.) are used so the capital outlay for the plant is low. Feed enters the mill, passes through the action zone and is discharged as a product. No recycle of oversize particles (having a size range greater than that desired) is possible. Since some large particles pass rapidly through the mill and other small particles have long residence times in the mill, a wide size distribution in the product results. Power utilisation is poor, since acceptable sizes of particles are still further reduced due to the excessive retention period in the action zone.

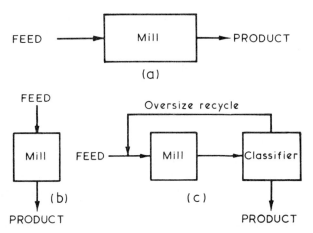

FIG. 4.7.   Methods of mill operation. (a) Open circuit grinding. (b) Free crushing.
(c) Closed circuit grinding.

4.4.2. FREE CRUSHING

With this method of operation residence time in the action zone is kept
short. When used in conjunction with open circuit grinding, this is
commonly accomplished by allowing the feed material to fall through the
action zone under gravity. Unnecessary breakdown of small particles is
limited so the formation of undersize particles (particles smaller than the
desired size range) is reduced. This mode of operation is more economic on
power consumption but, since some large particles rapidly pass through the
action zone, a wide size range of product can result.

4.4.3. CHOKE FEEDING

In choke feeding the discharge of product is restricted by inserting a screen
in the outlet from the machine. For a given feed rate, material remains
choked in the action zone of the mill until reduced to a size capable of
passing the screen. Since residence times can be long, excessive grinding of
smaller particles is likely, so undersize particles are produced at the expense
of a high power consumption. Choke feeding is useful when a finely divided
product is required. It affords a fairly large size reduction ratio from a single
machine.

4.4.4. CLOSED CIRCUIT GRINDING

The method of operation is shown diagrammatically in Fig. 4.7(c). The
residence time of material in the mill is kept short, either by gravity fall, or

by rapid transport through the action zone in a gas or liquid stream. The discharge stream from the mill passes to a classifying system where oversize material is removed and recycled back to the mill. In this way the mill works on bigger particles, so wasteful power consumption is minimised. The classification methods employed depend on the mode of transport. With a gravity or mechanical conveyor flow, vibrating screens are commonly used. With hydraulic or pneumatic transport, cyclone separators are often used.

4.4.5. WET MILLING

If the feed material is wet, or can be wetted without harm, this method of operation may be considered. The feed stock is ground as a suspension in a carrier liquid stream—often water. Dust problems associated with dry milling are overcome and hydraulic classification techniques such as elutriation, sedimentation and centrifugation may be employed for separating desired size fractions.

Very often in food processing the milling is part of an extraction process, a soluble constituent of the feed being transferred to the liquid stream for recovery by evaporation, as in corn milling.

Experience shows that power consumption is generally high with wet grinding. Mill wear may also be increased. Wet-milling tends to produce finer particles than those obtainable with dry milling operations. For this reason this mode of operation finds extensive application in ultrafine grinding applications (see also Section 5.2.2.6).

4.5.   DISINTEGRATION OF FIBROUS MATERIALS—SLICING, DICING, SHREDDING AND PULPING

4.5.1. INTRODUCTION

The foregoing principles of size reduction are applicable to frangible materials requiring reduction to granular or powdered forms when the feed is either dry, or contains little liquid. A wide range of substances fall into this category, including sugars, spices, peppers, nuts, cereals and dried foods. Many other foodstuffs requiring comminution (e.g. meat, fresh fruits and vegetables) have a fibrous structure and contain appreciable quantities of liquid. Being non-crystalline, the direct application of compressive forces may contribute little to their disintegration. Compressive forces do play a part in expression, another unit operation involving size reduction in which the object is to extract liquid (e.g. fruit juice) from the body of the material (Chapter 8).

In general, impact and shearing forces, often applied via a cutting edge, are used in the disintegration of fibrous materials. Much of the equipment used is similar to that used for dry, powdered materials. For example, hammers in a percussion mill can be replaced by a series of knives which apply the impact force along a thin cutting edge. Again, disc attrition mills may carry studs or serrations on the faces of the discs: these impart a tearing action.

In more specialised size reduction operations a uniformly sized and specific shape of particle may be required to simplify handling, aid rate processes such as dehydration or heat treatment, or to improve product appearance. Again, fibrous solids may require conversion into soft, semi-solid pulps, a common requirement in jam manufacture. These more specialised size reduction operations usually employ specially designed equipment. One of the commonest of these more specialised cutting operations is slicing.

4.5.2. SLICING

Sliced fruits are much in demand as a dessert dish. They present an attractive appearance, the portions produced being of a convenient size for eating. Rotary cutting knives are usually employed, the knives being set to cut the material being presented to them, often on a vibrating belt, into parallel slices of the desired thickness. In other fruit slicing operations the fruit is forced through a tube containing stationary knife edges arranged radially along the length of the tube. This type of assembly can produce decored, wedge shaped sections from firmer fruits such as apples.

4.5.3. DICING

Dicing—the cutting of material into cubes—usually follows a preliminary slicing operation which produces slices of the desired thickness. These slices are then fed onto a conveyor belt containing a series of studs which hold the slices in position as the belt carries them against a rotary knife assembly which cuts them into strips. The strips then pass through a further cutting zone at right angles to the stripping section. This produces the required cube.

4.5.4. SHREDDING

In shredding, the food material is torn into small fragments, the average size of the pieces depending on the type of machine and on residence time in the action zone. Shredding often precedes dehydration, the increase in surface aiding the rate process. Hammer mills are commonly used as shredders. The rotating shaft carries a number of discs, each having a series of impact edges around its periphery. The hammers can also be pivoted so as to produce a flailing action. Squirrel cage disintegrators—twin concentric cylindrical cages having their surfaces built up of cutting edges running along the length of the cylinders—are useful for shredding fibrous materials. The feed material is introduced into the inner cage and passes into the action zone between the cages, which rotate in opposite directions. The material is torn apart by the intense shearing and cutting action to which it is subjected, the shredded material passing through the outer cage to a product hopper.

4.5.5. PULPING

Pulping is another comminution operation, widely used in the processing of lower grade fruits separated during grading (Chapter 3). The fruit, which is edible but unacceptable for whole fruit processing, may be used in jam manufacture. A combination of pulping and sieving is used with many fruits and vegetables. A common form of pulper consists of a cylindrical perforated screen containing high speed rotating brushes. Material is fed to the inside of the cylinder, the brushes forcing pulped material through the perforations. Stalks, skins and stones pass over the screening surface as reject (Section 4.7.1). An alternative form of this machine has high speed paddles to help the breakdown of fruit. Screen sizes vary with the particular product requirement; finely dispersed, solid-liquid pulps being obtained with correct choice of perforations. Some fruits are softened by heating before pulping, the softening often leading to higher pulp yields.

4.5.6. ENERGY REQUIREMENT FOR A CUTTING OPERATION

Little work has been carried out on the energy requirement for a cutting operation. Friction and elastic deformation[4] of the material during cutting both play a part in the wasteful dissipation of energy during breakdown (Section 4.6). Well maintained cutting edges will reduce these losses.

4.5.7. MAINTENANCE OF CUTTING EDGES

Besides limiting energy losses, well sharpened knives also reduce the incidence of poor quality (i.e. badly bruised and torn) material which commonly arises when blunt or damaged cutting surfaces are used. For extended cutting edge life, knives should be made of hardened alloy steel or similar material and all foreign matter (stones, metal scrap, etc.) likely to damage the knives should be removed during the cleaning stage. Blade assemblies carried on high speed rotating shafts may well be in balanced pairs so their removal, sharpening and replacing should be performed with care.

4.6. ENERGY REQUIREMENTS FOR COMMINUTION OF SOLIDS

Little fundamental work on the energy consumption in such disintegration operations as cutting, shredding and dicing has been carried out. Somewhat more is known of the breakdown of friable materials. Two stages of breakage are recognised:

(1) initial fracture along existing fissures or cleavage planes in the body of the material;

(2) the formation of new fissures or crack tips, followed by fracture along these fissures.

A particle may be defined as a discrete element of a solid, regardless of its size.

When stress (force/area) is applied to a particle through the application of a force the particle may first deform and then break. Depending on the nature of the applied force and the mechanical resistance—all properties which describe the behaviour of a solid material under these conditions[4]— the material may either: (i) undergo elastic deformation, i.e. deform within the elastic limit and return to its original shape when the force is removed, or (ii) exceed the elastic limit and deform permanently (inelastic deformation), if sufficient stress is applied.

With increasing applied stress inelastic deformation continues until the yield stress of the material is exceeded. The particle may then rapidly rupture (brittle materials) or continue to deform (ductile materials) until finally breaking when the ultimate (breaking) stress is reached. The ultimate stress is a property of the material, but the size and structure of particles also influences their ease of breakdown and in consequence the energy required to reduce their size.

Particles contain planes of weakness along which breakdown may be initiated when the particle is stressed. With larger particles cleavage may occur along existing fissures (cleavage planes). With smaller particles new planes of weakness must be generated via crack-tips which are initiated under the influence of the stress. Since smaller particles contain fewer, if any, existing fissures, their breaking strength is higher. Greater energy is required to initiate new crack-tips so the energy required for particle breakdown increases as the size of the particles decrease. Elastic deformations are valueless in comminution since, although energy is utilised, no particle breakdown is initiated. The energy stored in straining the particle is lost when the stress is released. This and inter-particle friction make size reduction operations extremely inefficient with respect to energy utilisation.

It is generally accepted that little of the input energy to a comminution plant is usefully utilised in the breakdown operation. Only a small percentage of the energy supplied to the machine appears as increased surface energy in the solids. Figures of less than 2% are quoted, so grinding is a very inefficient process. Much of this input energy is lost in deforming the particles within their elastic limits and through friction between particles. This wasted energy appears as heat which, as we have seen, can lead to heat damage (Section 4.2.4).

Theoretical considerations suggest that the energy dE required to produce a small change dx in the size of unit mass of material can be expressed as a power function of the size of the material. Thus

$$\frac{dE}{dx} = -\frac{K}{x^n} \tag{4.5}$$

This equation has been used by a number of workers.

4.6.1. RITTINGER'S LAW (1867)

Rittinger considered that for the grinding of solids, the energy required should be proportional to the new surface produced and put $n = 2$.
Then

$$\frac{dE}{dx} = -\frac{K}{x^2}$$

or, integrating

$$E = K\left[\frac{1}{x_2} - \frac{1}{x_1}\right] \tag{4.6}$$

x_1 is the average initial feed size, x_2 is the average final product size. E is the energy per unit mass required for the production of this new surface and is usually measured in horsepower hour ton^{-1}. K is called Rittinger's constant and is a constant for a particular machine and material.

Rittinger's law has been found to hold better for fine grinding, where a large increase in surface results.

4.6.2. KICK'S LAW (1885)

Kick considered that the energy required for a given size reduction was proportional to the size reduction ratio, which requires that $n = 1$.

Then

$$\frac{\mathrm{d}E}{\mathrm{d}x} = -\frac{K}{x}$$

or

$$E = K\ln\frac{x_1}{x_2} \tag{4.7}$$

x_1/x_2 being the size reduction ratio (Section 4.1.4).

Kick's law has been found to hold more accurately for coarser crushing where most of the energy is used in causing fracture along existing fissures. It gives the energy required to deform particles within the elastic limit.

For many crushing operations the energy requirement suggested by Kick's law appears to be too low, whereas that required by Rittinger's equation appears to be excessive.

4.6.3. F.C. BOND (1952)—THIRD LAW OF COMMINUTION

In Bond's work,[11] n takes the value 3/2 giving

$$\frac{\mathrm{d}E}{\mathrm{d}x} = -\frac{K}{x^{3/2}}$$

or

$$E = 2K\left[\frac{1}{(x_2)^{1/2}} - \frac{1}{(x_1)^{1/2}}\right] \tag{4.8}$$

When x_1 and x_2 are measured in micrometres and E in kWh short ton^{-1} (907·16 kg),

$$K = 5E_i$$

where E_i is the Bond Work Index—the energy required to reduce unit mass of material from an infinite particle size to a size such that 80% passes a 100 micrometre sieve.

The Bond Work Index is obtained from laboratory crushing tests on the feed material. The third theory holds reasonably well for a variety of materials undergoing coarse, intermediate and fine grinding.

4.7. SCREENING

Screening is the unit operation in which a mixture of various sizes of solid particles is separated into two or more fractions by passing over a screen. Each fraction is more uniform in size than the original mixture. A screen is a surface containing a number of equally sized apertures. The surface may be plane (horizontal or inclined) or it may be cylindrical. Small capacity plane screens are called sieves. In general processing, screening is widely used for separating mixtures of granulated and powdered materials into size ranges. Some degree of overlap with other unit operations occurs since screens are used in filtration (Chapter 6) to separate coarse, or fibrous solid materials from a liquid phase and in the food industry for the sizing and grading of fruits and vegetables (Chapter 3). This section is concerned with the separation of solids on the basis of size.

Besides its use in the industrial separation of a feed material into two or more size ranges of particles for specific process purposes, screening, or sieving, is used in particle size analysis to determine particle sizes and size distributions of powdered materials.

4.7.1. SCREENING TERMINOLOGY

Undersize, fines or minus (−) *material*—material passing through a given screen.

Oversize, tails or plus (+) *material*—material failing to pass a given screen.

Either stream may be the desired (product) stream, or the undesired (reject) stream, depending on the particular application.

Screen aperture—the space between the individual wires of a wire mesh screen.

Woven wire sieves for laboratory particle size analysis were formerly designated by a mesh number, defined as the number of wires per lineal inch. Though this designation has now been deleted from the latest British Standard for Test Sieves (BS 410: 1986) and from the International Sieve Specification, it is still widely encountered in industry.

Screen aperture and mesh number are not the same. For a given screen aperture, the mesh number will depend on the thickness of the wire forming the screen.

Screen interval—the relationship between successively decreasing openings in a standard screen series.

Several different screen series are in use:

(a) Tyler Standard. This is a widely used series based on a 200 mesh screen having 0·0021 in diameter wires and a screen aperture of 0·0029 in. The ratio between apertures in consecutive screens is $(2)^{1/2}$. For closer sizing a Tyler series having a screen interval of $(2)^{1/4}$ is used.

(b) British Standards. This screen series is based on BS 410: 1986 'Test

Sieves'.[12] A 170 mesh screen will have a nominal aperture size of 90 μm and there is a screen interval of approximately $(2)^{1/4}$ between neighbouring screens.

(c) American Society for Testing Materials. ASTM-E 11. This series is based on an 18 mesh screen with a 1·0 mm aperture and a screen interval of $(2)^{1/4}$.

A number of sieves in both the BS and the US sieve series correspond to the International Standards Organisation (ISO) recommendations for test sieves. ISO 565 recommends a sieve series which corresponds to alternate sieves in the US series.

Diameter of a sieve fraction—The average diameter of a fraction passing a given sieve, but retained on the next smaller in the series, is often taken as the arithmetic average of the two screen apertures.

Diameter of solid particles—The particle dimension controlling its retention on a particular sized screen is often called its diameter. Particles encountered in industry are usually irregular in shape. An average diameter is used. This average diameter depends on the method of measurement so a number of different particle diameters are in common use. This can lead to confusion if the particular diameter used is not stated.

4.7.2. INDUSTRIAL SCREENS
Industrial screens are made from metal bars, perforated plates and cylinders, or woven wire cloth and fabrics. Materials of construction for screens handling foodstuffs include stainless steel, Monel metal and nylon fabric.

4.7.2.1. Grizzlies or bar screens
These are used for screening larger particles—pieces greater than 25 mm. They consist of a set of parallel bars, spaced to the desired separation. The bars are often wedge-shaped to minimise clogging (Fig. 4.8). They may be used horizontally or inclined at angles up to 60°. Vibrating grizzlies are available, the feed material passing over the screening surface in a series of jerks.

4.7.2.2. Vibrating screens
The simplest vibrating screens consist of a frame supporting a wire mesh screen or a perforated plate. They can be shaken mechanically or electromagnetically, the motion carrying feed material across the screen surface. They are normally inclined to the horizontal and are widely used in

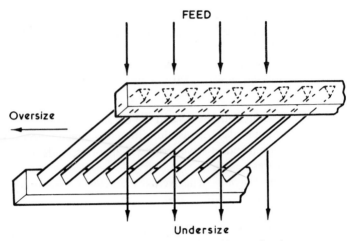

FEED

Oversize

Undersize

FIG. 4.8. A bar screen with triangular section bars.

grading fruits and vegetables, when perforated screens are used. These screens may be multi-deck units, a series of screens being mounted beneath each other, permitting separation of a given feed stock into several size ranges.

4.7.2.3. Reels or trommels

These units are revolving cylindrical screens mounted almost horizontally. Again the screening surface may consist of wire mesh or perforated sheet. Hexagonal cross-sections are also used since these lead to agitation which aids the separation of fine material. Wire mesh or fabric screens are used with powders and circular perforations for fruit and vegetable grading.

The capacity of a trommel increases with increasing speed of rotation until a critical speed is achieved. At speeds greater than this, the material does not cascade over the surface but is carried round by centrifugal force and separation is seriously impaired.

The critical speed of a trommel is given by equation (4.4)

$$N = \frac{42 \cdot 3}{(D)^{1/2}}$$

N is the number of revolutions of the trommel per minute, D is the diameter of the trommel in metres.

Specialised types of sizing equipment used in fruit and vegetable preparation are discussed in Chapter 3.

4.7.3. FACTORS AFFECTING THE EFFICIENCY OF A SCREENING OPERATION

Ideally, the object of screening is the complete separation of desired from undesired material. A number of factors can influence the degree of separation achieved.

(i) *Rate of feeding.* If the feed rate is too high, insufficient residence time on the screening surface will result. The screen becomes overloaded and material capable of passing leaves with the oversize.

The angle of inclination of the screen also influences residence time. Too steep an angle will result in insufficient residence time while too small an angle may restrict gravity flow across the screen.

(ii) *Particle size.* Even though sufficiently small, the particle will only pass the screen if its alignment, relative to the openings, is favourable. Large particles tend to impede the passage of smaller, and a preliminary separation may be required if a high proportion of bigger particles are present.

(iii) *Moisture.* The presence of moisture in the feed can cause adhesion between small and large particles. Undersize particles will be removed with the oversize materials.

(iv) *Worn or damaged screens.* Oversize particles will pass through the damaged area and the efficiency of the separation will be impaired. Damaged screens should be repaired immediately. Fine screens are very fragile and should be treated with great care.

(v) *Blinding (clogging) of screens.* Blinding or clogging of the openings is particularly likely to occur when the size of the particles is near to that of the screen aperture. Particles capable of passing are prevented from doing so and are carried over with the oversize. Blinded screens should be cleaned immediately or screening efficiency will suffer.

(vi) *Electrostatic charge.* In screening dry powders, surfaces may become charged. Small particles can clump together and leave the screening surface with the oversize, rather than the undersize, stream. Grounding the screen will avoid any agglomeration as well as preventing possible build-up of high-voltage static electricity in potentially explosive environments.[13]

4.7.4. LABORATORY SIEVING

For size analysis by screening, standard laboratory sieves up to 16 mm aperture are used. The usual range of particle size measured using this method is 50–3000 μm. The size of coarser particles is usually determined by direct measurement.

Details of laboratory particle size analysis techniques for powders using fine mesh test sieves are available in publications of the British Standards Institute. Of these, BS 3406 discusses powder sampling before sieve analysis and BS 1796: 1976 the method, its associated nomenclature and the presentation of results. British specifications for test sieves in the range 16 mm down to 32 μm are given in BS 410: 1986.

REFERENCES

1. Peleg, M. and Bagley, E. B., *Physical Properties of Foods*. AVI, Westport, Conn., USA, 1983.
2. North, R., Grinding practice as related to the characteristics of materials to be pulverised. *Trans. Inst. Chem. Eng.*, **32**(1) (1954) 56–60.
3. Lewis, M. J., *Physical Properties of Foods and Food Processing Systems*. Ellis Horwood and VCH, Chichester, England, 1987.
4. Loncin, M. and Merson, R. L., *Food Engineering Principles and Selected Applications*. Academic Press, New York, 1979.
5. Kent, N. L., *Technology of Cereals*, 3rd edn. Pergamon Press, Oxford, 1983.
6. McCabe, W. L., Smith, J. C. and Harriot, P., *Unit Operations of Chemical Engineering*, 4th edn. McGraw-Hill, New York, 1985.
7. Dexter, J. E., Martin, D. J. and Matsuo, R. R., The effect of roll flute orientation on durum wheat. Experimental milling performance and semolina quality. *Canadian Inst. Food Sci. Technol. J.*, **21**(2) (1988) 187–93.
8. Prem, H. and Prior, M., Impact mills for fine size reduction. *The Chemical Engineer*, **351** (December 1979) 841–4.
9. Brown, G. G. and Associates, *Unit Operations*. John Wiley and Sons, Chichester, England, 1950.
10. Podmore, H. L., Vibration grinding in close packed media systems. *Chemy Ind.*, **34** (1967) 1443–50.
11. Bond, F. C., Some recent advances in grinding theory and practice. *British Chemical Engineering*, **8** (1963) 631–4.
12. British Standard 410: 1986, British standard specifications for test sieves. British Standards Institution, London.
13. Stone, L. H., Protecting screening machines from product they process. *Chemical Engineering Progress*, **78** (December 1982) 64–8.

CHAPTER 5

MIXING AND EMULSIFICATION

5.1. MIXING

5.1.1. INTRODUCTION

Mixing operations in the food industries are of many types, involving solid, liquid and gaseous phases and mixers are frequently classified on the basis of the nature of the phases involved in the mixing process.

Two definitions of mixing often encountered are:

(i) An operation in which two or more components are interspersed in space with one another.

(ii) An operation which tends to remove non-uniformities in the properties of materials in bulk, e.g. colour, temperature, composition etc.

Though perfectly adequate for many mixing processes, e.g. blending of liquids, this approach can disguise the fact that in other applications, although components are interspersed in space and non-uniformities in properties reduced, the objective—mass transfer, or chemical reaction, for example—is something more than simple mixing.[1]

Regardless of the ultimate objective, the aim in the mixing device is to achieve a uniform distribution of the components by means of flow. The flow is normally generated by mechanical means.

The degree of uniformity attainable in a mixing process varies widely. With miscible liquids, or soluble solids in liquids, very intimate mixing is possible, though with more viscous liquids and widely differing densities mixing becomes more difficult to achieve. This is also the case where the amount of one of the components is small compared to others in the mix.

With immiscible liquids, paste-like materials and dry powders, the degree of uniformity obtainable is likely to be less.

The efficiency of a mixing process depends on the effective utilisation of the energy used to generate the flow of the components. The provision of adequate input energy, the design of the mechanical agency introducing the energy, the configuration of the containing vessel and the physical properties of the components are all important in the design of a mixer.

In the food industries the materials fed to a mixer may vary from low viscosity liquids to highly viscous pastes or dry powders. With liquid systems the flow conditions may be laminar or turbulent. However, a large transition region exists between the two.

Laminar mixing is normally associated with liquids having viscosities greater than about $10 \, kg \, m^{-1} \, s^{-1}$. These high viscosity fluids may also be non-Newtonian. Since the resistance to flow is high, flow currents are rapidly damped out and these fluids will require to be mixed in vessels carrying impellers which sweep out the greater proportion of the mixer vessel volume. The impellers (anchors, helical ribbons, helical screws) will be large diameter and their speed of rotation relatively low. However, high shear rates and associated extensional flows are produced in the laminar regions near the impellers and these deform and stretch the fluid elements, leading to an increase in surface area and a reduction in thickness of the elements each time they are exposed to the high shear regions.[1] Suspended solids, droplets or bubbles present in the fluid are reduced in size and dispersed.

Turbulent mixing is encountered when liquid viscosities are less than about $10 \, mkg \, m^{-1} \, s^{-1}$. The resistance to flow is less than in laminar mixing so properly directed flow currents initiated by a rotating impeller can circulate throughout the vessel. The impellers (propellers, turbines, simple paddles) can be considered as caseless pumps which impart energy to the fluid. Impeller diameters are smaller and impellers have higher speeds of rotation than is the case with laminar flow. Again, the rate of mixing is greatest near the impeller where the rates of shear are highest but, since mixing due to eddy diffusivity occurs along the complete flow-path, mixing is much more rapid than with laminar flow.

Though the newer, continuous 'in-line' mixers (Section 5.1.3.6) have become increasingly popular in recent years, mechanically agitated vessels are very widely used. Three basic types can be considered.

Type (1)—Stationary vessel containing a moving stirrer, agitator, paddle, i.e. an impeller or impeller assembly mounted on a rotating shaft (Fig. 5.1). Impellers mounted in vertical tanks are widely used for mixing low-

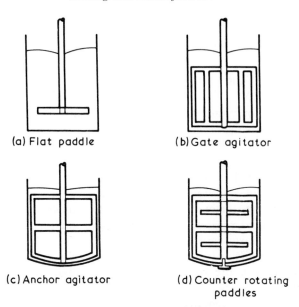

(a) Flat paddle

(b) Gate agitator

(c) Anchor agitator

(d) Counter rotating paddles

FIG. 5.1. Some typical paddle impellers.

viscosity liquids, free-flowing liquid/solid suspensions, and for the dispersion of gases in liquids.

Type (2)—Stationary vessel containing moving paddles, vanes, knives, ploughs, screws, etc. These mixers have been developed for mixing higher-consistency materials—viscous liquids, doughs, pastes, fats, etc.

Type (3)—Moving vessel containing moving and/or stationary paddles, vanes, knives, ploughs, screws, etc. Mixers in this category are used for very high consistency mixes—doughs, pastes and plastic materials.

These three classes of mixer cater for low, intermediate and high consistency mixes. Types (2) and (3) also handle dry powders. The objective, common to all three types, is the promotion of flow.

As the consistency of the components of the mix increases and the generation of flow becomes more difficult the type of impeller used changes from relatively small diameter propellers and turbines to larger paddles, screws etc., which sweep out a greater proportion of the containing vessel. The speed of rotation of the impeller system will also be less as will the fluid capacity handled. Though the smaller turbine and propeller impellers operate best under turbulent conditions (that is, with low viscosity, Newtonian liquids) they do find wide use for mixing moderately viscous or non-Newtonian systems. Godfrey[2] gives maximum viscosity values as -20 poise for propellers and 600 poise for turbines.

5.1.2. MIXERS FOR LIQUIDS OF LOW OR MODERATE VISCOSITY

The most commonly used form of mixier for handling low or moderate viscosity liquids is the mechanically-agitated impeller mixer. This type of mixer consists of one or more impellers, fixed to a rotating shaft, which create currents within the liquid. These currents should travel throughout the mixing vessel. It is not sufficient simply to circulate the liquid; if possible, turbulent conditions should be created within the moving stream.

When a moving stream of liquid comes into contact with stationary or slow-moving liquid, shear occurs at the interface and low-velocity liquid is entrained in the faster moving streams, mixing with the liquid therein. In order to achieve mixing in a reasonable time the volumetric flow rate must be such that the entire volume of the mixing vessel is swept out in a reasonable time.

The fluid power, P, required for moving a liquid by means of a pump is given by

$$P = QH\rho g \qquad (5.1)$$

where Q is the volumetric flowrate of the liquid of density ρ, H is the fluid head and g is the acceleration due to gravity.

Considering the mixer as a caseless pump,[3,4] this means that an input power, P, to the fluid can be thought of as generating a circulation rate, Q, in the mixing vessel, associated with a head, H, which is used in moving the fluid along its flow path while, hopefully, developing a high degree of turbulence. The degree of turbulence is highest near the impeller and the liquid should circulate through this region as frequently as possible. Thus mixing in lower viscosity systems is influenced by the degree of turbulence (head) and circulation rate (flow). Correct choice of impeller design determines a satisfactory balance of fluid input power between flow and head.

Some impellers, e.g. turbines, can be classified as 'shear type'. These generate large turbulent shear stresses near the impeller, making them suitable for dispersive mixing processes. Other 'circulation type' impellers, such as marine propellers, set up high rates of circulation throughout the vessel in the turbulent mixing of lower viscosity liquids. Anchors, helical ribbons and screws are circulation-type impellers that are good for the laminar blending of higher viscosity mixes.[4] The range of application for paddles, other than the simple variety, falls between these two.

In some cases average circulation times can be derived from the pumping capacity for specific impellers and terminal mixing times can be related to the average circulation rate.

For typical impeller-type mixers rotating in a vessel, understanding still lags behind that of other unit operations.[5] The problem stems from a lack of knowledge of internal flow dynamics and of the rheology of complex higher consistency liquids.

With low viscosity liquids the fluid velocity created by a rotating impeller has three components:

(a)　A radial component acting in a direction perpendicular to the shaft.
(b)　A longitudinal component acting parallel to the shaft.
(c)　A rotational component acting in a direction tangential to the circle of rotation of the shaft.

Both radial and longitudinal components generally contribute to mixing but the rotational component may not.

In the case of a vertically-mounted impeller mounted centrally in the mixing vessel, the rotational component promotes flow in a circular path around the shaft. The flow, which can be laminar, may lead to the formation of layers in the liquid. Little or no longitudinal flow may occur between these layers, the net result being that the vessel contents simply rotate with little mixing. If the relative velocity between the impeller blade and the liquid is low, the power that can be absorbed by the liquid is limited.

The tangential component of velocity can lead to the formation of a vortex at the surface of the liquid. As the speed of rotation of the impeller is increased this vortex deepens. Once the vortex reaches the suction of the impeller the power imparted to the liquid is suddenly reduced and air is drawn into the liquid. The introduction of air by means of vortex formation can be used to some advantage in certain circumstances, e.g. gas–liquid contacting in aerobic fermentations (Section 18.4.3.3(b)), but it is generally undesirable. Another disadvantage associated with rotational flow is that suspended particles may separate out under the influence of centrifugal force.

Vortexing, and the other disadvantages of rotational flow, may be reduced by positioning the agitator off-centre in the mixing vessel. Alternatively, baffles may be employed to interrupt this rotational flow and thereby reduce its effects. An effective method of baffling is to fix vertical

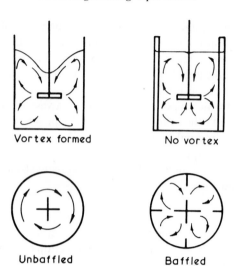

Vortex formed   No vortex

Unbaffled   Baffled

FIG. 5.2.   Flow patterns in baffled and unbaffled vessels with paddle or turbine agitators.

strips perpendicular to the wall of the vessel as shown in Fig. 5.2. Four such baffles are generally sufficient.

5.1.2.1. Paddle agitators

In its simplest form a paddle agitator consists of a flat blade fixed to a rotating shaft (Fig. 5.1(a)). The shaft is usually mounted centrally in the vessel and rotates at speeds in the range 20–150 rpm. The liquid flow has a high radial component in the plane of the paddle and also a high rotational component. Little vertical flow is developed. Baffling is normally employed to reduce swirling and vortexing (Fig. 5.2). Two- or four-bladed paddles are common. Pitched blades may be used to promote vertical flow. Multivane paddles or gate agitators may be used for more viscous liquids (Fig. 5.1(b)). Paddles designed just to clear the vessel walls (anchor paddles) are often used to promote heat transfer and minimise deposits on jacketed vessels (Fig. 5.1(c)). Counter-rotating multiblade paddles may be used to develop high localised shear where required (Fig. 5.1(d)). Paddles generally measure $\frac{1}{2}-\frac{3}{4}$ of the vessel diameter and the width of the blade is generally $\frac{1}{10}-\frac{1}{6}$ of its length. Paddle agitators are relatively easy to fabricate and can be coated with a variety of corrosion resistant materials. Single paddle agitators have a gentle mixing action often desirable when handling fragile, crystalline materials. They are useful for simple mixing duties, e.g. mixing of miscible liquids or preparation of solutions of solids.

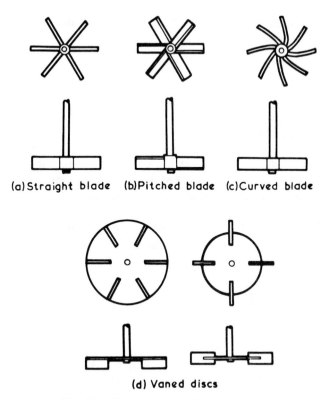

(a) Straight blade   (b) Pitched blade   (c) Curved blade

(d) Vaned discs

FIG. 5.3. Some typical turbine impellers.

5.1.2.2. Turbine agitators

A turbine agitator consists of an impeller with more than four blades mounted on the same boss and fixed to a rotating shaft (Fig. 5.3(a)). They are generally smaller than paddles, measuring 30–50% of the vessel diameter, and commonly rotate at speeds in the range 30–500 rpm. The shaft, again, is usually mounted centrally in the vessel. The simple straight bladed turbine generates strong radial and rotational currents. Baffling is normally employed to reduce swirling. Vertical flow is also set up due to deflection of the radial currents from the vessel walls (Fig. 5.2). The velocity of the liquid is relatively high and currents travel throughout the mixing vessel. High turbulence and shear are developed near the impeller itself. Impeller blades may be pitched to increase vertical flow (Fig. 5.3(b)). The vaned disc impeller (Fig. 5.3(d)) may be used for dispersing gases in liquids. Turbine agitators are useful for handling a wide variety of materials and are particularly effective in mixing moderately viscous liquids. The turbulence and shear developed close to the impeller make them useful for emulsion premixing (see Section 5.2.2.1).

5.1.2.3. Propeller agitators

These consist of short bladed impellers (usually measuring less than $\frac{1}{4}$ of vessel diameter) rotating at high speed (500 to several thousand rpm). The currents generated are primarily longitudinal and rotational (Fig. 5.4(a)) and are very persistent. Thus these comparatively small agitators are effective in quite large vessels when used with lower viscosity liquids. Because of the predominantly longitudinal nature of the flow currents, propellers are not very effective if mounted on vertical shafts located at the centre of the vessel. They are commonly mounted off centre and with the shaft at an angle to the vertical (Fig. 5.4(c)). In large tanks propeller shafts may be mounted through the side wall of the tank in a horizontal plane but off centre (Fig. 5.4(d)).

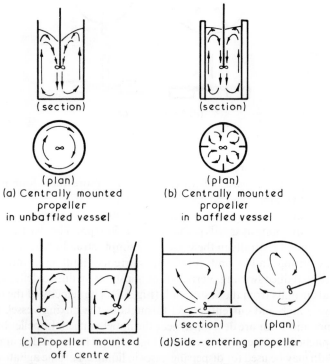

(a) Centrally mounted propeller in unbaffled vessel

(b) Centrally mounted propeller in baffled vessel

(c) Propeller mounted off centre

(d) Side-entering propeller

FIG. 5.4. Flow patterns in propeller agitated systems.

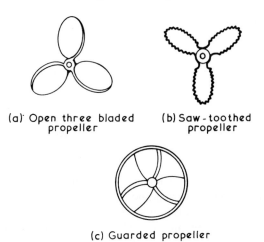

(a) Open three bladed propeller   (b) Saw-toothed propeller

(c) Guarded propeller

FIG. 5.5. Some typical propeller impellers.

Propeller agitators are most effective in mixing low viscosity liquids. Propeller blades cut and shear the material and can be used for dispersing solids and for emulsification duties. Some typical impeller designs are shown in Fig. 5.5.

5.1.2.4. Other types of impeller agitators

Other impellers employed for relatively low viscosity mixes include disc impellers, cone impellers and a wide variety of special designs for particular purposes. An example of one such special type is given in Fig. 5.6. This particular type subjects the material to high shear on being forced out through the slots and is recommended for emulsion premixing and liquid–liquid and solid–liquid dispersion.

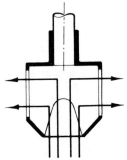

FIG. 5.6. Dispersator impeller. (By courtesy of Premier Colloid Mills Ltd.)

5.1.2.5. Mixing vessels

In practice these take various shapes, but the most commonly used design for lower viscosity liquids is a vertical cylindrical tank with a dished bottom. This minimises the dead spaces in corners, etc., which might occur in rectangular tanks, or cylindrical tanks with flat or conical bottoms. The filling ratio, i.e. ratio, liquid depth : vessel diameter, is usually 0·5–1·5 and 1·0 is recommended for most purposes. If tall vessels are used, one impeller should be installed for each vessel diameter of height. These and other recommendations for vessel and agitator designs are given by the EEUA.[6]

5.1.2.6. Power requirements for low viscosity liquid mixing systems

The power introduced into a liquid mixing system by an agitator is determined by its speed of rotation, the configuration of the mixer and the physical properties of the mixture. Using the method of dimensional analysis, Rushton *et al.*[7] related the power requirement to these various parameters. If linear dimensions such as the depth of liquid in the tank, the diameter of the tank, the number, dimensions and position of baffles are all in a definite geometrical ratio with the impeller diameter, then the power input to the agitator can be expressed as a function of the following variables:

Diameter of the impeller	D
Rotational speed of the impeller	N
Liquid density	ρ
Liquid viscosity	μ
Acceleration due to gravity	g

such that

$$P = f(N, D, \rho, \mu, g)$$

Dimensional analysis then gives

$$\frac{P}{D^5 N^3 \rho} = c\left(\frac{D^2 N \rho}{\mu}\right)^a \left(\frac{DN^2}{g}\right)^b \tag{5.2}$$

where a, b, and c depend on the system and its geometry; $P/D^5N^3\rho$ is the dimensionless power number, N_p; $D^2N\rho/\mu$ is the dimensionless Reynolds number, N_{Re}; DN^2/g is the dimensionless Froude number, N_{Fr}.

A number of workers have applied this equation to liquid mixing using impeller-type agitators in vertical cylindrical tanks. The Reynolds number represents the ratio of applied forces to the viscous drag forces. The Froude number represents the ratio of applied forces to gravity forces. Vortex formation is a gravitational effect and if suppressed, consideration of the Froude number is avoided. The Froude number can be neglected: (1) with baffled systems; and (2) with Reynolds numbers less than 10, when flow will be laminar.

For baffled systems the 'power equation' may be written as

$$\frac{P}{D^5 N^3 \rho} = c\left(\frac{D^2 N\rho}{\mu}\right)^a \tag{5.3}$$

Plots for N_p versus N_{Re} on log–log coordinates, so-called 'power curves' are available in the literature for particular mixer configurations. Power curves are independent of vessel size and find use in the 'scale-up' of liquid mixers from pilot-plant studies but it must be realised that a given curve is only applicable to the geometric configuration for which it was developed.[8]

5.1.3. MIXERS FOR HIGH VISCOSITY PASTES AND PLASTIC SOLIDS

The mixing of materials of high consistency, a common process in the food industry, involves the use of a wide variety of equipment of different designs. The materials handled by such equipment vary widely in physical properties and in many cases changes occur in these properties during the mixing operation. A further complication arises since, in many so-called mixing operations performed in this equipment, the object may not only be the production of a uniform mix. It may also involve the subjecting of materials to a particular type of mechanical action so as to obtain a product with certain desirable physical characteristics (e.g. in dough mixing). Many mixers are designed for specific duties and few general principles apply to mixers in this category; indeed the amount of engineering knowledge of high viscosity mixing processes, especially for non-Newtonian fluids, is quite limited.[2] Discussion in this section will be confined to mixers of a reasonably versatile nature having a number of applications.

One general principle which does apply to mixers for highly-viscous and paste-like materials is that their performance depends on direct contact between the mixing elements and the materials of the mix, in vessels designed for a high power input into small working capacities. Flow conditions will be laminar and processing times long to accommodate the high power required and the large stresses developed on the equipment.[9] The material must be brought to the mixing elements or the elements must travel to all parts of the mixing vessel. The local actions responsible for the mixing are complex. They have been described as kneading, in which the material is pressed against other adjacent material or against the vessel

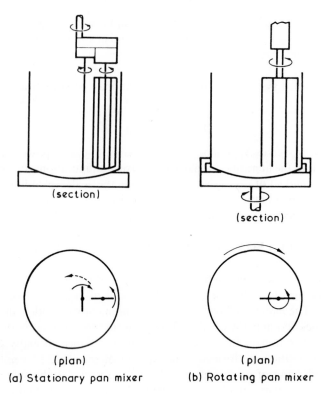

(section)

(section)

(plan)   (plan)
(a) Stationary pan mixer   (b) Rotating pan mixer

FIG. 5.7.   Pan mixers.

walls, and folding, in which fresh material is enveloped by already mixed material. Localised shearing develops and the material is stretched and torn apart by the action of the mixing elements. More recent work has thrown some light on prevailing mechanisms in laminar systems (see Edwards[9]).

In general, the higher the consistency of the mixture the greater should be the diameter of the impeller system and the slower the speed of rotation.

5.1.3.1. Pan mixers

These are of two general types. In the stationary pan mixer (Fig. 5.7(a)) the mixing elements move in a planetary path, visiting all parts of the stationary mixing pan. Elements are used singly or in pairs and are usually designed to provide only a small clearance between each other and the pan walls. In the rotating pan type, the mixing vessel is mounted on a rotating turntable (Fig. 5.7(b)). The mixing elements also rotate, but in one position,

FIG. 5.8.   Some special mixing elements ('tools') used in planetary type pan mixers. (By courtesy of Wodschow & Co., Copenhagen.)

and are located near the pan wall. Mixing elements vary in design depending on the duty.[10] Simple gate type elements conforming in general shape to the contours of the pan are common. Fork-like elements also find wide use. The blades may be twisted to give the desired mixing action and induce vertical motion. Some other typical element designs are shown in Fig. 5.8. Pans are removable either by raising or tilting the elements or by lowering the pan support.

5.1.3.2. Horizontal trough mixers (kneaders, dispersers, masticators)

These consist of a pair of heavy blades rotating on horizontal axes in a trough with a saddle-shaped bottom. The blades rotate towards each other at the top of their cycle and may follow tangential or interlocking paths. The material is drawn down over the point of the saddle and kneaded and sheared between the blades, the container walls and the bottom. The blades generally rotate at different speeds and may be independently driven or linked by gears. Blades vary in design but a common shape is that of the Z-blade or sigma blade element (Fig. 5.9). The vessel may be open or closed and may be evacuated. It may be jacketed for temperature control and usually tips up for emptying.

An overlooked mixer, developed some years ago in a previous era of government–industry cooperation, was designed to achieve short mixing times and high degrees of uniformity of components with highly viscous pastes and heavy paste-like materials. The main feature is a pair of rotors of special shape such that, when in contra-rotation, the tip of either one or other of the rotors is always in contact with the opposite rotor and with the walls of the mixing chamber. The mixing action is obtained by squeezing the material in the spaces between the rotors and expelling it through small clearances between them. The material to be mixed is gathered from the walls of the chamber and from the surfaces of the rotors by the rotor tips.

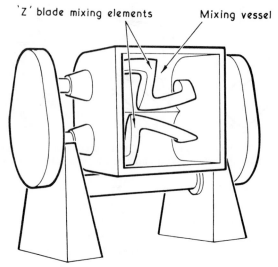

FIG. 5.9.   Z-blade (sigma-blade) mixer.

This action also serves to clean the mixer. Intense shearing action is said to result; the flow properties of the material do not influence the mixing; dead zones cannot exist so mixing is achieved uniformly and rapidly. It is claimed that one Maxta mixer will give the same throughput as at least four conventional Z-blade mixers of the same capacity while in many other applications mixing time is very much reduced.

5.1.3.3. Continuous paste mixers

A wide variety of devices are used to mix and knead viscous materials continuously. A common principle is to force the material through a series of obstructions (e.g. perforated plates, wire meshes, grids, etc.) by means of single or twin screw conveyors. The conveyors are rotated in troughs or cylindrical barrels with only small clearances between them and the walls of the retaining vessel; sometimes stationary teeth intermesh with the screws. The material is kneaded and sheared between the screws and the walls and further acted on mechanically by being forced through the obstructions. Examples of this principle are the working devices used in butter and margarine manufacture (Section 5.2.3).

A commercial mixer finding wide use in continuous, in-line mixing and blending applications, particularly with bakery mixes, batters, etc., is the Oakes continuous mixer (Fig. 5.10).[11] It consists of a toothed disc rotating between two toothed stators. High degrees of shear result giving high

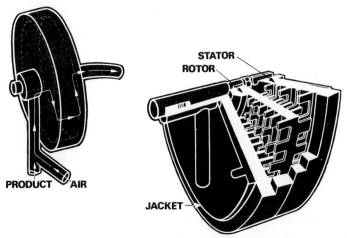

FIG. 5.10.   Diagram of Oakes continuous mixing head as used for air injection. (By courtesy of E. T. Oakes Ltd, Macclesfield.)

intensity mixing. A large volume, low intensity mixing machine—the Oakes continuous mixer-modifier—is also being used extensively in the UK for the continuous production of bread dough.[12]

5.1.3.4. Other devices
Many other devices are employed for mixing paste-like materials. Mixing or blending is sometimes achieved by passing the materials between rollers, or between a roller and another surface. Tumbling of the mass of material such as in butter churns (Section 5.2.3.1) is also employed. Colloid mills (Section 5.2.2.6) perform mixing operations. Other devices employ rotating knives to simultaneously reduce particle size and mix heavy materials.

5.1.3.5. Power requirements for higher viscosity liquid systems
The work of Rushton *et al.*[7] on power consumption in the mixing of low viscosity liquids has been extended to the laminar mixing of higher consistency systems.

For certain types of impellers—helical ribbons, helical screws, etc.—equations of a form similar to those developed for propellers and turbines (Section 5.1.2.6), but with constants specific to the different impeller geometries examined, are available in the literature (see Godfrey[2]). A knowledge of the power consumption for particular mixing processes is important in motor selection, as well as in gearbox and shaft design, particularly in the case of high viscosity liquids. The evaluation of different mixer designs for mixing rate and efficiency may also usefully be made on the basis of power consumption but insufficient data is currently available to allow mixer selection to be made on a quantitative basis.

5.1.3.6. 'In-line' mixers

An important development in continuous mixing, suitable for high capacity processing applications, is that of the in-line mixer. These units are an integral part of the pipe system so their use obviates the need for separate mixing tanks. This cuts down on space requirement, reduces the hold-up volume of product and also, by making 'cleaning in place' (CIP) (Section 17.3.3.2) easier, simplifies the cleandown problems associated with larger vessels.

In-line mixers may be of the 'dynamic' or 'static' variety.

Dynamic in-line mixers—in which flow is developed by a combination of pump pressure and a high-speed rotating element—are typified by the Oakes continuous mixer discussed in Section 5.1.3.3. In these particular units (which are very similar to the disc attrition mill, Section 4.3.3), a high-speed rotor moving adjacent to a shaped, close-clearance stator, develops intense shearing in fluids flowing continuously through the action zone. They are very widely used for the breakdown and dispersion of particles and droplets in liquids, and for the production of emulsions and stable foams.

'Static' in-line mixers utilise the movement of materials flowing over specially contoured stationary mixing elements situated in a tubular housing that constitutes part of the pipeline (Fig. 5.11). They find use in both laminar and turbulent mixing processes[13] and give effective mixing without the aid of moving parts.

The major variables with static in-line mixers are the flow rates and viscosities of the liquid components and applications involving materials having large differences in these properties are usually considerably more difficult. The number of mixing elements required increases with the difficulty of mixing. The degree of homogeneity achieved is said to increase exponentially with increased mixer length.[14]

FIG. 5.11. Assembly of Kenics static mixer elements. (By courtesy of Chemineer-Kenics, UK.)

In the operation of this type of mixer, fluids, flowing under pump pressure, are split and caused to flow along paths whose direction and lengths are dictated by the geometry and length of the unit. Though some units give lower pressure drops than others, these can be about ten times greater than those in a similar diameter empty pipe[15] so additional pumping energy is required. However, these mixers are said to require 10–100 times less energy compared with agitated vessels or extruders for high viscosity applications.[14]

The mixing elements can take a variety of geometric forms—helices, vanes or corrugated plates—different manufacturers of proprietary static-mixers offering their own configurations. Some 35 different static mixers are currently available and their performances differ widely.[14] Loncin and Merson[15] discuss one type in which the tubular housing contains elements generating helical flow paths a few centimetres in length, each juxtaposed 90° to the preceding element and each with the opposite spiral direction. As with other types of static mixer, mixing arises through a combination of flow splitting, changes in flow direction, and through the development and breakup of boundary layers, at successive elements. Fluids can be miscible or immiscible, and the units can handle gas/liquid systems. The consistency of the materials can be quite high. Any fluid that can be pumped through a pipe may be mixed in this way in any proportion from 1:1 to 100 000:1.[16]

Though originally developed for the laminar blending of viscous materials, static mixers are now generating interest in the processing of heat-sensitive liquids. Heat-transfer coefficients are considerably increased using static mixers. In the case of certain low pressure drop mixers, increases in heat-transfer coefficient of around 300% were obtained for increases in pressure drop of about 700%. Residence-time distribution characteristics are also much more uniform than in equivalent empty pipes and 'plug flow' can be approached.[14] This reduces the possibility of damage to heat-sensitive food liquids. Uniform residence-time distributions also leads to better control over chemical reactions so static mixers also have advantages in the design of continuous flow tubular reactors. Heat transfer and residence-time distribution aspects of static mixers are discussed by Godfrey.[13]

5.1.4. MIXERS FOR DRY SOLIDS

The dynamic behaviour of particles during mixing is complex. Early work in this field leant heavily on analogies with liquid-mixing systems which led to difficulties. Molecular diffusion is present in liquid systems and, in the case of single phase miscible liquids, although the molecules present may diffuse at different rates, a random distribution will be achieved within the confines of the system.[1] In solid–solid mixing, without the input of energy no mixing takes place since movement of the particles is not possible.

Solids mixing is generally regarded as arising from one or more of three basic mechanisms. These are: convection, i.e. transfer of masses or groups of particles from one location in the mixer to another; diffusion, i.e. the transfer of individual particles from one location to another arising from the distribution of particles over a freshly developed surface; shear, i.e. the setting up of slipping planes within the mass, also resulting in mixing of groups of particles. All three mechanisms may be employed in a mixing device, although a particular type may predominate in a specific type of mixer. Shear mixing is sometimes considered as part of a convective mechanism.

Considerable progress has been made since recognition and, more recently, understanding of another mechanism known as *segregation* or *unmixing*.

The importance of 'segregation' on the degree of homogeneity achievable in solids mixing cannot be overemphasised.

Segregation is now known to be brought about in the mixing of solids by:

(i) Differences in specific physical properties of the particles.
(ii) The nature of the movement initiating flow.

The physical properties influencing this mechanism are differences in particle size, density, shape and resilience, size difference being almost always the most serious cause of segregation.[1] Even very small differences in the 'size' of particles affect flow behaviour and the degree of mixing achievable in the mixing process. Experience indicates that materials with a size greater than $75\,\mu m$ will segregate readily but below $10\,\mu m$ no appreciable segregation will occur.[1]

Segregation occurs when particles in a group are free to change their positions, bringing about a change in packing characteristics. Since it is easier for smaller particles to move through spaces between adjacent particles the capability for movement of individual particles (mobility) is greater for smaller than for larger particles. Pouring, vibration and stirring mixtures of particles all give rise to segregation if the particles are free-flowing and techniques for successfully mixing and handling these mixtures rely on their ability to inhibit the freedom of particles to move in a non-random way.[17]

It is now accepted that the effectiveness of a mixing process must be related to both the flow properties of the components—the physical properties influencing 'flowability'—and to the design of the mixer.[18]

In the food industry it may be necessary for a mix to conform to customer product specifications or legal requirements. Practical tests are often applied to the mix to ascertain whether or not it is suitable for the purpose for which it was prepared, e.g. test baking of dry cake mixes. However, some method of following or controlling the mixing operation itself may be desirable. This usually involves sampling of the mix, analysis of the samples and statistical treatment of the results. A number of 'mixing indices' based on such procedures have been suggested. Many of these are reviewed by Weidenbaum.[19]

Any form of control of mixing operations involves sampling the mixture. The method of sampling, size, number and location of the samples all influence the usefulness of the control. The samples must be representative of the mixture and both the method of sampling and post-sampling handling must not allow segregation to alter the distribution of the particles in the sample.

The sample size that should be taken is related to the end use to which the product material is to be put and sample variance for a set of experimental results must be estimated at some sample size characteristic of this end use. A number of workers have used the term 'characteristic sample size' or 'scale of scrutiny' in this connection. Sampling methods are discussed by Weidenbaum[19] and Valentin.[20]

None of the many criteria of mixedness have found wide acceptance in practical mixing applications where an ideal mixture is likely to be regarded as a mixture produced at minimum cost and that satisfies the product specification at the point of use. Such a mixture may be far removed from any theoretical criterion of mixedness. It must also be re-emphasised that in practical mixing applications segregation is likely to arise unless the particles are very similar in size. This means that as mixing proceeds an equilibrium between mixing and unmixing is established. The degree of mixing achievable is dependent on the nature of the particles and on the movement characterised by the type of mixing device used. Once the mixing and de-mixing mechanisms reach a state of equilibrium, the state of the final mix is determined and further mixing will not produce a better result. It is the aim of the processor to select the mixer that gives a degree of mixing adequate for his process requirement at an acceptable cost. In some cases it may be possible to modify the nature of the ingredients to assist this selection.

If the size of the particles is not a specific product requirement then comminution to finer sizes can lead to higher quality mixes. Granulation, the use of 'coating processes' and controlled continuous mixing may also be considered in overcoming segregation and poor mixing.

Gross segregation does not arise when cohesive particles are mixed. With these particles surface forces—moisture bonding, electrostatic or van der Waal's forces—help to bind particles together, nullifying the tendency for them to separate.[1] Mixing times for cohesive powders may be increased but the final equilibrium mixture is of a much higher quality.[21]

It must be remembered that in industry a major requirement is for trouble-free powder handling—this suggests free-flowing particle systems but these can aggravate the problem of segregation. Though virtually non-segregating, cohesive powders can, on the other hand, cause intermittent flow and frequently total blockage of transfer-lines and hoppers. The designer of food mixing equipment may have to compromise between these two disadvantages.

Any tendency for segregation to occur must be recognised when selecting solids-mixing equipment. Segregation in a mixture of dry solids is readily detected by use of a 'heap test'. A well-mixed sample of the solids is poured through a funnel so as to form a conical heap. Samples taken from the central core and from the outside edge of the cone should have essentially the same compositions if segregation is not to be a problem. If the two samples have significantly different compositions then segregation will occur unless the choice of mixer is carefully made. Williams,[22] suggested that solids mixers could be classified into either of two groups:

(1) *Segregating mixers* have a mechanism mainly diffusive in character. This mechanism encourages the movement of individual particles making segregation more significant. Non-impeller type mixers are more likely to be of this type.

(2) *Less-segregating mixers* have mainly convective mixing mechanisms. These are typically impeller mixers in which blades, screws, ploughs, etc., sweep groups of particles throughout the mixing zone.

5.1.4.1. Tumbler mixers

These operate by tumbling the mass of solids inside a revolving vessel. These vessels take various forms and some typical examples are shown in Fig. 5.12. They may be fitted with baffles or stays to repeatedly redirect the movement of groups of the particles and so improve the performance of the mixer. Some have separately driven internal rotating devices to help break up agglomerates. The shells rotate at speeds up to 100 rpm, i.e. about half

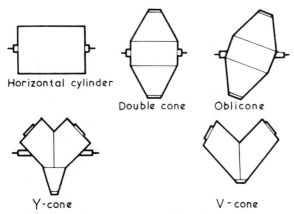

FIG. 5.12. Some typical tumbler mixer shapes.

the critical speed of the mixer[23] (see Section 4.3.4.1 for critical speed of a cylindrical drum). Working capacity is normally 50–60% of the internal volume. They are constructed from a wide variety of materials of construction (larger units are usually made of stainless steel) and are fitted with ports or valves for filling and emptying. Tumbler mixers are best suited to the gentle blending of particles with similar physical characteristics. Segregation can be a problem if particles vary, particularly in size and shape. According to Harnby,[23] an equilibrium mixture is usually reached in 10–15 min.

5.1.4.2. Horizontal trough mixers

These consist of semicylindrical horizontal vessels in which one or more rotating devices are located. For simple operations single or twin screw conveyors are adequate and one passage through such a system may suffice. For more demanding duties a ribbon mixer (Fig. 5.13) may be used. In a typical design of ribbon mixer, two counteracting ribbons are mounted on the same shaft. One moves the solids slowly in one direction while the other moves it quickly in the opposite direction. There is a resultant movement of solids in one direction and so the system can be used as a continuous mixer. Other types of ribbon mixers work on a batch system. Troughs may be open

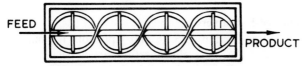

FIG. 5.13. Schematic drawing of open ribbon mixer (plan view).

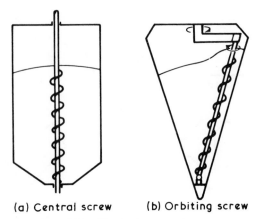

(a) Central screw   (b) Orbiting screw

Fig. 5.14.   Vertical screw mixers.

or closed (e.g. for use under pressure or vacuum or to minimise dust hazard) and may be jacketed for temperature control. Due to the small clearance between ribbon and trough wall, particle damage can occur and power consumption is high. Segregation can arise from the rolling motion but is generally not a serious problem.

The mechanism in this type of mixer is mainly convective, groups of particles being carried from one region to another by the ribbon-blades. This 'less-segregating' mixer is therefore used with materials that are likely to segregate during mixing.

5.1.4.3. Vertical screw mixers

A rotating vertical screw located in a cylindrical or cone-shaped vessel is another device used for mixing solids. The screw may be fixed centrally in the vessel (Fig. 5.14(a)) or it may rotate or orbit around the central axis of the vessel near the wall (Fig. 5.14(b)). The latter arrangement is more effective and stagnant layers near the wall are eliminated. Vertical screw mixers are quick and quite efficient and particularly useful for mixing small quantities of additives into large masses of material. Again a convective mechanism predominates so this type of unit will handle materials prone to segregation.

5.1.4.4. Fluidised-bed mixers

Fluidised beds (see Section 13.3.1.6 and Appendix I.2) may be used for mixing solids and are quite effective for particles with similar settling characteristics. Also, of course, the solid particles must have good fluidising characteristics. In addition to the fluidising air, high pressure jets of air causing spouting of the bed are said to improve the mixing.[24]

In the 'Airmix' fluidised mixer, the time required to reach equilibrium mixture quality is 1–2 min.[23] This compares favourably with the 15 min required to reach the same degree of mixing in tumbler and convective mixers and enables a smaller capacity unit to be used.

5.1.4.5. Other methods

Many other forms of mixer are used for solids blending. Heavy paddle mixers, pan mixers and Z-blade mixers have found some application in this field. Injecting additives into pneumatic lines carrying solid particles can sometimes be effective. Other devices employ centrifugal action or air jets to perform mixing operations.

5.1.5. APPLICATIONS FOR MIXING EQUIPMENT IN THE FOOD INDUSTRY

5.1.5.1. Low viscosity fluids

Examples of applications for impeller agitators include: blending of oils in the manufacture of margarine and cooking fats; diluting concentrated solutions; manufacturing fruit squashes; preparing liquid sugar mixtures for sweet manufacture; preparing brines and syrups; reconstituting dried products, e.g. milk powder; dissolving soluble dyes.

5.1.5.2. High viscosity liquids and pastes

Examples of applications for pan mixers, Z-blade mixers and other similar equipment include: dough and batter mixing in bread, cake and biscuit manufacture; preparation of meat and fish pastes; manufacture of chocolate products; blending of margarines, cooking fats and butter; whipping dairy and artificial creams; preparing cheese spreads and blending cheeses.

5.1.5.3. Dry solids

Applications for tumbler, ribbon and screw mixers include: blending of grains prior to milling; blending of flours and incorporation of additives to flours; preparation of custard powders, cake mixes and other such small goods; preparation of dry soup mixes; incorporation of additives in dried products (e.g. baby foods).

5.1.5.4. Unloading and handling of mixtures of solids

Pouring, shaking and vibrating a mixture of solid particles all encourage segregation if ingredients have significantly different particle sizes or densities. A well-mixed mixture can easily be destroyed by careless post-mixing handling. Dumping the mixture from a mixer outlet on unloading is a major cause of segregation, being in effect a large-scale heap test.

5.2. EMULSIFICATION

5.2.1. INTRODUCTION AND THEORY

Emulsification may be defined as that operation in which two normally immiscible liquids are intimately mixed, one liquid (the discontinuous, dispersed or internal phase) becoming dispersed in the form of small droplets or globules in the other (continuous, dispersing or external phase).

In most emulsions the two liquids involved are water and oil. Pure water and pure oil are seldom involved, however. The water phase may consist of solutions of salts, sugars or other organic and colloidal materials (hydrophilic materials). The oil phase may consist of oils, hydrocarbons, waxes, resins and other substances which behave like oil (hydrophobic materials). In order to form a stable emulsion a third substance, known as an emulsifying agent, needs to be included. The function and mode of operation of this third substance will be discussed later (Section 5.2.1.2).

When oil and water are mixed, two types of emulsion are possible. The oil may become the dispersed phase, giving an oil-in-water (o/w) emulsion. Alternatively the water may become the dispersed phase, producing a water-in-oil (w/o) emulsion (Fig. 5.15). The emulsion formed tends to exhibit most of the properties of the liquid that forms the external phase. An oil-in-water emulsion may be diluted with water, coloured with water soluble dyes and exhibit electrical conductivity corresponding to that of the aqueous phase. On the other hand a water-in-oil emulsion can only be successfully diluted with oil, coloured by oil soluble dyes and has a low electrical conductivity. Thus two emulsions of similar composition can have quite different characteristics depending on whether the oil or water is the external phase. The factors which influence the type of emulsion formed when oil and water are mixed include: the type of emulsifying agent used; the relative proportions of the phases; the method of preparation of the emulsion.

Emulsions with more complex structures may be produced by special techniques. These so-called multiple emulsions may be water-in-oil-in-water (w/o/w) or oil-in-water-in-oil (o/w/o) types. Discussion of such emulsions is outside the scope of this chapter. Matsumoto describes

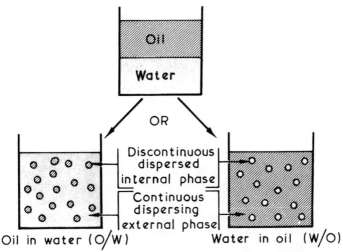

FIG. 5.15. Alternative types of emulsion.

methods for preparing w/o/w emulsions and mentions potential applications for them in the formulation and processing of foods.[25]

5.2.1.1. Interfacial tension

The interface between two immiscible liquids is a seat of free energy arising from an imbalance in the cohesive forces of the two liquids (interfacial tension). This energy causes the interface to contract to form the smallest possible interfacial area. In an emulsion the internal phase always tends to form spherical droplets representing the smallest interfacial area per unit volume of liquid. Further these droplets tend to coalesce to form larger ones, again reducing the interfacial area. In a crude emulsion this can proceed until the phases again completely separate.

On the other hand the formation of an emulsion involves the creation of a large number of new interfaces, contrary to the tendency to contract arising from interfacial tension. The higher the interfacial tension the more difficult it is to form an emulsion and the less stable the emulsion is likely to be. It is generally necessary to reduce the interfacial tension to form a stable emulsion. One important way of achieving this is by the use of emulsifying agents.

5.2.1.2. Emulsifying agents

These perform two functions in emulsification: they reduce the interfacial tension between the liquids to be emulsified and protect the emulsion formed

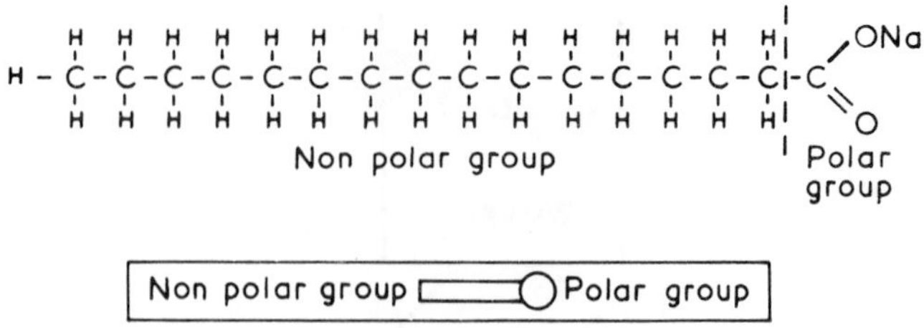

FIG. 5.16.   Sodium palmitate molecule.

by preventing the coalescence of the droplets of the internal phase. The substances used as emulsifying agents are numerous and varied and include: naturally occurring materials such as proteins, phospholipids and sterols; a wide range of synthetic materials such as esters of glycerol, propylene glycol, sorbitan esters of fatty acids, cellulose ethers, carboxymethyl cellulose and many others; finely divided solids such as bentonite and carbon black.

Most emulsifying agents consist of substances with molecules containing both polar and non-polar groups. Consider the simple example of a soap such as sodium palmitate with the structural formula given in Fig. 5.16. The hydrocarbon portion of the molecule is the non-polar group and the —COONa group is the polar group. For convenience the non-polar group will be represented by a rectangle and the polar group by a circle. In an emulsion such an agent is positively adsorbed at the interface between the phases and thereby reduces the interfacial tension. In becoming adsorbed the molecules of the emulsifying agent orientate themselves at the interface so that the non-polar groups, which have an affinity for the oil, will point towards the oil phase, while the polar groups will point towards the aqueous phase with which they have an affinity (Fig. 5.17). Thus a layer or film of emulsifying agent is formed at the interface. This interfacial film acts as a protective coating on the droplets of the internal phase, preventing them from coalescing under the influence of interfacial tension.

The phase in which the emulsifying agent is most soluble, as a general rule, tends to become the external phase. This occurs when the polar or non-polar groups in the emulsifying agent are slightly out of balance (i.e. when either the hydrophilic or hydrophobic properties of the agent show a slight predominance). If the groups in the molecules of the emulsifying agent are perfectly balanced then it shows no tendency to promote the formation of one type of emulsion more than the other. On the other hand if the polar and non-polar groups are grossly out of balance and one group dominates strongly then the substance is highly soluble in one or other of the phases. It

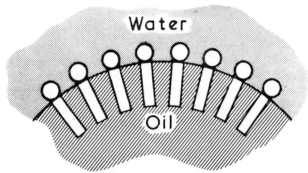

Fig. 5.17.   Orientation of emulsifying agent molecules at interface.

will not remain at the interface and hence will not act as an emulsifying agent. This is a simple empirical rule and there are exceptions.

An emulsifying agent may be selected for a particular application on the basis of its hydrophile–lipophile balance (HLB). This is defined as the ratio of the weight percentage of hydrophilic groups to the weight percentage of hydrophobic groups in the molecule. HLB values can be determined experimentally. HLB values for emulsifying agents range from 1 to 20. Agents with low values, 3–6, promote the formation of water-in-oil (w/o) emulsions while those with high values, 8–18, favour the formation of oil-in-water (o/w) types.[26]

Finely divided solids are also adsorbed at the interface in an emulsion and can act as emulsifying agents, although not very efficiently. Here, as a general rule, solids which are most easily wetted by the water phase promote oil-in-water emulsions and vice versa.

An emulsifying agent should, as far as possible, be specific in the type of emulsion it promotes. In the case of food emulsions, the agent should be non-toxic and many countries have regulations governing the use of emulsifying agents in foods. It should be relatively odourless, tasteless and colourless, and should be chemically and physically stable under the prevailing conditions of processing, handling and storage. It must be economic in price.

5.2.1.3. Methods of emulsification: general principles
In order to form an emulsion, work must be done on the system to overcome the resistance to the creation of new interfaces (arising from interfacial tension). Theoretically, this work of emulsification is equivalent to the product of the newly created surface and the interfacial tension. In addition, energy must be supplied to keep the liquids in motion and to

overcome frictional resistances. As a general principle, the work is done on the liquids by subjecting them to violent agitation. The type of agitation best suited to emulsification is that which causes the large droplets of the internal phase to be subjected to shear. By this action they are deformed and broken up into smaller, more finely dispersed, droplets. Provided conditions are suitable, the protective film of emulsifying agent is adsorbed at the interface and a stable emulsion is formed.

The time required for emulsification to occur varies with the emulsion formulation and the technique employed, and must be determined by experiment. For each case there is an optimum time below which a relatively unstable emulsion is formed. If agitation is continued much beyond this optimum time the emulsion may again suffer as the protective film can be damaged by excessive agitation. In fact, agitation is employed for breaking emulsions (see Section 5.2.3.1).

5.2.1.4. Preparatory steps

The following points should be considered in formulating emulsions:

(i) The emulsifying agent used must favour the type of emulsion required, i.e. o/w or w/o.

(ii) The phase volume (P/V) ratio (i.e. the percentage by volume of internal phase) affects the type of emulsion formed. The phase present in the larger proportion tends to become the external phase. Emsulsion with P/V ratios in excess of 50% are difficult to produce and handle.

(iii) The temperature of emulsification must be specified. Interfacial tension and viscosity fall with rise in temperature. The upper limit of temperature depends on the heat sensitiveness of the ingredients. Temperatures of up to 70°C are common for milk products while many products containing egg yolk solids, e.g. mayonnaise are emulsified at much lower temperatures.

As a general rule the two phases are best prepared separately. The emulsifying agent is generally added to the external phase, but there are exceptions. Certain hydrophilic gums and colloids are best dispersed in the oil phase to minimise swelling and the formation of lumps. Where premixing of the phases is practised, the internal phase is usually added gradually to the external while the latter is being agitated. Occasionally other premixing procedures are adopted or premixing is dispensed with altogether.

The account of the theory of emulsification and the role of emulsifying agents given in this section is a very simplified one. Many more detailed accounts are available in the literature.[27,28,29]

5.2.2. EQUIPMENT: PRINCIPLES, DESIGN FEATURES AND GENERAL APPLICATIONS

5.2.2.1. Mixers

Slow speed paddle agitators (see Section 5.1.2.1) find only limited application for premixing or emulsification duties because of the relatively mild mixing action. Pan and Z-blade mixers (Section 5.1.3) do perform emulsification duties, e.g. in dough mixing as a result of shear developed in the mass of viscous material. Other types of slow speed agitators consist of rotating vessels in which the contents are tumbled, e.g. butter and margarine churns (Section 5.2.3.1).

High speed mixers of the turbine and propeller type are much more effective as emulsion premixers and emulsifiers, particularly for low viscosity systems. Many special types of impeller have been designed for emulsification application, e.g. the type shown in Fig. 5.6.

Mixers are used for premixing the ingredients in the production of salad creams, artificial creams for cake filling, etc., and margarine (see Section 5.2.3.2). They are also used as emulsifers in the production of mayonnaise, processed cheeses, certain artificial creams and many other food emulsions.

5.2.2.2. Pressure homogenisers

Homogenisation is the term used to describe the operation in which the desired reduction in the size of the droplets of the internal phase is brought about by forcing the crude emulsion through a narrow opening at high velocity. A pressure homogeniser consists essentially of a homogenising valve and a high pressure pump. The valve provides an adjustable gap 15–300 μm wide through which the crude emulsion is pumped at pressures up to 10 000 psi (69 MN m^{-2}). On entering the gap the liquids are accelerated to velocities in the range 50–200 m s^{-1}. The droplets of the internal phase shear against each other, are deformed and disrupted. In many valves, as the liquids leave the gap they impinge on a hard surface set normal to the direction of flow and this further promotes disruption of the unstable droplets of the internal phase. The sudden drop in pressure as the liquids leave the gap and the collapse of bubbles due to cavitation probably also contribute to the reduction in droplet size.

A common type of valve design, the poppet valve, is shown in Fig. 5.18. The liquids travel between the valve and its seat causing it to lift against a

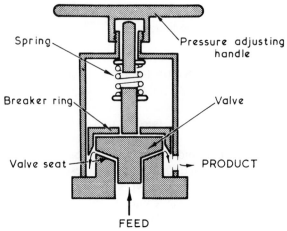

Fig. 5.18.   Principle of a simple (Poppet type) homogeniser valve.

strong spring. Adjustment of the tension on the spring provides the means of altering the homogenising pressure. On leaving the annular gap the liquids impinge on the breaker ring. An example of an alternative valve design is shown in Fig. 5.19. Many others are described in the literature. Single service valves are also available. These consist of cones of compressed wire fitting into conical seats. The liquids are forced through the multitude of channels in the valve body. These valves are discarded at the end of a day's run. By applying lower shear forces over a longer path homogenisation can be effected with less pressure than in more conventional valves.

Positive displacement pumps are necessary to supply the feed to the valve. For efficient results a steady feed rate is desirable. The most common system used is a multiple cylinder plunger pump which has three, five or seven cylinders with pistons working in sequence, driven via a crankshaft. In such a system the output varies up and down by about 20%. This can be further reduced by the use of high speed short stroke plungers.

The feed is usually introduced to the homogeniser as a crude premixed emulsion. Droplet sizes of the order of 0·1–0·2 μm are common, and may be as low as 0·02 μm.

Two stage homogenisation may be necessary to obtain satisfactory dispersion in some products. In milk products, salad creams and other emulsions in which proteins act as emulsifying agents, the small droplets formed after one passage through an homogenising valve at high pressure tend to cluster and clump together. This appears to arise from a poor

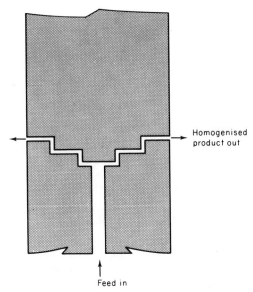

Homogenised product out

Feed in

FIG. 5.19. Homogeniser valve with stepped valve and seat.

distribution of emulsifying agent over the newly created surfaces and the fat globules becoming entangled within solid films of the agent. To overcome this, such materials may be passed through a second homogenising valve at a lower pressure, e.g. 400–500 psi (2·8–3·4 MN m^{-2}). By this means the clusters are broken up. Many modern designs of homogeniser valve are claimed to cope with such material in one stage only.

Pressure homogenisers find wide application in the food industry. These applications include the homogenisation of milk, low fat cream, evaporated milk and sterilised milk. Ice-cream mix exhibits good body and texture and high over-run when homogenised. Salad creams are often subjected to high pressure homogenisation, as are artificial creams, regenerated milk and cream products, cream soups, certain sauces and many other food products.[27–34]

5.2.2.3. Hydroshear (liquid whirl) homogeniser
The principle of operation of this type of homogeniser is illustrated in Fig. 5.20. The heart of the system is a simple cylindrical chamber assembly which has a tangential inlet port at its centre and two cone-shaped discharge nozzles at the ends of the chamber. The feed is introduced through a narrow orifice to give a high initial velocity. The liquid spreads to

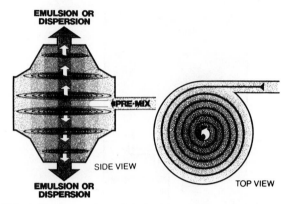

FIG. 5.20.   Principle of operation of the hydroshear homogeniser. (By courtesy of
APV Gaulin International S.A.)

cover the full width of the chamber wall, flows along the wall and is forced
towards the centre of the chamber rotating in ever decreasing circles and
accelerating. High internal shear develops between any two adjacent layers
of liquid because of the velocity differences created. An area of very low
pressure is created in the dead centre of the cylinder which is surrounded by
an area of intense cavitation accompanied by ultra-high frequency
vibration and shock waves. This results in the break-up of the droplets of
the internal phase and the formation of an emulsion. The feed is pumped in
at pressures up to 250 psi ($1750 \, \text{kN} \, \text{m}^{-2}$). This homogeniser does not
produce very fine droplets. It does produce uniform dispersions in the range
2–8 μm.

5.2.2.4. Microfluidiser

In this type of homogeniser one or two streams of the feed are pumped into
a chamber under high pressure, typically 16 000 psi ($110 \, \text{MN} \, \text{m}^{-2}$), and
velocity, typically $160 \, \text{m} \, \text{s}^{-1}$, where the fluid sheets interact resulting in
intense shear and turbulence which causes the release of energy and
cavitation. This leads to a break up of large droplets into smaller ones and
the formation of an emulsion. This equipment is said to produce very small
droplet sizes, less than 1 μm in diameter, within a narrow size range.[35]

5.2.2.5. Ultrasonic emulsification devices

The use of ultrasonic waves, i.e. sound waves having frequencies higher
than those the human ear can detect (about 16 kHz) provides another
means of dispersing one immiscible liquid in another to form an emulsion.

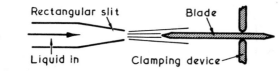

FIG. 5.21.   Principle of mechanical (wedge resonator) ultrasonic generator.

In a liquid irradiated with high energy ultrasonic waves each small region is alternately under tension and compression. During the negative half of the pressure cycle, when the liquid is under tension, any bubbles present in the liquid will expand. During the positive half of the cycle they will contract. Where the pressure amplitude is high and the bubbles are small the bubbles collapse violently during compression, i.e. cavitation. This can result in the release of a relatively substantial amount of energy. Cavitation can also occur in gas-free liquids, but the presence of dissolved gases and/or gas bubbles facilitates this phenomenon. The threshold intensity to produce cavitation increases with frequency (above about 10 kHz for water). Low frequency ultrasonic waves are best suited to duties where cavitation is desirable.

In a system consisting of two immiscible liquids, if cavitation occurs at the interface between the liquids, one phase will become dispersed in the other. Thus if the internal phase is added to the external phase while the latter is subjected to ultrasonic irradiation an emulsion can be formed.

There are three commonly applied methods of generating ultrasonic waves, namely: mechanical systems; systems employing magnetostrictive oscillators and piezoelectric crystal oscillators. The latter two methods are not generally applied to emulsification duties, except in cleaning where emulsification plays a part. Mechanical generators are finding increasing use in the food industry for emulsification applications.

The most common form of mechanical ultrasonic generator used for food emulsification is the wedge resonator. The principle of this type of generator is shown in Fig. 5.21. A blade with wedge shaped edges is positioned in front of a nozzle. Liquid is pumped through the nozzle and the jet emerging therefrom impinges on the leading edge of the blade and sets it vibrating. The blade is normally clamped at one or more nodal points and resonates at its natural frequency, imparting waves of ultrasonic frequency to the liquid. The intensity is not very great but is sufficient, in the proximity of the blade, to produce cavitation in the liquids and thus bring about emulsification. Liquids are normally supplied to the nozzles by means of gear pumps at pressures of the order of 50–200 psi (345–$1379 \, kN \, m^{-2}$). The frequency of vibration is usually in the range

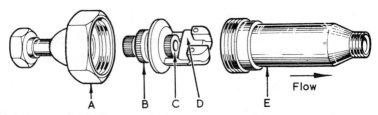

Flow

FIG. 5.22.   Ultrasonic homogeniser element. A, base; B, adjustable jet body; C, jet
insert; D, vibrating blade; E, resonant bell. (By courtesy of Ultrasonics Ltd.)

18–30 kHz and the disperse phase droplet size of the order of 1 to 2 μm. A
typical industrial ultrasonic homogeniser element is shown in Fig. 5.22.

The many applications for ultrasonic homogenisers in the food industry
include: the manufacture of salad creams, ice-cream mixes, cream soups,
essential oil emulsions, peanut butters, couverture chocolate, artificial
creams and baby foods. Units are also available for dispersing solids, e.g.
reconstituting dried milk powder, and other duties include producing
homogeneous fruit and vegetable purees, tomato juices and many other
similar tasks.[27,28]

5.2.2.6. Colloid mills

In principle a colloid mill consists of a stationary surface (stator) and a
rotating surface (rotor) separated by a small adjustable clearance through
which the crude emulsion is passed. In passing between these surfaces the
liquids are subjected to shear and turbulence resulting in the dispersion of
the internal phase.

A common form of mill consists of a frustrum shaped stator and
matching rotor turning on a horizontal axis. The clearance between stator
and rotor is adjustable (usually within the range of 50–150 μm) by
movement of the rotor horizontally. The feed is introduced under gravity at
the centre of rotation, passes between rotor and stator and is discharged at
the periphery (Fig. 5.23). Rotor speeds range from 3000 rpm for a 15 inch
(38·1 cm) rotor to 15 000 rpm for a $3\frac{1}{2}$ in (8·9 cm) rotor. Such mills are best
suited to handling low viscosity liquids.

For more viscous materials, mills with rotors turning on vertical axes
(often known as paste mills) are more generally employed (Fig. 5.24). Speeds
usually range from 3000 rpm for a 10-inch (25·4 cm) rotor to 10 000 rpm for
a $2\frac{1}{2}$-inch (6·4 cm) rotor. Such mills permit easier discharge of product and
cleaning.

Stators and rotors generally have smooth stainless steel surfaces, but
carborundum surfaces are also used. The latter are designed primarily for

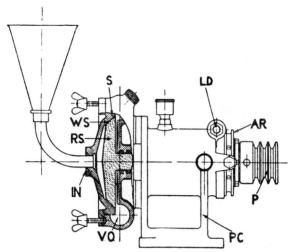

Fig. 5.23. High-speed colloid mill. IN, inlet; RS, rotor; S, stator; WS, working surfaces; VO, volute (outlet); AR, adjusting ring; LD, locking device; P, pulley; PC, pedestal casting. (By courtesy of Premier Colloid Mills Ltd.)

grinding solid materials but in some cases they give improved emulsification. Mills may be jacketed for temperature control. Such mills can produce fairly fine emulsions with internal phase droplet diameters of the order of 1–2 μm. One disadvantage is the incorporation of air into the product. This can result in poor performance of the mill and troublesome foaming.

Some mills are designed with corrugated rotors and stators (Fig. 5.25). By

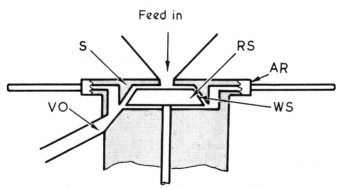

Fig. 5.24. Top-feed 'paste' colloid mill (diagrammatic). RS, rotor; S, stator; WS, working surfaces; VO, volute (outlet); AR, adjusting ring.

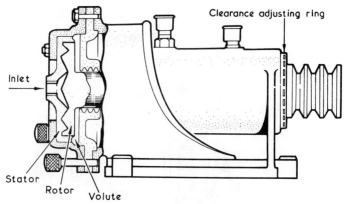

FIG. 5.25.　Corrugated colloid mill. (By courtesy of Premier Colloid Mills Ltd.)

correct design of such corrugations a progressive emulsification is obtained—the product may be discharged under pressure, up to 100 psi (690 kN m^{-2}), and aeration of the products is minimised.

Many other designs of mill are available incorporating different shaped rotors and stators. In some designs an impeller at the feed inlet induces flow of liquid countercurrent to the direction of the centrifugal effect of the rotor. This can have advantages for low viscosity liquids.

Colloid mills are generally more effective than pressure homogenisers for handling high viscosity products (greater than 1·0 N s m^{-2}). Homogenisers are more effective for very low viscosity materials (less than 0·2 N s m^{-2}). In the intermediate range of viscosities both systems are useful but the homogeniser generally tends to produce a smaller droplet size.

Colloid mills are used in the production of salad creams, mayonnaise, artificial creams and many other food emulsions. Paste mills are also applied to a wide variety of size reduction duties in the food industry including the production of meat and fish pastes and fruit purees.[27,28,30]

5.2.3. APPLICATIONS OF EMULSIFICATION IN THE FOOD INDUSTRY

5.2.3.1. Buttermaking

This is a unique example of emulsion technology. The raw material is milk, an oil-in-water emulsion. The final product, butter, is usually classed as a water-in-oil emulsion. Thus an inversion of the phases occurs during buttermaking. The changes in the emulsion structure during buttermaking are summarised in Fig. 5.26.

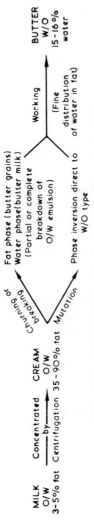

FIG. 5.26.   Changes in emulsion structure during buttermaking.

Batch churning methods are still very widely used. In a typical batch buttermaking operation, using fresh cream, the pasteurised milk is separated by centrifugation (Chapter 7) to produce cream containing 35–40% fat. This cream is rapidly chilled and held at a low temperature for a predetermined time (ageing). Chilling and ageing are important steps in controlling the solid:liquid fat ratio and hence the texture of the final product. Following ageing, the cream is subjected to churning and working. These two operations are essential steps in buttermaking. Churning involves agitation of the cream to bring about a partial breakdown of the oil-in-water emulsion. During agitation in a churn, air is incorporated and a foam produced. The fat globules in the cream accumulate at the air–plasma interface where they release a certain proportion of their liquid fat in non-globular form. Some of this free fat acts as a cement causing globules of fat which come into contact to bind together. As the foam bubbles form, burst and reform, more and more globules come together producing clusters or clumps of increasing size. Churning is continued until these clumps reach a predetermined size, clearly visible through inspection windows in the churn. After churning, the aqueous phase (buttermilk) is removed and the butter grains may be washed free of buttermilk with chilled water. Salt is added as required and the working of the butter commenced. This involves slow speed agitation of the mass of butter grains subjecting them to a kneading and folding action. The purposes of working are (a) to rupture more fat globules and produce more free fat, (b) to disperse the remaining water through the bulk of the fat in the form of fine uniform droplets and (c) to disperse the salt. Following working the butter is chilled and held in cool or frozen storage as required.

The final product appears as a homogeneous mass but its detailed structure is anything but uniform. Basically it consists of a continuous phase of free fat in liquid form containing crystals of free fat, globular fat which survived the churning and working, curd granules, gas bubbles and water droplets. A complete phase reversal does not occur, but the product is generally regarded as a water-in-oil emulsion. It is not a theoretically ideal model of an emulsion and its stability is due mainly to the semi-solid nature of the fat phase rather than any absorbed layer of emulsifying agent.

Most modern churns consist of large, hollow vessels which rotate about horizontal axes. They may contain stays or baffles to assist in the working stage of buttermaking. Some typical shapes are shown in Fig. 5.27. They are usually made of stainless steel with a polished surface on the outside and a sand blasted inner surface, to facilitate discharge of the finished butter. The churns are rotated at a range of speeds, the high speeds being used for

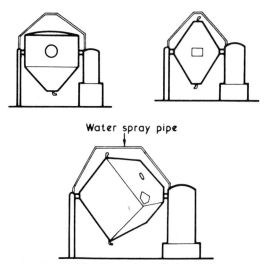

FIG. 5.27.   Typical metal churn shapes.

churning and the lower speeds for working. They may be connected to a vacuum line so that working can be carried out under reduced pressure.

'*Continuous*' *buttermaking techniques* are conveniently classified into groups as follows:

(a) Methods in which cream containing 35–40% fat is subjected to high speed churning and continuous working. Churning is normally achieved by high speed beaters and working by means of screws which knead the mass of butter grains and force them through perforated plates to produce a continuous ribbon of butter. The general principles of one such machine are shown in Fig. 5.28. Machines of this type are very widely used in large scale buttermaking.

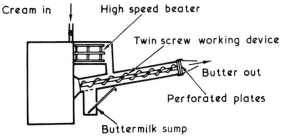

FIG. 5.28.   General principle of accelerated churning and working device (Fritz principle).

(b) Methods in which a concentrated cream (o/w emulsion), containing about 80% fat is prepared by reseparation and then subjected to cooling and mechanical treatment which results in an inversion of the phases to produce butter continuously. The phase inversion is carried out in a variety of equipment all of which involve agitating the concentrated cream in a jacketed system to bring about simultaneous cooling and phase inversion.

(c) Methods in which a highly concentrated cream is produced (o/w emulsion), the emulsion structure broken either before and during, or after, reseparation and a w/o emulsion formed from the separated phases. The emulsion is broken either in the separator or by passing the concentrated cream through an homogenising valve. Formation of the final w/o emulsion is achieved in some form of scraped surface heat exchanger which provides agitation and cooling simultaneously.[27,28,30−32,36]

5.2.3.2. Margarine and spreads

Margarine is a w/o emulsion made up of a blend of fats and oils in milk or water with emulsifying agents and other additives. As with butter, the water droplets are dispersed in a semi-solid fat phase containing fat crystals and liquid oil. The emulsifying agents are of the hydrophobic type and the other additives may include salt, flavours, colouring agents anti-spattering agents and vitamins.

In the batch methods of manufacture emulsification is usually brought about in churns either of the butter type or consisting of paddle agitators in a jacketed vessel. After churning, the margarine is chilled, tempered and then worked in a variety of devices designed to knead and fold the viscous emulsion to the desired consistency.

In the votator process for the manufacture of margarine on a continuous basis, the premixed ingredients are pumped through a series of scraped surface heat exchangers (Fig. 9.9) where simultaneous emulsification and cooling occurs. It then passes through a holding unit where the desired final texture is obtained.

Low calorie spreads usually contain more water than margarine, typically 50% water and 40% fat. Some are based on milk fat or combinations of milk and vegetable fats with acidified casein.[27,28,36,37]

5.2.3.3. Milk and its products

These provide further examples of emulsion technology. Milk is an oil-in-water emulsion containing 3–5% fat in the form of globules ranging in size from $<1\,\mu m$ to $>18\,\mu m$ (diameters). Unhomogenised milk, on standing, develops a cream layer due to reversible instability in the emulsion. This can be prevented by two-stage, pressure homogenisation which reduces the fat globule size to the order of 1–2 μm. Homogenised milk is also said to be more digestible and have a smoother appearance than unhomogenised milk. Milk, evaporated milk and cream, which is to be sterilised, is also homogenised to improve stability and texture. Ice cream mix is an oil-in-water emulsion usually containing 10–12% fat. The pasteurised mix is subjected to two-stage homogenisation before freezing. This influences the texture of the product and prevents separation during freezing and storage. As alternatives to pressure homogenisation, colloid mills and ultrasonic whistles have also been used to increase the stability of milk and milk products.[27,28,30,31,36]

5.2.3.4. Salad cream and mayonnaise

These are both oil-in-water emulsions. The former usually contains 30–40% oil and the emulsion is effected by pressure homogenisation. Mayonnaise usually contains more than 70% oil and, because of the unstable nature of a system with such a high P/V ratio, it is usually prepared by careful mixing at low temperature.[27,28,29,36]

5.2.3.5. Sausage meats and meat pastes

These are examples of meat products in which emulsification of the fat is important both to the texture of the product and its behaviour on cooking. Satisfactory emulsification is achieved by the correct use of mincers, bowl choppers and other specialised equipment.[27,28,31,36]

5.2.3.6. Cake and bread products

These are also influenced by the degree of emulsification of the fat in their formulation. Inadequate emulsification can result in a poor crumb structure and cakes and loaves of unsatisfactory shape and volume. Specialised mixing equipment is used to attain the desired degree of emulsification.[27,28,31,36]

REFERENCES

1. Nienow, A. W., Edwards, M. F. and Harnby, N., Introduction to mixing problems. In *Mixing in the Process Industries*, ed. N. Harnby, M. F. Edwards and A. W. Nienow. Butterworths, London, 1985, pp. 1–22.
2. Godfrey, J. C., Mixing of high-viscosity fluids. In *Mixing in the Process Industries*, ed. N. Harnby, M. F. Edwards and A. W. Nienow. Butterworths, London, 1985, pp. 185–201.

3. Oldshue, J. Y., Fluid mixing technology and practice. *Chem. Engng*, **90**(12) (13 June 1983), pp. 83–108.

4. Edwards, M. F., Mixing of low-viscosity liquids in stirred tanks. In *Mixing in the Process Industries*, ed. N. Harnby, M. F. Edwards and A. W. Nienow. Butterworths, London, 1985, pp. 131–44.

5. Mann, R., Recent progress in the modelling of mixers. *Process Engng*, **69**(8) (1988) 40–1.

6. Engineering Equipment Users Association (EEUA), Agitator Selection and Design. *Handbook No. 9* (revised). Constable and Co. Ltd., London, 1963.

7. Rushton, J. H., Costich, E. W. and Everett, H. J., Power characteristics of mixing impellers. *Chem. Engng Prog.*, **46**(8) (1950) 395–404.

8. Holland, F. A. and Chapman, F. S., *Liquid Mixing and Processing in Stirred Tanks*. Van Nostrand Reinhold, New York, 1966.

9. Edwards, M. F., Laminar flow and distributive mixing. In *Mixing in the Process Industries*, ed. N. Harnby, M. F. Edwards and A. W. Nienow. Butterworths, London, 1985, pp. 202–25.

10. McDonagh, M., Mixers for powder/liquid dispersion. *The Chemical Engineer*, **434** (March 1987) 29–32.

11. Thorne, J. G. M., Continuous mixing and dispersing. *Processing*, **22** (October 1976) 49–51.

12. Reid, J. G., Developments in continuous mixing and blending in bakeries. *Food Manufacture*, **45**(2) (1970) 36–40, 58.

13. Godfrey, J. C., Static mixers. In *Mixing in the Process Industries*, ed. N. Harnby, M. F. Edwards and A. W. Nienow. Butterworths, London, 1985, pp. 226–50.

14. Mutsakis, M., Streiff, F. A. and Schneider, G., Advances in static mixing technology. *Chem. Engng Prog.*, **82**(7) (July 1986).

15. Loncin, M. and Merson, R. W., *Food Engineering—Principles and Selected Applications*. Academic Press, New York, 1979.

16. Williams, G., How to buy a static mixer. *The Chemical Engineer*, **407** (October 1984) 30–7.

17. Harnby, N., Trends in powder mixing. *The Chemical Engineer*, **405** (July 1984) 22–3.

18. Miles, J. E. P. and Schofield, C., Some suggestions for the selection of solid–solid mixers. *Process Engng*. (September 1968) 77–81.

19. Weidenbaum, S. S., Mixing of solids. In *Advances in Chemical Engineering, Vol. II*, ed. B. T. Drew and J. W. Hoopes Jr. Academic Press, New York, 1968, pp. 211–337.

20. Valentin, F. H. H., The mixing of powders and pastes: Some basic concepts. *The Chemical Engineer*, **208**(5) (1967) 99–104.

21. Harnby, N., The mixing of cohesive powders. In *Mixing in the Process Industries*, ed. N. Harnby, M. F. Edwards and A. W. Nienow. Butterworths, London, 1985, pp. 78–94.

22. Williams, J. C., The mixing of dry powders. *Powder Technol.*, **2**(1) (1968) 13–20.

23. Harnby, N., The selection of powder mixers. In *Mixing in the Process Industries*, ed. N. Harnby, M. F. Edwards and A. W. Nienow. Butterworths, London, 1985, pp. 39–53.

24. Skidmore, J. A. H., Modern practice in dry solids mixing in industry. *Food Technol. Aust.*, **18**(10) (1966) 21–5.

25. Matsumoto, S., Review paper—W/O/W-type multiple emulsions with a view to possible food applications. *J. Texture Studies,* **17**(2) (1986) 141–59.
26. Lewis, M. J., *Physical Properties of Foods and Food Processing Systems.* Ellis Horwood, Chichester, England, 1987.
27. Dickinson, E. and Stainsby, G., *Colloids in Food.* Applied Science Publishers, London, 1982.
28. Becher, P. (ed.), *Encyclopedia of Emulsion Technology, Vol. 1. Basic Theory* (1983); *Vol. 2. Applications* (1985); *Vol. 3. Applications/Measurements* (1988). Marcel Dekker, New York.
29. Lissant, K. J. (ed.), *Emulsions and Emulsion Technology, Parts I and II* (1974); *Part III* (1984). Marcel Dekker, New York.
30. Farrall, A. W., *Food Engineering Systems Vol. 1. Operations.* AVI, Westport, Conn., USA, 1976.
31. Friberg, S. (ed.), *Food Emulsion.* Marcel Dekker, New York, 1976
32. Harper, W. J. and Hall, C. W., *Dairy Technology and Engineering.* AVI, Westport, Conn., USA, 1976.
33. White, G. W., Homogenisation of ice cream mixes. *Dairy Industry International,* **46**(2) (1981) 29–36.
34. Phipps, L. W., The high pressure dairy homogeniser. *Technical Bulletin 6.* The National Institute for Research in Dairying, Reading, England, 1985.
35. Korstvedt, H., Bates, R., King, J. and Siciliano, A., Microfluidization. *Drug and Cosmetic Industry,* **135** (November 1984) 36–7, 40.
36. Brennan, J. G., Emulsions in food technology. *Process Biochem.,* **5**(7) (1970) 33–7.
37. Andersen, A. J. C. and Williams, P. N., *Margarine,* 2nd edn. Pergamon Press, Oxford, England, 1965.

CHAPTER 6

FILTRATION AND MEMBRANE SEPARATION

6.1. FILTRATION THEORY

6.1.1. INTRODUCTION

Solid–liquid filtration, hereinafter called filtration, may be defined as that unit operation in which the insoluble solid component of a solid–liquid suspension is separated from the liquid component by passing the latter through a porous membrane or septum which retains the solid particles on its upstream surface, or within its structure, or both. The solid–liquid suspension is known as the feed slurry or prefilt, the liquid component that passes through the membrane is called the filtrate and the membrane itself is referred to as the filter medium. The separated solids are known as the filter cake, once they form a detectable layer covering the upstream surface of the medium. In practice, in order to obtain adequate recovery of the filtrate and/or a cake of adequate purity, the cake needs to be washed or blown free of filtrate once filtration ceases. In some operations air drying of the cake is also desirable. The equipment in which filtration, washing and drying is carried out, known as the filter, must provide a support for the filter medium, a space for the accumulation of the solids, channels for the introduction of the feed slurry, wash liquid, steam and/or air and for the removal of the filtrate, washings and exhaust air or steam. In addition to the filter itself, tanks must be provided for the feed slurry, filtrate and washings. A means of inducing the flow of filtrate through the filter and medium must also be provided.

The flow of filtrate may be brought about by means of gravity alone, by the application of a pressure greater than atmospheric upstream of the medium (pressure filtration), by applying a vacuum downstream of the medium (vacuum filtration) or by means of centrifugal force (centrifugal filtration). Filtration under the influence of gravity alone is limited in application to slurries containing very free-draining solids or with very low solids contents. It has very limited use in the food industry but is applied to water and sewage treatment. Such applications are treated in Chapter 18. Centrifugal filtration is dealt with in Chapter 7. Discussion in this chapter will be confined to pressure and vacuum filtration.

The applications for filtration in the food industry may be considered to fall into three categories. Category one embraces all those applications wherein slurries containing appreciable amounts of insoluble solids, i.e. more than one or two percent by weight, are separated into their solid and liquid components. Either the liquid or solid component, or both, may be valuable. In such operations a cake is formed on the upstream surface of the medium and the process is known as cake filtration. The second category is termed clarification and involves removing small quantities of insoluble solid from a valuable liquid. Here the object usually is to produce a clear liquid and the solids are generally unwanted. In such filtrations a cake may build up on the medium or alternatively, where the amount of solids is very small, they may become enmeshed within the structure of the medium. The third category, often referred to as microfiltration, involves the removal of very fine particles, of the order of 1 μm or less, and is generally directed at removing microorganisms from liquid foods.

6.1.2. GENERAL THEORY

The following brief treatment of the theory of filtration is applicable only to those cases where cake build-up occurs. More detailed accounts of filtration theory are available in Refs 1–7.

In the initial stages of filtration the first particles of solid to encounter the filter medium become enmeshed in it, reducing its open surface area and increasing the resistance it offers to the flow of filtrate. As filtration proceeds a layer of solids builds up on the upstream face of the medium and this layer, or cake, increases in thickness with time. Once formed, this cake in fact becomes the primary filtering medium. Filtrate passing through a filter encounters three types of resistance, namely (a) that offered by the channels and ports of the filter itself, (b) that offered by the filter medium, and (c) that offered by the filter cake. The total pressure drop across the filter is equivalent to the sum of the pressure drops resulting from these three resistances. Usually the pressure drop through the channels and ports of the filter itself is neglected in calculations.

If $-\Delta p$ is the total pressure drop across the filter and $-\Delta p_c$ and $-\Delta p_m$ the pressure drops across the cake and medium respectively then

$$-\Delta p = -\Delta p_c - \Delta p_m \tag{6.1}$$

6.1.3. FILTER CAKE RESISTANCE

The pressure drop across the filter cake may be related to the flow rate of filtrate by the expression[2]

$$-\Delta p_c = \frac{\alpha \eta w V}{A^2} \left(\frac{dV}{dt} \right) \tag{6.2}$$

where $-\Delta p_c$ = pressure drop across the cake, η = viscosity of filtrate, w = mass of solids deposited on the medium per unit volume of filtrate, V = volume of filtrate delivered in time t, A = filter area normal to the direction of flow of filtrate, α = specific resistance of the cake.

α physically represents the pressure drop necessary to give unit superficial velocity (see Appendix I.1) of filtrate of unit viscosity through a cake containing unit mass of solid per unit filter area. α is related to the properties of the cake by

$$\alpha = \frac{k(1-X)S_0^2}{X^3 \rho_s} \tag{6.3}$$

where X = porosity of the cake, i.e. the fraction of the total volume that is void; S_0 = specific surface area of the solid particles in the cake (surface area per unit volume); ρ_s = density of the solids; k = constant (5 for random packed particles of definite size and shape).

In a cake composed of rigid non-deformable solid particles α is independent of $-\Delta p_c$ and does not vary throughout the depth of the cake. Such a cake is known as *incompressible*.

Many slurries contain non-rigid, deformable solid particles or agglomerates of particles. The resistance to flow in cakes, formed from such solids, depends on the pressure drop and also varies throughout the depth of the cake, being highest near the filter medium. Such cakes are called *compressible*. Since α varies throughout the depth of a compressible cake, an average value for specific resistance for the entire cake must be used in equation (6.2). This average specific resistance must be measured experimentally for each slurry. To apply equation (6.2) at different pressures the relationship between the average specific resistance and $-\Delta p_c$ must be determined experimentally.

6.1.4. FILTER MEDIUM RESISTANCE

By analogy with equation (6.2) the filter medium resistance may be defined by the equation

$$-\Delta p_m = \frac{R_m \eta}{A} \left(\frac{dV}{dt} \right) \tag{6.4}$$

where $-\Delta p_m$ = pressure drop across the medium; R_m = filter medium resistance.

It is usual to assume that R_m is constant during any filtration cycle and to determine its value by experiment. When treated thus, R_m also includes the resistance to filtrate flow offered by the filter channels.

From equations (6.1), (6.2) and (6.4)

$$-\Delta p = -\Delta p_c - \Delta p_m = \frac{\eta}{A}\left(\frac{\mathrm{d}V}{\mathrm{d}t}\right)\left(\frac{\alpha w V}{A} + R_m\right)$$

or

$$\frac{\mathrm{d}V}{\mathrm{d}t} = \frac{A(-\Delta p)}{\eta\left(\dfrac{\alpha w V}{A} + R_m\right)} \tag{6.5}$$

Equation (6.5) is a general expression for the rate of flow of filtrate. Its application to filtration under different conditions is outlined below.

6.1.5. CONSTANT PRESSURE FILTRATION

When $-\Delta p$ is maintained constant, equation (6.5) may be integrated thus:

$$\int_0^t \mathrm{d}t = \frac{\eta}{A(-\Delta p)}\left(\frac{\alpha w}{A}\int_0^V V\,\mathrm{d}V + R_m\int_0^V \mathrm{d}V\right)$$

i.e.

$$t = \frac{\eta}{(-\Delta p)}\left[\frac{\alpha w}{2}\left(\frac{V}{A}\right)^2 + R_m\left(\frac{V}{A}\right)\right] \tag{6.6}$$

Equation (6.6) is a general expression for the filtration time during constant pressure filtration.

To use equation (6.6), values of α and R_m must be determined experimentally.

Equation (6.5) may be written in the form:

$$\frac{\mathrm{d}t}{\mathrm{d}V} = KV + B \tag{6.7}$$

where

$$K = \frac{\alpha w \eta}{A^2(-\Delta p)} \tag{6.8}$$

and

$$B = \frac{R_m \eta}{A(-\Delta p)} \tag{6.9}$$

Equation (6.7) represents a straight line if dt/dV is plotted against V.

Thus if a constant pressure filtration is carried out and values of V for various values of t recorded, a graph of dt/dV versus V can be constructed as shown in Fig. 6.1. The slope of this line is K and the intercept on the ordinate when $V = 0$ is B. Thus values of α and R_m can be determined from equations (6.8) and (6.9).

For incompressible cakes equation (6.6) can be used directly at different pressures. For compressible cakes however the relationship between α and $-\Delta p$ needs to be determined experimentally by carrying out filtration runs at at least two different constant pressures. Empirical equations may be fitted to the results obtained. Two such equations have been suggested.[2]

$$\alpha = \alpha_0(-\Delta p)^s \tag{6.10}$$

and

$$\alpha = \alpha_0'[1 - \beta(-\Delta p)^{s'}] \tag{6.11}$$

where $\alpha_0, \alpha_0', s, s'$ and β are empirical constants. Equation (6.10) is used more commonly than (6.11) but the latter is applicable over a wider range of pressure drops. The average specific resistance is more correctly a function of $-\Delta p_c$ than $-\Delta p$. However, during most of a filtration cycle $-\Delta p_c$ is large compared with $-\Delta p_m$ and so little error arises in relating α to $-\Delta p$. s in equation (6.10), known as the compressibility coefficient, is zero for incompressible cakes and rises towards 1·0 as compressibility increases.

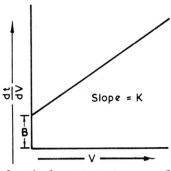

Fig. 6.1. Plot of results from constant pressure filtration run.

Having determined values for α_0 and s then equations (6.10) and hence (6.6) can be used for constant pressure filtration calculations at different pressures.

6.1.6. CONSTANT RATE FILTRATION
If filtration is carried out at constant rate then

$$\frac{dV}{dt} = \text{constant} = \frac{V}{t} \tag{6.12}$$

Equation (6.5) may be written:

$$-\Delta p = \left(\frac{\eta\alpha w V}{A^2 t}\right)V + \left(\frac{\eta V R_m}{At}\right) \tag{6.13}$$

or

$$-\Delta p = K'V + B' \tag{6.14}$$

Equation (6.14) represents a straight line if $-\Delta p$ is plotted against V. The slope of the line is K' and the intercept to the $-\Delta p$ axis when $V = 0$ is B'. Thus for incompressible cakes α and R_m can again be determined by experiment and equation (6.13) used for cycle calculations.[5]

For compressible cakes the relationship between α and $-\Delta p_c$ must again be determined by experiment. If a relationship of the form shown in equation (6.10) is assumed to apply, equation (6.2) may be modified to:

$$(-\Delta p_c)^{1-s} = [-(\Delta p - \Delta p_m)]^{1-s} = \frac{\eta\alpha_0 w V}{A^2}\frac{V}{t} \tag{6.15}$$

which may be written:

$$[-(\Delta p - \Delta p_m)]^{1-s} = K''t \tag{6.16}$$

where

$$K'' = \frac{\eta\alpha_0 w}{A^2}\left(\frac{V}{t}\right)^2 \tag{6.17}$$

If it is assumed that $-\Delta p_m$ is constant throughout a constant-rate filtration then by plotting $-\Delta p$ versus t, passing a smooth curve through the points and extrapolating the curve to the $-\Delta p$ axis, an approximate value for $-\Delta p_m$ can be obtained. If $\log t$ is then plotted against $\log [-(\Delta p - \Delta p_m)]$ and a straight line obtained, the slope of this line is $1 - s$. K'' can also be obtained from the above log–log plot or calculated from equation (6.16). α_0 may be calculated from equation (6.17). If at the first attempt the log–log plot is not a straight line then further approximations for $-\Delta p_m$ need to be made.

For some applications a combination of constant rate and constant pressure may be used, i.e. increasing the pressure in the early stages of filtration and maintaining it constant in the later stages. In other cases a more complex pressure/time pattern may be more appropriate. Graphical techniques may be used to estimate filtering times under such conditions. The choice of operating conditions largely depends on the characteristics of the feed slurry and are usually determined by laboratory trials.[8]

6.1.7. WASHING THE CAKE

In most filters, cake washing is carried out by substituting wash liquid for the feed slurry when filtration is complete. Thus the wash liquid follows the same paths through the cake as the filtrate. In such an operation if the physical properties of the wash liquid, notably viscosity, are the same as the filtrate, the rate of washing will be approximately equal to the final rate of flow of filtrate. Since washing is usually carried out at constant pressure the rate of washing will remain approximately constant. This behaviour is only approximate since 'channelling' which can occur in the cake may alter flow rates.

The concentration of filtrate solids in the wash liquid generally varies with time to the general pattern shown in Fig. 6.2, curve A. Under optimum conditions up to 90% of the solubles in the cake may be removed in the initial stage a–b. Washing is continued until the soluble solids content of the washings reaches an economic limit.

In the plate-and-frame press (Section 6.2.1) fitted with wash plates, the

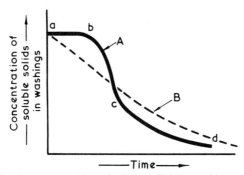

Fig. 6.2.   Variation in concentration of soluble solids in washings with time. Curve A: Displacement washing (applicable to most filters). Curve B: Thorough washing (applicable to plate-and-frame presses fitted with wash plates).

wash liquid follows a different path to that of the filtrate. It travels through twice the cake thickness and has only half the filtering area available as compared with the filtrate. Thus the rate of flow of wash liquid is approximately a quarter of the final filtration rate. The change in soluble solids concentration in the washings is then more gradual and uniform as in Fig. 6.2, curve B.[1,5,8]

6.1.8. APPLICATION OF THEORY

The general expressions for rate of filtration at constant pressure and rate may be used for interpreting the effects of changes in operating conditions on throughput, downtime, etc., and scaling up plant. They should always be regarded as approximate guides, however, and should be supported by practical trials where at all possible. The filtering characteristics of slurries are very sensitive to methods of preparation and handling, and where small-scale tests are used to obtain data to apply to larger-scale operations it is important to use slurries as nearly as possible identical to those which are to be filtered on the industrial equipment and to use methods of preparation and handling similar to the full-scale methods. Such precautions are particularly important when compressible cakes are encountered. Compressible cakes are common in food filtration.

6.1.9. FILTER MEDIA

The main functions of the filter medium are to promote the formation of a cake of solids and to support it once formed. The medium should offer the minimum resistance to flow consistent with the rapid formation of a filter cake. It must be strong enough to support the cake and retain its strength under the extreme conditions occurring during the operation. Its surface characteristics should be such as to facilitate cake removal. The medium must be non-toxic and chemically compatible with the material being filtered. It must not be too expensive.

Filter media may be rigid or flexible. Rigid media may be loose, such as sand and/or gravel, diatomaceous earths, or charcoal. Such loose media are seldom used alone in food applications. Fixed rigid media are also used. These include porous carbon, porcelain, fused alumina, perforated metal plates, rigid wire meshes or edge media (see Section 6.2.1.5). Such rigid media are available in the form of plates, discs, tubes and other shapes.

Flexible media may consist of woven fabrics of cotton, silk, wool, and jute. Many synthetic materials are finding applications, including nylon, polypropylene, polythene, polyvinylchloride and co-polymers and terylene. Glass fibre and flexible metal meshes are also used as media. Non-woven materials are also used, including cotton and wool fibres, and paper pulp. These are available in preformed pads of various shapes. Asbestos, once widely used as a filter aid, is no longer acceptable. Alternative fibrous media are being investigated.[9,16]

All the types of media mentioned above can be obtained with specified pore sizes to suit particular filtration applications. The only reliable method of selecting a medium for a particular duty is by practical trials. Further information on filter media is available in Refs 1, 2, 5 and 6.

When the solids to be filtered off are very finely divided or are of a slimy, highly compressible character the filter medium tends to block quickly and only short runs are possible. In such circumstances materials known as filter aids are often used. These usually consist of comparatively large, inert, non-compressible solid particles of different shapes. They may be applied by mixing with the feed slurry or they may be suspended in a clear liquid, often some filtrate from a previous run, which is then passed through the filter so that a precoating of the filter aid builds up on the medium. The filter aid forms a rigid lattice structure on the medium and provides numerous channels through which the filtrate can flow, thus slowing up the plugging of the medium and prolonging the filtration cycle. Sometimes a combination of precoating and premixing is used. Kieselguhr, or diatomaceous earth, is commonly used as a filter aid. Paper pulp, carbon, fuller's earth and many other materials are also used as filter aids. As with filter media, filter aids are available in a wide range of grades to suit particular applications.[1,2,5,6]

6.2. FILTRATION EQUIPMENT—PRINCIPLES, DESIGN FEATURES AND GENERAL APPLICATIONS

6.2.1. PRESSURE FILTERS

In pressure filters a superatmospheric pressure is maintained upstream of the medium to induce the flow of filtrate through the system. This upstream pressure is achieved by pumping the feed slurry into the filter. Pressure filters may be operated at constant pressure throughout filtration or the pressure may be gradually increased so as to maintain a constant flow rate of filtrate. Various combinations of these two basic methods may also be used. Since centrifugal pumps are commonly employed, constant rate followed by constant pressure filtration is a common combination as this corresponds to the feed-discharge characteristics of such pumps. In particular, when handling compressible solids, a low initial pressure is

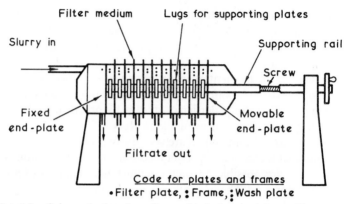

FIG. 6.3.   Schematic drawing of assembled plate-and-frame filter press.

desirable to minimise plugging of the medium. The maximum pressure used in pressure filters is usually of the order of 25–75 psig (276–621 kN m^{-2}) but some filters operate at much higher pressures.

6.2.1.1. Vertical plate pressure filters (filter presses)

A vertical drainage plate supporting a filter medium is the basic filtering element in a vertical plate stress. A commonly used design is the *plate-and-frame press*. In this type of filter grooved plates, covered on both sides with

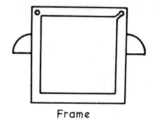

Frame

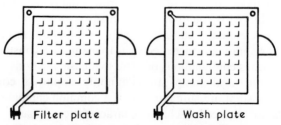

FIG. 6.4.   Schematic drawings of plates and frame.

filter medium, alternate with frames in a rack (Fig. 6.3). The assembly of plates and frames can be squeezed tightly together by a screw, hydraulic or pneumatic mechanism to form a liquid-tight unit. The filter medium also acts as a gasket, preventing leakage between the plates and frames. Both plates and frame are provided with openings at one corner and when the press is closed these openings form a channel through which the feed slurry is introduced. In addition, the hollow centre of each frame is connected by an auxiliary channel to this feed channel (Fig. 6.4). The feed slurry enters the frames and the cake builds up in the hollow centre of the frames. The filtrate passes through the medium and on to the grooved surfaces of the filter plates from where it is removed via an outlet channel in each plate. Filtration is continued until the flow of filtrate drops below a practical level or the pressure reaches an unacceptably high level, due to the cake packing tightly in the frames. After filtration, washing of the cake may be carried out by replacing the flow of feed slurry with wash liquid. However, more effective washing is obtained by the use of special wash plates (Fig. 6.4). These are arranged in the press so that every second plate is a wash plate. During filtration these wash plates act as filter plates. During washing the outlets from the wash plates are closed and the wash liquid introduced on to their surfaces through a special inlet channel. The flow path for both filtration and washing when wash plates are used is shown in Fig. 6.5. The cake is removed manually after opening the press.

Another common design of filter press is known as the *recessed-plate press*. In this filter the cake accumulates within recesses in the plates and no frames are used. The feed is usually introduced centrally and removed via an outlet on the corners of each plate (Fig. 6.6). For washing, the feed slurry is replaced by wash liquid entering through the same inlets. Membrane plates consist of recessed plates covered with flexible membranes. These can be inflated with compressed air to squeeze out excess liquid from the cake. If this is done part way through a filtration run, with certain cakes it can reduce the filtering time compared with conventional plates.

Many other types of vertical plate filters are available. Larger presses have facilities for lifting or moving plates and frames mechanically. Automated plate presses are available from which the cake is discharged by movement of the filter cloth after each short cycle.[8]

The vertical plate filter has found very wide application in industry. It is simple in design and operation, compact, flexible and can be used to handle a wide variety of types of slurry. It is relatively cheap initially. On the other hand labour costs and filter cloth consumption are high and washing of the cake is not always efficient.

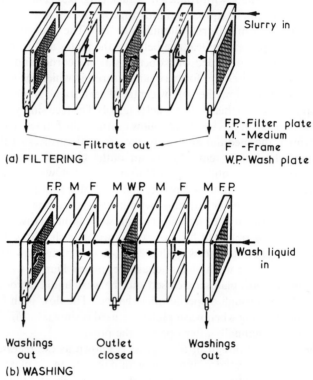

FP.-Filter plate
M. -Medium
F -Frame
W.P.-Wash plate

FIG. 6.5. Flow paths of liquid through plate-and-frame press, fitted with wash plates, during (a) filtering and (b) washing.

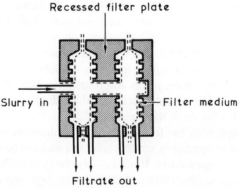

FIG. 6.6. Schematic drawing (sectional view) of a recessed-plate press.

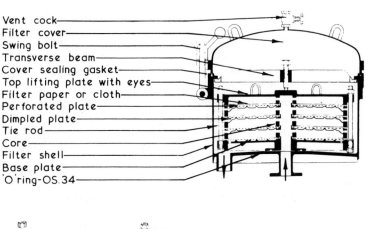

Vent cock
Filter cover
Swing bolt
Transverse beam
Cover sealing gasket
Top lifting plate with eyes
Filter paper or cloth
Perforated plate
Dimpled plate
Tie rod
Core
Filter shell
Base plate
O'ring-OS.34

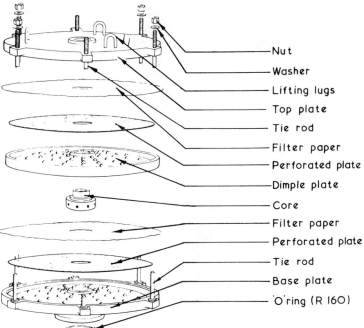

Nut
Washer
Lifting lugs
Top plate
Tie rod
Filter paper
Perforated plate
Dimple plate
Core
Filter paper
Perforated plate
Tie rod
Base plate
O'ring (R 160)

FIG. 6.7. Horizontal plate filter. (Top) Calmic E type high duty pressure filter. (Bottom) Calmic filter element assembly sequence. (By courtesy of Calmic Engineering Co. Ltd.)

6.2.1.2. Horizontal plate filters

This type of filter consists of a number of horizontal plates, suitably designed to allow free drainage of the liquid, assembled in a vertical stack in a cylindrical pressure vessel. The filter medium covers the top surface of the plates. The feed slurry is introduced through a central duct (as in Fig. 6.7) or through a hollow annular inlet. The cake builds up on the upper surfaces of the medium and the filtrate passes through the medium on to the drainage plates and out through an annular or central outlet. After filtration, the feed is replaced by wash liquid and washing carried out by displacement. Blowing of the cake with steam or air is carried out where required. For cake removal, the plates are usually lifted vertically out of the shell and the solids removed manually. Some units have mechanical devices to aid cake removal.

The horizontal plate filter is compact. The horizontal plates promote uniform cake build up. The units are readily cleaned or sterilised if required, and cake washing is effective. Simple units have relatively high labour requirements and are normally available only in relatively small sizes, e.g. up to 30 in (76·2 cm) diameter and up to 24 plates per unit. They are most useful for removing small quantities of solids (e.g. as polishing filters) or for short cycles, particularly where very clean conditions are important.

6.2.1.3. Shell-and-leaf pressure filters

These filters have a filter leaf as the basic filter element. A filter leaf consists of a wire mesh screen or grooved drainage plate over which the filter medium is stretched. The leaf may be suspended from the top or supported

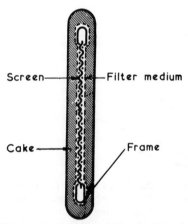

FIG. 6.8.   Schematic drawing of filter leaf (sectional view).

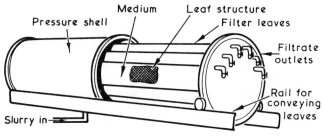

(a) Stationary leaf filter, open for cake discharge

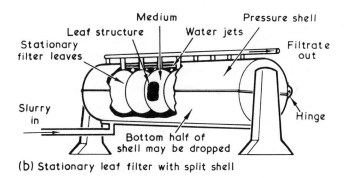

(b) Stationary leaf filter with split shell

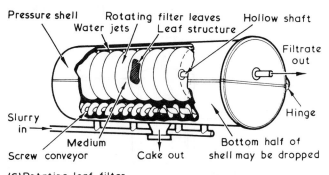

(C) Rotating leaf filter

FIG. 6.9.   Schematic drawings of some common horizontal shell-and-leaf pressure filters.

from the bottom or centre. The supporting member is usually hollow and forms an outlet channel for the filtrate (Fig. 6.8).

In horizontal shell-and-leaf filters the filter leaves are mounted vertically in a horizontal pressure-tight vessel. The feed slurry is introduced under pressure into the shell and the cake builds up on the outer surfaces of the leaves. The filtrate passes through the medium and drains from the inner structure of the leaves into the outlet channel provided. Leaves may be rectangular or circular in shape and may be stationary as shown in Fig. 6.9(a), (b), or rotating slowly about a horizontal axis as in Fig. 6.9(c). The rotation of the leaves at 1–2 rpm promotes uniform cake build up. Filtration is continued until the cake thickness reaches a predetermined value, and then washing is carried out either by replacing the slurry with wash liquid or alternatively by sluicing down the cake using water jets, reslurrying, and refiltering it. Cake removal is achieved either by withdrawing the leaves from the shell and cleaning them manually (Fig. 6.9(a)) or by sluicing down the cake with the bottom half of the shell open (Fig. 6.9(b)). Some such filters can discharge dry cake continuously from the shell by means of screw conveyors (Fig. 6.9(c)), if the cake can be satisfactorily removed from the leaves by 'blowing back' with compressed air. Compressed air may also be employed for loosening the cake prior to sluicing down. In vertical shell-and-leaf pressure filters, rectangular leaves are mounted vertically in a vertical cylindrical pressure vessel (Fig. 6.10).

Shell-and-leaf filters are flexible and can be economic in the use of labour, especially where cake discharge from the closed shell is possible. On the other hand the cake formed is not usually as dry as in presses. Classification of solids and uneven cake build up can occur. They have a higher capital

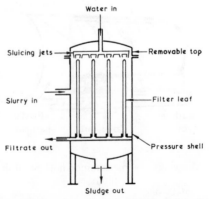

FIG. 6.10. Schematic drawing of vertical shell-and-leaf pressure filter.

cost than plate filters. Pressures used do not normally exceed about 60 psig ($0.52 \, \text{MN m}^{-2}$), but some units can work at 250 psig ($1.85 \, \text{MN m}^{-2}$). They are best suited to long filtration runs with slurries of unchanging characteristics.

6.2.1.4. Shell-and-tube pressure filters

These filters incorporate a cylindrical tube, instead of a leaf, as the basic filter element. The tubes are usually suspended vertically from the filtrate take-aways in vertical pressure vessels. Tubes may be made of perforated metal, wire mesh, plastics or porous stone. Their features are similar to shell-and-leaf filters but they usually have smaller capacities and are almost always used with a precoating of filter aid.

6.2.1.5. Edge (pressure) filters

A stack of closely spaced rings or discs, often known as a filter pile, forms the basic feature of an edge filter. The discs are mounted one above the other on a fluted rod and held in position between a boss and nut (Fig. 6.11). The edges of the discs are separated by gaps of the order of $0.001–0.01$ in ($25.4–254 \, \mu\text{m}$) by means of projections on the rings. The required number of these filter piles may be fixed in a header plate and enclosed in a pressure vessel (Fig. 6.12).

In operation, a precoat of filter aid is built up at the edges of the discs. The feed is introduced under pressure into the shell and the cake builds up over the precoat. Filtrate passes through the precoat, through the spaces between the discs and out via the grooves in the supporting rod. Premixing of filter aid with the slurry is usually practised in addition to precoating. Cake is removed when filtration and washing are complete by back blowing and/or back flushing through the filtrate outlet and removing the sludge formed through a bottom outlet.

Edge filters are constructed of metal (usually stainless steel) or plastic (compatible with the product). They are economical in labour requirements and use no filter cloth. They are most suited to the removal of small quantities of finely divided solids to produce very clear liquids (i.e. clarifying or polishing).

6.2.1.6. Continuous pressure filters

Rotary drum and disc filters can be operated as continuous pressure filters. However, they are far more commonly used as continuous vacuum filters and so will be described in detail in Section 6.2.2. Cake discharge is the

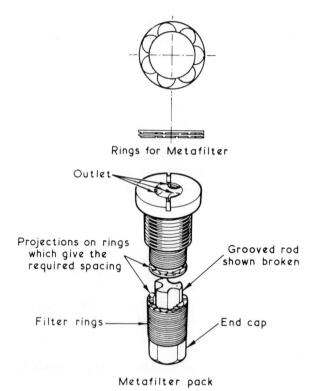

Rings for Metafilter

Metafilter pack

FIG. 6.11.   Filter pile. (Diagram reproduced by courtesy of Stella-Meta Filters Ltd.)

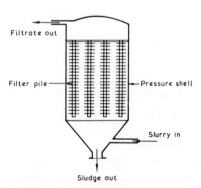

FIG. 6.12.   Schematic drawing of assembled edge filter.

biggest problem. Some units employ a self-sealing screw conveyor to continuously remove the cake from the shell. Others use pressure receivers operated singly or in pairs. The latter arrangement permits intermittent discharge of the cake. They are best suited to handling large throughputs of standard slurry where pressures greater than atmospheric are advantageous (e.g. for volatile or hot filtrates).

6.2.2. VACUUM FILTERS

In vacuum filters a subatmospheric pressure is maintained downstream of the medium and atmospheric pressure upstream. Because the pressure drop across the filter is limited to one atmosphere, they are not suited to batch operation. Some types of leaf filter, tube filters and edge filters are operated under vacuum but continuous vacuum filters are far more common. Because the upstream pressure is atmospheric, cake discharge, and hence continuous operation, is facilitated. Most vacuum filters are operated at constant pressure drop, except during the initial stages when the system is being evacuated.

6.2.2.1. Continuous rotary drum vacuum filters

As its name implies, this type of filter consists of a cylindrical drum rotating about a horizontal axis. In one very common design, the surface of the drum consists of a number of shallow compartments formed between dividing strips running the length of the drum (Fig. 6.13). Each compartment is connected, by one or more pipelines, to an automatic rotary valve situated centrally at one end of the drum. The drum is partly submerged in an open tank of slurry. Filter medium covers the entire drum surface and is supported by perforated plates, grids or wire meshes to provide drainage space between the medium and the floor of each shallow compartment. The drum rotates at speeds of the order of 0·1–2 rpm. Consider one compartment on the drum surface, e.g. the shaded one shown in Fig. 6.13(a). As the drum rotates and this compartment becomes submerged in the slurry, a vacuum is drawn on it by means of the automatic rotary valve. Filtrate flows through the medium and out through the drain pipe from the compartment and is directed to the filtrate receiver by means of the valve. A layer of cake builds up on the outer surface of the medium. As the compartment emerges from the slurry the cake is sucked free of filtrate. As it proceeds further on its cycle the drainings from the compartment are diverted to another receiver by means of the rotary valve and wash liquid is applied to the cake by means of sprays. As the compartment passes from beneath the sprays the cake is sucked free of

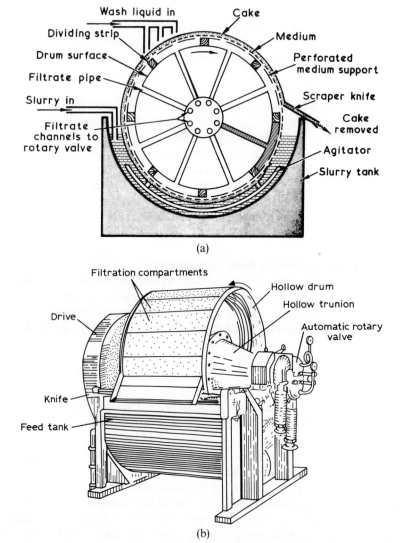

FIG. 6.13.   Rotary drum vacuum filter. (a) Principle of operation. (b) General view (reprinted from Cheremisinoff and Azbel,[5] by permission of the author).

washings. Further on its cycle the compartment is disconnected from its vacuum source and compressed air is introduced beneath the filter medium for a short period, loosening the cake from the surface of the medium. This is again controlled by the automatic rotary valve. The cake is removed by means of a scraper knife. Then, as the compartment becomes submerged in the slurry again, vacuum is re-applied and a new cycle commences. Thus each compartment behaves as an individual filter operating in a sequence which results in the continuous delivery of filtrate and discharge of cake.

Many alternative designs of drum filter are available. Feed is normally applied by rotating the drum partly submerged in a slurry tank. As an alternative, for quick-settling solids, top-feeding may be used. In this system the slurry is fed to a distributor trough on top of the drum, whence it flows on to the medium surface. An alternative system of cake removal employs an endless belt which passes around the drum and upon which the cake builds up. At the point of discharge of the cake the belt passes over rollers to effect cake removal. In other designs, closely spaced strings (string-discharge) or coiled wires (coil filter) are used instead of a belt. In the precoat drum filter a layer of precoat material up to 3 in (7·62 cm) thick is applied to the drum before use. As the drum rotates, a thin layer of this precoat, together with the thin cake formed thereon, is removed by an advancing knife edge. The precoat filter is mainly applicable to slurries with low solids contents and where thin, highly deformable cakes are formed.

The advantages of rotary drum vacuum filters are low labour costs, large capacity for the space occupied and flexibility in cake thickness. On the other hand they are limited in use to fairly permeable cakes which discharge readily. Dry cakes are difficult to obtain and the capital cost of the equipment, including vacuum equipment, is relatively high. As with all vacuum filters they are not suited to handling very hot filtrates or volatile materials. Their best field of application is in handling large volumes of slurry of standard characteristics with reasonably free draining properties.

6.2.2.2. Rotary vacuum disc filters

Such a filter (Fig. 6.14) consists of a number of circular filter leaves mounted on a horizontal axis about which they rotate. Each disc is fitted with a cake removal device and is divided into sections, each of which has an individual outlet to the central shaft. These outlets form a continuous channel through which the filtrate and wash flow from all sectors at the same angle. These channels terminate in a rotary valve similar to that used on drum filters. In operating each disc behaves as a drum filter, the cycle being controlled by the rotary valve.

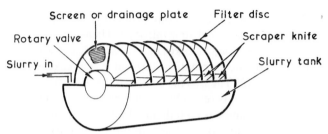

FIG. 6.14. Schematic drawing of rotary vacuum disc filter.

6.2.2.3. Other types of continuous vacuum filters

These incorporate rotating tables, endless moving belts and other forms of support for the filter medium and cake. Scroll conveyors, rollers, pulleys and devices for lifting or inverting the filter medium support are employed for discharging the cake.[1-8]

6.3. APPLICATIONS FOR FILTRATION EQUIPMENT IN THE FOOD INDUSTRY

6.3.1. GENERAL SOLID/LIQUID SEPARATION

In the extraction of sugar from sugar cane the mill juice contains insoluble solid impurities. Most of these are removed by treatment with lime and heating. A flocculent precipitate is formed which settles leaving a relatively clear raw sugar juice. However the mud thus produced may contain only 5% by weight of insoluble solids and is filtered to recover more juice. Large capacity plate-and-frame presses or rotary drum vacuum filters are used for this purpose. At a later stage in refining the raw sugar, filtration is used again to clarify juice.

Juice obtained from sugar beet by extraction with water also contains insoluble impurities. Most of these are removed by a two-stage settling operation after preliminary flocculation. The supernatant juice is then filtered using plate-and-frame, shell-and-leaf, shell-and-tube or rotary drum vacuum filters with the application of filter aids. The sludge from the settlement tanks may also be filtered to recover more juice.[10-12]

Filtration is applied at several stages during the refining of edible oils. The crude oil after extraction or expression contains insoluble impurities, e.g. fragments of seeds, cell tissue, etc. These are removed by filtration. After decolourisation of oil, bleaching earths are filtered off. If the oil is hydrogenated (hardened) the catalysts used for that process are recovered by filtration. Plate-and-frame, recessed plate, horizontal plate and vertical leaf filters are used for these duties. To remove the higher melting point fractions, oil may be cooled slowly and the solidified portion filtered off on a belt filter (winterisation).[13-15]

Other applications include filtration of starch and gluten suspensions for which rotary drum vacuum filters are usually used and, in brewing, filtering mash and recovering yeast after fermentation for which plate-and-frame presses are generally employed.

6.3.2. CLARIFICATION BY FILTRATION

In brewing, beer is clarified after cooling. A common type of filter for this duty is a plate-and-frame press using sheets made of cellulose, aluminium oxide and zirconium oxide fibres, with added kieselguhr, as filter medium. Insoluble polyvinyl pyrrolidone may also be incorporated into the sheet material to absorb phenolic materials associated with beer haze.[16,17] Wine is clarified at different stages of production: after racking, after decolourising and just before bottling. Filter aids are used with plate-and-frame, leaf or precoated rotary drum vacuum filters.[18] Other liquids clarified by filtration include: fruit juices, vinegar, yeast and meat extracts, salad and table oils, brines, sugar syrups and jellies.[19]

6.3.3. REMOVAL OF MICRO-ORGANISMS BY FILTRATION

The term microfiltration is often used to describe the application of filtration to the removal of micro-organisms (yeasts and bacteria) from liquid foods. For this purpose, unwoven, fibrous media are used. The mechanism of filtration is complex as micro-organisms fail to penetrate these media although their pore size should permit them to so do. The fibres hold the negatively charged micro-organisms electrostatically. It is usual to clarify the feed prior to microfiltration. If the objective is to obtain a sterile product the assembled filter must be sterilised before use. Horizontal and vertical plate filters and tubular filters are commonly used for this purpose. Microfiltration can be used as a substitute for, or a supplement to, other methods of reducing the number of viable organisms in liquid foods. Beer and wine are the main products which are treated in this way but some fruit juice products and yeast extracts may also be microfiltered.[2,16,18] In recent years membranes have been used increasingly in place of fibrous media for the removal of micro-organism from liquid foods. Membrane technology is discussed in Section 6.4 below.

(*Note:* Grateful acknowledgement is hereby made for information received from Messrs Dorr-Oliver Co. Ltd, Johnson-Progress Ltd, Calmic Engineering Co. Ltd and Stockdale Engineering Ltd.)

6.4. MEMBRANE SEPARATION—ULTRAFILTRATION AND REVERSE OSMOSIS

6.4.1. INTRODUCTION

A number of novel methods for the separation of various solutes from solutions of liquid foodstuffs have found increasing acceptance in recent years. Several are based on the use of membranes and at least two— ultrafiltration and reverse osmosis—now have important commercial applications in food processing.

Ultrafiltration and reverse osmosis (also known as hyperfiltration) are both pressure activated membrane separation techniques in which solutes of different molecular weights are separated from solution. The major difference between the two is in the pressure required to effect separation and, in consequence, in equipment and pumping costs. In the food industry, ultrafiltration is used mainly for fractionation—separation of different solutes on the basis of molecular size—and reverse osmosis for the concentration of solutions and the purification of water.

6.4.1.1. Ultrafiltration (UF)

As commonly defined (Section 6.1.1), filtration is a unit operation used to separate solid particles from a fluid by passage through a porous membrane. The membrane retains the particles but permits fluid to pass. The pore size required decreases as the size of the particles being separated decreases. Filters of a variety of types are available and, for separating very small particles (as small as $0.1~\mu m$), so-called 'microfilters' are used.[20]

At the sub-micron level, the membrane pore size is approaching a size capable of preventing the passage of larger molecules in solution. Membranes capable of selectively preventing the passage of larger solute molecules in solution by means of micropores in a membrane structure when subjected to relatively low pressures (in the range $0.1–1.0~\mathrm{MN\,m^{-2}}$ ($1–10$ atm)) are known as *ultrafiltration membranes*. In operation, ultra-filtration is concerned with the separation of high molecular weight large molecules from low molecular weight small molecules capable of passing the membrane.

6.4.1.2. Reverse osmosis (RO)

In an attempt to find new methods for the desalination of sea-water, Reid and Breton[21] noticed that homogeneous thin films of commercial cellulose acetates of varying degrees of acetylation were, under high pressures ($5–10~\mathrm{MN\,m^{-2}}$ ($50–100$ atm)), permeable to water molecules though, to a large extent, preventing the passage of sodium ions and chloride ions.

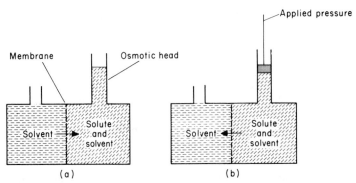

FIG. 6.15.   Principle of reverse osmosis. (a) Natural osmosis. (b) Reverse osmosis.

Though salt rejections of up to 99% were obtained, the resulting water permeation rates were much too low to permit exploitation as a commercial desalination process. By preparing films of cellulose acetate from specific mixed solvents containing swelling agents, Loeb and Sourirajan[22] obtained high salt rejections but at much higher rates of permeation. Since this discovery in the 1950s, cellulose acetate-based (and other) membranes, suitable for a variety of different separation purposes, have been developed,[23,24] though the purification of water is still a major application of what are now called reverse osmosis membranes.

Reverse osmosis (Fig. 6.15) is concerned with the separation of different molecules of low molecular weight and of a size comparable to water molecules. However, inorganic and small organic molecules are unable to pass across the membrane and normally only water molecules pass. This means that a mechanism, other than simple filtration or molecular sieving, based on molecular size must play a part in the separation.

6.4.2. OSMOTIC EFFECT IN MEMBRANE SEPARATION

When liquid flows through the micropores in a membrane, energy is expended in overcoming the resistance to flow. This energy loss manifests itself as a drop in pressure exactly as in flow through pipelines. Pressure must be applied to the liquid on the upstream side of the membrane if flow is to occur. With smaller pore sizes (tighter membranes), higher applied pressures will be required to maintain a particular flow rate. For a particular membrane, increasing the applied pressure results in larger *flux* values, at least initially. In the case of permeable membranes, a second pressure component, not experienced in conventional filtration, arises. This is osmotic pressure.

It is well known that when an ideal, semi-permeable membrane separates a solution from its pure solvent, then solvent molecules pass spontaneously across the membrane from the solvent to the solution. In general, solvent molecules pass from a region of lower concentration to a region of higher concentration. The driving force for the flow of solvent molecules is the difference in chemical potential on the two sides of the membrane. This phenomenon is called osmosis. The flow of solvent across the membrane continues until the fluid pressure developed in the concentrated solution is sufficiently high to prevent the passage of further solvent molecules (Fig. 6.15). At equilibrium this pressure is called the osmotic pressure of the solution. The osmotic pressure of a solution is a characteristic for a particular solvent–solute system. This spontaneous flow of solvent molecules across a permeable membrane by osmosis as in the opposite direction to that required in membrane separations.

In reverse osmosis the object is to promote the flow of solvent molecules (*permeate*) through the membrane, from the more concentrated solution to the less concentrated, thereby leaving the solution (*retentate*) still more concentrated.

Since the osmotic pressure developed opposes the desired flow, a reverse pressure, sufficient to overcome both it and the resistance to flow encountered in the membrane at the desired rate of flux, must be applied to the retentate side if solvent molecules are to pass the membrane.

A study of the colligative properties of dilute solutions under ideal conditions gives Van't Hoff's equation with osmotic pressure, π, as

$$\pi = RT\left(\frac{c}{MW}\right) \tag{6.18}$$

The equation, which is only an approximation, shows that osmotic pressure is inversely proportional to the molecular weight, MW, of the solute, which means that smaller molecular weight compounds in solution give rise to higher values of osmotic pressure. R is the universal gas constant, c is the concentration and T is the absolute temperature. The greater osmotic pressures arising from the presence of smaller molecules means that significantly higher operating pressures must be applied to the retentate side to effect transfer across the membrane. Cheryan[25] lists osmotic pressures for some simple food systems.

For larger molecules, e.g. solutes with molecular weights greater than about 500, the osmotic pressure developed is small so low applied pressures can effect the fractionation of larger molecules (e.g. the separation of proteins from lactose). This is the province of ultrafiltration where pressures as low as $0.1-1.0\,\mathrm{MN\,m^{-2}}$ (1–10 atm) are capable of maintaining acceptable permeate flows through the 'loose' membranes which characterise UF processes.

With low molecular weight solutes—inorganic electrolytes, smaller organic molecules, etc.—the osmotic pressures developed are very much higher. In addition, the 'tight' membranes necessary to effect their separation, offer a greater resistance to flow. 'Tight' RO membranes show virtually no pores, when viewed by scanning electron microscope whereas with 'looser' ultrafiltration membranes, pores $(0.001-0.02\,\mu\mathrm{m}$ diameter) are discernible. Not surprisingly then, in reverse osmosis considerably higher pressures, in the range $5-10\,\mathrm{MN\,m^{-2}}$ (50–100 atm), are required to effect separation.

Operating pressures apart, the distinction between reverse osmosis and ultrafiltration is not clear-cut. In both, the chemical nature and the structure of the membrane surface in contact with the feed solution can influence the separation and permeability characteristics of the membrane under the operating conditions of the process. Membranes for both reverse osmosis and ultrafiltration can be produced in a similar manner and manufacturers have developed membranes with a range of pore-size distributions giving a gradual variation in permeability and separation properties. This gradation in membrane properties means that RO and UF applications can overlap.[26]

Membrane performance is frequently characterised in terms of 'rejection' or 'retention' factor (depending on whether the permeate or the concentrate is being considered) and 'molecular weight cut-off'.

The retention or rejection factor, R, is defined as

$$R = \frac{c_\mathrm{f} - c_\mathrm{p}}{c_\mathrm{f}} \qquad (6.19)$$

where c_f is the concentration of a particular molecular species in the feed and c_p that of the species in the permeate.

Molecular weight cut-off is also used to characterise membrane performance. This is the molecular weight value above which 100% of a particular solute present in solution does not pass the membrane. It is a nominal value. Ideally, in fractionation using membranes, total removal or retention of a particular component is desired but, besides molecular size, electrochemical behaviour and the structure of the component can also influence separation and, for these reasons, rejections of specific components from a permeate by a commercial membrane are more likely to be around 95%. Capabilities of commercial membranes are characterised by the manufacturer using model systems. Cut-offs should be specified for particular molecular weight values but since results for particular food systems are likely to vary from these, pilot-scale trials, with the particular system being considered, are recommended before investing in large scale plants.

6.4.3. MEMBRANES

6.4.3.1. General operational requirements

General requirements for membranes suitable for food processing purposes are as follows:

(1) The membrane must be capable of giving the degree of separation (molecular weight cut-off) required, at high permeate flow rates and over extended periods of time.

(2) Membranes must be capable of withstanding effective cleaning and disinfection to the requirements necessary for satisfactory hygienic operation.

(3) Membranes should possess considerable strength to give a long 'in-place' life under the operating conditions experienced.

Satisfying these requirements can be difficult in some applications.

6.4.3.2. Membrane flow

Although microfiltration membranes are often considered to be microporous sieves for the removal of colloidal and other suspended matter, other than for the removal of larger molecules in solution this simple approach does not completely describe the flow across UF membranes. All RO membranes are considered to incorporate an extremely thin film which is non-porous, so mechanisms other than those based simply on fluid mechanics must be responsible for transport across a part of these membranes.

A number of models have been proposed to explain the flow of material across membranes. Earlier models proposed include:

(a) *Capillary flow model.* This simple model, considered more applicable to 'looser' ultrafiltration membranes, is based on laminar flow through fine capillaries and the Hagan–Poiseuille equation for flow through a circular pipe is used to determine the flux across the membrane. This is the approach used by Carman for flow in porous beds.[27] It might be expected to apply to porous membranes which approximate the conditions postulated and where a filtering or sieving action predominates. However, this model takes no account of concentration polarisation or fouling (Section 6.4.4), nor of interactions between the solute or solvent and the membrane.

(b) *Solution–diffusion model.* This model, for reverse osmosis, postulates the dissolution of participating species (solvent and solutes) in the material of the membrane, followed by molecular diffusion across the barrier. Since both the solubilities and the rates of diffusion of the various molecular species present will not be the same for different components, this model appears to explain the selectivity of reverse osmosis membranes to various components in solution.

(c) *Preferential sorption–capillary flow model.* This model also suggests that two mechanisms are responsible for membrane transport. It was originally put forward to explain desalination, the first reverse osmosis process. The model, discussed by Sourirajan,[28] a pioneer in the field of reverse osmosis, postulates that a porous membrane in contact with an aqueous solution is of a chemical nature such that it has a preferential sorption for water or preferential repulsion for solute. A multimolecular layer of preferentially sorbed pure water exists at the membrane–solution interface. The interfacial water is continuously removed by flowing under pressure through capillaries in the membrane. On an infinitesimally thin layer of the membrane surface film at the interface, a critical pore diameter of twice the thickness of the pure water layer must be maintained for maximum separation and permeability. Away from the film–solution interface, in the bulk of the membrane, capillary flow occurs, the connecting pores being of larger diameter so the resistance to the flow of permeate would be low. The most important consequence of this mechanism is that the process is governed by surface phenomena; hence, the chemical interaction between the surface and the solution is a controlling parameter in reverse osmosis. Though scanning electron microscopy does not appear to reveal the presence of pores in the surface film of reverse osmosis membranes, the structure of RO membranes currently in use correspond quite closely to this model. These and more recent models are discussed by Cheryan.[25]

6.4.3.3. Structure of membranes

Most membranes for both reverse osmosis and ultrafiltration have either 'asymmetric' or 'composite' structures. Asymmetric membranes are cast from a single material having a total thickness of 0·1–0·2 mm. They consist of an ultra-thin active layer of dense polymer, some 0·1–1·5 μm thick, supported on a relatively thick, porous polymer substructure, the pore size frequently increasing in diameter in the bulk of the membrane. For added support the membrane laminate is normally attached to a rigid but porous backing structure.

Composite asymmetric membranes—a more recent development—also consist of a very thin active film but in this case placed on top of a highly porous sublayer of different material, such as polysulphone, which itself may be supported on a polypropylene backing.[24]

6.4.3.4. Membrane materials

The first polymers to be successfully employed in membrane separation processes were made from cellulose esters. These can be constructed with various porosities according to need. However the cellulose acetate membranes commonly used are subject to hydrolysis in strongly acidic and mildly alkaline conditions. The recommended pH range for use is 3–7, but hydrolysis is a minimum at pH 4·5–5·0. Cellulosic membranes are unable to withstand temperatures exceeding 35–40°C and they are also attacked by chlorine, a common sterilising agent in the food industry. Cellulosic membranes are also subject to microbial and enzymic attack.

Though originally finding wide use, cellulose acetate membranes have gradually been superceded in the food industry since the introduction of polysulphone ultrafiltration membranes which have good chemical and

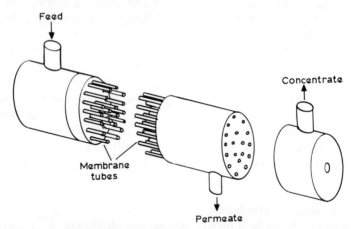

FIG. 6.16.   Ultrafiltration module, tubular membranes, Paterson Candy International (PCI). Membranes 12·5 mm diameter, 3·6 m long: each module has 18 tubes, total area 2·5 m². Module outside diameter 10 cm. (Reprinted from Robinson, R. K., *Modern Dairy Technology. Vol. 1.* Elsevier Applied Science Publishers, London, 1986, p. 243.)

thermal stability as well as mechanical strength. Difficulty was experienced in producing conventional asymmetric, non-cellulosic reverse osmosis membranes but this was overcome using the composite membrane method of construction. One approach using this technique is to form a conventional, very porous polysulphone membrane and overlay this with a very thin layer of a polyamide or other dense polymer. These new generation materials can be used at temperatures up to 80°C with acid and alkaline cleaning solutions and can withstand oxidative conditions better than cellulose acetate membranes.

Inorganic membranes, which extend the applicability of membrane separation still further, are now being developed. An example of this is a commercially available module for UF applications. These have zirconium oxide membranes supported on carbon tubes. They can be sterilised with steam and can tolerate the whole pH range as well as temperatures above 100°C. They also possess considerable mechanical strength, an important requirement for membranes subjected to high pressures that could consolidate or collapse if insufficiently strong.

6.4.3.5. Membrane configurations

Four different membrane geometries are available—tubular, flat-sheet, spirally-wound and hollow-fibre membranes, the latter being normally used for water treatment.

The main difference between the three types used in the food industry is the size of the flow paths through the unit. Modules with narrow flow channels may be more prone to fouling and are not as easy to clean as those with greater flow areas. Again, with more viscous feed liquids, the pressure drops developed due to friction are greater in narrow passages and may restrict the flow rates obtainable through some units. However, hold-up volumes are considerably greater with larger channels and membrane separation area per unit of plant volume correspondingly less. The main features of the four types are as follows.

(a) *Tubular membranes.* Here the membrane is carried on the side of a support tube to give a circular flow channel up to 25 mm in diameter. In one module used widely in the food industry (Fig. 6.16), this membrane tube is carried in a second, perforated stainless steel tube. Numbers of these tube assemblies are fitted inside an outer stainless steel permeate collection shroud. The membrane tubes are individually attached to header-plates at both ends, the tube bundle being sealed inside the collection shroud. The flow path brings the feed solution to the inside of the membrane tubes via

Food Engineering Operations

an inlet header-plate where, as it flows over the cylindrical membrane surface, permeate passes radially through the membrane to the collection shroud for separate removal. The retentate leaves through an outlet header-plate and is usually recirculated (Section 6.4.4.1). With cross-flow filtration inside tubes, the circular flow path is large compared with other types of membrane configuration. Since tubular membranes are designed to operate with the feed solution in highly turbulent flow they are easier to clean if particulate material is in suspension. Concentration polarisation and possible fouling are said to be suppressed to a greater extent than is the case with flat-sheet and spirally-wound membranes where, since flow paths can be as small as 0·5 mm, flow is likely to be laminar.

The generation of highly turbulent flow in larger diameter flow paths means that the energy consumption for pumping is greater with tubular membranes. Since these units also have a higher hold-up volume, they occupy more plant space for the membrane area required than those with narrow flow passages. This can be an important consideration with large capacity plants.

(b) *Flat-sheet membranes.* These are used in assemblies somewhat similar in construction to a hybrid of the plate- and frame-filter press and the plate-heat exchanger (Fig. 6.17), although the overall shape of commercial units vary, being rectangular, circular or oval. Using this analogy, membrane

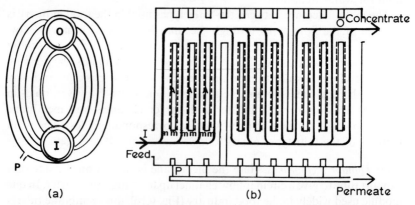

(a)   (b)   Permeate

FIG. 6.17. Ultrafiltration module, flat sheet membranes. Danish Sugar Corporation (DDS). (a): membrane support plate for module 37; I, inlet port; O, outlet port; P, permeate outlet, dimensions 38 cm × 31 cm, channel height 1·3 mm at centre, 1·8 mm at periphery. (b): membrane assembly; A, support plates; m, membranes. (Reprinted from Robinson, R. K., *Modern Dairy Technology. Vol. 1.* Elsevier Applied Science Publishers, 1986, p. 244.)

sheets replace filter cloths and are placed either side of a thermoplastic support plate (equivalent to a filter plate). A number of these membrane–plate–membrane combinations are clamped together and, in conjunction with special seal rings, entry and exit holes at the top and bottom of the support plates mate up with holes in the membrane surfaces to form (as in a plate heat exchanger), a retentate flow path connecting the spaces between successive pairs of membranes. Liquid flows through the narrow gap between adjacent membrane surfaces. In some units specially shaped ribs on the surface of the support plates both increase the size of the flow channels and modify the direction of the retentate flow paths over the surface of the membranes. This helps to increase turbulence and promote mixing in order to break up the boundary layer and so mitigate the effect of concentration polarisation. Narrow drain channels behind the membranes carry permeate out of the unit.

Other modifications of the flat-sheet membrane module carry spacer plates which direct the flow of liquid over the surface of the membranes. Seal rings, support plates and spacers, if used, are often fabricated in polysulphone.

Advantages claimed for flat-sheet equipment are low hold-up volume for a given membrane area and lower energy costs than other types. In operation, the initial feed liquid is split so as to flow in series to the space between the membrane pairs of adjacent plates arranged in groups. The liquid passes over the two membrane surfaces in cross-flow mode. The number of membranes in a group is adjusted so as to minimise the overall pressure drop.[24] After separation, permeate flows along the drain channels behind the membranes to outlet ports on the support plates. The retentate passes on to more membrane–plate combinations, the number of combinations used depending on the necessary membrane area for the process.

Attempts to reduce pressure losses while increasing flow velocities and boundary layer break up in the narrow channels of flat-sheet membrane modules have led to a variety of support plate designs. The objective is to reduce concentration polarisation and the risk of gel formation and fouling while, at the same time, keeping energy costs low.

(c) *Spiral-wound flat-sheet membranes.* These are tubular variations of the flat-sheet membrane, several varieties being produced by different manufacturers. In one widely used type (Fig. 6.18), two flat sheets of membrane, separated by a plastic spacer sheet, are placed between two further sheets of porous support medium. This combination of sheets is wrapped around a central tube which connects, via perforations in its

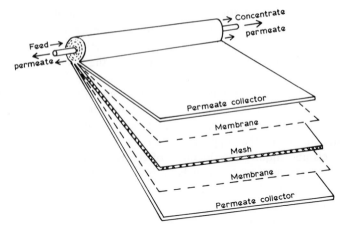

FIG. 6.18. Ultrafiltration module, spirally wound membrane, Abcor. Length 84 cm, diameter 11 cm, membrane spacing 0·7 mm, area 5 m². Three such sections are housed in series in a stainless steel tube to make one module, 3 m long, membrane area 15 m². Schematic diagram to show the formation of the spiral. (Reprinted from Robinson, R. K., *Modern Dairy Technology. Vol. 1.* Elsevier Applied Science Publishers, London, 1986, p. 245.)

surface, with the porous material along one edge of the sandwich. The spiral-wound roll, its ends partially sealed to isolate the porous layers, is contained inside a cylindrical outer tube. Feed liquor enters at one end of the outer tube and, under pump pressure, finds its way through the space between the membrane surfaces. The plastic spacer decreases the resistance to flow and also acts as a turbulence promoter to help reduce concentration polarisation. As the liquid passes over the membrane surfaces, permeate flows radially through the membrane and, via the flow paths afforded by the porous support media, drains through the perforations in the surface of the central tube to be discharged through ports at either end of this inner tube. Retentate leaves at the discharge end of the outer tube. As with other flat-sheet modules, energy costs are said to be less than with tubular membranes and hold-up volumes are relatively small compared to the tubular type. Even with spacer sheets separating the membranes the retentate flow path is still relatively small so these units are easily blocked. Unlike plate and frame modules they cannot be dismantled for cleaning. If coarser particulate material is suspended in the liquid being treated some form of feed pre-cleaning—centrifugal clarification and/or microfiltration—may need to be considered.

(d) *Hollow-fibre membranes.* One of the most widely used RO systems (mainly for the upgrading of low quality water) is that based on the use of narrow bore hollow-fibre membranes of an asymmetric polyamide marketed by Du Pont. The use of very narrow bore hollow fibres (about 40 μm bore and 80 μm overall diameter) allows an extensive membrane surface to be accommodated in a relatively small volume. Since the fibres are thick-walled they are also able to withstand high pressures without collapsing.

Bundles of fibres, each fibre attached to a header plate at either end, are wrapped around a porous support tube which is sealed inside an outer tube. The fibres almost fill the annular space between the two tubes. Feed water, entering the central porous feed tube under pressure, flows through the tube wall and over the outside of the fibres in the annulus, using the extremely narrow spaces between them as flow channels. Permeate (usually pure water) flows through the tube walls and, via the hollow centre of the fibres, to the header plate and product outlet. The retentate, containing the concentrated water salts, is rejected.

Although, using other membrane configurations, reverse osmosis is increasingly used for the concentration of certain liquid foods—fruit juices, sugar solutions, milk and whey products—the risk of fouling in the very small flow passages associated with hollow-fibre membrane modules is considered to be high. Other than for laboratory scale investigations, these units do not appear to have found commercial application with food liquids.

As mentioned previously, hollow-fibre reverse osmosis membranes are used extensively in the food and other bio-industries for the production of pure water for process purposes.[29]

6.4.4. ULTRAFILTRATION AND REVERSE OSMOSIS SYSTEMS
6.4.4.1. Basic features
Although a variety of systems are in use for UF and RO, basically they are very similar.

Feed liquid from a storage vessel is fed, under pump pressure, via a manifold to the appropriate number of membrane modules necessary to give the surface area for the desired separation at the required rate. Permeate passing through the membrane is taken off. In most applications in the food industry the retentate (enriched concentrate) is the desired stream. The particular type of membrane is selected for the degree of separation (cut-off) it is hoped to achieve with the particular feed at the required throughput.

It must be remembered that membranes are constructed on the basis of compromise between high rates of permeation and sharp cut-off values. It is unrealistic to expect that a commercial membrane will give complete cut-off of a specific solute, hence complete separation of different solutes of very similar molecular weight. The shape and electrical potentials of solute molecules and the nature of any charges on the membrane may also influence the passage of specific molecules. The molecular weights might need to differ by as much as an order of magnitude, or even more, for very high degrees of separation to occur.

A useful modification to some ultrafiltration processes that helps in the purification of the concentrate stream is to dilute the feed with water as separation proceeds. The modified process is known as *diafiltration* and it assists in the removal of small molecules that are capable of passing through the membrane. Washing-out more smaller molecules than would normally permeate in straightforward ultrafiltration results in a more enriched concentrate. Diafiltration finds use in the dairy industry.[30] The process can be valuable for removing certain contaminants from retentate streams.

Generally, differences in the design of a membrane separation plant and its mode of operation are more concerned with minimising the capital and operating costs for a unit which performs satisfactorily. 'Once-through' systems (Fig. 6.19(a)) are used in water treatment but the membrane areas needed can be high. With food liquids, to keep the required area within realistic limits, 'recirculating' systems are usually used since permeate fluxes (because of higher viscosities, increased fouling, etc.) are likely to be lower than those in water treatment. For small scale batch operation, the concentrate is passed back to the feed tank (Fig. 6.19(b)), recirculation continuing until the desired degree of concentration is achieved. Energy costs are high when operating in this way since the pressure energy given to the liquid is totally dissipated on recycling to the feed tank.

In the 'feed and bleed' mode of operation, frequently used with larger plants, part of the pressurised retentate passes repeatedly over the membrane surfaces while the permeate is continuously removed. When the product concentration reaches the required value, part is bled off via a back pressure valve, the feed pump supplying fresh liquid to compensate for that removed as product and permeate. Operation is then continuous. The retentate recirculation rate is kept high to promote turbulence in order to limit concentration polarisation and membrane fouling. Since the concentration in the recycle is almost as high as that of the product, average flux rate will be low. The average retention time is relatively low, however, which reduces the risk of microbial growth in the plant.

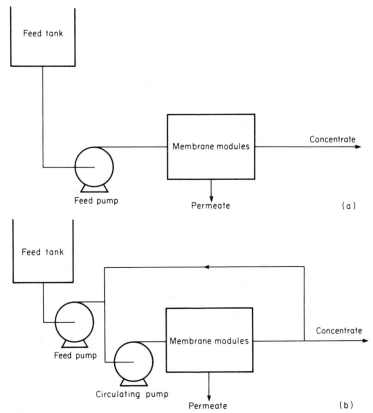

Fig. 6.19. (a) Once-through system. (b) Recirculating system.

With high capacity plants, multi-stage continuous operation is recommended. This employs as many as six stages, each stage being a separate feed and bleed system. A reducing volume of bleed concentrate passes forward through each stage so the concentration of the retentate progressively increases. The membrane area required falls in successive stages as the volume of liquid processed decreases.

A heat exchanger is often included in ultrafiltration plants to permit temperature control. In this way it is possible to avoid temperatures at which microbial growth is rapid. The maximum growth of mesophilic bacteria occurs at around 37°C. Reducing the temperature of the feed liquor increases its viscosity and also decreases the solubility of many solutes so the risk of concentration polarisation and fouling becomes greater. Although permeate rates usually increase at higher operating temperatures, many food liquids are heat sensitive, e.g. with some proteins, denaturation can occur at temperatures of 60°C. For these reasons the temperature of food liquids are often maintained at about 50°C during RO or UF. With some food liquids, pasteurisation before membrane separation is advantageous. This reduces the number of micro-organisms entering the plant and minimises growth rate during ultrafiltration. Because of the possibility of microbial fouling, and also because concentration polarisation leads to membrane fouling, regular, satisfactory 'cleansing' operations assume great importance in RO and UF processes if optimum production rates are to be consistently achieved. In common with all food and other bio-processing plants, hygienic design principles and facilities for 'cleaning in place' (CIP) must be included in the design of the overall system (Chapter 17).

6.4.4.2. Concentration polarisation
As with all fluid–solid flow systems, when feed liquid flows over membrane surfaces a boundary layer develops. The membrane surface itself can be deep within the laminar sublayer where retentate crossflow velocity is very low. Since the membrane surface is rejecting larger solute molecules in a region of very low flow, the rate of transport of solute away from the membrane to the mainstream flow is low so concentration of solute occurs at the membrane surface. This accumulation of solute at the interface rapidly results in the formation of a viscous layer which resists the flow of permeate through the membrane. This phenomenon is called concentration polarisation and it leads to a rapid reduction in permeate flux. Concentration polarisation arises in both RO and UF separations but the higher solute concentrations normally encountered in the retentate make the problem more acute in ultrafiltration. Rapid fouling often results. Various membrane designs and different operating techniques have been suggested to combat the drop in flux, as well as the risk of fouling, resulting from concentration polarisation (Section 6.4.3.5).

6.4.4.3. Membrane fouling
In the region of higher concentration caused by concentration polarisation at the interface, the likelihood of solute coming out of solution and depositing on the membrane increases. In fact, concentration polarisation is often associated with severe membrane fouling. The nature of the fouling is likely to depend on the flow velocities at the interface, the solubility of solutes present and on the properties of the membrane and the solution in contact with it. Some higher molecular weight solutes tend to form gels on

the surface of the membrane. If the gel is also compressible, then the resistance to permeate flow may be greatly increased at higher pressures. The formation of gels appears to be related to both the cross-flow shearing forces developed in the retentate near the interface and the permeate flow through the membrane.

In addition to fouling arising from concentration polarisation, the presence of colloidal and fine particulate material in suspension in the feed can quickly give rise to fouling due to direct deposition of these solids on the membrane surface, particularly if feed flow velocities are low. Membrane pores are easily plugged and the flux is then rapidly reduced. Highly turbulent retentate flows may help to keep the solids in suspension but a wiser precaution, if solids are present, is to clarify the feed using centrifugal clarifiers or polishing filters before membrane treatment.

6.4.5. ADVANTAGES OF ULTRAFILTRATION AND REVERSE OSMOSIS

These membrane separation processes take place without phase change so energy requirements[24] are less than those of conventional concentration operations, such as evaporation or freeze concentration. The energy requirement for the evaporation of water, for example, is about $25 \, kW \, m^{-2}$ whereas with RO the requirement is only about one tenth of this amount. Membrane separation offers other advantages compared to evaporation. Since no heating is needed to effect phase change, the risk of heat damage to heat labile foods is minimised, aroma losses due to the stripping of volatile substance on vaporisation are avoided and large volumes of cooling water (an increasingly more expensive commodity) are no longer required. This suggests that where a choice between reverse osmosis and evaporation is available the former offers significant advantages. The degree of concentration which can be achieved by reverse osmosis, however, is limited because of the reduction in flux (hence production capacity) at higher viscosities.[24] This can be a disadvantage. An increasingly common compromise, used particularly in the dairy sector, is to pre-concentrate a dilute food liquid using reverse osmosis and then follow this by an evaporation stage if further concentration is required.

6.4.6. APPLICATIONS OF REVERSE OSMOSIS AND ULTRAFILTRATION

We have seen that the demarcation between ultrafiltration and reverse osmosis is not always clearcut. Because of the smaller osmotic effect, considerably lower pressures are required to effect separation by UF than is the case with RO. The chemical nature of the membrane may play a more significant role in RO but similar membranes can be found performing in both categories of separation.

It is in the application of the methods that the differences become more apparent. Reverse osmosis is very widely used in water treatment,[29] being more concerned in the separation of pure water as permeate, e.g. from ground waters and surface waters (Section 18.2.2) having low concentrations of dissolved solids, in desalination and in the treatment of brackish waters, etc.

Reverse osmosis does find use in the food industry for the concentration of low molecular weight organic materials in dilute aqueous solution. Reverse osmosis is used for the concentration of milk—whole milk, skim milk and buttermilk—before evaporation or fermentation (in certain cheese and yogurt manufacture).

In the dairy sector of the food industry, two by-products produced in enormous quantities are cheese whey and skim milk. Before the advent of membrane separation some of the skim milk was used as animal feed and some concentrated by evaporation and then spray-dried to produce skim milk powder for use in confectionery, ice cream, etc. Although highly pollutory, the whey was usually discarded. An early use of ultrafiltration was to partially concentrate the milk proteins whey contains in the production of whey protein concentrates (WPC). The concentrate is further enriched by evaporation and spray-drying to give WPC powders containing up to 65% protein.[31] These possess useful functional and nutritional properties.[32] The manufacture of whey protein concentrates is now firmly established since they can have a wide range of functional properties, depending on the method of manufacture, making them useful as food ingredients. However, the functionality can be significantly modified by relatively minor changes in processing. Much work has been carried out on the utilisation of these concentrated proteins in the human diet and a variety of formulated foods containing them are now on the market. The lactose and mineral salts in the whey are removed in the permeate. The treatment of whey permeate for the demineralisation and recovery of lactose is still the main use of reverse osmosis in the food industry. Other uses for the whey permeate are being extensively investigated and alcohol is one product being commercially produced.

Though the list of laboratory and pilot scale investigations into the use of RO and UF membrane systems for both the concentration and fractionation of food systems continues to grow it is in the dairy industry that commercial exploitation has been the greatest.[30,33] Much development work remains to be done if the same degree of success is to be achieved in other sectors of the food industry.

REFERENCES

1. Purchas, D. B., *Industrial Filtration of Liquids*, 2nd edn. Leonard Hill Books, London, 1971.
2. Orr, C., *Filtration Principles and Practices* (two vols). Marcel Dekker, New York, 1977.
3. Coulson, J. M., Richardson, J. F. with Backhurst, J. R. and Harker, J. H., *Chemical Engineering, Vol. 2*, 3rd edn. Pergamon Press, Oxford, 1978.
4. Foust, A. S., Wenzel, L. A., Clump, C. W., Maus, L. and Bryce Anderson, L., *Principles of Unit Operations*, 2nd edn. John Wiley, New York, 1980.
5. Cheremisinoff, N. P. and Azbel, D. S., *Liquid Filtration*. Ann Arbor, Woburn, Mass., USA, 1983.
6. Green, D. W. (ed.), *Perry's Chemical Engineers Handbook*, 6th edn. McGraw-Hill, New York, 1984.
7. McCabe, W. L., Smith, J. C. and Harriott, P., *Unit Operations of Chemical Engineering*, 4th edn. McGraw-Hill, New York, 1985.
8. Purchas, D. B. and Wakeman, R. J. (ed.), *Solid/Liquid Separation Equipment Scale-up*, 2nd edn. Uplands Press Ltd and Filtration Specialists Ltd, London, 1986.
9. Dal Cin, M., Deep filtration. *Enotecnico*, **22**(2) (1986) 205–12.
10. Jenkins, G. H., *E. Hugot's Handbook of Cane Sugar Engineering*, 2nd edn. Elsevier, Amsterdam, 1972.
11. Birch, G. G. and Parker, K. J. (ed.), *Sugar Science and Technology*. Applied Science Publishers, London, 1979.
12. McGinnis, R. A., *Beet-Sugar Technology*, 2nd edn. Beet Sugar Development Foundation, Fort Collins, Colo., USA, 1971.
13. Hamilton, R. J. and Bathi, A. (ed.), *Fats and Oils: Chemistry and Technology*. Applied Science Publishers, London, 1980.
14. Hamilton, R. J. and Bathi, A. (ed.), *Recent Advances in Chemistry and Technology of Fats and Oils*. Elsevier Applied Science Publishers, London, 1987.
15. Swern, D. (ed.), *Bailey's Industrial Oil and Fat Products. Vols 1 and 2*. John Wiley, New York.
16. Hough, J. S., Briggs, D. E., Stevens, R. and Young, T. W., *Malting and Brewing Science. Vol. II. Hopped Wort and Beer*, 2nd edn. Chapman and Hall, London, 1982.
17. Pollock, J. R. A. (ed.), *Brewing Science. Vol. 3*. Academic Press, New York, 1987.
18. Amerine, M. A., Kunkee, R. E., Ough, C. S., Singleton, V. L. and Webb, A. D., *The Technology of Winemaking*, 4th edn. AVI, Westport, Conn., USA, 1980.
19. Nelson, P. E. and Tressler, D. K., *Fruit and Vegetable Juice Processing*, 3rd edn. AVI, Westport, Conn., USA, 1980.
20. Bertera, R., Steven, H. and Metcalfe, M., Development studies of crossflow microfiltration. *The Chemical Engineer*, **404** (June 1984) 10–14.

21. Reid, C. E. and Breton, E. J., *J. Appl. Polymer Sci.*, **1** (1959) 133.
22. Loeb, S. and Sourirajan, S. *Adv. Chem. Ser.*, **38** (1962) 117.
23. Michaels, A. S., Tailored membranes. In *Advances in Preconcentration and Dehydration of Foods*, ed. A. Spicer. Applied Science Publishers, London, 1974, pp. 213–50.
24. Madsen, R., Theory of membrane filtration. In *Evaporation, Membrane Filtration, and Spray Drying*, ed. R. Hansen. North European Dairy Journal, 1985, pp. 179–286.
25. Cheryan, M., Membrane separations: mechanisms and models. In *Food Properties and Computer-Aided Engineering of Food Processing Systems*, ed. R. P. Singh and A. G. Medina. Kluwer Academic Publishers, Dordrecht, The Netherlands, 1989, pp. 367–91.
26. Minh, S. and Billigheimer, P. J., Membranes in downstream processing. *The Chemical Engineer*, **416** (July/August 1985) 48–51.
27. Carman, P. C., Fluid flow through granular beds. *Trans. Inst. Chem. Eng.*, **15** (1937) 150–66.
28. Sourirajan, S., *Reverse Osmosis*. Logos Press, London, 1970.
29. Pohland, H. W., Reverse osmosis. In *Handbook of Water Purification*, ed. W. Lorch. McGraw-Hill (UK), London, 1981, pp. 285–335.
30. Glover, F. A., Ultrafiltration and reverse osmosis for the dairy industry. Technical Bulletin 5, National Institute for Research in Dairying, Reading, England, 1985.
31. Lewis, M. J., Concentration of proteins by ultrafiltration. In *Developments in Food Proteins*, ed. B. J. F. Hudson. Applied Science Publishers, London, 1982, pp. 91–130.
32. Kinsella, J. E., Functional properties of proteins in foods: A survey. *Critical Reviews in Food Science and Nutrition*, **7**(3) (1976), 219–80.
33. Robinson, R. K. (ed.), *Modern Dairy Technology. Vol. One. Advances in Milk Processing*. Elsevier Applied Science Publishers, London, 1986.

CHAPTER 7

CENTRIFUGATION

7.1. INTRODUCTION AND THEORY

Centrifugation may be defined as a unit operation involving the separation of materials by the application of centrifugal force. Here the applications of centrifugation are discussed under three headings, viz. separation of immiscible liquids, separation of insoluble solids from liquids and centrifugal filtration. Other applications for centrifugal equipment are mentioned elsewhere in this text, for example: separation of gas–solid systems (cyclone separator, Chapter 13); separation of vapour–liquid systems (entrainment separators, Chapter 12).

7.1.1. SEPARATION OF IMMISCIBLE LIQUIDS

The centrifugal force, F_c, acting on an object of mass m, rotating in a circular path of radius R, at an angular velocity of ω is:

$$F_c = mR\omega^2 \qquad (7.1)$$

and

$$\omega = \frac{\pi N}{30} \qquad (7.2)$$

where N = rotational speed (rpm) and ω = angular velocity (rad s^{-1}).

Thus the magnitude of the centrifugal force depends on the radius of rotation, the speed of rotation and the mass of the body or, for a unit volume of material, the density of the material. If two immiscible liquids A and B with densities ρ_A and ρ_B respectively are placed in a cylindrical bowl which is rotated about a central axis, the more dense liquid A will tend to move towards the wall of the bowl and form an annular ring near its inner

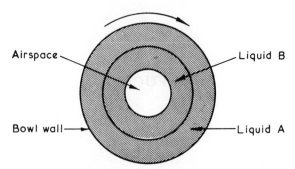

FIG. 7.1. Separation of immiscible liquids in a cylindrical bowl (plan view).

surface as shown in Fig. 7.1. The less dense liquid B will be displaced towards the centre of rotation and form an inner annular ring again as in Fig. 7.1. If provision is made for introducing the liquid feed continuously to the bowl and for tapping off from the two liquid layers separately, separation of the liquids can be achieved. The feed is usually introduced to the bottom of the bowl by a centrally located pipe and the liquids removed from each layer by a weir system such as that illustrated in Fig. 7.2. The cylindrical interface, of radius R_i, separating the two phases is known as the neutral zone. In practical systems this interface is not as clearly defined as Fig. 7.2 suggests. The dense liquid flows out over a circular weir of radius R_A and the lighter liquid over one of radius R_B. If we assume that the liquid rotates at bowl speed, that is, that slippage and friction are negligible, then the drop in pressure, arising from centrifugal force, between R_i and R_A must

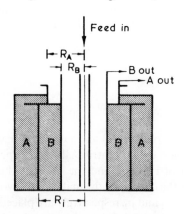

FIG. 7.2. Separation of immiscible liquids in a cylindrical bowl with submerged weir (sectional view).

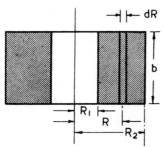

Fɪɢ. 7.3. Annular ring of liquid in cylindrical centrifuge bowl.

equal the pressure drop between R_i and R_B. If this was not so the interface would not be stable at radius R_i.

Consider an annular ring of liquid of thickness $(R_2 - R_1)$ as shown in Fig. 7.3. The centrifugal force, dF, acting on the volume element dR thick and of mass dm at radius R is:

$$dF = \omega^2 R \, dm \tag{7.3}$$

but

$$dm = 2\pi \rho b R \, dR \tag{7.4}$$

where $\rho = $ density of the liquid; $b = $ height of the liquid layer in the centrifuge. Therefore

$$dF = 2\pi \rho b \omega^2 R^2 \, dR \tag{7.5}$$

The pressure drop over the element is dP and

$$dP = \frac{\text{Force}}{\text{Area}} = \frac{2\pi \rho b \omega^2 R^2 \, dR}{2\pi b R} = \rho \omega^2 R \, dR \tag{7.6}$$

The pressure drop over ring of liquid $(R_2 - R_1)$ thick is

$$\Delta P_{(R_2 - R_1)} = \omega^2 \rho \int_{R_1}^{R_2} R \, dR = \frac{\omega^2 \rho (R_2^2 - R_1^2)}{2} \tag{7.7}$$

Returning to the system shown in Fig. 7.2 and using equation (7.7) the pressure drops over the two liquid layers are:

$$\Delta P_{(R_i - R_A)} = \frac{\omega^2 \rho_A (R_i^2 - R_A^2)}{2} \tag{7.8}$$

$$\Delta P_{(R_i - R_B)} = \frac{\omega^2 \rho_B (R_i^2 - R_B^2)}{2} \tag{7.9}$$

If the neutral zone is to remain stable then

$$\frac{\omega^2 \rho_A (R_i^2 - R_A^2)}{2} = \frac{\omega^2 \rho_B (R_i^2 - R_B^2)}{2} \tag{7.10}$$

$$R_i = \left(\frac{R_A^2 - (\rho_B / \rho_A) R_B^2}{1 - \rho_B / \rho_A} \right)^{1/2} \tag{7.11}$$

(*Note*: In deriving the above expression it is assumed that the inner liquid radius is that of the outlet in each case. Cresting of the liquids, particularly at high throughputs, may render this assumption invalid and adjustments need to be made to the equations above.)

Thus the radius of the neutral zone depends theoretically on the radii of the two phase outlets and the liquid densities. For example, for two liquids of known densities, if R_B is fixed then as R_A is increased so R_i increases. This affords a means of controlling R_i, that is controlling the relative size of zone A to zone B in the centrifuge. In zone A light liquid is effectively stripped from a mass of dense liquid, while in zone B dense liquid is more effectively removed from a mass of light liquid. If, therefore, the duty to which the centrifuge is put involves stripping a mass of dense liquid free of light liquid, that is a pure dense phase is required, then the dwell time in zone A should exceed that in zone B. In such a case R_A would be reduced, thus reducing R_i and increasing the relative size of zone A to zone B. An example of such a duty is the separation of cream from milk where the object is to minimise the fat (light phase) content of the separated milk (dense phase). If the requirements were reversed, *e.g.* if the operation involved stripping small amounts of water from an edible oil, then R_A would be increased, increasing the size of zone B. In practice it is common to control R_i by varying R_A with R_B fixed.

Equation 7.11 also shows that R_i depends on the relative densities of the two phases. If the difference in density is very small the neutral zone becomes unstable. The difference between ρ_A and ρ_B should not be less than about 3%.[1] It has also been found that the best separation is achieved if the feed is introduced to the bowl at a point near the neutral zone.[1-4]

7.1.2. SEPARATION OF INSOLUBLE SOLIDS FROM LIQUIDS

The term *centrifugal clarification* is often used to describe the removal of small quantities, a few percent or less, of insoluble solids from a liquid by centrifugal means. Equipment used for this purpose is usually operated on a batch principle. The separated solids build up in the centrifuge bowl and have to be removed periodically. The terms *desludging* or *decanting* are sometimes used to describe the removal of larger quantities of insoluble solids from a liquid by centrifugal means. In equipment used for this purpose there is provision made for the removal of the insoluble solids from the bowl during its operation which is then continuous.

If a liquid containing insoluble solids with a greater density than the liquid is fed to a rotating cylindrical bowl, the solids will move towards the bowl wall. If one outlet is provided for the liquid near the centre of rotation, e.g. if the outer exit (radius R_A) in the bowl shown in Fig. 7.2 is closed off, then those particles of solid which reach the bowl wall will remain in the bowl. Those particles which do not reach the bowl wall will be carried out in the liquid. The fraction remaining in the bowl and the fraction passing out in the liquid will be controlled by the rate of feed, i.e. the dwell time in the bowl.

Consider a solid particle of diameter D_p in the liquid in the bowl shown in Fig. 7.3. If it is assumed that this particle moves radially at its terminal velocity under laminar flow conditions, the radial velocity of the particle is:

$$v_t = \frac{\omega^2(\rho_s - \rho_l)D_p^2 R}{18\eta} \tag{7.12}$$

where v_t = terminal velocity of particle; ρ_s and ρ_l = densities of solid and liquid respectively; D_p = diameter of particle; R = distance of the particle from centre of rotation; η = viscosity of liquid.

Since the gravitational effect is very small compared with the centrifugal effect and since we are interested mainly in the movement of the smallest particles, these assumptions seem reasonable.[3,4]

The time required for a particle to travel an elemental radial distance dR is

$$dt = \frac{dR}{v_t} = \frac{18\eta}{\omega^2(\rho_s - \rho_l)D_p^2} \frac{dR}{R} \tag{7.13}$$

Assume that half of all those particles present in the feed with a particular diameter, D_{pc}, are removed during their passage through the bowl. Most particles with diameters greater than D_{pc} will be removed from the liquid while most particles of a smaller size will remain in the liquid. D_{pc}, as here defined, is known as the 'cut-point' or 'critical' diameter. Assume that clarification is being carried out in a simple cylindrical centrifuge as shown in Fig. 7.4(a), and that all particles are distributed uniformly over the cross section of the annular ring of liquid at the base of the bowl and flow upwards to the discharge point with equal velocity. All particles of diameter D_{pc} contained in the outer half of the cross sectional area of the ring of

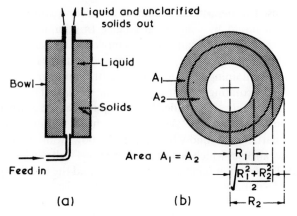

FIG. 7.4.   Principle of simple cylindrical centrifugal clarifier.

liquid will reach the bowl wall and be removed from the liquid. The maximum distance a particle in this zone has to travel to reach the bowl wall is

$$\left[R_2 - \left(\frac{R_1^2 + R_2^2}{2} \right)^{1/2} \right]$$

see Fig. 7.4(b). The time required for a particle of diameter D_{pc} to travel this distance is

$$t = \frac{18\eta}{\omega^2(\rho_s - \rho_l)D_{pc}^2} \int_{\left(\frac{R_1^2 + R_2^2}{2}\right)^{1/2}}^{R_2} \frac{dR}{R}$$

$$= \frac{18\eta \ln\left(\dfrac{R_2}{[(R_1^2 + R_2^2)/2]^{1/2}} \right)}{\omega^2(\rho_s - \rho_l)D_{pc}^2} \tag{7.14}$$

The minimum residence time for a particle in the bowl is V/q, where V is the volume of liquid held in the bowl at any time, and q is the volumetric flow rate of liquid through the bowl.

Thus for a particle of diameter D_{pc} to be separated out

$$\frac{V}{q} = \frac{18\eta \ln\left(\dfrac{R_2}{[(R_1^2 + R_2^2)/2]^{1/2}} \right)}{\omega^2(\rho_s - \rho_l)D_{pc}^2} \tag{7.15}$$

Equation 7.15 may be written in the form

$$q = 2\left[\frac{g(\rho_s - \rho_l)D_{pc}^2}{18\eta}\right]\left[\frac{\omega^2 V}{2g \ln\left(\frac{R_2}{[(R_1^2 + R_2^2)/2]^{1/2}}\right)}\right] \quad (7.16)$$

$$= 2 . v_g . \Sigma \quad (7.17)$$

where g = acceleration due to gravity; v_g = sedimentation velocity of a particle of diameter D_{pc} in a gravitational field; Σ = characteristic of the centrifuge, equivalent to the area of a gravity settling tank with similar settling characteristics to the centrifuge (i.e. one which will remove half of all particles of diameter D_{pc}).
Now

$$\frac{1}{2 \ln\left(\frac{R_2}{[(R_1^2 + R_2^2)/2]^{1/2}}\right)} \simeq \frac{(3R_2^2 + R_1^2)}{2(R_2^2 - R_1^2)} \quad (7.18)$$

Therefore

$$\Sigma \simeq \frac{\omega^2 V(3R_2^2 + R_1^2)}{2g(R_2^2 - R_1^2)} \quad (7.19)$$

For a simple cylindrical bowl such as that shown in Fig. 7.4(a)

$$V = \pi(R_2^2 - R_1^2)b$$

where b = height of the bowl.
Therefore

$$\Sigma \simeq \frac{\pi\omega^2 b(3R_2^2 + R_1^2)}{2g} \quad (7.20)$$

Alternative values of Σ are given in the literature for different types of bowl, e.g. for a disc-bowl centrifuge (see Section 7.2.1.2)

$$\Sigma = \frac{2\pi\omega^2(S - 1)(R_x^3 - R_y^3)}{3g \tan \Omega} \quad (7.21)$$

where S = number of discs in stack; R_x and R_y = outer and inner radius of stack; Ω = conical half angle of discs.
For centrifuges of the same type but of different sizes to have the same performance, that is, to clarify out particles of a particular diameter and above, the quantity q/Σ should be the same. This provides a useful guide for scaling up calculations. These expressions apply best to simple cylindrical

bowls at low or moderate feed rates. The more complex the centrifuge the more difficult it is to apply simple analyses such as these. Extrapolation on the basis of constant value of q/Σ cannot be made between different types of centrifuge, e.g. tubular-bowl and disc types, without special correction factors being introduced.[3-8]

7.1.3. CENTRIFUGAL FILTRATION

This term describes another method of separating insoluble solids from liquids involving centrifugal force. However, in this case the mechanism of separation is filtration and the flow of the filtrate is induced by centrifugal means. The general principle of the centrifugal filter is shown in Fig. 7.5. The slurry is fed into a rotating bowl with a perforated wall, which is lined with a suitable filter medium. The solids are thrown to the bowl wall and form a filter cake through which the filtrate passes, under the influence of centrifugal force, then through the filter medium and perforated basket wall.

Direct comparison of pressure filtration and centrifugal filtration reveals certain differences. In the latter both the centrifugal force and the filtering area increase with increase in radius. Centrifugal force acts on the filtrate passing through the cake and on the cake itself supplementing the hydraulic pressure head. For a comparatively simple system (such as that shown in Fig. 7.5) assuming an incompressible cake and neglecting kinetic energy changes in the filtrate, the rate of flow of filtrate through a centrifugal filter may be expressed as:

$$q = \frac{\rho\omega^2(R_3^2 - R_1^2)}{2\eta\left(\dfrac{\alpha M_c}{[2\pi b(R_3 + R_2)/2][2\pi b(R_3 - R_2)/ln(R_3/R_2)]} + \dfrac{R_m}{2\pi b R_3}\right)}$$

$$= \frac{\rho\omega^2(R_3^2 - R_1^2)}{2\eta\left(\dfrac{\alpha M_c}{A_a A_l} + \dfrac{R_m}{A_m}\right)} \tag{7.22}$$

where q = volumetric flowrate of filtrate; ρ = filtrate density; ω = angular velocity; η = filtrate viscosity; α = specific cake resistance; M_c = mass of solid cake in basket; R_1 = radius of inner surface of the liquid ring; R_2 = radius of the inner surface of the cake; R_3 = radius of inner surface of bowl; A_a = arithmetic mean cake area; A_l = logarithmic mean cake area; A_m = area of filter medium; R_m = resistance of filter medium; b = height of basket. (see Chapter 6, Sections 6.1.3 and 6.1.4 for definitions of α and R_m.)

Such an equation applies only to cakes of uniform thickness. In most

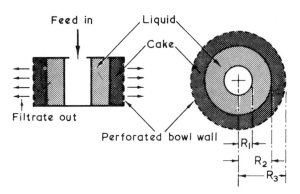

(a) Sectional view (b) Plan view

FIG. 7.5. Principle of simple centrifugal filter.

practical cases cakes are thicker near the base than the top. Such systems give a filtration rate 5–20% greater than a cake of constant thickness of similar volume and permeability.[4,6,7,9]

7.2. EQUIPMENT—PRINCIPLES, DESIGN FEATURES AND GENERAL APPLICATIONS

As equation (7.1) shows, the centrifugal force is proportional to the radius of rotation. The self stress developed in a bowl wall is proportional to the square of the radius of the bowl.[3] The latter factor usually determines the upper speed limit of a bowl. Centrifugal separators are available in two general classes, small diameter high speed machines and large diameter lower speed machines. The centrifugal force developed in the former class is generally greater than in the larger machines. When describing the performance of centrifugal separators the term *relative centrifugal force* (RCF) is often used. This is the ratio of the maximum acceleration developed in a centrifuge bowl ($\omega^2 R$) to the acceleration due to gravity (g). It is often referred to as the 'g' force or 'g' factor. Industrial machines usually develop RCF values in the range $700g$ to $22\,000g$. Laboratory 'bottle' centrifuges can develop up to $34\,000g$ and ultracentrifuges up to $360\,000g$ Some centrifuges are best suited to liquid–liquid separation, others to solid–liquid separation. Many can perform both tasks. It is also possible to obtain three product streams from a separator, viz a light phase (oil) stream, a dense phase (aqueous) stream and a concentrated slurry of insoluble solids.

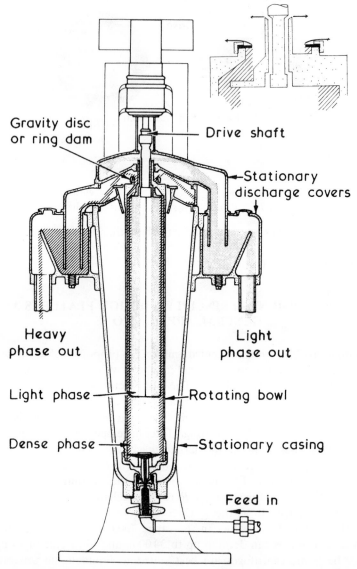

Gravity disc or ring dam

Drive shaft

Stationary discharge covers

Heavy phase out

Light phase out

Light phase

Rotating bowl

Dense phase

Stationary casing

Feed in

Fig. 7.6. Tubular bowl centrifuge (Sharples Super Centrifuge). (By courtesy of Pennwalt Ltd.) The insert shows how the heavy phase discharges over the gravity disc (solid black) while the light phase discharges through channels in the drive shaft.

7.2.1. LIQUID–LIQUID CENTRIFUGAL SEPARATORS

Tubular-bowl centrifuge. This type of centrifuge consists of a long, narrow, cylindrical bowl rotating at high speed in an outer stationary casing. The bowl is usually suspended from the top with a guide provided for the base. The feed is introduced through a stationary pipe to the bottom of the bowl and quickly accelerated to bowl speed by means of vanes or baffles. The two liquids are removed from the annular layers formed through a circular weir system as shown in Fig. 7.6 and discharge into stationary covers. Control over the neutral zone radius, as discussed in Section 7.1.1, is achieved by fitting rings with different internal diameters to the dense phase outlet. Such rings are often known as 'gravity discs' or ring dams. Bowls have diameters in the range 4–5 in (10–12·5 cm) and length-to-diameter ratios from 4 to 8. Bowl speeds up to 15 000 rpm generate up to 13 000*g*. Capacities are in the range 2–16 gall min^{-1} (9–73 dm^3 min^{-1}). Tubular-bowl centrifuges can also be used for clarification of liquids (see Section 7.2.2 below).

Disc-bowl centrifuge. In this type of centrifuge a relatively shallow, wide cylindrical bowl rotates at moderate speed in a stationary casing. The bowl is usually bottom driven. The feed is normally introduced to the bottom of the bowl through a centrally located feed pipe from above. The bowl contains a number of closely spaced metal cones, called discs, which rotate with the bowl and are located one above the other with a fixed clearance between them, Fig. 7.7(a). The discs have one or more sets of matching holes which form channels through which the feed material flows, Fig. 7.7(b). Under the influence of centrifugal force the dense phase, travelling towards the bowl wall, streams down the undersides of the discs while the light phase, displaced towards the centre, flows over the upper faces of the discs, Fig. 7.7(c). The liquids are thus divided into thin layers and the distance any drop of one liquid must travel to get caught up in, and removed in, the appropriate outgoing stream is very small. Also considerable shearing is said to take place at the liquid–liquid interface between the countercurrent streams of liquid which can help to break up certain types of emulsions and improve separation.[1,6] The separation efficiency of a disc-bowl centrifuge is much better than that of a cylindrical bowl of the same dimensions without discs, rotating at a similar speed. The separated liquids are removed by means of a weir system, and again different gravity discs on the dense phase outlet may be used to control the neutral zone position. In some machines provision is made for introducing the feed near the neutral zone by substituting different discs at the bottom of the stack with holes at the appropriate radius. Bowl diameters range from 8 to 40 in (20–102 cm) and the spacing between the discs is of the order of 0·02–0·05 in (0·5–1·3 mm). A

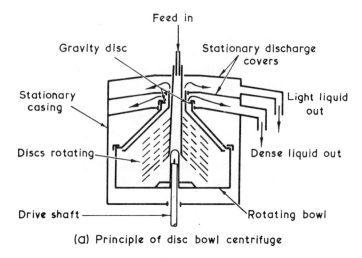

(a) Principle of disc bowl centrifuge

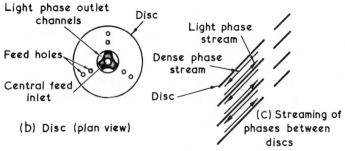

(b) Disc (plan view)

(c) Streaming of phases between discs

FIG. 7.7.   Principle of disc-bowl centrifuge.

typical 12-in diameter bowl rotating at 6400 rpm develops 7000g. Machines with capacities up to 500 gall min^{-1} (2273 dm^3 min^{-1}) are available. Hermetic separators are available from which streams may be discharged through paring chambers or centripetal pumps at pressures up to 100 psi (690 kN m^{-2}). Such units are useful where foaming is a problem, for handling volatile liquids and limiting exposure to the atmosphere. Disc-bowl separators may also be used for clarification of liquids (see Section 7.2.2 below).

7.2.2.   INSOLUBLE SOLID–LIQUID CENTRIFUGAL SEPARATORS

Both tubular and disc-bowl centrifuges may be used for clarifying small quantities of solids from liquids. If the dense phase outlets are closed off and the liquid is removed through the central outlet, then most of the solid particles with diameters greater than the 'cut-point' diameter as defined in Section 7.1.2 will remain as a deposit on the bowl wall. This is a batch operation and, when the solids build up on the bowl wall results in contamination of the outgoing liquid, the operation must be stopped, the bowl dismantled and cleaned out. As the amount of solids in the feed increases so does the frequency of cleaning and the cost of the operation.

The solids capacity of tubular-bowl machines is low, 2–4·5 kg, so for economical operation the insoluble solids content of the feed should not normally exceed 0·5%. However, industrial models do generate up to 13 000g and are efficient at removing very fine solids. When used for this purpose they are often referred to as polishing centrifuges. The solids capacity of disc-bowl separators is in the range 2–20 kg. However, again, they are only used to clarify liquids containing small amounts of insoluble solids, preferably less that 1%. Both clarification and liquid–liquid separation may be carried out simultaneously.

A cylinder-bowl (multichamber) centrifuge is also available. The bowl is divided into a number of annular chambers to facilitate separation of insoluble solids. Again it is batch operated and used for liquids containing relatively small amounts of solids.

Solid-bowl clarifier. Where large volumes of liquid containing small quantities of solids (1–2%) with good settling characteristics need to be

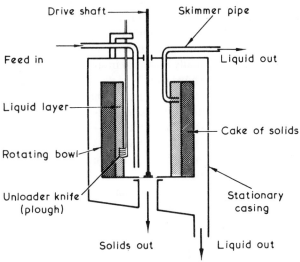

FIG. 7.8. Principle of solid-bowl clarifier.

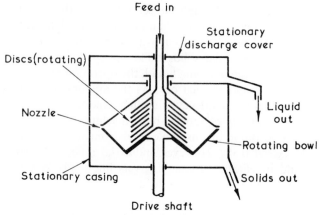

FIG. 7.9.   Principle of nozzle-discharge centrifuge.

clarified, simple large diameter, 24–42 in (60–108 cm) cylindrical bowls, without discs, may be used (Fig. 7.8). These are operated on a batch principle and, when a cake of solids of the maximum thickness is formed, the feed is cut off, excess liquid removed with a skimmer pipe and the solids cut out with a knife or plough and dropped through an opening in the bowl floor.

For applications outside the capacities of the batch machines described above, centrifuges are available which provide for the continuous or intermittent discharge of insoluble solids in the form of slurries from the bowl. Some examples of these machines are described below.

Nozzle-discharge (self-cleaning) centrifuge. This machine is of the disc-bowl type but the bowl is usually biconical in shape (Fig. 7.9). A number of ports are spaced around the bowl usually at its largest diameter. These may number from two to twenty four and range in diameter from 0·03 to 0·08 in (0·76–2·00 mm). The size of the ports is selected to suit the particle size of the solids in the feed. From 5 to 50% of the feed is continuously discharged through the ports in the form of a slurry. The solids concentration in the slurry is usually not more than 25% v/v. By recycling a proportion of the nozzle discharge this may be increased to 40% v/v in some cases.

A number of machine designs are available which feature intermittent solids discharge. The **valve-discharge centrifuge** is similar in design to the nozzle-discharge machine described above but valves are fitted in the solids discharge ports. These valves can be opened at desired intervals to discharge the solids. In the **self-opening centrifuge** (shown in Fig. 7.10) the lower section of the bowl moves vertically and is actuated by hydraulic

CLARIFYING — BOWL CLOSED   BOWL CLEANING WITH TOTAL DISCHARGE

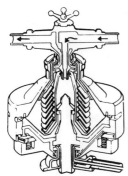 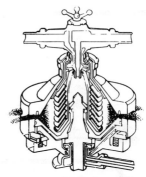

FIG. 7.10. Self-opening centrifuge. (By courtesy of Alfa-Laval Co. Ltd.)

pressure which, when high, keeps the discharge ports closed. When the pressure is released the lower part of the bowl descends, opening the ports and permitting discharge of the solids. The action is swift, taking only a fraction of a second. In these machines the discharge operation may be triggered by timers. Alternatively, self-triggering systems are available in which the build-up of solids in the bowl is monitored to provide a triggering signal for the discharge of the solids. Self-triggering should lead to higher separation efficiency because the solids are ejected before they have reached and possibly clogged the disc stack and very little liquid should escape with the solids. This is very important when dealing with feeds of varying solids content. Such machines can handle feed with up to 6% v/v solids and the solids released are generally drier than those discharged continuously. There is a wide range of machine designs available to suit specific products and process specifications.

When the solids content of the feed exceeds that which can be handled by the centrifuges described above or where the solids settle very readily, **decanting (conveyor-bowl) centrifuges** may be applicable (see Fig. 7.11). Both the conveyor (scroll) and the imperforate bowl rotate in the same direction but a few rpm differential is induced by a gearbox which rotates with the bowl. Sedimented solids are conveyed to one end up a conical section, known as the beach, to be discharged. The clarified liquid decants over an adjustable weir at the other end of the bowl. The weir will adjust the 'pond' depth and consequently the extent of any dry beach and thus the performance of the machine can be optimised. Such machines can deal with a wide range of slurry concentrations up to 90% v/v. As long as a slurry is pumpable the machine will accept it. Bowl diameters range from 6 to 54 in

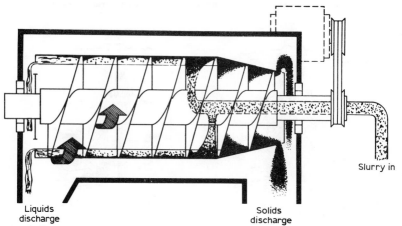

Slurry in

Liquids
discharge

Solids
discharge

FIG. 7.11.   Principle of conveyor-bowl centrifuge. (Reproduced with the permission of Alfa-Laval Sharples Ltd, Camberley, Surrey, England.)

(15–137 cm) with length-to-diameter ratios of 1·5–3·0 and rotate at 1600–8500 rpm. They develop 2000–3000g and are best suited to separating medium and coarse particles. Particle sizes less than about 2 μm are normally not separated. The liquid from such decantors may be passed through tubular or disc-bowl clarifiers for final polishing. Washing of the solids inside the centrifuge is possible but is only effective in the case of coarse granular or spherical solids. A higher speed decantor developing, up to 5000g, is now available.

Many of the machines described above are designed for cleaning in place (CIP) and remote operation. Some have been in operation continuously for many months, if not years, in food applications without the need for shut down. Control and automation has been developed to monitor the mechanical aspects of these machines, for example lubrication and vibration.

7.2.3.   FILTERING CENTRIFUGALS (BASKET CENTRIFUGES OR DEWATERING CENTRIFUGES)

This type of equipment is used for handling slurries which lend themselves to separation by filtration, that is suspensions of fairly large particulate solids or crystalline materials which form suitably porous cakes.

Batch filtering centrifugal. Such a unit is shown in Fig. 7.12. The cylindrical metal basket with a perforated wall is suspended from the end of a vertical shaft. A filter medium lines the inside of the basket wall. In a typical cycle, the feed is introduced with the basket rotating at moderate

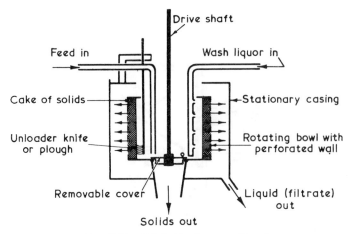

FIG. 7.12. Batch filtering centrifugal.

speed. The bowl is then accelerated and filtration occurs through the cake of solids formed on the bowl wall. Wash liquid may be sprayed on to the cake and the cake spun dry at high speed. The basket is then slowed down, the cake cut out with an unloader knife or plough and removed through an opening in the basket floor. The filter medium is rinsed and the cycle repeated.

Bowls diameters are usually in the range 12–60 in (30–152 cm) with diameter-to-height ratios of 1–3. Speeds of rotation range from 2100 rpm for small bowls to 600 rpm for larger models, developing from 800*g* to 300*g* respectively. Cycle times vary from 3 to 30 min. The cycle may be manually controlled or automated to varying degrees.

Fully automatic batch centrifuges are also available. These rotate at a constant speed throughout the cycle. Feed and wash liquid are introduced automatically and the cake cut out with a hydraulically operated knife or plough and discharged through a chute. Bowl diameters are usually in the range 12–48 in (30–122 cm). They rotate about horizontal axes at between 2500 and 1000 rpm, developing up to 1250*g*. They are best suited to handling feeds that are consistent in composition, have a high concentration of insoluble solids which have good draining characteristics. They have cycle times in the range 0·5–1·5 min. Delicate crystals may suffer mechanical damage due to the action of the plough.

Continuous filtering centrifugals are also available. These may feature cylindrical or conical perforated bowls. The **reciprocating conveyor (push-type) centrifuge** is an example of the former (see Fig. 7.13). The feed enters the

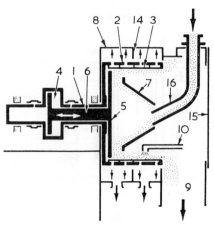

FIG. 7.13. Schematic drawing of single-stage push-type centrifuge. 1, Hollow shaft; 2, basket; 3, sieve of basket; 4, hydraulic drive for pusher; 5, pusher member; 6, pusher shaft; 7, inlet funnel; 8, casing; 9, catcher; 10, washing device; 14, separating wall; 15, door; 16, feed pipe. (By courtesy of Escher Wyss (UK) Ltd.)

rotating basket through a rotating funnel which accelerates it gently to bowl speed. A layer of solids 1·00–3·00 in (2·5–7·6 cm) thick forms on the bowl wall. This layer is moved forward towards the open end of the basket by a reciprocating pusher with a stroke of up to 3 in (7·6 cm) which operates in the range of 20–100 strokes min^{-1}. On each return stroke of the pusher, the feed funnel, which reciprocates also, delivers feed to the freshly exposed basket wall. The cake may be washed as shown and is finally spun off the open lip of the basket into a stationary casing. Basket diameters range from 8 to 48 in (20–122 cm) and develop from about 600g to 3000g. The basket wall is usually in the form of a bar screen with spacing in the range 0·005–0·020 in (0·13–0·50 mm). Crystal damage is reduced by the gentle acceleration and deceleration of the feed and discharged solids respectively. With some materials buckling of the cake layer in front of the pusher may occur and cake washing is not always effective.

A **multistage push-type centrifuge** is shown in Fig. 7.14. The stages are arranged in a telescopic fashion and alternate baskets reciprocate in an axial direction while the remainder are stationary axially. Thus each basket acts as a pusher for the following one. In such a machine the total distance the cake has to be pushed in each basket is less than in the single stage unit for a given total centrifuging time. Thus problems associated with buckling of the cake layer are minimised. The loosening of the cake occurring on transfer from one stage to the next is said to improve filtration and washing,

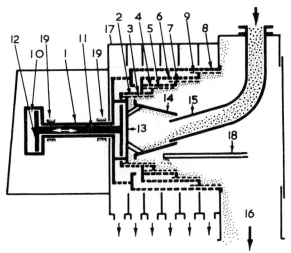

FIG. 7.14. Schematic drawing of multi-stage push-type centrifuge. 1, Hollow shaft; 2, first stage; 3, sieve covering; 4, second stage; 5, sieve covering; 6, third stage; 7, sieve covering; 8, fourth stage; 9, sieve covering; 10, pressure cylinder; 11, piston rod; 12, piston; 13, pusher member; 14, inlet funnel; 15, inlet pipe; 16, catcher; 17, casing; 18, washer pipe; 19, bearing. (By courtesy of Escher Wyss (UK) Ltd.)

and also the power consumption is more uniform and lower than in large single stage units.

The **screen-conveyor centrifuge** (shown in Fig. 7.15) is an example of a filtering centrifuge featuring a conical bowl. The helical conveyor turns slightly faster than the bowl and moves the filter cake towards the wide end

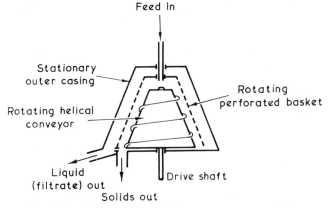

FIG. 7.15. Principle of vertical screen-conveyor system.

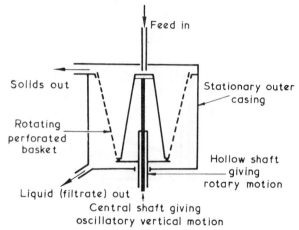

FIG. 7.16.   Principle of vibrating screen centrifuge.

of the bowl from where it is discharged. The **constant angle bowl** is similar in design to the above but without the conveyor. The cone angle is slightly larger than the angle of repose of the solids at any stage in their drying cycle so that the solids move towards the wide end of the bowl from where they are discharged. The selection of the proper cone angle and suitable screen surface is critical for each application. In the case of the **vibrating** or **oscillating screen centrifuge** (shown in Fig. 7.16) the basket oscillates in a vertical direction while rotating, thus causing the solids to move to the top for discharge.

7.3. APPLICATIONS FOR CENTRIFUGAL EQUIPMENT IN THE FOOD INDUSTRY

Tubular-bowl centrifuges are used in edible oil refining for degumming the crude oil, separation of soapstock after neutralisation of the free fatty acids and in subsequent washing stages to purify the oil. Other applications include the separation of animal blood into plasma and haemaglobin and the clarification of fruit juices, cider and sugar syrup for clear sweet manufacture.

Disc-bowl centrifuges are used in the dairy industry for separating cream from milk in edible oil refining for separation of soapstock and washings and for clarification of vegetable, citrus oils and fruit juices.

The various **solid–liquid separators**, described above, have found very many applications in the food and biotechnology industries including: in the dairy industry for separating milk, buttermilk and whey; in oil refining for degumming, soapstock separation, separation of washings, dewaxing and winterisation; in winemaking for the clarification of juices and wines at various stages, juice recovery from tank bottoms and recovery of wine/alcohol from fermented lees; in brewing for the recovery of yeast and clarification of beer; dewatering of corn, wheat and rye starches. The type of bowl and solids discharge system used depends on the nature of the feedstock and the required characteristics of both the liquid and solid components.

Decanting centrifuges have found increasing use in industry in recent years. Applications include: recovering animal and vegetable protein, viz. casein and soya protein; harvesting single cell protein; separating coffee, tea and cocoa slurries; desludging fish oils; separating fat from comminuted meat; meat deboning; separating blood meal from coagulated blood; clarifying tallow; extracting olive oil; separating fish blood water and fish press liquor; dewatering trub, solids separated from wort in brewing; clarifying liquor from pressed spent grain and recovering tartrates from distilled wine lees.

Filtering centrifugals are used extensively in sugar refining for recovering, washing and drying sugar crystals. Other applications include: separating juice from comminuted fruits and vegetables; recovering vegetable proteins and separating starch from potato slurry. They are also used in freeze concentration operations (Section 9.5.2).

(*Note*: Grateful acknowledgement is hereby made for information received from Messrs Alfa-Laval Ltd, Alfa-Laval Sharples Ltd and Westfalia Separator AG.)

REFERENCES

1. Trowbridge, M. E., Problems in the scaling-up of centrifugal separation equipment. *The Chemical Engineer*, **40**(162) (1962) A73–A87.
2. Lavanchy, A. C. and Keith, F. W., Jr, Centrifugal Separation. In *Kirk Othmer Encyclopedia of Chemical Technology. Vol. 4*, 2nd edn. John Wiley, New York, 1964, pp. 710–58.
3. Coulson, J. M., Richardson, J. F. with Backhurst, J. R. and Harker, J. H., *Chemical Engineering. Vol. 2*, 3rd edn. Pergamon Press, Oxford, England, 1978.
4. Foust, A. S., Wenzel, L. A., Clump, C. W., Maus, L. and Bryce Anderson, L., *Principles of Unit Operations*, 2nd edn. John Wiley, New York, 1980.
5. Ambler, C. M., The evaluation of centrifugal performance. *Chem. Engng Prog.*, **48**(3) (1952) 150–8.
6. Green, D. W. (ed.), *Perry's Chemical Engineer's Handbook*, 6th edn. McGraw-Hill, New York, 1984.

7. McCabe, W. L., Smith, J. C. and Harriott, P., *Unit Operations of Chemical Engineering*, 4th edn. McGraw-Hill, New York, 1985.
8. Records, F. A., The continuous scroll discharge decanting centrifuge. *The Chemical Engineer*, **281** (January 1974) 41–7.
9. Records, F. A., Filtration theory in cyclic centrifuges. *Chem. Proc. Engng*, **52** (November 1971) 47–51.

CHAPTER 8

SOLID–LIQUID EXTRACTION AND EXPRESSION

8.1. SOLID–LIQUID EXTRACTION (LEACHING, WASHING)

In the food and biochemical industries the transfer of mass between phases is often of interest. The phases may be solid, liquid or gaseous and two or more phases may be involved in any one transfer operation. Often when a phase contains more than one component the individual components differ in their tendencies to transfer to another phase or phases. For example, one of the components in a liquid may be more volatile than the others and so transfer more readily to a gaseous phase. This is the basis of distillation operations. Alternatively one component may be more soluble in another phase and so transfer between phases more readily than the other components in the system. This is the basis of solvent extraction operations. Where such differences exist between the components in a phase and that phase is placed in intimate contact with another phase or phases then mass transfer may occur between the phases and result in the redistribution of the components among them. Thus the composition of all the phases may change. In this way a separation of the components of a phase may be brought about.

Solid–liquid extraction is an example of such a separation operation in which a desired component, the *solute*, in a solid phase is separated by contacting the solid with a liquid, the *solvent*, in which the desired component is soluble.

Separation operations of this kind are carried out in single or multiple steps or *stages*. A stage is a unit of equipment in which two or more phases are brought into contact, maintained in contact for a predetermined period and then separated mechanically from each other. During the period of contact mass transfer of components between the phases takes place and

199

they approach a state of equilibrium. An *equilibrium* (*ideal* or *theoretical*) stage is one in which the phases are intimately mixed and retained in contact for a time sufficient to allow thermodynamic equilibrium to be achieved between the phases before they are separated, In an *actual* (*real*) stage a true state of equilibrium is not reached and so the change in composition is less than that theoretically possible. *Stage efficiency* may be defined as the ratio of the compositional change brought about in an actual stage to that which would have occurred in an equilibrium stage under the same operating conditions.

In a solid–liquid extraction stage the solvent is brought into intimate contact with the solid, solid and solvent are held in contact for the required time and then the mixture is separated into two streams: a 'clear' liquid stream or *overflow* stream consisting of a solution of the solute in the solvent and a 'residue' stream or *underflow* stream consisting of the insoluble solid component with some solution adhering to it. In this context an equilibrium stage may be defined as a stage in which the solution adhering to the solid in the underflow stream has the same composition as the clear liquid constituting the overflow stream. In an actual stage the concentration of the solute in the overflow stream would be less than in the solution adhering to the solid in the underflow stream.

8.1.1. SINGLE STAGE CALCULATIONS

Consider an equilibrium stage as shown diagrammatically in Fig. 8.1, where L_2 and L_1 represent the total mass (or mols) of the overflow streams entering and leaving the stage, S_0 and S_1 represent the total mass (or mols) of the underflow streams entering and leaving, Y is the mass (or mol) fraction of a component in the L stream, X is the mass (or mol) fraction of a component in the S stream. If the two streams are thoroughly mixed in the stage then a mixture of mass ε results. Let Z represent the mass (or mol) fraction of a component in this mixture. Mass balances may be carried out on the stage as follows.

Total mass balance:

$$S_0 + L_2 = \varepsilon \tag{8.1}$$

Mass balance for component 'a'

$$S_0 X_{a0} + L_2 Y_{a2} = \varepsilon Z_{a1} \tag{8.2}$$

Mass balance for component 'b'

$$S_0 X_{b0} + L_2 Y_{b2} = \varepsilon Z_{b1} \tag{8.3}$$

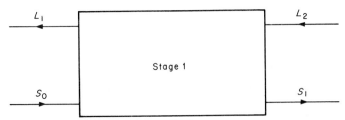

FIG. 8.1.   An equilibrium stage.

In a three component system (a ternary system) a mass balance for the third component '*c*', similar in form to equations (8.2) and (8.3) may be written. However, this may not be necessary as the mass fraction of '*c*' in the streams may be obtained by difference since

$$X_a + X_b + X_c = 1 \qquad (8.4)$$

and

$$Y_a + Y_b + Y_c = 1 \qquad (8.5)$$

Considering component '*a*', from equations (8.1) and (8.2) the relationship

$$S_0 X_{a0} + L_2 Y_{a2} = (S_0 + L_2) Z_{a1} \qquad (8.6)$$

may be written. Rearranging (8.6)

$$\frac{S_0}{L_2} = \frac{Y_{a2} - Z_{a1}}{Z_{a1} - X_{a0}} \qquad (8.7)$$

A similar expression may be written for component '*b*' thus

$$\frac{S_0}{L_2} = \frac{Y_{b2} - Z_{b1}}{Z_{b1} - X_{b0}} \qquad (8.8)$$

Thus the composition of the mixture in the stage can be obtained from a knowledge of the masses and compositions of the streams entering. If the compositions of the incoming streams are represented graphically as shown in Fig. 8.2 then the composition of the mixture can be shown to lie on a straight line between the points representing the compositions of streams S_0 and L_2, and the position on that line will be such that the ratio S_0/L_2 is equal to the distance from L_2 to ε divided by the distance from ε to S_0. This is known as the *inverse lever-arm rule*. If these lengths are expressed in terms of distances on the axes rather than the line $S_0 L_2$ itself, then

$$\frac{S_0}{L_2} = \frac{Y_{a2} - Z_{a1}}{Z_{a1} - X_{a0}} = \frac{Y_{b2} - Z_{b1}}{Z_{b1} - X_{b0}}$$

i.e. equations (8.7) and (8.8).

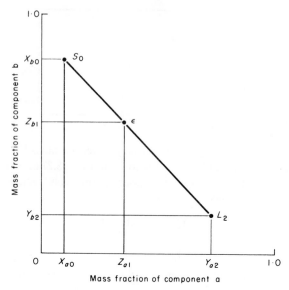

Fig. 8.2. Graphical representation of the composition of incoming streams and mixture in an equilibrium stage.

Subtraction of streams may also be carried out graphically. If Δ represents the mass (or mols) difference between the S and L streams then a total mass balance is

$$\Delta = S - L \tag{8.9}$$

and a component balance is

$$\Delta X_\Delta = SX - LY \tag{8.10}$$

where X_Δ is the composition of the Δ stream. If such a subtraction is represented graphically the composition of the stream will lie on a straight line drawn through the points representing the compositions of the S and L streams but beyond S from L. In Fig. 8.3 graphical addition and subtraction are represented diagrammatically.

When equilibrium conditions have been established in the stage and if the mixture still consists of two phases then the composition of the phases will depend on the equilibrium relationship between them. This relationship will be specific to each system and will also depend on the operating conditions. When subsequently the two phases are separated the masses of the outgoing streams will be related to their compositions by

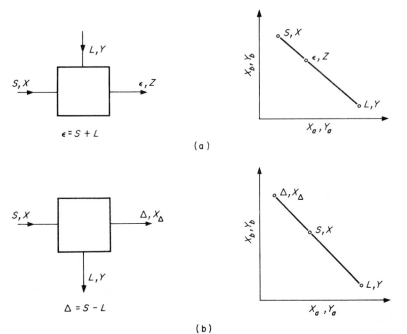

FIG. 8.3. Graphical addition and subtraction of streams. (a) Graphical addition; (b) graphical subtraction.

mass balances similar to those applicable to the incoming streams thus

$$\varepsilon = S_1 + L_1 \tag{8.11}$$

$$\varepsilon Z_{a1} = S_1 X_{a1} + L_1 Y_{a1} \tag{8.12}$$

$$\varepsilon Z_{b1} = S_1 X_{b1} + L_1 Y_{b1} \tag{8.13}$$

8.1.2. MULTISTAGE CALCULATIONS

Since the two phases leaving an equilibrium stage are by definition in equilibrium those equilibrium conditions represent the maximum degree of separation of the components that can be obtained in a single stage. Further changes in composition may be achieved by contacting one of these phases with a fresh quantity of the other phase. For example in a solid–liquid extraction operation the underflow stream from an equilibrium stage may be contacted with fresh solvent to bring about further extraction of the solute. This application of fresh solvent to the underflow from each stage may be continued until the concentration of solute in the underflow reaches a satisfactorily low level. However, this technique

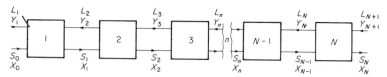

FIG. 8.4.   Multistage, countercurrent mass transfer system. N refers to last stage in the system; n refers to any stage.

requires large quantities of solvent and the solution obtained when all the overflow streams are bulked will be relatively weak in solute. Thus the costs of recovery of the solute will be relatively high.

An alternative procedure for obtaining maximum separation of components is to use a multistage countercurrent system such as that shown in Fig. 8.4. The two phases enter at opposite ends of a series of stages and flow countercurrent to each other through the series. In a solid–liquid extraction system of the countercurrent type the underflow from stage 1 enters stage 2 where it is contacted with overflow from stage 3. The concentration of solute in the overflow from stage 3 will be less than that in the solution adhering to the solid in the underflow from stage 1. The two streams entering stage 2 will not be in equilibrium and will tend to move towards that state. Thus a change in composition of the two streams will occur. A similar change, not necessarily of the same magnitude, will occur in each stage of the series and result in a relatively large change in the composition of the streams after they have passed through the complete series.

For some purposes it is convenient to consider a mass balance on a complete countercurrent series, treating it very much like one equilibrium stage, as follows.

Total mass balance:

$$S_0 + L_{N+1} = S_N + L_1 = \varepsilon \qquad (8.14)$$

where ε is the total mass of the mixture in the system.

Component mass balance:

$$S_0 X_0 + L_{N+1} Y_{N+1} = S_N X_N + L_1 Y_1 = \varepsilon Z_\varepsilon \qquad (8.15)$$

where Z_ε is the average composition (mass fraction) of a component in the mixture in the series.

Also

$$Z_\varepsilon = \frac{S_0 X_0 + L_{N+1} Y_{N+1}}{S_0 + L_{N+1}} = \frac{S_N X_N + L_1 Y_1}{S_N + L_1} \qquad (8.16)$$

Thus the value of Z_ε may be obtained graphically by the application of the inverse lever-arm rule from a knowledge of the masses and compositions of the streams entering or leaving the system.

8.1.2.1. Net flow concept

Between each pair of stages of a countercurrent system two streams pass one another (see Fig. 8.4). The net flow is the difference in mass flow rate between these two streams. The net flow concept may apply to the total mass flow or to the flow of one or more components in counterflowing streams. Since there is no accumulation of total mass or components in the system the net flow is constant throughout the system. It is of course a fictitious quantity since the streams are not actually subtracted one from the other.

The total net flow Δ is given by:

$$\Delta = S_0 - L_1 = S_n - L_{n+1} = S_N - L_{N+1} \qquad (8.17)$$

The net flow of a component is given by:

$$\Delta X_\Delta = S_0 X_0 - L_1 Y_1 = S_n X_n - L_{n+1} Y_{n+1} = S_N X_N - L_{N+1} Y_{N+1} \quad (8.18)$$

where X_Δ is the mass fraction of the component in the fictitious net flow stream. Also

$$X_\Delta = \frac{\Delta X_\Delta}{\Delta} = \frac{S_0 X_0 - L_1 Y_1}{S_0 - L_1} = \frac{S_n X_n - L_{n+1} Y_{n+1}}{S_n - L_{n+1}}$$

$$= \frac{S_N X_N - L_{N+1} Y_{N+1}}{S_N - L_{N+1}} = \frac{\text{net flow of component}}{\text{total net flow}} \qquad (8.19)$$

It is possible to locate Δ on a composition diagram by graphical subtraction. The point representing the composition of $\Delta(X_\Delta)$ must be on a straight line through the points representing the compositions of the streams S_0 and L_1 (i.e. X_0 and Y_1 respectively) and also on a straight line through the points representing the compositions of streams S_N and L_{N+1} (i.e. X_N and Y_{N+1} respectively). It can thus be located as shown in Fig. 8.5. Since the total mass and component net flow rates are constant from stage to stage X_Δ must also lie on a straight line through X_1, Y_2; X_2, Y_3; X_3, Y_4; etc. This common point, the delta point, provides a means of relating the compositions of streams leaving adjacent stages.[1,2]

8.1.3. STAGE-TO-STAGE CALCULATIONS

Frequently it is necessary to estimate the number of equilibrium stages required to bring about a specified degree of extraction. Alternatively

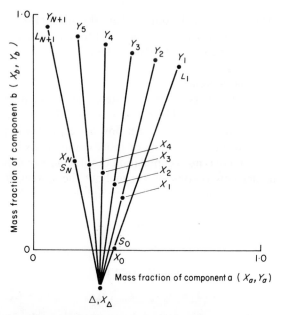

FIG. 8.5. Graphical location of the delta point.

information may be required on the performance of a system with a specified number of stages. Such information may be obtained by stage-to-stage calculations. These may be started at either end of the series of stages. For example, if Y_1, the composition of the solution stream leaving the system, is known then X_1 can be obtained from a knowledge of the equilibrium relationships between the streams. In order to obtain a value for Y_2 some relationship between the streams S_1 and L_2 needs to be established. The delta point, derived from a consideration of the net flow of material between stages, may provide this stage-to-stage link. Thus with alternate use of equilibrium data and the delta point it is possible to progress from stage to stage until the specified end value of X_N is reached. In this way the number of equilibrium stages can be estimated. If the number of stages is known then this same technique may be used to obtain a value for X_N (or Y_1, if the calculation is started from the other end of the series, stage N).

The composition of each stream in a countercurrent extraction system may be represented graphically on a triangular diagram as shown in Fig. 8.6. In this diagram the right angle vertex represents pure insoluble solids. The abscissa (where $X_s = 0$) represents mixtures of insoluble solids and

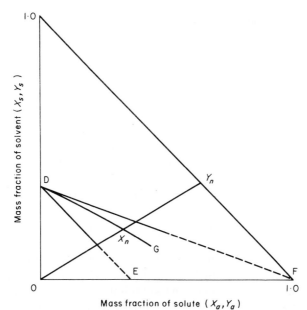

Fig. 8.6. Composition diagram showing underflow lines.

solute. The vertical coordinate (where $X_a = 0$) represents mixtures of insoluble solids and solvent. The hypotenuse represents mixtures of solute and solvent ($X_c = 0$). Some such triangular diagrams may be divided into saturated and unsaturated regions or two-phase regions. However, in most practical applications for solid–liquid extraction a single unsaturated solution is formed and subdivision of the triangle is unnecessary. If the quantity of solution (or solvent) adhering to unit mass of insoluble solids in the underflow from each stage is known, the composition of the underflow may be represented by a line on this diagram. If the mass of solution (or solvent) retained per unit mass of insoluble solids is the same from each stage the system is said to operate under *constant underflow* conditions. If the mass of *solution* per unit mass of insoluble solids is constant for all stages the composition of the underflow may be represented by a line such as DE in Fig. 8.6. The equation to this line is:

$$X_s = \frac{k}{(k + 1)} - X_a \qquad (8.20)$$

where X_s = mass fraction of solvent in the underflow, X_a = mass fraction of solute in the underflow, k = mass of solution retained per unit mass of insoluble solids.

This line may be drawn by locating points D

$$\left(X_a = 0, X_s = \frac{k}{(k+1)} \right)$$

and E

$$\left(X_s = 0, X_a = \frac{k}{(k+1)} \right)$$

on the vertical and horizontal axes respectively.

If the mass of *solvent* per unit mass of insoluble solids in the underflow from all stages is the same then the underflow composition may be represented by a line such as DF in Fig. 8.6. The equation to this line is:

$$X_s = \frac{K}{(K+1)} - \frac{K}{(K+1)} X_a \tag{8.21}$$

where $K =$ the mass of solvent retained per unit mass of insoluble solids. Line DF may be drawn by locating points D ($X_a = 0$, $X_s = K/(K+1)$) and F ($X_s = 0$, $X_a = 1$). If neither the mass of solution or solvent retained per unit mass of insoluble solids remains constant from stage to stage then the values obtained experimentally from each stage may be plotted on the triangular diagram to give a curved line such as line DG in Fig. 8.6.

Any straight line connecting the right angle vertex 0 ($X_s = 0$, $X_a = 0$) with the hypotenuse ($X_c = 0$) will intersect the underflow line at a point representing the composition of the underflow in equilibrium with the clear solution whose composition is represented by the point of intersection of the first line with the hypotenuse. Thus in Fig. 8.6 underflow whose composition is represented by point X_n is in equilibrium with clear solution of composition Y_n. In this example it is assumed that line DG is the underflow line. By definition, in an equilibrium stage, this means that the mass fraction of solute in the solution retained by the insoluble solids in the underflow leaving stage n is the same as that in the clear solution represented by point Y_n. Further, since the right angle vertex represents insoluble solids and point Y_n clear solution the ratio 'clear solution/ insoluble solids' in the underflow, represented by point X_n, may be obtained by the application of the inverse lever-arm rule and is equivalent to the ratio of the distances $0X_n/X_nY_n$. Note that for line DE, for constant 'solution' underflow, this ratio is constant.

The delta point (see Section 8.1.2), may be located on the triangular composition diagram by extending straight lines through Y_{N+1}, X_N and Y_1, X_0 until they intersect as shown in Fig. 8.7. By connecting the right angle

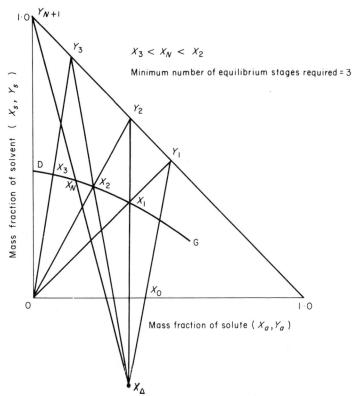

FIG. 8.7. Graphical method of determining the minimum number of equilibrium stages.

vertex 0 and point Y_1 with a straight line, X_1 may be located where this straight line intersects the underflow line DG. By extending a straight line through X_Δ and X_1 to intersect the hypotenuse, Y_2 may be located. By connecting Y_2 to 0, X_2 may be located and following that Y_3, as shown in Fig. 8.7. This procedure may be followed until the value of X_n obtained is equal to or less than the specified final value X_N. The number of straight lines connecting 0 with the hypotenuse represents the minimum number of equilibrium stages required to reduce the mass fraction of solute in the underflow to X_N. In the example shown in Fig. 8.7 the minimum number of stages required is 3. If the number of stages is specified, then provided sufficient data is available to locate the delta point, the same procedure may be used to calculate X_N (or Y_1 if the procedure is started at stage N).[1-3]

The number of actual stages required to obtain a specified degree of

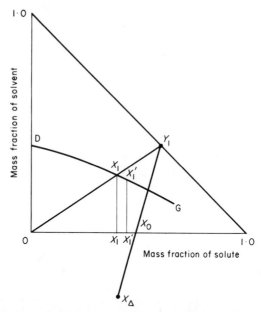

FIG. 8.8. Graphical representation of stage efficiency.

extraction will be greater than the estimated number of equilibrium stages. If the stage efficiency is determined and found to be independent of concentration then the number of actual stages is equal to the number of equilibrium stages divided by the stage efficiency. If the efficiency varies from stage to stage then it must be taken into account at each stage when using the graphical method for estimating the number of actual stages required. For example in the case shown in Fig. 8.8 the underflow composition, X_1, in equilibrium with the overflow composition, Y_1, is shown. If the actual composition of the underflow leaving stage 1 is found to be X_1' then this is the value that should be used to obtain Y_2 graphically. Stage 1 efficiency in this case is $(X_0 - X_1')/(X_0 - X_1).$[2]

8.1.4. RATE OF EXTRACTION

The extraction of solute from a solid particle is usually considered to take place in three stages. The solute first dissolves in the solvent. The solute in solution diffuses to the surface of the solid particle. Finally the solute moves from the surface of the solid particle, where it is assumed to be in the form of a saturated solution, into the bulk of the solution. Any one of these three steps could limit the rate of extraction. It is usually assumed that, when a correct choice of solvent has been made, the solution of the solute takes place rapidly and does not greatly influence the overall rate of extraction. It is difficult to quantify the rate of movement within the solid particle due to the complex structure of most solids. The rate of movement of solute from the saturated layer at the surface of the particle to the bulk of the solution may be described by the expression:

$$\frac{dw}{dt} = KA(C_s - C) \tag{8.22}$$

where dw/dt = rate of mass transfer of solute, A = area of solid–liquid interface, C_s and C = concentrations of solute at the surface of the solid and in the bulk of the solution respectively, K = mass transfer coefficient.

In a single stage extraction unit where V is the total volume of the solution and is constant, then

$$dw = V\,dc$$

and so

$$\frac{dc}{dt} = \frac{KA(C_s - C)}{V} \tag{8.23}$$

Integrating this expression within the limits $-t = 0$, $C = C_0$ to $t = t$, $C = C$,

$$\int_{C_0}^{C} \frac{dc}{C_s - C} = \int_{0}^{t} \frac{KA}{V}\,dt$$

gives

$$\ln\left(\frac{C_s - C_0}{C_s - C}\right) = \frac{KA}{V}t \tag{8.24}$$

If pure solvent is used initially, *i.e.* $C_0 = 0$

$$\ln\left(\frac{C_s}{C_s - C}\right) = \frac{KA}{V}t \tag{8.25}$$

Thus the solution approaches saturation at an exponential rate.[2,4]

Factors which influence the rate of extraction include:

(*a*) *The area of the solid–liquid interface.* According to equation (8.22) the rate of mass transfer from the surface of the solid is directly proportional to this area. Thus a reduction in particle size should result in a greater rate of extraction, due to the increased area and a reduction in the distance the solute has to move within the solid to get to the surface. However, there are limits to the degree of comminution desirable to obtain the best results in

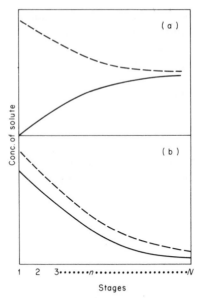

FIG. 8.9.   Graphical representation of concurrent and countercurrent extraction
systems. (a) Concurrent system; (b) countercurrent system. - - - - - - Solid; ———
solution.

many practical cases. Too fine a solid may impede the flow of solution
through the bed of solid in an extractor and in some cases cause undesirable
substances to be released into the solution (see Section 8.1.6).

(*b*) *Concentration gradient.* The concentration gradient between that at
the surface of the solid and that in the bulk of the solution is also important.
The solvent must be selective with respect to the solute to be extracted. It
must also have a low enough viscosity to permit good circulation through
the bed of solid. Countercurrent systems of extraction enable control to be
exercised over the concentration gradient so that extraction can continue
even when the concentration of solute in the solid is low. This facilitates
more complete recovery of solute as compared with that attainable in single
stage or multistage concurrent systems (see Fig. 8.9).

(*c*) *Temperature.* Elevation of temperature usually increases both rate of
solution of solute in solvent and rate of diffusion of solute through the
solution. It usually, therefore, leads to an increased rate of extraction.
Limits on temperature for some materials may need to be imposed, to avoid
undesirable physical and/or chemical changes which could impair product
quality (see Section 8.1.6).

(*d*) *Rate of flow of solvent*. In general the higher the velocity and the more turbulent the flow of solvent over the surface of the solid, the higher the rate of extraction. When fine solids are being extracted mechanical agitation is often employed. In the case of most food applications the solvent is made to flow, under the influence of gravity or with the aid of a pump, through a static bed of the solid. Excessive agitation of the solid can sometimes lead to undesirable disintegration of the solid particles.

8.1.5. EXTRACTION EQUIPMENT—PRINCIPLES, DESIGN FEATURES AND GENERAL APPLICATIONS

In the food industry solid–liquid extraction is mainly applied to relatively coarse, particulate materials, usually greater than 200 mesh in size. In many cases the solid has a cellular structure. The equipment used includes single and multistage static tanks and continuous moving-bed extractors. Vigorous movement of the solid is seldom desirable.

8.1.5.1. Single stage extractors

The simplest form of extractor consists of an open tank, fitted with a false bottom which supports a bed of the solid to be extracted. The solvent is distributed over the surface of the bed of solid, percolates down through it and the solution is removed through a drain beneath the false bottom. In food applications extraction is often carried out at high temperatures and pressures. In the case of oil extraction the solvent is relatively volatile. For these reasons and also for hygienic considerations, vessels are usually totally enclosed and capable of withstanding the required pressure. A simple single stage extraction unit is shown diagrammatically in Fig. 8.10. Provision may be made for recirculating the overflow. A heater may be incorporated in the feed line and/or recirculation line to enable the temperature of the solution to be maintained at the desired value. Some units are jacketed for this purpose. Such cells may be filled manually or with the aid of a conveyor or some other mechanical device. The solid residue is removed manually or dumped through an outlet in the base of the cell. Where volatile solvents are being used, it is possible to incorporate a solvent recovery and recycling system in such units. This enables a relatively concentrated overflow to be obtained (see Fig. 8.11). Large cells may need to be fitted with perforated shelves, chains or some other internal structures to support the bed of solid and minimise consolidation which would impair the flow of solution through the bed. Single stage units are used for pilot plant and small scale commercial operations for the extraction of oil from seeds, beans, and nuts, coffee solubles from ground,

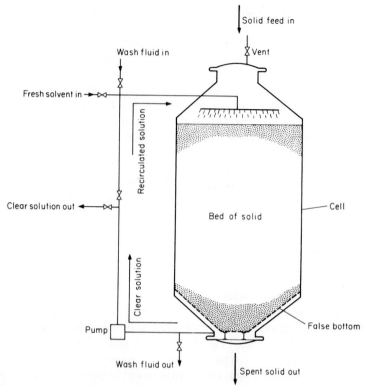

FIG. 8.10. Single-stage, enclosed extraction cell.

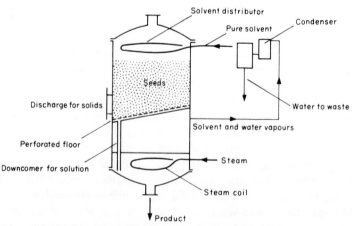

FIG. 8.11. Single-stage extractor with solvent recycle. (Reproduced from *Chemical Engineering*[2] by courtesy of Pergamon Press.)

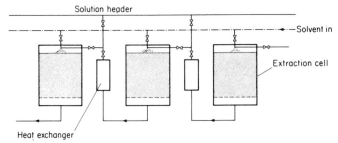

FIG. 8.12. Multistage, countercurrent, static-bed extraction system.

roasted beans and tea from dried leaves. Unless a solvent recovery system is included the bulked overflow from such operations will be relatively dilute, necessitating expensive solute recovery procedures.

8.1.5.2. Multistage static-bed systems

In order to carry out countercurrent extraction a number of cells may be arranged in series as shown in Fig. 8.12. Each cell in the circuit contains a charge of solid and the solution from the adjacent cell is introduced into the top of the cell, percolates through the bed of solid, leaves via an outlet beneath the false bottom and passes on to the next cell in the series. Heaters may be interposed between cells as required. Two header pipes are usually used, one to carry solution when a cell is being bypassed, the other to carry solvent or wash liquid. The solid is not physically moved from one cell to the next, countercurrent to the direction of flow of the solution. However, a countercurrent effect is obtained as follows: at any particular time one or more of the cells is isolated from the circuit. In Fig. 8.13 three cells are

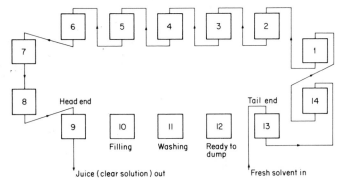

FIG. 8.13. Multistage, countercurrent extraction battery showing flow of solution at one particular point in time.

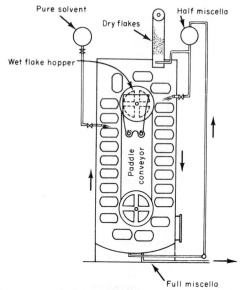

FIG. 8.14.   Bollmann extractor (being used for oil extraction; miscella is solution of oil in solvent). (Reproduced from *Unit Operations of Chemical Engineering*[6] by courtesy of McGraw-Hill.)

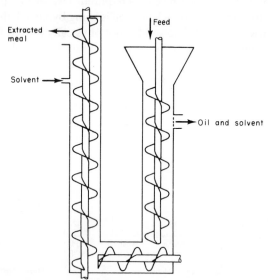

FIG. 8.15.   Hildebrandt extractor. (Reproduced from *Unit Operations of Chemical Engineering*[6] by courtesy of McGraw-Hill.)

shown to be thus isolated. At the time depicted in this diagram, cells numbered 10, 11 and 12 are being filled, washed and emptied respectively. The fresh solvent is being introduced into cell 13 and clear solution removed from cell 9. When the solid in cell 13 is fully extracted, this cell will be isolated from the circuit and cell 10 introduced in its place. The fresh solvent will then enter into cell 14 and clear solution leave from cell 10. By proceeding in this way, isolating cells in turn around the circuit, the benefits of countercurrent extraction may be obtained.

The number of cells in a countercurrent system can vary from 3 to 14 and the capacity of individual cells may be as high as 10 tons of solid. Such systems are used for the extraction of coffee, tea, oil and sugar from beet.

8.1.5.3. Continuous, moving-bed extractors

Very many designs of moving-bed extractors are available. Most operate on a counter-current principle, but some employ a combination of concurrent and countercurrent flow of solid and solution. The following are some examples of moving-bed extractors used for food applications.

Bollmann (*Hansa-Mühle*) *extractor* (Fig. 8.14). This is basically a bucket elevator, contained within a vapour-tight vessel. The buckets are perforated to permit throughflow of solution. Each bucket has a capacity of up to 40 kg of solid and takes about 1 h to complete a cycle. Fresh solvent is introduced near the top of the left hand leg of the unit as shown in Fig. 8.14. The solvent flows down through the buckets, countercurrent to the direction of movement of the solid, and into a sump at the base. This solution is pumped to the top of the right hand leg and flows concurrently through the downward moving solid. The final concentrated solution collects in another sump at the base from where it is pumped to filters and on to the next stage of the process. The fresh solid is fed from a charge hopper into the buckets at the top of the right hand leg. As each bucket reaches the top of the left hand leg, having completed a cycle, it is inverted and the spent solid is discharged into a hopper from which it is removed by a conveyor. Such extractors are mainly used for the extraction of oil from bean flakes and seeds.

Hildebrandt extractor (*or diffuser*) (Fig. 8.15). This extractor consists of two vertical, cylindrical towers, connected at the bottom by a short, horizontal cylinder. Each cylinder contains a screw conveyor, with perforated blades. These conveyors move the solid from the top of the short tower down to its base, across to the base of the second, taller tower and up to the discharge port at the top of this tower. Fresh solvent is introduced

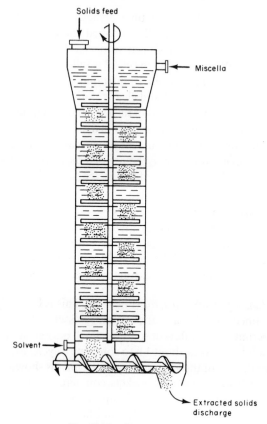

Solids feed

Miscella

Solvent

Extracted solids
discharge

FIG. 8.16. Bonotto extractor.

near the top of the taller tower, below the level of the spent solid discharge port. The solvent flows, under gravity, countercurrent to the direction of movement of the solid. It passes through screens and out via a port near the top of the short tower, below the inlet for fresh solid. The screw turn at about 1 rpm and the capacities of such units may be as high as 40 tonnes h^{-1}. They are used for the extraction of oil from bean flakes and sugar from beet.

Bonotto extractor (Fig. 8.16). This unit consists of a single, vertical tower, divided into sections by horizontal plates. Each plate has an opening through which the solid can pass downwards and these openings are positioned 180° from each other on successive plates. The solid is fed onto

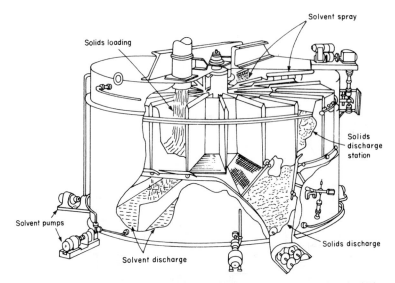

FIG. 8.17.   Rotocel extractor. (By courtesy of Dravo Corporation, Chemical Plants Division.)

the top plate. A rotating wiper blade moves the solid to the opening in this top plate through which it falls onto the plate below. Each plate is fitted with a wiper blade and the solid follows a spiral path down through the tower, and is discharged at the base. Fresh solvent enters at the base and is pumped upwards, countercurrent to the direction of flow of solid, to a discharge port at the top of the tower. This unit is mainly used for oil extraction from nuts and seeds.

Rotocel extractor (Fig. 8.17). In this extractor a cylindrical tank, divided into a number of sector-shaped cells, rotates slowly over a compartmented, stationary tank, covered with a wire mesh screen or perforated disc. Solid is fed into each cell as it passes beneath a conveyor feeder. After completing a cycle, spent solid is discharged through an opening in the perforated floor and removed by a screw conveyor. Fresh solvent is sprayed onto the solid just before it is discharged. The solvent percolates through the solid in the cell and into one of the compartments in the stationary tank beneath. From there it is pumped up and sprayed onto the solid in the preceding cell in the sequence. This occurs in each cell and so a countercurrent effect is obtained. Rich solution is removed from the compartment beneath the cell which has just been charged with fresh solid. Such units have been applied to sugar beet and oil extraction.

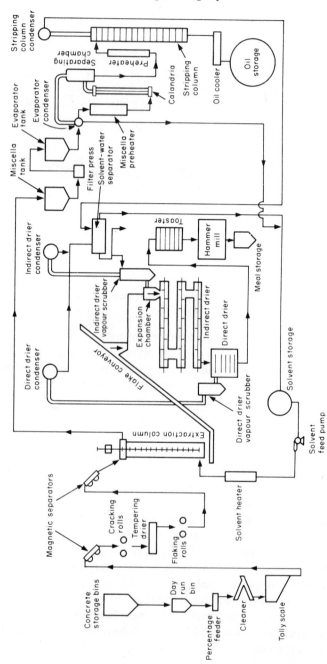

FIG. 8.18. Flow diagram for solvent extraction of soybeans. (Reproduced from *Unit Operations*[3] by courtesy of John Wiley and Sons.)

Many other designs of extractor are available, some for specialised applications such as coffee or sugar beet. Solid–liquid centrifugal separators (see Section 7.2.2) are also used for countercurrent extraction or washing, for example in the preparation of yeast extract and the recovery of protein isolates.[1–3,5,6]

8.1.5.4. Complete extraction plants

The units described in the preceding section are where the actual mass transfer of solute from solid to solvent occurs. However, in a complete extraction process many other operations may need to be carried out to obtain products of the desired character and quality. The solid feed material usually has to be prepared for the extraction operation. This may involve cleaning, trimming, peeling, size reduction and heat treatment. The spent solid from the extractor may have to be stripped of solvent, dried and milled or otherwise modified for its end use. The rich solution from the extractor has to be separated into solvent and solute. This usually involves filtration, concentration and separation, by settling, centrifugation or crystallisation. The solute may need to be further treated for its end use. If the solvent is to be recycled it may need to be further purified by steam stripping, filtration and separation. An example of a complete extraction plant is shown in Fig. 8.18.

8.1.6. APPLICATIONS FOR SOLID–LIQUID EXTRACTION IN THE FOOD INDUSTRY

8.1.6.1. Extraction of sugar from sugar beet

Sugar is extracted from sliced beets using water as the solvent. Multistage, countercurrent, static-bed systems, such as that shown in Fig. 8.12, are commonly used. Some moving-bed extractors also find application in this field, particularly those shown in Figs. 8.15 and 8.16. The beet is sliced to provide an increased surface area for extraction while at the same time limiting the amount of cell damage. Excessive cell damage can result in undesirable non-sugar compounds being released into the solution. Temperature control is important. Too high a temperature can lead to peptisation of the beet cells and contamination of the solution with non-sugar compounds. Temperatures range from 55°C in the early stages of extraction to 85°C in the later stages. The final solution, produced by extraction, usually contains about 15% dissolved solids. This is purified by settling and filtration and concentrated by vacuum evaporation. Crystallisation of the sugar from the concentrated solution is brought about as indicated in Section 9.5.2. The crystals are separated from the syrup by centrifugation and air dried.[6,7]

8.1.6.2. Extraction of edible oil

Solvent extraction is often used as an alternative to or in combination with expression for the recovery of oil from beans, nuts and seeds. It usually results in more complete recovery of oil, as compared with that attainable by expression, with less than 1% of oil remaining in the spent solid. Extraction is also used to a limited extent for the recovery of oil from fish products, such as livers, and meat byproducts, such as crackling. The solvents used in oil extraction are usually light petroleum fractions of the hexane (BP 63·5–69°C) or heptane (BP 90–99°C) type. Cyclic hydrocarbons such as cyclohexane (BP 71–85°C) are also used. Such solvents are highly flammable and great care is necessary in their use. Non-flammable solvents such as trichloroethylene (BP 86·5°C) have also been used but they are toxic and so also difficult to handle and with certain products the spent cake is itself toxic to cattle. Carbon disulphide has been used for olive oil extraction and acetone and ethyl ether for fish livers. Recently considerable interest has been expressed in the use of isopropyl alcohol and ethyl alcohol as solvents. Batch extractors are only used for relatively small scale, or specialised operations. Most oil extraction plants include some type of moving-bed extractor. All the types described in Section 8.1.5.3 find application in this field. Pretreatment of the feed, such as size reduction and heating, can greatly influence yield and quality of the product. Quite a complex series of operations are necessary to recover the solvent from the solution and the spent solid as exemplified by the flow sheet for soybeans in Fig. 8.18. Soybeans, peanuts, cottonseed and flaxseed are among the materials from which oil is extracted by solvent extraction.[8]

8.1.6.3. Manufacture of instant coffee

A typical flow diagram for the manufacture of instant coffee is shown in Fig. 8.19. Extraction is an important stage in such a process. The ground, roasted beans are extracted with hot water to produce a solution containing about 25–30% solids. Extraction is usually carried out in a countercurrent, multistage, static-bed system, consisting of from 5 to 8 units. At any one point in time one cell is isolated from the circuit while the spent solid is discharged and fresh ground introduced. Tall cylindrical pressure vessels are used with heat exchangers interposed between cells. When first introduced into the battery, the grounds are extracted with water at a temperature less than 100°C. As extraction proceeds the solution

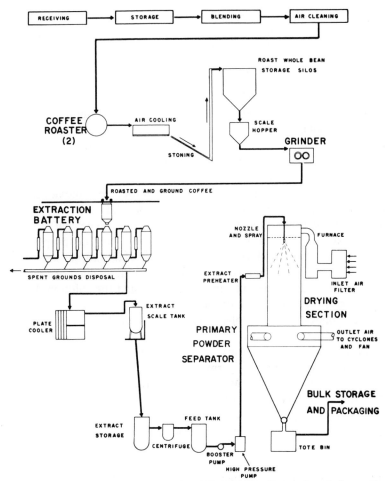

Fig. 8.19. Flow diagram of instant coffee plant. (Reproduced from *Food Dehydration*[9] by courtesy of AVI.)

temperature is raised up to a maximum of about 180°C. In the latter stage of extraction some hydrolysis of insoluble carbohydrate material occurs resulting in an increase in soluble solids. The rate and degree of extraction are influenced by many factors. An increase in temperature can result in increased yield of solubles but too high a temperature may impart an undesirable flavour to the product due to excess hydrolysis. A small particle size favours a high rate of extraction, but if the grind is too fine movement of solution in the towers is impaired and excess oil may be released into the solution. Cycle times, usually in the range $\frac{1}{2}$–1 h, and the ratio water:coffee grounds, usually in the range 7:2–5:1, also influence extraction. Some specially designed, continuous extractors are also used for the extraction of coffee grounds.[9-12]

8.1.6.4. Manufacture of instant tea

Extraction of dried, blended leaves with hot water is an essential stage in the manufacture of instant tea. Extraction may be accomplished in a 3–5 stage, static-bed system. Temperatures usually range from 70°C in the initial stages of extraction to 90°C in the final stages. To improve the rate of flow of solution through the cells they may be evacuated after filling with leaves and the pressure restored to atmospheric level with carbon dioxide gas. The final solution usually contains from 2·5 to 5% solids. Some continuous, countercurrent towers and moving-bed extractors, somewhat similar in principle to the Rotocel (Fig. 8.17), are also used for this purpose. The solution of soluble tea solids is then stripped of volatile aroma constituents and concentrated by vacuum evaporation, to a solids content of from 25 to 50%. The aroma constituents are added back and the solution dried by spray, vacuum-belt or freeze drying.[9,10]

Other applications for solvent extraction include: the extraction of essential oils from flowers; the separation of cell fragments from hydrolysed yeast; the recovery of grape sugar from pomace and the extraction of oil from wheat germ, rice bran, coconut and other sources. Countercurrent extraction, using a single screw extractor and operated intermittently, has been used to produce juices from fruits and vegetables. Higher yields of good quality juice were obtained as compared with traditional methods based on expression.[13]

8.1.6.5. Extraction with supercritical carbon dioxide

A relatively recent development in solid–liquid extraction is the use of carbon dioxide, usually in the form of a supercritical fluid, as a solvent. Supercritical carbon dioxide has the characteristics of both a gas and a liquid. It has the density of a liquid and acts as a liquid solvent, but it diffuses easily like a gas. The advantages of this solvent include: it is highly volatile and so can be separated easily and completely from the solute, it has a low viscosity; a high diffusivity; is non-toxic, non-inflammable and cheap. The main disadvantage is the requirement for high pressure extraction vessels leading to high capital and running costs. In Fig. 8.20 a pressure–temperature diagram for carbon dioxide is presented. Shown are the boiling line, melting line and sublimation line which separate the areas of

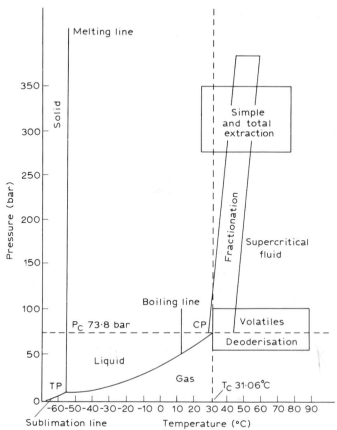

FIG. 8.20. Pressure–temperature diagram for carbon dioxide. TP, triple point; CP, critical point; P_c, critical pressure; T_c, critical temperature.

liquid, gaseous and solid carbon dioxide. Subcritical liquid carbon dioxide is found in the triangle formed by the boiling line, melting line and line of critical pressure, i.e. from $-55°C$ to $+31°C$ and from 5–74 bar $(0.5–7.4\,MN\,m^{-2})$. The supercritical region is above the line of critical pressure and to the right of the line of critical temperature. Both subcritical and supercritical carbon dioxide are non-polar solvents. The solvent power of supercritical carbon dioxide increases with increase in temperature and pressure. In so-called *simple extraction*, where a single component is to be extracted from an insoluble matrix, the carbon dioxide should be used at its highest solvent power, i.e. at the highest temperature and pressure possible for each application. The upper limit of temperature is determined by the heat sensitivity of the material being extracted while the pressure limit will be determined by the capital and running costs of the equipment. High solvent power is also beneficial when all soluble matter is to be extracted, so-called *total extraction*. For deodorisation or extraction of highly soluble compounds, supercritical carbon dioxide with low solvent power is used, i.e. in a state close to the critical point (Fig. 8.20). When fractionation of the extract according to solubility is desired, then a stepwise increase in solvent power is applied. This is best started in the gaseous state near the critical point and pressure and temperature raised according to the solubility of the least soluble compounds to be extracted.[14-16]

Two industrial applications for supercritical carbon dioxide are decaffeination of coffee and preparation of concentrated extracts from hops. In the first of these applications, supercritical carbon dioxide is used as an alternative to water or methylene chloride for the solvent extraction of caffein from green coffee beans. Moist beans are loaded into the extractor vessel and supercritical carbon dioxide is circulated through the system, extracting the caffein. The carbon dioxide then passes to a scrubbing vessel where the caffein is washed out with water. As an alternative to wet scrubbing, the caffein laden carbon dioxide may be passed through a bed of activated charcoal to remove the caffein. In another variation on this last process, charcoal pellets may be placed in the extractor with the beans. The pellets are later separated from the beans by screening. The product is of good quality due to the selectivity of carbon dioxide for caffein and its stability, which prevents it reacting with the coffee constituents.[12,16]

A good quality hop extract should contain the volatile oil in good condition, the soft resins (particularly the α-acids) and little else. Supercritical carbon dioxide produces such good quality extract. A multistage, countercurrent, static-bed system may be used for this application (Fig. 8.21). This is comprised of four extractor vessels made to high specification. One of these vessels is out of the cycle at any one time. Supercritical carbon dioxide percolates up through the hop pellets in each vessel in turn. The solution of extract in carbon dioxide (miscella) enters the shell side of a condensor/evaporator where the carbon dioxide evaporates, precipitating out the extract, which is automatically discharged from the unit. The carbon dioxide from the condensor/evaporator is recompressed, cooled and enters the tube side of the condensor/evaporator. As it condenses, the heat released evaporates carbon dioxide from the miscella in the shell side. The condensed carbon dioxide flows to the carbon dioxide tank from where it is fed via a chiller back to the extraction battery. A transfer tank from which either liquid or gaseous carbon dioxide can be fed

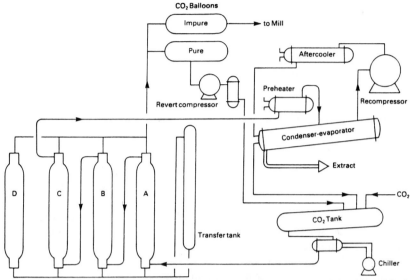

FIG. 8.21. Flow diagram of plant for the extraction of hops with supercritical carbon dioxide (adapted from Moyler[20]).

to any extractor and two balloons for the temporary storage of pure and impure carbon dioxide gas complete the system.[16-18]

Other potential applications for supercritical fluid extraction which have been investigated include: decaffeination of tea; extraction of flavour compounds from fruits and spices; concentration of flavour compounds in citrus oils; extraction of oil from nuts and seeds; fractionation of oils and fatty acid esters.[16,19-21]

8.2. EXPRESSION

8.2.1. INTRODUCTION

Many materials—fruits, vegetables and seeds contain valuable liquid constituents within the cell structure composing them. Groundnuts, coconuts, soya beans, sunflower seeds and olives, for example, yield edible oils and fats, while juices from a variety of fruits are used in the manufacture of various soft drinks and wines. The cell walls normally require disruption before this liquid constituent can be separated and some form of pre-treatment such as pulping or heating is often required.

Though interest has centred on the liquid being extracted, in some cases the residues have found use as animal feed. In traditional oilseed processing priority has been given to the production of oil rather than to the oilseed residue. Interest in protein utilisation has highlighted the possibility of the oilseed wastes as alternative sources of protein for human food sources. To avoid protein denaturation during processing it may be necessary to modify the traditional extraction methods. Traditionally, separation is accomplished by either solvent extraction—as in the recovery of fats from animal and vegetable materials[8]—or by mechanical expression. Expression, the unit operation considered here, is the separation of liquids from solids by the application of compressive forces and is often used in the food and beverage industries.

To maximise the extraction of product, expression may be preceded by comminution. In this two-stage process, the feed is first reduced to a pulp and the liquid subsequently separated from the pomace by expression. In the alternative, single-stage process, cell rupture and expression of product take place without the separate size reduction stage. The two-stage process maximises the yield of expressed liquor but product quality may be poorer due to increased passage of finely divided solids. In addition, with some fruit juice extractions, the more juice extracted the poorer the quality of the resulting liquor due to the passage of both increased amounts of solid and also undesirable organic compounds extracted from ruptured skins, seeds, etc. With grape-juice in wine production, for example, these components impart astringency, bitterness and browning to finished wines. Repeated pressings to maximise liquor production in the single-stage process similarly yield poorer quality finished products. Giving higher throughputs with lower capital and operating costs, single-stage expression is said to be more economical than two-stage operation.[22]

The efficiency of an expression process depends on several factors including:

(i) The yield stress of the solid phase (i.e. its resistance to deformation).
(ii) The porosity of the cake formed.
(iii) The viscosity of the liquid expressed.
(iv) The compressive force applied.

Other complex compressibility, permeability and water binding characteristics play a part in the dewatering. Some of these properties are partly response-related and are influenced by the way the expression is carried out.[23]

The rate of flow of liquid through the interstices of the cake or pomace can be influenced by the type of pulp and its previous history. The rate of expression of fruit pulp, apple for example, may vary with the particular variety of a fruit.[24] Climatic and soil conditions during growth, maturity at picking and any metabolic changes occurring during the interval between harvesting and processing the fruit may also play a part.

For a fuller discussion of the factors affecting expression and the development and use of mathematical models incorporating these factors to predict expression parameters for use in the design of equipment, see Orr[25] and Schwartzberg.[23]

8.2.2. EXPRESSION EQUIPMENT
A number of methods are available for expressing the liquid from a solid–liquid matrix. Some methods are essentially batch operations while others are suitable for continuous operation.

The methods include:

8.2.2.1. Hydraulic pressing
Three types of hydraulic press are in common use:

(*a*) *Plate press.* The pulp to be expressed is placed in heavy cotton filter bags, or cloths, which are placed between grooved pressure plates arranged

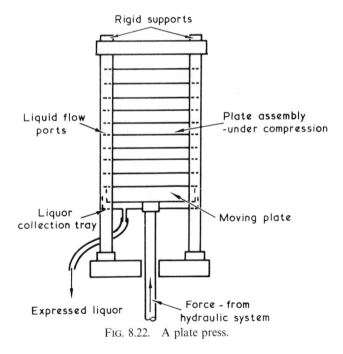

FIG. 8.22.   A plate press.

in a vertical stack. Hydraulic pressure is applied across the ends of the stack, pressures of 31–62 MN m^{-2} (2–4 tons in^{-2}) being developed. The pulp, in the form of relatively thin layers, experiences a compressive force. Keeping the layers thin permits reasonably rapid draining of liquor through the cake interstices and across the grooved plate faces to a common receiver (Fig. 8.22).

Filling, pressing, opening and cleaning of these batch units requires a high labour usage. In an attempt to achieve maximum extraction more economically, presses capable of exerting increasing pressures in several stages have been developed. In these units the assembly of plates moves beneath a series of pressure heads each exerting a higher pressure than the preceding head. The pressure should be increased gradually, since rapid changes can lead to sharp decreases in bed voidage with a consequent drop in drainage rate.

(*b*) *Cage press*. For this type of press, a finely perforated cylinder carries an internal pressure plate (platen) which can be moved backwards and forwards within the cylinder, hydraulically (Fig. 8.23). The design of the

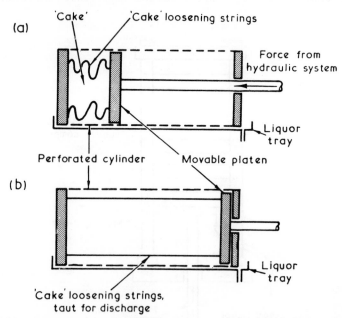

FIG. 8.23.   A cake press. (a) Cake under compression. (b) With hydraulic pressure released for cake discharge.

system allows close control over the pressure exerted on a pulp charge inside the cylinder. Liquid expressed from the cake on compressing passes through the perforations. Plastic strings connected between the pressure plate and the closed end of the cylinder act as drainage channels during compression, thus assisting the rate of expression. Older presses may have chains or ropes fitted in place of plastic strands. With some cage presses, the pressure plate is withdrawn after an initial compression. The strings, on tightening, loosen the cake. Combining this action with rotation of the cylinder breaks down the cake, which can then be recompressed. Several pressings are normally performed on a given charge.

(c) *Elastic membrane press.* In this type of press, also known as a *tank press*, an elastic membrane fixed longitudinally across the diameter of a closed, cylindrical tank divides the inside volume, when empty, into two, roughly equal, volumes. The solid–liquid mixture to be expressed is fed into the vessel shell on one side of the membrane via side openings—the pressing zone. As filling proceeds the membrane distends, allowing the pressing zone to virtually fill the whole of the shell. Air, admitted under pressure, on the other side of the membrane, is then used to pneumatically pressurise and compress the mixture. Expressed juice finds its way to outlet ports in an inner wall of the pressing zone, then flows along juice channels before leaving the press for pump transfer to appropriate storage vessels. After expression, the pomace is loosened by rotating the vessel, this same action initiating discharge of expressed solids and their removal from the vessel. The automatically controlled cycle takes 1·5 h, and, because of the low but continuously applied pressure over the extended membrane, produces maximum yields of high quality juices with minimal solids content.[26]

8.2.2.2. Continuous presses

To reduce the high labour requirements associated with hydraulic expression, continuous presses have been developed.

(a) *Roller press.* In this type of unit, a compressive force is applied by passing the pulp between heavy rollers. Modifications of this method have been developed to improve the separation of liquid from solid. For instance simple crushing rolls of the type used for expressing juice from sugar cane have directional drainage grooves (Menchaerts grooves) on the roller surfaces. These grooves direct the liquors away from the compressed cake thus reducing re-wetting.[27]

Pulp is fed between the rollers as shown in Fig. 8.24. Liquid is expressed

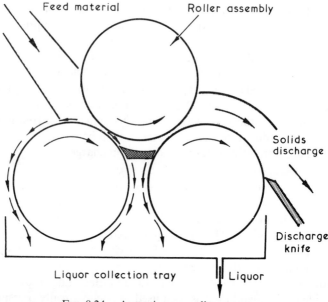

FIG. 8.24.   A continuous roller press.

from the pulp and flows to a collection launder. Solid passes to the third delivery roller where it is removed by a 'doctor' knife. In other types of roller presses, drums similar in design to those used in drum filtration are used. The face of the drum is perforated and covered by a filter cloth. Dewatering rollers bear against the face of the drum. Pressing takes place between the drum and the rollers. Liquid is drawn through the filter cloth and into the perforated drum the interior of which may be maintained under reduced pressure to aid flow. The cake is removed by 'doctor knife' or 'string discharge'.

   (*b*) *Screw press.* In this unit, known in the oil milling industry as an 'expeller',[8] fruit pulps or oilseed meals are fed to a thick-walled cylinder containing a rotating polished screw having a gradually decreasing pitch. Material trapped between the screw and the inside of the cylinder barrel passes through a gradually reducing flow area, experiencing an increasing compressive force. The walls of the cylinder contain fine perforations or slots covered by adjustable screens, through which expressed liquor drains from the cake. The expressed cake leaves the unit through an adjustable discharge port (Fig. 8.25). Power consumption in these units is high. Power is dissipated in friction and may raise the product temperature appreciably.

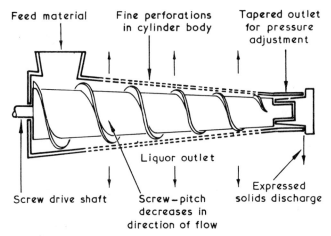

Feed material   Fine perforations   Tapered outlet
in cylinder body   for pressure
adjustment

Liquor outlet

Screw drive shaft   Screw-pitch   Expressed
decreases in   solids discharge
direction of flow

FIG. 8.25. A continuous screw press.

The risk of thermal degradation to heat sensitive materials can be reduced by the use of hollow water-cooled screws. The degree of compression achieved can be varied by adjusting the area of the discharge port and by varying the speed of rotation of the worm. Shaft speeds fall in the range 5–500 rpm, depending on application, and barrel pressures of 138–276 MN m^{-2} (20 000–40 000 psi) are achieved. Good separations at throughputs of up to 8500 kg h^{-1} (200 tons 24 h^{-1}) are reported with the residual cake containing 4–5% of liquid. With certain fruits, passage of fine particles with the liquid can present problems. In such cases, subsequent clarification by centrifugation or filtration may be required.

(*c*) *Belt press.* This type of continuous press is very similar to the belt filter which has been finding increasing use in compression filtration in recent years. In 'twin-belt' units, two separate, horizontal continuous belts (press belt and filter belt) are rigged so as to form a narrow gap between them as they run parallel to each other and in the same direction.[25] The press belt is superimposed above the filter belt and drive, and return drums at each end of the system control the direction and speed of the two belts. Rollers situated under the permeable filter belt support it over the filtering length of the unit, while press rollers similarly hold the upper, impervious, press belt at the desired separation distance. The wet solids are fed onto the filter belt and pass into the narrow gap between the two belts. The compression generated expresses the liquid which passes through the filter belt to a collection trough. Dewatered solids can be removed by a 'doctor knife' at the outlet end of the press. In single-belt presses, hollow return and/or drive drums with perforated faces can be used to separate the liquid expressed as the solid–liquid matrix fed onto the inside of the belt is pressed between the belt and the drum.

8.2.3. APPLICATIONS

Hydraulic presses are widely used for batch operations in fruit juice processing. Screw presses also find use in this field but are often used as 'finishers' following a prior pulping and thickening process. In modern fruit-juice technology, enzymes are used in the preparation of the fruit mash to ensure that it is suitable for pressing. The use of specific enzymes to provide the correct degree of pectin degradation is necessary to prevent both increase in viscosity due to the presence of soluble pectins and the retention of juice by insoluble protopectins.[28] Both hydraulic and expeller-type screw presses are used in the extraction of oils during oil milling, the oil being expressed from clean, oil bearing seeds after cooking and conditioning in steam cookers.[8] Roller presses are widely used in expressing juices from sugar cane.[27] Continuous screw presses are used in wine making. They achieve high yields of liquid and are easily cleaned, but solids and phenolic component levels in the extracts are very high.[26] Belt presses give juices comparatively low in suspended solids but are not very easy to maintain and clean. They are also extremely costly.[26] Tank presses, though expensive, are finding growing use in wine making. They are said to be capable of extracting high-quality juices while giving maximum yields with minimal solids.[26]

Schwartzberg,[23] discusses the uses of expression and gives a comprehensive list of materials frequently subjected to expression.

REFERENCES

1. Foust, A. S., Wenzel, L. A., Clump, C. W., Maus, L. and Bryce Anderson, L., *Principles of Unit Operations*, 2nd edn. John Wiley, New York, 1980.
2. Coulson, J. M., Richardson, J. F. with Backhurst, J. R. and Harker, J. H., *Chemical Engineering. Vol. 2,* 3rd edn. Pergamon Press, Oxford, England, 1978.
3. Brown, G. G. (ed.), *Unit Operations.* John Wiley, New York, 1955.
4. Charm, S. E., *Fundamentals of Food Engineering*, 2nd edn. AVI, Westport, Conn., USA, 1971.
5. Green, D. W. (ed.), *Perry's Chemical Engineer's Handbook*, 6th edn. McGraw-Hill, New York, 1984.
6. McCabe, W. K., Smith, J. C. and Harriott, P., *Unit Operations of Chemical Engineering*, 4th edn. McGraw-Hill, New York, 1985.

7. McGinnis, R. A. (ed.), *Beet-Sugar Technology*, 2nd edn. Beet Sugar Development Foundation, 1971.

8. Swern, D. (ed.), *Bailey's Industrial Oil and Fat Products*, 4th edn. John Wiley, New York, 1982.

9. Van Arsdel, W. B., Copley, M. J. and Morgan, A. I., Jr (ed.), *Food Dehydration*. Vol II, 2nd edn. AVI, Westport, Conn., USA, 1973.

10. Masters, K., *Spray Drying Handbook*, 4th edn. George Godwin, 1985.

11. Sivetz, M. and Desrosier, N. W., *Coffee Technology*. AVI, Westport, Conn., USA, 1979.

12. Clarke, R. J. and Macrae, R. (ed.), *Coffee. Vol. 2.* Elsevier Applied Science Publishers, London, 1987.

13. McPherson, A., It was squeeze or g, now it's CCE. *Food Technol. Aust.*, **39**(2) (1987) 56–60.

14. Brogle, H., CO_2 as a solvent: its properties and applications. *Chem. Ind.*, **12** (1982) 385–90.

15. Bott, T. R., Fundamentals of carbon dioxide in solvent extraction. *Chem. Ind.*, **12** (1982) 394–6.

16. Rizvi, S. S. H., Daniels, J. A., Benado, A. L. and Zollweg, J. A., Supercritical fluid extraction: operating principles and food applications. *Food Technol.*, **40**(7) (1986) 56–64.

17. Volbrecht, R., Extraction of hops with supercritical CO_2. *Chem. Ind.*, **12** (1982) 397–9.

18. Gardner, D. S., Industrial scale hop extraction with liquid CO_2. *Chem. Ind.*, **12** (1982) 402–5.

19. Calame, J. P. and Steiner, R., CO_2 extraction in the flavour and perfumery industries. *Chem. Ind.*, **12** (1982) 399–402.

20. Moyler, D. A., Liquid CO_2 extraction in the flavour and fragrance industries. *Chem. Ind.*, **18** (1988) 660–2.

21. Temelli, F., Chen, C. S. and Braddock, R. J., Supercritical fluid extraction in citrus oil processing. *Food Technol.*, **46**(6) (1988) 145–50.

22. Fellows, P., *Food Processing Technology: Principles and Practice.* Ellis Horwood, Chichester, England, 1988.

23. Schwartzberg, H. G., Expression-related properties. In *Physical Properties of Foods*, ed. M. Peleg and E. B. Bagley. AVI, Westport, Conn., USA, 1983.

24. Rebouillat, S. and Scwartzberg, H. G., Dynamic and static filtration resistance during mechanical expression. In *Food Engineering and Process Applications. Vol. 2. Unit Operations*, ed. M. Le Mageur and P. Jelen. Elsevier Applied Science Publishers, London, 1986.

25. Orr, C. (ed.), *Filtration: Principles and Practice. Part I.* Marcel Dekker, New York, 1977.

26. Vine, R. P., The use of new technology in commercial wine making. In *Food Technology International Europe 1987*, ed. A. Turner. Sterling, London, 1987.

27. Hugot, E., *Handbook of Cane Sugar Engineering*, 2nd edn. Elsevier, Amsterdam, 1972.

28. Veal, K., Key stages in fruit-juice technology. In *Food Technology International Europe 1987*, ed. A. Turner. Sterling, London, 1987.

CHAPTER 9

CRYSTALLISATION

9.1. INTRODUCTION

Crystallisation processes are used for two purposes in the food industry. A liquid material may be separated by crystallisation into a solid and liquid phase differing in composition, one or both fractions becoming products of the process. Alternatively no separation of the solid phase is attempted and all the raw material is retained in the product.

If separation is to be effected, it is necessary to obtain the maximum deposition of one component in crystalline form, to remove substantially all the crystals formed from the liquid and to carry out these operations so that the minimum of liquid is removed either through wetting the surface of the crystals or by being trapped within them. In order to separate the crystals from their 'mother liquor' it is desirable to have the crystals of comparable size. Uniformity of crystal size may also be aesthetically desirable. Hence crystallisation procedures involving separation are generally designed to produce individual crystals of a specified size and shape. In crystallisation procedures not involving separation the control of crystal size is also important. For instance the texture of confectionery such as fondant creams and fudges is dependent on the size of the crystals produced during their manufacture, as is also the texture of butter (see Chapter 5).

The process of crystallisation can be initiated either by cooling or by evaporation. To illustrate the differences between these two methods, consider a solution of sucrose in water. From the equilibrium diagram for a sucrose–water system (Fig. 9.1) it can be seen that the quantity of ice or crystalline sucrose that can be recovered in the pure state by cooling a solution is limited. At a temperature fractionally above the 'eutectic

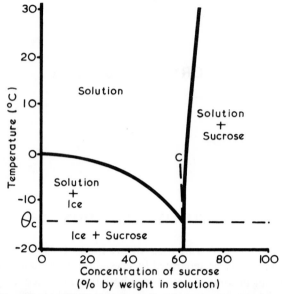

FIG. 9.1.   The equilibrium diagram for the sucrose–water system.

temperature' (θ_c) the system consists of crystals of one component in equilibrium with a solution at the eutectic concentration (C), while at a temperature fractionally below θ_c the equilibrium state is a single solid phase. The saturation line for sucrose, i.e. the line separating the 'solution' and 'solution + sucrose' zones, is very steep over the range shown in the diagram. Therefore a saturated solution of sucrose in water, over this range, has a concentration only very slightly above the eutectic concentration C and the yield of sucrose from cooling such a solution will be correspondingly limited. On the other hand, over 80% of the water in a 20% solution of sucrose in water can be recovered as ice by freezing.

Since only the water is volatile in the sucrose–water system this component may be driven off by heating, so raising the concentration to that level at which crystallisation of sucrose occurs. In this instance the solution could be evaporated to dryness and all the sucrose recovered in crystalline form, an operation which could not be accomplished by cooling the solution.

The sucrose–water system has a particularly simple equilibrium diagram. Even two component systems may have more complex diagrams, e.g. in a case such as NaCl, where an aqueous solution of the material can crystallise both in hydrated and anhydrous forms. Systems having more than two components will exhibit a more complex pattern of behaviour and the desired product may no longer be a single component but a mixture of several. Crystallisation in such systems can still be promoted by cooling and/or evaporation, and crystallisation processes may be classified on the basis of the method used.

In these more complex systems the degree to which separation can be achieved (i.e. the extent to which desirable material may be concentrated in the fluid or removed with the crystals) depends on the composition of the system. In some instances, say in sugar refining and salt production, the solution may be regarded as being composed of a solute, a solvent and certain impurities. The impurities may increase or decrease the solubility of the solute in the solvent. Occasionally impurities have no significant influence and sometimes a mixed crystal is formed. A solubility coefficient (c) can be defined by:

$$c = \frac{\text{solubility of solute in impure solution at given temperature}}{\text{solubility of solute in pure solvent at same temperature}}$$

If the impurities are such that c is greater than unity these are said to 'salt in' the solute and if c is less than unity the solute is said to be 'salted out'. It is interesting to note, in this connection, that the normal impurities found in sugar cane juice are such that $c < 1$ while the reverse is true for beet sugar juice.[1]

9.2. NUCLEATION

If a solution of a solute in a solvent is progressively cooled, or if the solvent is progressively evaporated, crystallisation does not commence immediately the concentration of one component of the solution increases above its saturation value at the temperature of the solution. The immediate effect is to produce a supersaturated solution in which crystal nucleation may, or may not, occur. The degree of supersaturation of a solution is measured in terms of the supersaturation coefficient (S):

$$S = \frac{C}{C_0} \tag{9.1}$$

where C = concentration (w/w) of solute in solvent at a given temperature, C_0 = concentration (w/w) of solute in solvent in a *saturated* solution at the same temperature. Obviously the solution is supersaturated if $S > 1$ and $S = 1$ defines the solubility curve.

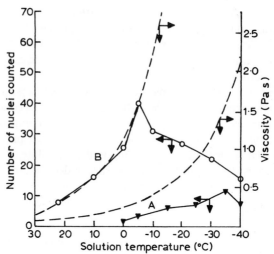

FIG. 9.2. Spontaneous nucleation in supercooled citric acid solutions in relation to the degree of supercooling and the viscosity of the solution. (From Mullin and Leci.[2])

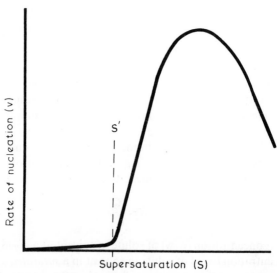

FIG. 9.3. Diagrammatic representation of the relationship between the rate of nucleation in a solution and supersaturation of the solution.

Crystallisation in supersaturated solutions can be initiated by the addition of solute crystals. Crystallisation might then proceed by the deposition of material on the faces of these added crystals alone, without nucleation of new crystals. Alternatively, the presence of the added solute crystals may give rise to the formation of additional crystal nuclei in the solution (secondary nucleation—see below). Alternatively crystals of similar structure to the solute crystals, dust or gas bubbles may also initiate crystallisation, as may the application of mechanical shock or ultrasonic vibrations (heterogeneous nucleation). These are the principal mechanisms of nucleation encountered in industrial crystallisation operations.

In supersaturated solutions free, as far as possible, from any crystalline material or foreign particles, crystallisation can still take place, nuclei being generated from the solution itself (homogeneous nucleation). The rate at which homogeneous nucleation occurs is a function of the supersaturation. Figure 9.2 shows the results of experiments on the rate of nucleation in supersaturated citric acid solutions. Solution A had a concentration equivalent to 4·6 kg of citric acid monohydrate per kg excess water giving a saturation temperature of 62°C. Solution B was more concentrated (7 kg kg^{-1}; saturation temperature 85°C). As may be seen, when the solution was held at progressively lower temperatures (and so the supersaturation increased) the rate of nucleation also increased up to a maximum value, after which a fall was observed. This fall in nucleation rate occurs when the viscosity of either solution is higher than 1·5 Pa s. It has been observed in some other systems, particularly in melts, which generate high viscosity at high supersaturations or supercoolings. Thus the stability of the supersaturated sugar solutions that compose high-boiled confectionery (e.g. barley sugar) is attributed to the very high viscosity of the product. When high-boiled sweets are 'pulled' (i.e. as occurs in the manufacture of peppermint rock) the air bubbles incorporated in the mass act as sites for nucleation.[3]

The nucleation behaviour shown by the experiments mentioned above is shown in generalised diagrammatic form in Fig. 9.3. The nucleation rate (v) is zero at $S = 1$ and increases only very slowly at first as the supersaturation increases. The rate then rises much more rapidly and then finally may fall again.

Although the conditions existing in crystallisation operations in food processing and in the manufacture of food ingredients are such that homogeneous nucleation will not be the dominant process, a simple theory based on homogeneous nucleation will serve to demonstrate important principles that will find application in these processes.

Consider a spherical crystal of radius r. The mass (N) of this crystal, in moles, will be given by

$$N = \frac{4\pi r^3 \rho}{3M} \qquad (9.2)$$

where ρ = density of the crystal and M = molecular weight of the material of the crystal.

The surface area (s) of this crystal will be given by

$$s = 4\pi r^2 \qquad (9.3)$$

If this crystal is growing outward radially in a supersaturated solution, differentiating equations (9.2) and (9.3) gives

$$\frac{dN}{dr} = \frac{4\pi r^2 \rho}{M} \qquad (9.4)$$

and

$$\frac{ds}{dr} = 8\pi r \qquad (9.5)$$

whence

$$\frac{ds}{dN} = \frac{ds}{dr} \cdot \frac{dr}{dN} = \frac{2M}{r\rho} \qquad (9.6)$$

The rate of change of surface area with mass is, therefore, small when a crystal is large and high when it is small.

A crystal will grow or shrink in a solution depending on the balance between the driving force for solution and the driving force for deposition.

Consider a large (effectively infinite) crystal—one for which ds/dN can be taken to be zero. Let the activation energy for solution be E J mol^{-1} of solute transfered at a specified absolute temperature (T). Then, on the basis of an Arrhenius relationship, the driving force for solution will be proportional to

$$\exp\left(-\frac{E}{RT}\right)$$

For a small crystal the situation is different since any loss of mass will be accompanied by appreciable loss of surface area and a corresponding release of surface energy (cf. the surface tension in the interface between a liquid and a gas). Let this surface energy be σ J m^{-2}. Then the energy needing to be supplied will be reduced correspondingly.

The net energy requirement per mole transferred will now be

$$E - \sigma \frac{\mathrm{d}s}{\mathrm{d}N} = E - \frac{2M\sigma}{r\rho}$$

for a spherical crystal.

Therefore, the driving force for solution, in this case, will be proportional to

$$\exp\left(-\frac{E}{RT} + \frac{2M\sigma}{RTr\rho} \right)$$

Thus the driving force for solution will be higher for a small crystal than for a large one.

Now consider two crystals, one large and one small, each in a solution with which it is in equilibrium. The driving force for deposition from each solution onto the respective crystal will be proportional to the concentration of solute in that solution. Let this be C_0 in the case of the large crystal and C in the case of the small crystal.

Then

$$\frac{C}{C_0} = \frac{\exp\left(-\dfrac{E}{RT} + \dfrac{2M\sigma}{RTr\rho} \right)}{\exp\left(-\dfrac{E}{RT} \right)} = \exp\left(\frac{2M\sigma}{RTr\rho} \right) \tag{9.7}$$

Now, if a solution is in equilibrium with crystalline solute it is said to be saturated and its concentration is the solubility of the solute in the solvent. Thus, C is the solubility of a small crystal and C_0 the solubility of a large crystal in the same solvent. It is C_0 which is normally taken to be the solubility of a solute in a solvent. A solution of concentration C would be regarded as supersaturated, with a supersaturation of $S = C/C_0$.

Equation (9.7)—the Ostwald–Freundlich equation—leads to two conclusions. Firstly, small crystals are more soluble than large crystals and, if crystals of mixed size are present to excess in a solution, the material of the small crystals would tend to re-enter the solution and deposition would take place on the larger, less soluble crystals, for which the solution would be supersaturated. This process is accelerated if there are continuing fluctuations in the temperature of the system, which has clear implications for the storage of crystal-containing materials such as ice cream or other frozen foods.

Secondly, equation (9.7) leads to an explanation of nucleation behaviour.

Combining equations (9.1) and (9.7), the radius (r^1) of the smallest spherical crystal stable in a solution of supersaturation S is given by:

$$r^1 = \frac{2\sigma M}{\rho RT \ln(S)} \tag{9.8}$$

Thus if crystal formation is to occur spontaneously in a solution, crystal nuclei of radius r^1 or greater must be formed. If the minimum energy to effect this is W, kinetic considerations suggest that the rate of nucleus formation (v) will be given by:

$$v = k \exp\left(-\frac{W}{RT}\right) \tag{9.9}$$

W is made up of two components, the energy (W_s) required to form the surface of the crystal nucleus—which is positive—and the energy required to form the bulk of the nucleus, (W_v). As the substance of the crystal is a more condensed state of matter than the solution from which it was generated, W_v is a negative quantity. W_s is immediately obtainable from the surface area of the nucleus

$$W_s = 4\pi(r^1)^2\sigma \tag{9.10}$$

W_v can be obtained from thermodynamic considerations. What is required is the change of Gibbs Free Energy (F) of the material of the crystal.

Now, by definition,

$$F = H - TS = U + PV - TS \tag{9.11}$$

where H, S, U, P and V have their usual meanings of enthalpy, entropy, internal energy, pressure and volume, respectively. Differentiating equation (9.11),

$$dF = dU + P\,dV + V\,dP - T\,dS - S\,dT \tag{9.12}$$

Now if energy dQ is absorbed by a system, resulting in that system doing work on the surroundings

$$dQ = dU + P\,dV \tag{9.13}$$

and, by the definition of entropy,

$$dQ = T\,dS \tag{9.14}$$

Substituting equation (9.14) in equation (9.13) gives

$$dU = T\,dS - P\,dV \tag{9.15}$$

and substituting equation (9.15) in equation (9.12)

$$dF = V dP - S dT \qquad (9.16)$$

If, as in nucleus formation, the process is at constant temperature then $dT = 0$ so

$$dF = V dP \qquad (9.17)$$

As with liquid droplets, the internal excess pressure within the spherical nucleus will be

$$\frac{2\sigma}{r^1}$$

so, from equation (9.17),

$$W_v = V \Delta P = \frac{4}{3}\pi(r^1)^3 \cdot \frac{2\sigma}{r^1} = \frac{8\pi(r^1)^2\sigma}{3} \qquad (9.18)$$

and, from equations (9.10) and (9.18),

$$W = W_s - W_v = 4\pi(r^1)^2\sigma - \frac{8\pi}{3}(r^1)^2\sigma = \frac{4\pi}{3}(r^1)^2\sigma \qquad (9.19)$$

so, substituting for r^1 from equation (9.8) and W from equation (9.19), equation (9.9) may be re-written

$$v = k \exp\left\{ -\frac{16\pi}{3}\left(\frac{\sigma}{RT}\right)^3\left(\frac{M}{\rho \ln(S)}\right)^2 \right\} \qquad (9.20)$$

While equation 9.20 is based on far too crude a model to give a quantitative explanation of homogeneous nucleation behaviour, it does have a form which relates to Fig. 9.3—showing little nucleation at low supersaturations and then a sudden steep rise in nucleation rate thereafter. The rise in the nucleation rate is so rapid that, in practice, a certain supersaturation (S' in Fig. 9.3) may be defined so that, effectively, no spontaneous nucleation occurs at supersaturations below S'. This supersaturation defines the 'supersolubility curve' (Fig. 9.4). At supersaturations above S' (the 'labile zone') nucleation occurs spontaneously in the solution. At supersaturations between S' and unity (the 'metastable zone') spontaneous nucleation is negligible though crystals of solute added to the solution ('seed material') will grow in size by crystallisation on their surfaces and secondary nucleation (see below) may occur in seeded solutions. In the impure sucrose solutions handled during sugar refining, the value of the critical

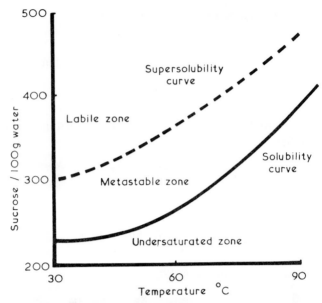

FIG. 9.4. Approximate supersolubility diagram for sucrose.

supersaturation defining the supersolubility curve is found to increase as the purity decreases.[1]

Three basic approaches are possible to nucleation in industrial processes. First, finely divided solute crystals may be added to a solution which is maintained in the metastable zone of supersaturation and these seed crystals grown to finished size without any further nucleation. If it is assumed that each seed crystal supplied grows to a finished crystal of the same shape, the mass of seed material required for a given finished weight of product with a given average crystal size will rise as the cube of the characteristic linear dimension of the seed particles. Clearly, very finely divided seed material is required if its mass is to be kept to reasonable proportions.

Secondly, nuclei may be formed from the solute already in the solution by holding the solution in the labile zone. In industrial crystallisation the feedstock lacks the extreme purity and the process lacks the other conditions necessary for homogeneous nucleation to dominate and so, rather than refining equation (9.20) which assumes such nucleation, empirical relationships are often used of the form

$$v = n(c - c_0)^m \qquad (9.21)$$

where v = the rate of nucleation, c = the concentration of the solute in the nucleating solution, c_0 = the concentration of the solute in a saturated solution and m and n are constants.

The constant m is known as the 'order' of the nucleation process. This is usually higher than 2 and can go up to above 8.[4]

Thirdly, once crystals have been established—whether by seeding or by spontaneous nucleation in the labile zone—further crystal nuclei can be formed by secondary nucleation. This occurs particularly when the solution is agitated and in the upper ranges of supersaturation of the metastable zone.

The supersaturation of the solution has to be sufficiently high that the nuclei formed from the existing crystals do not redissolve in the solution. There are several explanations for this secondary nucleation, some of which may fit the facts better in one situation than in another. For instance, small fragments may be broken from the existing crystals as they collide with each other, with the walls or agitators. Foreign particles which have not heretofore taken part in the process could become activated by contact with a crystal face and then serve as crystal nuclei. Alternatively, partly integrated units, weak outgrowths or weak conglomerates may be stripped off the crystal surfaces or torn apart by the viscous drag of passing fluid. It has been shown that in some systems the existing crystals have to be greater than a certain size to cause secondary nucleation, perhaps because they have to be large enough to induce sufficiently strong eddies for this last process to take place.

The phenomenon of secondary nucleation means that the metastable zone (see Fig. 9.4) can be subdivided with an upper part adjacent to the labile zone and a lower part lying adjacent to the undersaturated zone. In the lower section, the metastable zone proper, there will be neither appreciable primary or secondary nucleation and crystallisation will take place only by deposition on pre-existing crystals. In the upper section (or intermediate zone) there will be no primary nucleation—either heterogeneous or homogeneous—but the presence of pre-existing crystalline material will lead to secondary nucleation. The boundary between these two sub-divisions depends on the conditions in the crystalliser. Agitation, in general, aids secondary nucleation and the more vigorous the agitation the lower the supersaturation at which secondary nucleation occurs and therefore the narrower becomes the true metastable zone.

Crystallisation can either be a batch or continuous operation. The growing of seed crystals to a finished size in the metastable zone is clearly a batch process and would be used where crystals of particular size uniformity are required. Alternatively, a batch of crystal nuclei may be produced either in the labile zone and/or by secondary nucleation and then crystallising conditions changed (either by dilution of the solution by the addition of raw feedstock or by increasing the temperature) so that growth of that batch of nuclei to finished size takes place iń the metastable zone.

A continuous crystallisation process requires a continuous supply of crystal nuclei and so implies operation under conditions of primary and/or secondary nucleation at all times. Some means of size classification of the crystalline material must be incorporated into the process so that crystals of finished size may be removed from the mass of growing crystals. In such a system not all crystals nucleated will grow to finished size. The relatively high solubility of small crystals may result in them being sacrificed to larger, but still growing, crystals nearby.

Since the degree of supersaturation of a solution influences its nucleation behaviour, control of supersaturation is important. This is particularly true in the sugar industry where direct-reading electrical instruments have been developed to measure supersaturation. The measurement of this quantity involves the determination of both the temperature and concentration of the solution. While the former measurement is straightforward, the latter must be approached indirectly. Boiling point elevation, viscosity and electrical conductivity have been used as indications of the concentration of sugar solutions.[5]

9.3. CRYSTAL GROWTH

Subsequent to nucleation or the addition of seed material, crystals will grow in a supersaturated solution, drawing material from the liquid phase. The relationship between rate of deposition ($R \, \mathrm{kg \, m^{-2} \, s^{-1}}$) and solution concentration has been represented empirically by an equation similar to equation (9.21)

$$R = f(c - c_0)^g \qquad (9.22)$$

where f and g are constants. The value of g is generally between 1 and 2.

The rate of growth of a crystal in a solution depends both on the transport of material to the surface of the crystal and on the mechanism of surface deposition. Stirring the solution during crystallisation will reduce the effect of the first factor but, even when there is no mechanical agitation, transport of material to the surface is not necessarily the rate-determining factor. Experimental evidence suggests that the rate of growth of sucrose

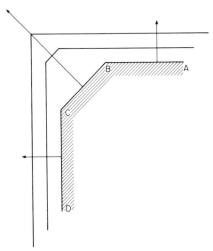

Fig. 9.5. The modification of the shape of a crystal due to the differential growth rates of its surfaces. The diagram shows a section through the corner of a crystal. The initial crystal has a face BC growing at three times the rate of faces AB and CD. These latter faces overlap the former during the growth of the crystal, as shown.

crystals is diffusion controlled only above 40–45°C and sodium chloride crystals above 50°C. The presence of impurities may also affect the rate of crystal growth, generally reducing it, though the reverse effect has been reported.

The external form, or 'habit', of a crystal depends on the conditions of growth. The different faces of a growing crystal do not all advance at the same rate. This can lead to a fast-growing face being overlapped by slower-growing faces on its boundaries and 'growing out'; that is, being absent from the finished crystal (Fig. 9.5). The rate of face advance not only varies between faces, but the dependence of face advance on the degree of supersaturation also varies. Crystals grown rapidly from highly super-saturated solutions tend to develop extreme habits, the crystals growing into long needles or having a dendritic (tree-like) structure.

The reason for this is that crystals of this shape have a high specific surface and so can more easily dissipate the heat released as material in solution deposits on the crystal in a lower energy state. In the case of deposition from the vapour phase, say in the deposition of frost on the evaporator of a mechanical refrigerator, the energy release is higher than from a solution and crystals of extreme habit are very frequently formed.

The presence of 'impurity' compounds in the solution can also affect the shape of the crystals by selectively influencing the growth rates of different crystal faces. Materials that have this effect are known as 'habit modifiers'. A habit modifier may be a naturally occurring impurity or a material deliberately added to produce habit modification. As an example of the first category the effect of raffinose in beet sugar production can be cited. Raffinose occurs naturally in sugar beet and its concentration is increased by prolonged cool storage. In the extracted sugar syrups it has the effect both of slowing the rate of growth of the sucrose crystals and modifying their habit.[6] Up to 0·5% of raffinose in the sucrose has no significant effect. Between 0·5 and 1·0% raffinose gives the sucrose crystals a distinctive cubic appearance. Peculiar flat crystals are produced as the level reaches 2% and above this concentration the presence of the raffinose leads to thin, narrow plates of sucrose, sometimes almost needle-like. These changes affect both the appearance of the product and its bulk density.

Examples of the deliberate addition of habit modifiers are given in Section 9.5, but it should be appreciated that the actual solvent itself may be regarded as a habit modifier. It is, after all, a material foreign to the crystal. Thus crystals of one material, formed from different solvents, can have different habits. This should be borne in mind in solvent fractionation of fats (see Section 9.5.1), where a choice of solvents is possible. An extreme form of habit modification is crystal inhibition, where growth is reduced to negligible proportions on all faces.

Modification of the shape of the growing crystal also occurs when such crystals come together and adhere. This gives rise to 'twinned' crystals, when the original crystals join together at a definite mutual orientation, and to crystal aggregates when the original crystals join in random orientation. When a fraction of the crystals formed in a solution aggregate, the irregular and comparatively large crystals formed influence both the subsequent processing operations and the final product. Furthermore, some of the solution from which they developed can be trapped in the interstices of the aggregated crystals, reducing the purity of the crystalline phase of the system. The formation of aggregates depends on the extent and duration of crystal–crystal contacts during the process of crystallisation. Stirring during crystallisation reduces the tendency to aggregate formation, as does the presence of surface active agents and a high dielectric constant in the crystallising solution.[7]

The tendency of crystals to aggregate, or 'cake', subsequent to the crystallisation process depends, to an extent, on the crystal habit. Near-spherical crystals of uniform size will have few points of contact with one another while crystals of the same shape but with a wide distribution of size will be able to pack more densely giving more contact points at which adhesion may occur. Likewise, needle-shaped crystals can be in line contact and plate-like crystals in face contact with each other, increasing the risk of generating strong mechanical bonds. The process of caking involves the drying out of hydrated films on the surface of the crystal. A saturated solution of sodium chloride in water would be in equilibrium with an atmosphere at 78% relative humidity. Therefore crystals of pure sodium chloride would take up water from the atmosphere and become damp if stored at a higher humidity than this. To remain dry and free-running pure salt crystals would require storage at humidities below 78%. Even small quantities of impurity can affect this situation drastically. Traces of calcium chloride in the sodium chloride, for instance, would lead to caking at much lower humidities since a saturated calcium chloride solution has an equilibrium relative humidity of only 32%. It may not be practicable to avoid products being contaminated with traces of such hygroscopic materials, so other methods of reducing the tendency to cake may be adopted. Fine inert powders dusted on to the crystal surface can be effective. For instance, table salt may be dusted with magnesium carbonate and icing sugar with tricalcium phosphate or cornflour.

9.4. POLYMORPHISM

Some substances can crystallise in a variety of different forms due to differing molecular arrangements within the crystal lattice. These forms can be distinguished by their physical properties, and X-ray diffraction has been widely used in their investigation. This phenomenon, which is quite distinct from the modifications to crystal shape due to differing growth habits, is known as polymorphism. Two types of polymorphism are distinguished, reversible (enantiotropism) in which there is a reversible transition between two forms at a definite transition temperature and irreversible (monotropism).

In the food industry polymorphism is of particular technological importance in fat crystallisation. Many triglycerides can crystallise in a distinct number of crystal structures, each giving a solid of a different melting point. Almost all triglyceride polymorphism is monotropic. In this irreversible type of polymorphism a lower melting point crystal can only transform into a form with a higher melting point. It is easy to supercool fats down to the temperature of fusion of the lowest melting point form (i.e.

the least stable form). Thereupon, crystallisation takes place rapidly in the lowest melting point form of crystal. These crystals can then transform to crystals in the higher melting point forms, the rate of transformation being a function of temperature. If the crystals are melted and the liquid fat recooled, low melting point crystals can again be produced.

9.5. CRYSTALLISATION PROCESSES IN THE FOOD INDUSTRY INVOLVING SEPARATION

9.5.1. FAT FRACTIONATION
Vegetable oils—particularly cottonseed oil and lightly hydrogenated (105 iodine value) soybean oil—are used as proprietary salad oils and in the manufacture of mayonnaise. These oils contain some glycerides with melting points sufficiently high that they deposit solid crystals at the temperature of a cool larder (say 5°C). This would spoil the appearance of a salad oil and impair its pouring properties. It could also break the emulsion in a mayonnaise. The winterisation process[8] removes sufficient of these high melting point glycerides by fractional crystallisation to prevent this turbidity occurring during low temperature storage of the oil. The major difficulty of the process lies in growing the glyceride crystals in such a way that, on removal, they entrain as little as possible of the oil product. Large crystals are found to be the most favourable form for this process, so the cooling is carried out very slowly keeping the degree of supercooling, and hence the rate of crystal nucleation, low. The cooling and crystallisation process is spread over a period of two or three days and once nucleation has occurred, to prevent crystal breakdown, the crystallising oil is not stirred. At the end of the crystallisation process the mixture must be moved to filters in such a way that crystal damage is again minimised. The high melting point fats removed in this way can be utilised for other products, e.g. in the manufacture of margarine. This is an example of the so-called 'dry' fractionation process. Milkfats have also been fractionated in this way. While the flavour of butter or butteroil is appreciated in many foods, the wide melting range of these materials is a problem, particularly for some pastry products where a relatively high melting point fat is desired. Increasing the melting point by chemical treatments—hydrogenation and inter-esterification is possible but can affect the flavour. Controlled cooling of milkfat to 26°C to produce large crystals of the higher melting point triglycerides enables two fractions to be produced, one melting at about

40°C and the other, with a somewhat higher colour and flavour, melting at about 25°C. This last has found application in other, more fluid, food formulations.

In contrast to milkfat, the cocoa butter used in chocolate manufacture has a very small melting range, being hard—almost brittle—at room temperature and melting almost completely at body temperature (*c.* 37°C). The experience of eating chocolate derives from this unique property of cocoa butter among natural fats, which in turn comes from the particular balance of triglycerides in its composition. Cocoa-butter-equivalent fats for use in chocolate-like formulations, or for addition to chocolate where this is permitted, can be produced from other oils and fats by fractionation from a solvent solution. Again, this process is preferred to chemical modification of oils by hydrogenation, since to produce a suitable hardness at ambient temperature would result in a material that would not be sufficiently fluid at body temperature and so would given a waxy mouth-feel. Hexane, 2-nitropropane and acetone can be used as solvents. Acetone is preferred for producing cocoa butter analogues from palm oil since it produces a high melting point crystal which is not only more desirable in its chemical make-up, but is also easier to filter.

9.5.2. FREEZE CONCENTRATION

This process involves the fractional crystallisation of ice from liquid foods. Although this process is traditional (it has long been used to enhance the alcoholic content of cider) it has found only limited and spasmodic use in the food industry. It has been employed, or recommended, for producing citrus juice concentrates to be preserved by freezing, for concentrating alcoholic beverages and adjusting the alcohol content of wines, for concentrating vinegar and for the preliminary concentration of liquid foods prior to freeze drying.

The advantage of this method of concentration is that heat degradation is eliminated and high quality products may be produced. Its disadvantages are threefold. Firstly the degree of concentration achievable is limited (see Section 9.1). Secondly, suspended matter in the feed can serve as heterogeneous nuclei. This can lead to concentrates which are pale in colour and lacking in flavour since pigmented particles and suspended essential oils are removed from the system at the centre of ice crystals. Thirdly, the process has proved more expensive than evaporation. The capital cost of the plant is not the only feature contributing to the economics of the process, since the fraction of the soluble solids of the feed material discharged with the ice crystals or melted water rather than with

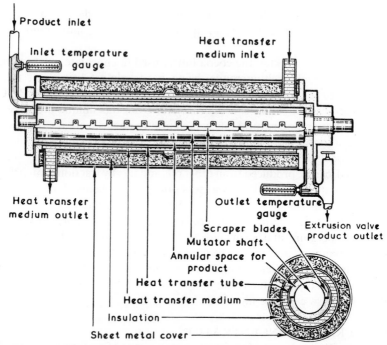

FIG. 9.6.   Cross-sections of the 'Votator' type scraped surface heat exchanger. (By courtesy of A. Johnson & Co.)

the concentrate is highly important. Process improvements over the years have been directed to cost-effective reduction of this loss.[9]

The problem to be solved is the generation of ice crystals substantially free of inclusions of mother liquor and the separation of these from the system clean of any adhering concentrate. One process attempts this operation by first passing the solution to be concentrated through a scraped surface cooler (Fig. 9.6) to produce a slurry of crystal nuclei. In this unit the fluid to be cooled flows through the annular space between the cylindrical cooling surface and the axial rotor (or 'mutator') revolving within it. Blades mounted on the rotor bear against the cooling surface and continuously scrape the cooled product from it. The slurry from this unit is then fed into a crystalliser vessel, where it rises through a fluidised crystal bed. Here the nuclei from the cooler redissolve, because of their higher solubility, the water depositing on the larger ice crystals forming the bed. The solution, freed of its load of nuclei and so concentrated, is mixed with new feed-stock and recycled. The crystals in the fluidised bed, through impact, become

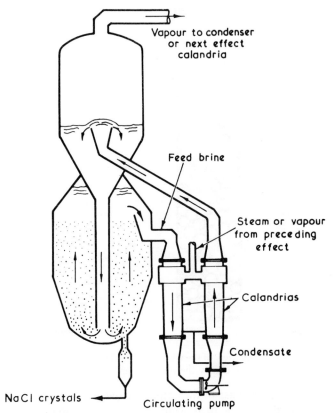

FIG. 9.7. Diagrammatic view of a 'Krystal' evaporative crystalliser for sodium chloride. (By courtesy of A. W. Bamforth, Crystallization Specialist, Stockton-on-Tees.)

abraded to spheroids, the debris either redepositing or forming new crystals. The system is generally similar to that shown in Fig. 9.7 except that crystals are formed by cooling instead of by evaporation. As a crystal increases in size it falls towards the base of the bed and is removed together with concentrated liquor. The crystals must now be freed from this concentrate, which is the product, and their large size and spherical shape aid this process.

First the majority of the liquor is drained, pressed or centrifuged from the crystals to form the product. The crystals are then taken to a wash column for purification. This device is shown diagrammatically in Fig. 9.8. The heater at the base of the column melts the crystals, the majority of the melt

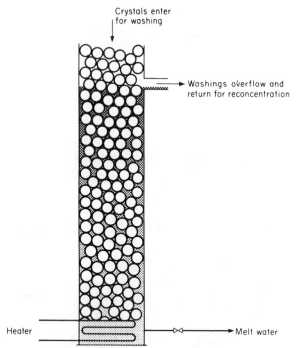

Crystals enter for washing

Washings overflow and return for reconcentration

Heater

Melt water

FIG. 9.8.   Diagrammatic view of the wash column. The crystals are shown enlarged to clarify the mode of operation.

water escaping at the base of the column. However, the rate of outflow is controlled so that some melt water rises through the crystal bed, in countercurrent flow to the crystals, washing their surfaces as it goes. The washings from the column can then be returned to the system.

A process analogous to freeze concentration has been investigated as an alternative to multiple stage flash evaporation in the production of potable water in locations where only brackish water or sea water are available. In this process it is the ice crystals—being formed of substantially pure water—which are harvested and re-melted to give the product stream. Because of the large volume flows that are required, direct contact of the feedstock by a boiling refrigerant gas was used, rather than indirect cooling in any form of heat exchanger, to limit the capital cost of the plant.

9.5.3.   SALT MANUFACTURE

In coastal areas with high insolation (i.e. exposed to considerable solar radiation), sea water is evaporated in shallow lagoon-like salt pans by

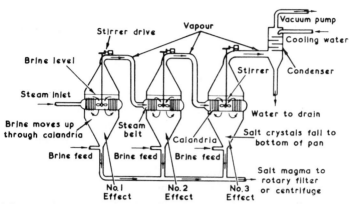

FIG. 9.9. Diagrammatic representation of a triple effect salting evaporator. (By courtesy of ICI Mond Division.)

natural agencies. Elsewhere factory methods are employed for salt production. Much salt was heretofore made by evaporation of brine at, or just below, its boiling point in open pans to give coarse crystals ('pan salt').

The feed brine could be concentrated by multiple stage flash evaporation and might have experienced primary nucleation before entering the open pan where the surface evaporation developed the greatest supersaturation in the adjacent liquid. Crystal nuclei, held by surface tension in the surface, grew by accretion to their edges into hollow pyramids, apex downwards, with stepped sides. When the surface tension could no longer support the crystal, it fell to the base of the pan, through the concentrated brine, where it continued to grow until it was removed, dried and packed.

The crystals produced by this process (and even the fragments resulting from their fracture) had a high specific surface, a low bulk density and, by virtue of their relatively large surface area, a rapid rate of solution. Even though the process was wasteful of heat and labour, making the product relatively expensive, such salt commanded a market where its specific properties were essential. However, the production of salt in multiple effect vacuum evaporators (see Fig. 9.9 and Chapter 12) now dominates.

A temperature difference of about 13°C across each calandria is sufficient to maintain adequate heat transfer in salt manufacture and the presence of the salt in the boiling solution raises the boiling point of the water about 9°C. Thus the vapour given off is superheated by this amount and will condense at a temperature 9°C lower in the calandria of the next effect. There will therefore be a temperature difference of about 22°C in the boiling temperature of the solutions in adjacent effects and, in the triple effect evaporator shown in Fig. 9.9, about 44°C between the boiling temperatures in the first and third effects. In the third effect an adequate crystallisation rate is obtained with a boiling temperature of 46°C and the vapour produced can be condensed with water at ambient temperature. The boiling temperature in the first effect will be about 90°C, which is quite acceptable since salt is completely stable at this temperature.

The crystals formed in such units are suspended in the circulating brine and grow until they are large enough to settle to the base of the evaporator body. The system is continuous but, due to the build-up of impurity salts in the evaporating brine, the latter must be completely replaced periodically. The normal crystal form of 'vacuum salt' is cubical. The addition of a trace of potassium ferrocyanide to the brine as a habit modifier results in a dendritic form of crystal. A coarse crystal of rounded form ('Granular Salt') is also produced. Crystals of this form may be manufactured in an Oslo-type crystalliser (see Fig. 9.7) in which a salt-solution, supersaturated by flash evaporation, passes through a fluidised bed of growing crystals.

A circulating pump moves the brine through submerged calandrias in which it is heated. The brine then passes up into a flashing chamber where, with the release of hydrostatic pressure, it boils to give a supersaturated solution in which nucleation takes place. It then passes down into the lower, crystallising, chamber which has a somewhat conical lower section. Thus as the brine moves upwards it does so with ever decreasing velocity until the widest cross-section is reached.

Initially the crystals will be sufficiently small to circulate with the brine throughout the system but, as they grow in size, so their settling velocity will increase until it exceeds the minimum velocity in the crystallising chamber. A fluidised bed of growing crystals is now formed in the chamber. The crystals in this bed will be classified according to size with the smallest at the top and the largest (with the highest settling velocity and so requiring the largest upward brine velocity to fluidise them) at the bottom. The finished crystals are removed from the bottom of the bed and new crystals, resulting from either primary or secondary nucleation, will replace them at the top of the bed.

The shape of the finished crystals is related to their size. The larger the crystal required the greater the brine velocities in the system must be to keep them fluidised and the more vigorous become the impacts (crystal–crystal, crystal–wall, etc.) that the crystals suffer. Finished sodium chloride crystals of 0·8 mm size (settling velocity 50 mm s^{-1}) will be obtained with well-defined edges and corners. Finished crystals of 3 mm (settling velocity over 200 mm s^{-1}) will need such high brine velocities in their production that they will be almost spherical in shape,[10] which in this case is the desired form, giving a low specific area (in $m^2 kg^{-1}$).

9.5.4. SUGAR MANUFACTURE

Sucrose solutions cannot be boiled above 85°C because coloured impurities are produced. Below 55°C the crystallisation rate is unsatisfactorily slow. The boiling point elevation of the crystallising syrup will be about 10°C and, due to the high thermal resistance in the fluid on the solution side of the calandria, the temperature difference across the calandria would have to be in excess of 20°C. Thus it is not possible to use multiple effect evaporation in crystallising sugar and single effect, short-tube evaporators are normally employed. The high fluid viscosities and the requirement for uniform crystal size also lead to batch operation. Uniformity of crystal size for aesthetic reasons is required in a number of grades of sugar prepared for retail sale. In manufacture, changes in crystal size and distribution can have marked effects on the surface, shape and density of products, such as biscuits.

The normal procedure today is to draw a quantity of syrup into the evaporator, sufficient to cover the calandria, and concentrate this to a metastable supersaturated solution. Seeding and operation in the metastable zone of supersaturation (Section 9.2) are normal practice. Syrup is added as the process proceeds, the syrup/crystal mixture (or massecuite) level rising in the evaporator body. At the end of the process the syrup/crystal ratio is allowed to fall ('tightening the massecuite') to a degree limited by the need to maintain the massecuite sufficiently fluid.

After the finished massecuite has been discharged from the pan it is centrifuged to separate the crystals from the syrup and the latter is fed to another evaporator pan. A brief re-heating of the massecuite may be practised to reduce the syrup viscosity and permit more rapid separation in the centrifuge. This re-heating may even be achieved within the centrifuge assembly itself. Between two and four evaporation stages may be used, the syrup becoming increasingly impure as it passes from stage to stage and crystal growth becoming consequently slower due to the increasing viscosity of the syrup and the increasing concentration of non-sugar substances such as salts that have an inhibiting effect on crystal growth. In the final stage of crystallisation in the manufacture of raw cane sugar, crystal growth is so slow that it is uneconomic to complete this process in the pan and the massecuite is discharged into crystallisers. These are tanks where the massecuite is cooled in a controlled manner to maintain the syrup in the metastable zone in order to complete the crystallisation process. The tanks are equipped with stirring apparatus designed to minimise crystal breakage.

9.6. CRYSTALLISATION PROCESSES IN THE FOOD INDUSTRY NOT INVOLVING SEPARATION

9.6.1. THE CRYSTALLISATION OF SUCROSE IN FOODS

The texture, or mouth-feel, of a number of types of sugar confectionery (e.g. coconut ice, fudge and fondant creams) depends, among other things, on the size of the sugar crystals present in the product. Controlled cooling and agitation produces the appropriate degree of nucleation on which crystal size will ultimately depend.

One recent development in sugar manufacture itself falls within the category of crystallisation without separation. Since the crystallisation of sucrose is an exothermic process, if nucleation is initiated in a sufficiently concentrated sucrose solution, say by heating it under pressure and then bringing about a sudden temperature fall by allowing it to escape to atmospheric pressure through an orifice with consequent flash evaporation, the resultant crystallisation can release sufficient heat to evaporate the remaining water. Since nucleation and growth are both very rapid under these circumstances, many minute crystals (15–40 μm) are formed and agglomerate chaotically as crystallisation and drying continue to form a micro-porous matrix which can then be prepared as a particulate product. There is, of course, no separation involved since, for instance, when low purity syrups are used, all solids in the feed are retained in the product. Indeed, materials such as flavourings may be added to the feed and, provided they can withstand the temperatures involved in the process, they become trapped in the narrow capillary pores. Thus a variety of ingredients with a range of functional properties can be formulated.

9.6.2. THE CRYSTALLISATION OF ICE IN FOODS

General comments on the influence of ice crystal size on frozen foods are given in Chapter 14. However ice cream, which is eaten in a partly frozen condition, warrants mention here. Small ice crystals are required for a smooth texture since crystals greater than 55 μm can be detected on the palate and give a coarse, icy texture to the product. The requisite intense nucleation can be achieved in a scraped-surface heat exchanger (Fig. 9.6). Here the ice cream mix is rapidly cooled to a temperature where nucleation occurs freely. The mechanical agitation not only speeds the cooling but leads to conditions favouring secondary nucleation. The frozen product leaves this heat exchanger in a plastic condition, where it can be formed into the required portions. Subsequently it may be hardened by further prolonged cooling. This is a process of crystal growth.

It has already been noted that solubility is a function of crystal size and that crystals in products have therefore a tendency to increase in size and reduce in number during storage. A stabiliser is added to the ice-cream mix partly to retard this re-crystallisation and inhibit the growth of large ice crystals during primary freezing.[11] This stabiliser is a gel-forming agent, such as carboxymethylcellulose (CMC) which reduces the mobility of the liquid water and acts as a habit modifier, reducing the rate of growth of the ice crystal faces.[5]

9.6.3. LACTOSE CRYSTALLISATION IN FOODS

There is about 5% lactose in cows' milk and it contributes about 40% of the total solids. A saturated aqueous solution at 20°C contains 16% lactose and this solubility is reduced in the presence of sucrose. Thus, in products with a high milk solids content, lactose crystallisation can be a problem. Lactose crystals dissolve slowly in the mouth and if they are over 30 μm long they impart an objectionable sandy texture to the product. For a satisfactorily smooth texture crystals should be no more than 10 μm long.[12]

In ice cream, the growth of objectionably-sized lactose crystals will be promoted by storage, particularly at fluctuating temperatures (see Section 9.6.2) and so is not a problem in ice cream consumed immediately on freezing. For products which will be stored, the milk-solids-not-fat content must be limited to prevent too high a lactose concentration.[11]

In sweetened condensed milk the excess lactose is crystallised out as small crystals by cooling to a temperature where the product is supersaturated with lactose but not too viscous (say 30°C), seeded with fine lactose crystals and then held at a constant temperature with agitation to obtain secondary nucleation. Alternatively, the hot product may be pumped through cooling coils which may be precoated with an already treated batch of material to provide the initial supply of crystals for secondary nucleation.

9.6.4. FAT CRYSTALLISATION

Margarine is a water-in-oil emulsion, the oil phase of which contains a mixture of different base materials and thus a whole range of differing triglycerides. At room temperature a finished table margarine will have only about 20–25% of the triglycerides in solid form and these solid fat crystals will be of the order of 3–10 μm. Too large crystals will give a grainy texture, too small will give a product lacking in plasticity.[13]

To produce the desired crystal formation, the emulsion is spread on the surface of a chilled drum or passed through a scraped surface heat exchanger (Fig. 9.6), where it will rapidly supercool and nucleate. The material emerging from this process is too hard, with too much solid triglyceride. Slight warming and mechanical working of the material causes recrystallisation to the required final composition.

Peanut oil is liquid at room temperature and can separate from peanut butter. Peanut butter is therefore stabilised by producing a matrix of fine crystals of added solid fat in the material. These crystals are produced with extreme habits to complex as much oil as possible. Hydrogenated peanut oil was used for this purpose, but it can lose some of its stabilising power in storage due to enantiotropic recrystallisation (see Section 9.4). Other fats are therefore now used.[8]

Ice cream mix is a formulation containing, generally, about 6–12% fat, 7·5–11·5% milk solids (not fat) and 13–18% sugars together with stabilisers (to increase the viscosity and to control ice crystal growth—see Section 9.6.2) and emulsifiers. After homogenisation to achieve an oil-in-water emulsion, the mix is cooled to 4°C, at which temperature the fats are supercooled, and held for some hours in a process known as ageing. During this time some fat crystallisation takes place. A complex structure is developed around the emulsified fats with crystallised triglycerides surrounding a still fluid core. Emulsifier and protein fractions themselves become adsorbed onto this solid fat on the surface of the globule. In the vigorous agitation during the freezing process some of the membranes that have been developed round the fat globules rupture releasing liquid fat. Air is incorporated into the mix during freezing ('over-run') and this liquid fat then coats and stabilises the fine air bubbles. The solid fat in the outer layers of the fat globules, however, prevents the coalescence of the fat phase.

In the manufacture of chocolate products, whether in the form of cast blocks or enrobed over some base or filling, account must be taken of the polymorphism of cocoa butter. At a temperature of 49°C or higher, no fat crystals will be present in chocolate. Cooling with stirring to, say, 25–28°C is required to induce fat crystallisation and the viscosity of the material will rise markedly. The material is unsuitable for use in this condition, however, because of the presence of fat crystal nuclei in a form (the β' form) which is unstable at room temperature. Raising the temperature to about 32°C will convert these to the stable β form and also reduce the viscosity. This whole process is known as 'tempering' and in the tempered chocolate about 2% of the fat present will be crystallised. The use of untempered chocolate is unsatisfactory because the transformation of fat crystals from the unstable to the stable form in the finished product would spoil its appearance (fat bloom).

When used subsequent to tempering, the chocolate will appear solid after only a relatively small proportion of the fat has solidified on the nuclei generated in the tempering process. Further crystallisation as the product cools results in a shrinkage of the chocolate which, in the case of cast products, aids their release from the mould. Too rapid cooling is to be avoided as it could result in the generation of fresh unstable nuclei.

REFERENCES

1. Hugot, E., *Handbook of Cane Sugar Engineering*, 3rd edn. Elsevier, Amsterdam, 1986.
2. Mullin, J. W. and Leci, C. L., Some nucleation characteristics of aqueous citric acid solutions. *J. Crystal Growth*, **5** (1969) 75.
3. Lees, R. and Jackson, E. B., *Sugar Confectionery and Chocolate Manufacture*. Leonard Hill, Aylesbury, England, 1973.
4. Mullin, J. W., Bulk crystallisation. In *Crystal Growth*, ed. B. R. Pamplin. Pergamon Press, Oxford, England, 1975, pp. 289–325.
5. Mullin, J. W., *Crystallisation*, 2nd edn. Butterworths, London, 1972.
6. McGinnis, R. A. (ed.), *Beet Sugar Technology*, 2nd edn. Beet Sugar Development Foundation, Fort Collins, Colo., USA, 1971.
7. Van Hook, A., *Crystallisation, Theory and Practice*, ACS Monograph No. 152. Van Nostrand Reinhold, New York, 1961.
8. Weiss, T. J., *Food Oils and Their Uses*. AVI, Westport, Conn., USA, 1970.
9. Thjissen, H. A. C., Freeze concentration of food liquids. In *Proceedings of the 3rd International Congress of Food Science and Technology*. IFT, Chicago, 1971, pp. 491–8.
10. Bamforth, A. W., *Industrial Crystallization*. Leonard Hill, London, 1965.
11. Hyde, K. A. and Rothwell, J., *Ice Cream*. Livingstone, Edinburgh, Scotland, 1973.
12. Webb, B. H. and Whittier, E. O. (ed.), *Byproducts from Milk*, 2nd edn. AVI, Westport, Conn., USA, 1970.
13. Anderson, A. J. C. and Williams, P. N., *Margarine*, 2nd edn. Pergamon Press, Oxford, England, 1965.

CHAPTER 10

HEAT PROCESSING I

10.1. INTRODUCTION

The manufacture of foods involves two broad types of conversions—those concerned primarily with physical changes and those in which irreversible chemical changes are the main purpose of the activity. Physical conversions, such as size reduction and centrifugation, are conventionally regarded as *unit operations*. Conversions in which the main effects are chemical in nature are referred to as *unit processes*.

Using these conventions, the subject of food processing may be rationalised. Thus, instead of considering foods on a commodity basis, it is more convenient to deal with these in groups, each of which is based on a common, physical or chemical, conversion activity. The unit process of 'heat processing' embraces baking, boiling, frying, grilling, blanching and other conversion activities where the application of heat is used primarily to effect chemical changes in the food. This chapter is concerned with the food engineering aspects of the unit process of heat processing.

10.2. MODES OF HEAT TRANSFER INVOLVED IN HEAT PROCESSING OF FOODS

Heat flow, in some foods, is susceptible to analysis on the bases of the classical theories of conduction, convection or radiation (see Appendix II). However, in many cases, combinations of two or all three modes of heat transfer are effective simultaneously, and mathematical treatments become either very involved or impracticable. The situation is further complicated by the fact that heat processing, in changing the chemical nature of the food, also brings about changes in its physical properties. Thus, viscosity and density change, often continuously, during heating, and such changes profoundly affect the thermal behaviour of the food. Added to this is the fact that there is a dearth of knowledge relating to the physical and thermal properties of foods. Finally, foods are seldom of simple geometric shape or of homogeneous composition. From the foregoing, the difficulties of applying any precise mathematical treatment to heat flow in most practical systems becomes obvious. Nevertheless, much progress has been made in the mathematical treatment of heat transfer. These treatments, although invaluable in assisting our understanding of the interaction of the factors controlling heat flow in foods, are either excessively generalised or too specific or too empirical.

10.3. METHODS OF HEAT GENERATION FOR HEAT PROCESSING

Heat is generated from four main sources of energy:

  (i)   Solid fuels, e.g. coal, coke or wood.
 (ii)   Liquid fuels, e.g. fuel oils, paraffin or kerosene.
(iii)   Gaseous fuels, e.g. coal gas, natural gas, petroleum gases, etc.
(iv)   Electrical energy generated from solid, liquid, gaseous or nuclear fuels or by water power.

World consumption of primary energy in 1985 comprised: petroleum 38%, gas 20%, coal 30%, hydroelectricity 7% and nuclear and other sources 5%. In the UK the primary energy split was similar at: petroleum 38%, gas 24%, coal 30% and nuclear and other sources 8%.[1]

The selection of the source of heat for the heat processing of foods involves consideration not only of the general economic properties of the source of energy but also of the effects of the fuel and its by-products on the food. In general, the best compromise must be arrived at considering the following requirements:

  (i)   The lowest fuel cost per unit of useful heat.
 (ii)   The lowest capital and maintenance costs for combustion and transfer equipment.
(iii)   The lowest direct labour cost per unit of useful heat.
(iv)   The lowest fire and explosion hazard in dusty conditions.
 (v)   The lowest risk of product contamination by the fuel and its by-products.

(vi) The maximum of flexibility in operation and control.
(vii) The maximum of reliability in continuity of supply.

In addition to the foregoing process considerations, acceptable energy sources must also satisfy increasingly demanding environmental standards. Radioactive by-products of atomic or nuclear fuels are an obvious example but visual pollution (e.g. pylons, power stations, etc.) and thermal pollution, causing overheating of streams and rivers, are also important considerations affecting fuel selection. Finally, atmospheric contamination by dust, smoke and noxious emissions such as volatile metal compounds (e.g. tetra-ethyl lead) and oxides of sulphur and nitrogen (which cause 'acid rain') are a matter of active public concern.

10.3.1. SOLID FUELS

Coal of various types represents the most abundant source of non-renewable energy throughout the world, but although stocks will last for several hundreds of years, they are finite. Renewable solid fuels, such as wood, and other biomass (bulk plant material) fuels will become increasingly important as fossil reserves are depleted.

The average properties of solid fuels, compiled from various sources, are compared in Table 10.1. From this it may be seen that these fuels are characterised by high sulphur and ash contents. Additionally, coal and anthracite often contain traces of volatile, toxic materials like lead and arsenic compounds and they are dusty to handle. These facts contra-indicate the use of such fuels in food processing other than for steam raising or indirect fired equipment. In any application it is vital to prevent product contamination by the fuel, its fumes or its ash, by isolating the burners and the fuel storage bunkers from the production area.

10.3.2. LIQUID FUELS

Table 10.1 indicates the properties of some typical liquid fuels. Of these, petroleum-derived fuel oils of various viscosities represent the most widely used group of industrial heating fuels. British Standard Specifications[2] are accepted as basic requirements for oil fuels sold in the UK, whilst in the USA specifications are laid down by the American Society for Testing and Materials (ASTM). The gross calorific values of these fuels are reasonably constant, whatever the grade, at around 41 MJ litre^{-1} (175 000 Btu gall^{-1}). The price of fuel oils decreases as the viscosity increases but the higher viscosity oils must be kept hot enough to allow them to be pumped from storage to the burners. The lower price is, therefore, offset, to a certain extent, by the capital and maintenance costs of the additional equipment involved.

TABLE 10.1
Average properties of UK fuels

	Gross calorific value (MJ kg^{-1})	Sulphur (%)	Moisture (%)	Ash (%)
Solid				
Anthracite	32·5	1	8	8
Coal	29	2	5–10	8
Coke	28	1	0·5–5	1–5
Wood (air dried)	14	—	12	4–5
Liquid				
Kerosene	46·5	0·2 max.	neg.	—
Gas oil 34 sec.[a]	45·5	0·75 max.	0·05 max.	0·01 max.
Fuel oil 220 sec.[a]	43·5	3·2 max.	0·5 max.	0·05 max.
Fuel oil 950 sec.[a]	43	3·5 max.	0·75 max.	0·07 max.
Fuel oil 3 500 sec.[a]	42·5	3·5 max.	1·00 max.	0·10 max.
Gaseous				
Natural Gas (North Sea)	37·2 MJ m^{-3}	neg.	neg.	neg.

[a] Viscosity, seconds Redwood I at 100°F (38°C).

When used in the food industry, liquid fuels are best restricted to use in indirect fired equipment since the combustion by-products may contain unacceptably high levels of oxides of sulphur and nitrogen. Additionally, there is an ever-present risk of contamination by odours and smuts arising as a result of incomplete combustion. Finally, fuel oils are characterised by pungent odours so that it is imperative to ensure that valves and pipelines are completely leakproof and that the oil storage area is isolated from the production area.

10.3.3. GASEOUS FUEL

Natural gas, although representing only 10% of the world fossil energy reserve, is an important fuel with attractive properties (see Table 10.1).

North Sea gas is 90% methane; it is practically free from water, sulphur and other impurities; it has a high calorific value and is non-toxic. No on-plant storage of gas is required (cf. solid and liquid fuels), but its use presents a fire and explosion risk.

In the food industry, the properties of gas—combined with its flexibility, ease of control and low labour involvement—make it an attractive fuel for both direct and indirect fired equipment. In the former application, the levels of oxides of nitrogen in the combustion by-products and consequent contamination of the food muust be carefully monitored.

10.3.4. ELECTRICITY

Although electricity is not a primary source of heat energy it is widely used for industrial heating. Due to the low efficiency of conversion of primary energy in electricity generation (only about 40% in the UK), electricity is a costly source of heat. This is offset, to a certain extent, by the high thermal efficiencies obtainable in electrical heating systems. In the food industry, electricity offers excellent flexibility and control, low fire and explosion risk and excellent hygiene and cleanliness properties. In spite of these advantages, electrical energy finds only specialised application in the UK food and allied industries where the energy used comprises: petroleum 48%, gas 29%, electricity 12%, and solid fuel 11%.[3]

Nuclear power stations provide about 5% of the world's energy demand. Despite serious problems of safety and environmental acceptability, this energy source will continue to expand.

10.3.5. RENEWABLE ENERGY SOURCES

At current rates of consumption, world reserves of petroleum and natural gas will last for 30–40 years, whilst proven reserves of coal are expected to last for several centuries. Although new discoveries and techniques may expand stocks of fossil fuels, these are finite and will become progressively more expensive. Consequently, considerable efforts are being made to develop renewable sources of energy. These include: water power, hydro power, solar radiation, geothermal energy and biofuel generation.[4]

Hydro power uses the energy of falling water or of waves or tides to drive machines. Hydro-electric generators are well established as a renewable energy source and provide about 7% of the world's energy demand. Wave energy may be harnessed via floating platforms or floating plates, giving a pumping action which may be used to generate electricity. Unfortunately, although potentially the resource is vast, the unpredictable and oscillatory nature of sea waves presents serious engineering problems.

Tidal energy is much more predictable and tides have been harnessed successfully (e.g. the 240 MW tidal La Rance generator in France). However, the high capital cost and long lead times of installations, coupled with difficulties of matching tide periodicity with regular power demands are drawbacks.

Wind power may be converted into electrical energy using modern, turbine-type aerogenerators which are available in Europe in capacities from a few kilowatts upwards. Assembled in groups on 'wind farms', installations generating tens of megawatts have been reported. Noise, interference with radio and TV, and restriction to remote, windy sites are said to be drawbacks.[5]

Solar radiation falling annually on the Earth's surface is said to be equivalent to 5×10^{14} barrels of oil[5] (cf. the world proven fossil energy reserves equivalent to 5×10^{13} barrels of oil). Unfortunately the intermittent and diffuse nature of this potentially enormous energy source makes exploitation difficult and expensive. Solar radiation fixation may be achieved by the following:

(i)   Using solar panels which comprise flat plate-type heat exchangers painted matt black. The panels absorb solar energy, transferring it to a heat exchange fluid (water).

(ii) Using focussing mirrors to concentrate solar radiation to generate steam and hence electricity.

(iii) Using photovoltaic cells which convert solar radiation directly to electricity.

Geothermal energy is produced by heat accumulated in subterranean reservoirs as steam, hot water or hot rocks. Such energy has been estimated as being equivalent to 5×10^{13} barrels of oil.[5] Dry steam fields are used in Italy, New Zealand and the USA and hot water (approx. 80°C) accumulations are important energy resources in these countries and also in the USSR.

Biofuels may be generated from biomass produced by plants or micro-organisms, which may then be burnt directly as fuel or alternatively used to produce gaseous (e.g. methane), liquid (e.g. ethanol) or solid (e.g. charcoal) fuels. The biomass may occur as a by-product—such as sugar cane or beet residues—or as animal wastes, etc. Alternatively, crops may be cultivated specifically for energy production. Plants suitable for agrochemical fuel production include fast growing trees, such as eucalyptus, oil-bearing plants, such as sunflowers or oil palms, and crops, such as maize, soybeans and grasses.

Fermentation of sugar cane in Brazil to yield ethanol which is mixed with petroleum to produce motor fuel ('gasohol') and a similar process in the USA using maize are examples of the application of large scale biofuel production. However, such processes, although successful in fixing solar energy, exhibit a high energy input/output ratio and, in all but a few favourable areas of the world, generate expensive energy.

In general, with the exception of hydro power, renewable energy sources are uncompetitive with fossil sources. However, depletion of fossil reserves and the improving technology of biofuel production, coupled with increasing public concern regarding the environment, will make renewable sources relatively more attractive as time passes.

10.4. METHODS OF APPLYING HEAT TO FOOD

10.4.1. INTRODUCTION

Foods are heated by indirect or direct methods. In indirect heating, heat is applied to the food through heat exchangers, the products of combustion being isolated from the food. In direct systems the heat energy is passed directly into the food without the intervention of heat exchangers, the products of combustion being in direct contact with the food. The methods of heat application in use and under development for the heat processing of foods may be classified as follows:

(i) Indirect heating by:
  (a) Vapours or gases such as steam or air.
  (b) Liquids such as water and organic heat exchange liquids.
  (c) Electricity, in resistance heating systems.
(ii) Direct heating:
  (a) Using gas, oil and solid fuels.
  (b) Using infra-red energy.
  (c) Using electricity, by dielectric or microwave methods.

10.4.2. INDIRECT HEATING METHODS

These systems comprise, basically, four components: (i) a combustion chamber where the fuel is burnt and its products of combustion disposed of; (ii) a heat exchanger where the heat of combustion is taken up by a heat transfer fluid; (iii) a transfer system in which the heated transfer fluid is passed to the heat user and (iv) a heat exchanger at the user-end of the system where the transfer fluid exchanges its heat with the food. Figure 10.1 illustrates typical vapour and liquid systems serving jacketed heat-users. Components (i) and (ii) above constitute a boiler in these cases. Types of boiler, their design and application are discussed elesewhere.[6]

Variations of this basic system include:

(i)   the use of gaseous transfer media such as air or steam which are passed into or over the food;
(ii) heating the food by contacting it directly with a heat exchanger.

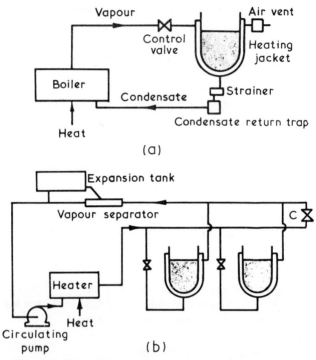

Fig. 10.1. Simple fluid heating systems. (a) Vapour system. (b) Liquid system—the control valve C automatically maintains a constant pressure between the delivery and return manifolds.

10.4.2.1. Indirect heating of foods by vapours or gases

Saturated steam and air are commonly used heat transfer media. Steam may be used for heating in either its saturated or its superheated form; it may also be used to operate electrical generators and vacuum ejectors and as a motivator for machinery. No other material possesses these unique properties, and for this reason a source of steam is an essential requirement in most food plants.

Thermodynamically, saturated steam is also exceptional. When applied as a heat transfer medium it has a high latent heat and a high thermal conductivity, which are advantageous. On the other hand, it has a high vapour pressure and low critical point which are disadvantageous. In its other properties, steam has much to recommend it to the food processor: it is non-toxic, fire and explosion proof and odourless; it is produced from a cheap and abundant raw material. In normal practice, saturated steam is used for food processing up to temperatures in the region of 200°C. Above this, the cost of the necessary high pressure equipment starts to become unduly high. Perry[6] gives much useful information relating to steam as a heating vapour.

At temperatures above its saturation temperature, steam behaves as any other gas and, although it has somewhat better thermal properties than air, it is comparable with the latter as a heat transfer medium. Superheated steam, therefore, finds little heating application in the food industry although the Dole aseptic canning process uses superheated steam to effect sterilisation of cans and lids (Section 11.4.2.1).

Air is a poor heat transfer fluid since it has low specific heat and thermal conductivity. Nevertheless, air is used for the heating of canned foods in the Ekelund cooker (Section 11.3.3.2) for baking (Section 10.5.2) and in fluidised bed cooking. In all these cases transfer is by forced convection. In hot-air driers, air acts both as a heat and mass transfer medium (Section 13.3.1). Air is, of course, non-toxic and non-contaminating although it can bring about deterioration in foods which are sensitive to oxidation.

10.4.2.2. Indirect heating of foods by liquids

Liquids such as water, mineral oils, chlorinated hydrocarbons and fused salts are used for general process heating. With the exception of water, these liquids find application in high temperature processing since they have the advantage of low vapour pressures. The more important properties of some typical heating liquids are set out in Table 10.2.

High temperature hot water is a most useful medium at temperatures up to 200°C when advantage may be taken of its high specific heat and thermal conductivity. Additionally, in the absence of oxygen, there is little corrosion and, since evaporation is absent, scale formation is minimal. The other liquids all possess odours so that great care must be taken to prevent leaks if product contamination is to be avoided.

10.4.2.3. Indirect heating of foods by electrical resistance heating

The generation of heat by the flow of current through a resistor is known as resistance heating. Process vessels may be heated in this manner by attaching resistors to the vessel walls or by immersing sheathed resistors in the material to be heated (immersion heating). The heating elements used are generally made from spirally wound, nickel–chromium wires. They may take the form of rigid platens fixed to the vessel wall or may comprise flexible jackets for vessels or tapes for pipelines and valves. These elements work at temperatures up to 800°C so that, since heat transfer into the food is

TABLE 10.2
Properties of some heat exchange fluids

	M.pt. (°C)	B.pt. (°C)	S.ht.[a] (kJ kg⁻¹ °C⁻¹)	Enthalpy[a] above 0°C (kJ kg⁻¹)	Thermal conductivity (J m⁻¹ s⁻¹ °C⁻¹)	Vapour pressure (kN m⁻²) at temperature (°C) given in parentheses	Practical operating range (°C)
	M.pt. (°C)	B.pt. (°C)	$S.ht.^{a}$ $(\text{kJ kg}^{-1}\,^{\circ}\text{C}^{-1})$	Enthalpy^{a} above 0°C (kJ kg^{-1})	Thermal conductivity $(\text{J m}^{-1}\text{s}^{-1}\,^{\circ}\text{C}^{-1})$	Vapour pressure (kN m^{-2}) at temperature (°C) given in parentheses	Practical operating range (°C)
Water	0	100	4·3	625	0·68	1 540 (200)	0→200
Steam	—	—	2·0	2 740	0·17	—	100→200
Air	—	—	1·0	150	0·03	—	—
o-Dichlorobenzene	−22	180	1·6	490	0·11	600 (260)	−17→260
Mineral oil	—	—	2·3	350	0·12	10 (316)	10→320
Organosilicate	—	>320	2·0	300	0·13	13 (316)	10→320
Diphenyl/Diphenyloxide	12	260	2·2	580	0·13	1 500 (400)	15→400

^{a} Measured at 150°C.

primarily conductive, high rates of transfer may be produced at the point where it is required and with a high degree of control.[7] Resistance-heated baking ovens are common; resistor banks are located within the oven cavity, heat being conveyed to the food by a combination of conduction, convection and radiation.

10.4.3. DIRECT HEATING METHODS

The risks attendant upon the direct heating of foods by solid, gaseous and liquid fuels have been indicated (Section 10.3) but numerous direct fired baking ovens, malt kilns and driers are encountered in the food industry. Solid fuels, gas and fuel oil are used in this way, gas being favoured because of its freedom from potential contaminants.

Direct heating, by means of electrode boilers,[8] finds use in special steam-raising applications when steam is required either intermittently or at a user-point uneconomically remote from the main steam source. This method, although of high thermal efficiency, is only an economic possibility in special circumstances or when a cheap source of electric power is available.

Induction heating, that is heating in a material by means of the currents induced in that material by an alternating magnetic field,[9] is only applicable to electrically conducting substances. Thus, although widely used in many other branches of industry, induction heating finds little application in the food industry. Inductively heated reaction vessels would appear to have applications in food processing because of their precisely-controllable area-heating characteristics and fast heating properties.[10]

Direct heating by infra-red energy generated by radiants heated either electrically or by fuels is important in food processing both as a heating method and as a contributor in equipment heated by other direct and indirect systems.

10.4.3.1. Infra-red heating of foods

This is carried out by means of banks of radiant heaters located in a tunnel through which food is conveyed. Electrically heated radiants are of two types, medium temperature heaters and high temperature heaters. In medium temperature heaters, filaments operating at 500–1000°C are sheathed in metal or silica tubes. These generate energy at an intensity of around 15 kW m^{-2}. High temperature radiators comprise either tungsten filament lamps or filaments sheathed in quartz tubes. These operate at filament temperatures of about 2500°C and are available with energy outputs of 10–65 kW m^{-2} depending on type. Although some of the heat is

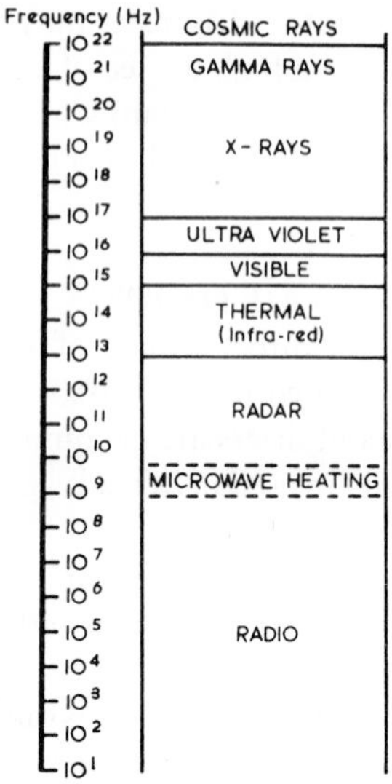

Frequency (Hz)

10^{22}	COSMIC RAYS
10^{21}	GAMMA RAYS
10^{20}	
10^{19}	X - RAYS
10^{18}	
10^{17}	
10^{16}	ULTRA VIOLET
10^{15}	VISIBLE
10^{14}	THERMAL (Infra-red)
10^{13}	
10^{12}	
10^{11}	RADAR
10^{10}	
10^{9}	MICROWAVE HEATING
10^{8}	
10^{7}	
10^{6}	
10^{5}	RADIO
10^{4}	
10^{3}	
10^{2}	
10^{1}	

FIG. 10.2.   The electromagnetic spectrum.

transferred convectively, the majority of the energy is radiated in the infra-red with a range of wavelengths between 0·75 and 350 μm (Fig. 10.2).

Radiant energy is transformed into heat only on absorption, a process described by Beer's Law which states:

$$I = I_0 \exp(-\alpha x) \qquad (10.1)$$

where I is the amount of radiation transferred to depth x in the material, I_0 is the incident intensity of radiation and α is the absorption coefficient of the heated material. Practical systems involve selective radiators (see Appendix II) so that absorption varies from zero ($\alpha \rightarrow 0$) at some wavelengths, to complete absorption ($\alpha \rightarrow \infty$) at other, selective wavelengths. Only wavelengths up to about 50 μm are of practical importance in food heating. Water and aqueous systems absorb best at wavelengths around 1 μm. Ideally, for maximum absorption, it is necessary to produce an intense, narrow spectrum tuned to the absorption bands of the substance to be heated but, in practice, realisation of this can only be partial. The relevant theory is discussed briefly in Appendix II.3 and more fully elsewhere.[11]

When absorption of infra-red energy occurs, it is characterised by low penetration, and produces rapid surface cooking of the food. This results in rapid sealing and browning of the outer layers. Water and volatile flavours tend to be retained, making the food more juicy and flavoursome.

Penetration to the centre of the food-piece is mainly by conduction, which is often a slow process. It is important, therefore, when using this method of heating, to ensure that an adequate final centre-temperature is obtained. Radiant heating has many applications in food processing such as: grilling; toasting; baking; cooking; specialised dehydration procedures, e.g. drying of sugar cubes and nuts and in freeze drying; melting of fats and as a component of other heating methods, e.g. in direct fired boilers and ovens.[12]

10.4.3.2. Dielectric heating of foods
Two other methods of direct electrical heating—dielectric heating and microwave heating—have been the subject of intense investigation by the food industry over the last decade. These are now well established as valuable heating methods in certain fields of heat processing. Additionally, these methods appear to have considerable potential, as yet unexploited, in several new applications. Both methods use high-frequency energy and, to avoid interference in radar, television and radio transmissions, the frequencies permitted for use for industrial, scientific and medical purposes are regulated by international agreement (Table 10.3).

From Table 10.3 it will be seen that the permitted frequencies fall into two bands—those below 300 MHz being loosely called radio frequencies (or RF) and are used in dielectric heating, whilst those above 300 MHz are

TABLE 10.3
High frequencies for industrial, scientific and medical purposes
(International Telecommunication Union. Radio Regulations, Geneva 1976)

Frequency (MHz)	Wavelength	
$13.56 \pm 0.05\%$	22.1 m	
$27.12 \pm 0.6\%$	11.1 m	
$40.68 \pm 0.05\%$	7.4 m	
$433.92 \pm 2.0\%$	69.2 cm	
915 ± 25^a	32.8 cm	⎰ Allocated only to Region 2 (Greenland
$2\,450 \pm 50$	12.2 cm	⎱ and N. and S. America)
$5\,800 \pm 75$	5.2 cm	
$22\,125 \pm 125$	1.4 cm	

[a] *Note:* The Wireless Telegraphy Regulations 1971 (SI.1675. HMSO) permits the use of the frequency range 886–906 MHz in radio frequency heating apparatus subject to limitations on the maximum radiated field strength and maximum terminal voltage of the apparatus.

called microwaves and are used in microwave heating. In fact, the whole band of permitted frequencies are radio waves, the phenomena of dielectric heating and microwave heating being essentially similar. The differences are solely due to the different frequencies used, which determine the extent of energy penetration and the type of equipment employed.

Dielectric heating theory. Dielectric heating is defined[9] as heating in an electrically insulating material by the losses in it when subjected to an alternating electric field. The material to be heated constitutes a dielectric sandwiched between capacitor plates connected to a capacitive, high-frequency, alternating generator. Heating is brought about by molecular friction due to the rapid orientation of the electric dipoles under the influence of the high-frequency alternation of the applied field.

The power (P) developed in a parallel plate capacitor is given by the relationship:

$$P \propto E^2 . f . \frac{A}{d} . \varepsilon_r . \tan \delta \qquad (10.2)$$

where E = electrical field strength, f = frequency, A = area of the dielectric, d = thickness of the dielectric, ε_r = relative dielectric constant of the dielectric, $\tan \delta$ = loss tangent of the dielectric. ($\varepsilon_r \tan \delta$ is referred to as the 'loss factor' of the dielectric.)

For P to be maximal, E, f, A and $\varepsilon_r \tan \delta$ must be as high as possible whilst d should be as small as possible. The system is, however, subject to the following restraints:

(i) The applied voltage is limited by the dielectric strength of the material being heated, and by the occurrence of 'flash-over' between the capacitor plates. For these reasons industrial equipment is usually limited to about 15 kV.

(ii) Designers of equipment are limited in the frequencies they may use and also by the fact that the cost of high-frequency capacitative generators increases steeply at frequencies above about 100 MHz. Commercial dielectric heaters therefore use the lower frequencies, 27 MHz being a common frequency.

(iii) The dimensions A and d of the food-piece are often predetermined, e.g. biscuits, fish pieces and so on. There is some flexibility in the case of bulk fluid foods, but in practice the maximum dimension (L) of a capacitor is limited by $L < \lambda/16\sqrt{\varepsilon_r}$ where λ is the wavelength involved. The thickness d is limited by 'flash-over' between the plates.

(iv) The loss factor, '$\varepsilon_r \tan \delta$', is a property of the dielectric (the food) and is both frequency and temperature dependent.

Equipment design. Dielectric heating equipment generally comprises a low-loss belt which conveys the food at a controlled rate between the plates of the capacitor. The top plate may be raised or lowered to control the heat generated in the product, and power input is also variable. It is usual to fit traps at the input and outlet points of the conveyor in order to limit RF leakage. Heaters capable of dissipating 160 kW of energy in the food with an efficiency of about 50% are usual, although units generating many hundreds of kilowatts have been installed.[13]

Characteristics of dielectric heating. This type of heating has the following characteristics:

(i) The rate of heating is very fast compared with conventional methods.

(ii) The fastest heating point occurs at some depth below the surface of the food so that heat losses are minimised.

(iii) Local overheating is minimised and this, in conjunction with (i), reduces heat damage to the food.

(iv) Because of its speed, dielectric heating saves working space.

(v) It is clean, continuous in operation and is well suited to automatic control.

(vi) There is no surface browning of the food.

(vii) Energy is generated directionally so that the orientation of the food unit in relation to the capacitor plates is of great importance in determining the magnitude of the ratio A/d.

Food-processing applications of dielectric heating. Dielectric heating is used to thaw frozen eggs, meat, fruit juices and fish and to melt fats, chocolate and butter. The method finds application in the baking of biscuits (Section 10.5.2.1). Other applications include the heating of peanuts for confectionery manufacture and the drying of sugar cubes and crispbread.[13]

Obviously, since about 2 kWh of energy is required to evaporate 1 kg of water, this method is unsuitable for the removal of water in bulk.

10.4.3.3. Microwave heating of foods

Microwaves are regarded as those electromagnetic radiations having frequencies in the range of 300–300 000 MHz. For reasons already discussed, industrial equipment is limited to the frequencies given in Table 10.3, 897 and 2450 MHz are commonly used frequencies.

Microwave heating theory. As in the case of dielectric heating, only the briefest outline of the relevant theory can be given here but excellent descriptions are available elsewhere.[14]

Although, as in dielectric heating, microwaves generate heat by molecular-dipole vibration, the former is electrostatic whereas the latter is a radiation phenomenon. Microwave heating differs from dielectric heating only in using higher frequencies and these dictate the use of a different type of equipment. The basic power equation (equation 10.2) applies, but the considerations involved differ in the following respects:

(i)   Because of the higher energy associated with the higher frequencies used in microwave heating, the same energy input may be achieved by the application of a lower voltage. Hence dielectric stress within the food is reduced and 'flash-over' is largely eliminated.

(ii) The food dimensions A and d are no longer restraints. The shape and size and orientation of the food are of importance only in respect of ensuring adequate 'through heating'.

(iii) Loss factors are higher at the higher frequencies used in microwave heating. This implies a lower voltage stress on the food for the same energy input.

(iv) In microwave heating the penetration of the radiation assumes great importance. If the food is transparent then no heating results. It is convenient to measure the penetration in terms of the penetration depth D at which the energy is reduced to 1/eth of its incident value.[14]

Penetration depth is given by the following equation:

$$D \simeq \frac{\lambda_0}{2\pi(\varepsilon_r \tan \delta)^{1/2}} \qquad (10.3)$$

where $\lambda_0 =$ wavelength in free space.

Penetration is, therefore, inversely proportional to frequency. For example, for water at $95°C$, $D = 29.5$ cm at 915 MHz and 4.8 cm at 2450 MHz.

For the foregoing reasons it will be clear that the frequency selected for use in a purely radiative phenomenon, such as microwave heating, is a matter of great importance if the best result is to be obtained.

Equipment design. Microwave heaters comprise a high-frequency generator (such as a magnetron) from which energy is transported by

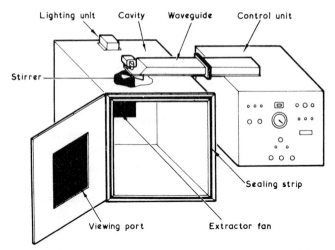

Lighting unit   Cavity   Waveguide   Control unit

Stirrer

Sealing strip

Viewing port   Extractor fan

FIG. 10.3.   A microwave oven. (By courtesy of Elliott Electronic Tubes Ltd, Borehamwood, England.)

means of a hollow, rectangular waveguide or by a coaxial cable to a heating chamber (Fig. 10.3). This latter may be either a metal oven or tunnel, effectively water-trapped at each end, through which passes a low-loss belt carrying the food to be heated. In either case the heating cavity must be accurately matched, electrically, to the generator, otherwise the resulting mismatch causes overheating of the power tube which could be damaged as a consequence.

Alternatively, food may be conveyed through the waveguide which then becomes the heating chamber. Movement of the food through the heating zone counteracts field inequalities which, in fast-heating processes such as microwave heating, result in large temperature gradients within the food.

Domestic and catering ovens operating at 0·5–2 kW are now common. Magnetrons generating up to 30 kW at 897 MHz and up to 5 kW at 2450 MHz are available and these, used singly or in combination, provide the processor with considerable flexibility. Industrial heaters generating as much as 130 kW have been reported. Clearly, equipment of this power must be carefully safeguarded to prevent energy leakage and the design of microwave heating equipment has received much attention.[13]

Food-processing applications of microwave heating. Microwaves are used to heat precooked, frozen foods and, in conjunction with the browning effect of infra-red heaters, for the cooking of food in canteens and hospitals where speed is important. Industrially, microwaves are used for precooking chicken, for apple-juice evaporation and in potato-crisp finishing. Investigational work has indicated promising applications, e.g. in the pasteurisation of fruit juices; in reducing mould counts in bread, cakes and jam; in bread baking and in accelerated freeze drying (Section 13.3.4).[13,15]

Safety considerations in the use of microwaves. The human body is a 'lossy' entity and current indications are that exposure to microwaves results predominantly in thermal effects, the eyes and testicles being specially susceptible to heat change. It is reported that non-thermal biological effects such as enzyme inactivation and protein modification have been demonstrated in animals exposed to microwave energy. A situation of uncertainty exists regarding human sensitivity and more information is required on this important subject. In the USA a maximum RF leakage level of 5 mW cm^{-2} is specified,[14] and equipment is engineered to ensure that this limit is not exceeded. As indicated previously, the energy source is tuned to match the heating cavity so that a leak of any magnitude would result in a mismatch causing the magnetron to stop working. Modern microwave equipment is fitted with foolproof safety devices and may be regarded as inherently safe.

10.5.   FOOD CONVERSION BY HEAT PROCESSING

10.5.1.   THE BLANCHING PROCESS
Blanching is an important heat process in the preparation of vegetables (and some fruits) destined for canning, freezing or dehydration. Primarily, blanching is carried out to inactivate enzymes or to destroy enzyme substrates such as peroxides. Blanching is effected by heating the food *rapidly* to a predetermined temperature, holding it at this temperature for a predetermined time and then either *rapidly* cooling the material or, alternatively, passing it to subsequent processing without delay. If unblanched food is processed (e.g. as a canned conduction-heating pack) it may well be an appreciable time in reaching a temperature sufficiently high to inactivate enzymes. In low-temperature processes, such as vacuum evaporation, spray drying and freeze drying, enzyme inactivation temperatures may not be reached at all. In both these cases, residual enzyme activity in the food may cause the development of undesirable odours, flavours and colours during processing and storage.

In addition to destroying enzymes, blanching also brings about the following changes:

(i)   The raw material is cleaned and the bacterial load is reduced.
(ii) Cellular gases are expelled, reducing can corrosion and assisting the attainment of adequate headspace vacua during canning.
(iii) The food is softened and shrinks, so filling of containers is facilitated.
(iv) Texture may be improved, especially in dehydrated foods.
(v)   Undesirably, blanching may lead to loss of heat-sensitive vitamins and to leaching out of water-soluble nutrients.[16] Over-blanching causes texture damage.

10.5.1.1. Blanching methods

The two methods of blanching in general use are: (i) immersion blanching using hot water, and (ii) steam blanching. Immersion blanching involves passing the food at a controlled rate through a perforated drum rotating in a tank of water thermostatically controlled to the blanching temperature (75–100°C). Alternatively, the food is suspended in water, heated to blanching temperature and is then pumped through a serpentine holding tube (pipe blancher). Immersion blanching leads to high loss of solubles in some foods, and scrupulous plant hygiene is necessary if thermophile contamination is to be avoided.

Steam blanchers utilise saturated steam at atmospheric or at low pressure ($150 \, kN \, m^{-2}$). The food is conveyed through the steam chamber on a mesh belt or by means of a helical screw, the residence time being controlled by the conveyor speed. The blanched product is discharged through an outlet lock to a washer and cooler. Steam blanching tends to give lower blanching losses than immersion blanching but has a reduced cleaning effect on the food so that an 'after washer' is necessary. Generally, steam blanchers are easier to sterilise than water blanchers.

Microwave blanching has been applied to fruits and vegetables packaged in film bags[17] and would appear to offer some advantages, such as microbiological cleanliness and low losses of nutrients. The method, although costly, may well find specialised applications.

10.5.1.2. Blanching problems

These arise, firstly, in ensuring uniform heat-treatment and, second, in controlling blanching losses and the effluent disposal difficulties caused by these. *Individual Quick Blanching* (IQB) claims to alleviate these problems.[18] This is a modified three-stage steam-blanching process in which pieces of food are rapidly heated as a thin layer ($\sim 5\,kg\,m^{-2}$) followed by holding as a deep bed, where equilibration takes place, after which the food is cooled by chilled air. This permits shorter retention time, giving improved yield and quality and reduces effluent volumes and strength.

Peroxidase is the most heat-stable enzyme present in vegetables and is easy to detect, consequently it is used as a blanching indicator. However, it is not always necessary to produce complete inactivation. Sliced green beans, peas and carrots showing residual peroxidase activity have shown adequate storage quality at $-20°C$. With other vegetables (e.g. Brussels sprouts) zero peroxidase activity is essential. Again, peroxidases from different sources exhibit different heat resistances, e.g. spinach peroxidase has a z-value (see Chapter 11) of $15°C$ whereas green bean peroxidase has a z-value of $49°C$.

Uniformity of heat treatment, particularly in continuous blanchers, is difficult to attain, being controlled by many variables, such as:

(i) The residence time, which itself is controlled by the type of flow—streamline, turbulent or (rare but desirable) plug-type. A spread of residence times is usual so that blanching to zero peroxidase leads to a high degree of overblanch.

(ii) Piece size, which has a large effect on the rate of heat penetration so that non-uniformity of piece size inevitably causes some overblanching.

(iii) Piece shape, which also affects heat penetration and controls the flow pattern within the blancher and hence influences piece residence time.

Finally water quality is important, e.g. hard water ($> 200\,ppm$) causes toughening of peas whereas very soft water ($< 50\,ppm$) or water containing sodium chloride or sodium hexametaphosphate causes excessive softening of peas.

10.5.2. THE BAKING PROCESS

The baking of farinaceous foods like bread, biscuits and cakes, is an important food-conversion activity. In yeast-raised foods such as bread, which is the biggest preoccupation of the baker, a series of complex, temperature-dependent chemical reactions take place during baking (Fig. 10.4). Since these reactions determine the properties of the converted food, the heating must be carefully controlled if the desired colour, flavour,

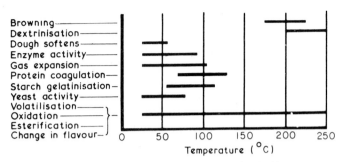

FIG. 10.4.   The reaction in bread during baking.

aroma and texture are to be obtained. The chemical changes taking place are discussed, in detail, elsewhere.[19]

Baking ovens form an important group of heat processing equipment and include a wide array of types which may be classified on the following bases:

Heating Method:	(i)	Indirect by solid fuel, oil, gas or electricity.
	(ii)	Direct by gas, air or electronically.
Design Types:	(i)	Batch—peel or draw-plate ovens.
	(ii)	Continuous—rotary hearth, reel, tunnel and multicycle tray ovens.

10.5.2.1. Heating of baking ovens

In indirectly fired ovens the food is heated mainly by radiant heat transfer. Hot combustion gases or electrical energy are used to heat the walls of batch ovens or to heat radiators located above and below the baking band in continuous ovens.

Conventional direct heating by gas is effected by locating ribbon-type gas burners above and below the baking band. Heat transfer, in this case, is by a combination of radiation and natural convection.

In direct forced-convection baking, air, drawn from the baking chamber, is heated directly by gas burners. The hot gases are then forced by a recirculating fan back into the chamber through nozzles located above and below the baking band.[20-22] According to Gales and Petty[21] the relationship $Nu \propto Re^x . Pr^y$ for forced convection (Appendix II) approximates, in this system, to $h \propto G^{0.78}$ (where h = heat transfer coefficient and G = mass flow of heated air) when air velocities around $0.5 \, m \, s^{-1}$ are used with moderate nozzling. The advantages of this type of oven are: shortened baking times, high thermal efficiency and excellent control (since h is roughly proportional to the air-speed). Additionally, changing the oven temperature or heating up from cold is speeded since the thermal mass of the system is low.

Dielectric heating is firmly established in the post-baking of biscuits. In thin food sections, such as biscuits, browning and dehydration down to about 10% moisture may be effected in the first 60% of travel through conventional tunnel ovens. The rest of the baking time is required to reduce the moisture content to around 2% whilst retaining the desired biscuit colour. This last stage may be performed rapidly (15–20 s) by passing the partly finished biscuits through a dielectric oven. This has the effect of increasing the throughput of highly expensive tunnel ovens and is, therefore, financially attractive. Additionally, better control over moisture contents is claimed.[23]

10.5.2.2. Types of baking oven
Batch ovens, heated directly or indirectly, are in general use and consist of a baking cavity into which the food is charged either singly, on a long-handled shovel (or peel), or in batches on trays. Charging and discharging is facilitated by fitting this oven with a sliding hearth (the draw-plate oven).

The smaller continuous ovens include the rotary-hearth oven in which the food is charged on to a heated sole plate which rotates horizontally. The speed of rotation is adjusted so that the baked product may be removed continuously as fresh material is charged. In the reel oven the food is conveyed within the oven chamber on trays slung between two wheels which rotate vertically, using the ferris wheel principle. Charging and discharging takes place at the same point. These two types of oven give uniform baking results, the effects of local hot-spots being minimised by the movement of the food.

The multicycle tray oven conveys the food on a serpentine path through the baking chamber, the food being carried on trays suspended from chains. Loading and unloading is usually carried out at the same point. Such ovens are characterised by high capacity and economic use of floor space.

In tunnel ovens the food is carried on an endless conveyor belt which passes, at controlled speed, through a series of independently controllable heating sections. The food enters at one end of the tunnel, which may be 100 m long, and is discharged at the other end. Tunnel ovens are expensive to buy and occupy a large floor area, but their capacity, flexibility and accuracy of control has established their wide application in large-scale baking. There is an extensive literature on baking oven design.[19,20]

10.5.3. EXTRUSION COOKING

Extrusion, a process whereby food is forced through a restricting orifice (or die) producing mixing and forming of the food, is a well established procedure in the manufacture of pasta, sausages, etc. Extension of this process to include controlled, continuous heating of the food undergoing extrusion is called extrusion cooking.

10.5.3.1. Extrusion cooking equipment

At its simplest, an extrusion cooker comprises a flighted Archimedean screw rotating in a tightly fitting barrel which is equipped with a feeder at its inlet end and having a die at its outlet end. Heating is effected by:

(i) energy dissipated by the shearing of the viscous dough-like food mass within the barrel,

(ii) conductively, via electrically- or steam-heated jackets surrounding the barrel, or

(iii) by injecting steam into the barrel.

Cooling may be brought about if required by circulating chilled water through jackets surrounding the barrel.

The combined effects of compression of the food mass by the rotating screw, the heat supplied and generated and compression by the die produce high pressures (up to 60 atm) and elevated temperature (up to 200°C) within the extruder. As the heat-treated food is forced through the outlet die by the rotating screw, the sudden drop in pressure of the plastic extrudate causes rapid expansion and moisture loss which cools the product evaporatively to give a rigid, or semi-rigid, product having the cross-sectional profile of the die.[24]

Variations and extensions of the basic extrusion cooking process include the following:

(i) Continuous premixers and preconditioners, such as screw or ribbon mixers, in which dry ingredients are mixed and treated with metered amounts of water, oils, etc., to provide a uniform feed material of the appropriate moisture content.

(ii) Vibratory or rotary volumetric feeders, or weigh-belt feeders, used to deliver metered flows of dry preconditioned raw material whilst metering pumps are used to inject liquids, such as water or oils, into the feed section of the cooker. Extrusion cookers are very sensitive to feed rate variations which cause system instability. This, unless corrected, results in rapid blockage of the outlet dies and eventual shut-down of the equipment.

(iii) Screws tapered and fitted with flights having variable pitch and depth, permitting variations in degree of mixing or back-mixing, shear rate and compression. Both single-screw and double-screw extruders are available commercially. The latter comprise a pair of closely intermeshing screws which may be co- or contra-rotating. They differ from single screw extruders in both operation and in the type of product produced. In general, single-screw devices involve larger shear forces and hence high power consumption, with large temperature differences within the material being processed. Advantageously, the single-screw extruder has a lower capital cost and is much less complex than its twin-screw counterpart.[25,26]

(iv) Barrels may be parallel sided or may be tapered to increase compression and shear. Jackets may be fitted to produce conductive heating or cooling and inspection windows and ports for insertion of sensors for measuring temperature, pressure, etc., may be provided.

(v) Dies are available in a wide variety of cross-sectional profiles, e.g. circular (giving rods), square (giving bars) and slot-like (giving sheets). The die is usually carried in a die-plate which is rigidly

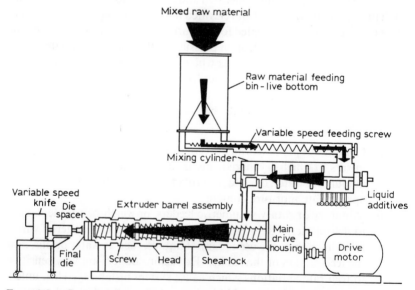

Fig. 10.5. Cross-section of a typical extrusion cooker. (From Smith and Ben-Gera.[27])

attached to the barrel outlet and which is usually preceded by a distributor plate designed to equilibrate the high pressure generated in the extrudate being delivered to the die-plate.

(vi) Cutting knives revolving parallel to the face of the die-plate are used to cut the extrudate into sections of length determined by the speed of rotation of the cutter in relationship to the linear speed at which the extrudate is discharged through the die-plate.

(vii) Finishing equipment includes continuous flakers, driers, toasters and devices for dusting or spraying the extrusions with solid or liquid flavourings or other additives.

A typical extrusion cooking plant is depicted in Fig. 10.5.

10.5.3.2. Applications of extrusion cooking

As a result of the rapid acceptance of this method of high-temperature short-time heat processing, applicational knowledge has outstripped theory. In spite of intense research activity, detailed knowledge of what is taking place in the barrel is sparse and, when available, specific to particular systems. It is generally accepted that foods undergoing extrusion cooking are subjected to a complex series of reactions including hydration, shearing, homogenisation, starch gelation, protein denaturation, melting, solubilisation, plastification, inactivation of micro-organisms and enzymes, orientation of molecules and aggregates, forming, shaping, expansion and drying. The complexity of these processes, interacting and occurring both simultaneously and sequentially, suggests that theoretical understanding will accumulate only slowly. It is likely that extrusion cooking will remain an empirical technology for some time to come.

Application of this process is now widespread, embracing production of breakfast foods, snack- and pet-foods and of nutritious pre-cooked infant foods. Flat breads, crackers and biscuits are now produced on extrusion cookers. The ability of the cooker to convey and heat viscous materials is used in the continuous production of boiled sweets either by anhydrous melting of sucrose or boiling of concentrated sugar solutions. Filled products, e.g. snacks containing more than one component, may be produced by co-extrusion. This involves synchronisation of two extruders producing different components, which are then combined at a special die. A relatively recent development is the extrusion of so-called 'half-products' in the form of dense sections or pellets which, on dropping into hot fat, expand to form hot ready-to-eat bite-sized pieces with a crisp-like texture in a range of flavours.[28]

REFERENCES

1. Anon., *Statistical Review of World Energy*. British Petroleum, London, 1986.
2. Anon., Petroleum fuels for oil engines and burners. BS 2869. British Standards Institution, London, 1970.
3. Boardman, J., Effecting efficient energy usage. *Food Processing*, **47**(5) (1986) 29–31.
4. Twidell, J. and Weir, A. D., *Renewable Energy Sources*. Spon, London, 1986.
5. Knight, B., Renewable sources of energy. *Shield International*. British Petroleum, London, 1980.
6. Perry, J. H., *Chemical Engineers Handbook*, 6th edn. McGraw-Hill, New York, 1984.
7. Barber, H., *Electroheat*. Granada, London, 1983.
8. Horsley, M. E., Electrode steam and hot water boilers. *Digest No. 70*. Institute of Electrical Engineers, London, 1984.
9. Anon., Glossary of terms used in industrial high frequency induction and dielectric heating. BS 2759, Section 1. British Standards Institution, London, 1956.
10. Hobson, L. and Day, J., Induction heating of vessels. *J. Inst. Elect. Engng Educ.*, **22** (1985) 129–42.
11. Hankins, W. C., *The Application of Electric Infra-Red Heating to Industrial Processes*. British National Committee for Electroheat, London, 1981.
12. Ginzburg, A. S. and Growchowski, A., *Applications of Infra-Red Radiation in Food Processing*. Leonard Hill, London, 1969.
13. Anon., *Dielectric Heating for Industrial Processes*. British National Committee for Electroheat, London, 1983.
14. Copson, D. A., *Microwave Heating*. AVI, Westport, Conn., USA, 1975.
15. Metaxas, A. C. and Meredith, R. J., *Industrial Microwave Heating. IEE Power Engineering Series 4*. Peter Peregrinus, London, 1983.
16. Selman, J. D., The blanching process. In *Developments in Food Preservation—4*. Elsevier Applied Science Publishers, London, 1987, pp. 205–80.
17. Anon., In the bag microwave processing. *Food Trade Review*, **51**(3) (1981) 22–3.
18. Lazar, M. E., Lund, D. B. and Dietrich, W. C., IQB—a new concept in blanching. *Food Trade Review*, **42**(3) (1972) 13–15.
19. Matz, S. A., *Bakery Technology and Engineering*. AVI, Westport, Conn., USA, 1972.
20. Alderson, G. P., Which oven? *Bakers Review* (19 October 1984), 21–39.
21. Gales, D. R. and Petty, H. H., Oven developments—The forced convection oven. *Food Trade Review*, **30**(3) (1960) 56–64.
22. Anon., Baking and ovens. History of heat technology. *Bakers Digest*, **58**(2) (1984) 12–16.
23. Anon., Up to 30% more biscuits with RF post baking. EC4290. The Electricity Council, London, 1982.
24. Harper, J. M., *Extrusion of Foods. Vols I and II*. CRC Press, Boca Raton, Fla., USA, 1981.
25. Van Zuilichem, D. J., Alblas, B., Reinders, P. M. and Storp, W., A comparative study of the operational characteristics of single and twin screw extruders. In

Thermal Processing and Quality of Foods, ed. P. Leuther, J. C. Cheftel, C. Ericksson *et al.* Applied Science Publishers, London, 1983, pp. 33–44.

26. Jowitt, R. (ed.), *Extrusion Cooking Technology*. Applied Science Publishers, London, 1984.

27. Smith, O. B. and Ben-Gera, I., The application of high temperature short time extrusion cooking in the food industry. *Food Process Engineering. Vol. I. Food Processing Systems*, ed. P. Linko, Y. Mälkii, J. Oikku and J. Larinkari. Applied Science Publishers, London, 1980, pp. 726–44.

28. Eckett, A., Snacks. A look into pasta. *Food Processing*, **54**(4) (1985) 25–7.

PART III

PRESERVATION OPERATIONS

CHAPTER 11

HEAT PROCESSING II

11.1. MICROBIOLOGICAL CONSIDERATIONS

11.1.1. INTRODUCTION

When foods are preserved by heat, the heating process serves to reduce the concentration of micro-organisms in the food. It may also inactivate enzymes present (see Section 10.5.1). The heating operation forms only part of the total preservation process, which can include, e.g. the addition of chemical preservatives, suitable packaging of the product or storage at reduced temperatures. It is not a necessary requirement of the heating operation that it should eliminate all viable organisms from the material. Sound cans of food, particularly cans of cured meat products, frequently contain viable organisms.[1] What is required is that the resulting product should be both acceptable to the consumer and safe to eat at the end of a predetermined storage period under defined conditions.

It is convenient to divide heat processes into three categories, involving heating (i) to temperatures below 100°C; (ii) to a temperature of 100°C; (iii) to temperatures above 100°C.

Heat processes below 100°C are usually termed pasteurisation processes and generally they are designed to inactivate all pathogenic organisms and some, but not necessarily all, of the spoilage organisms which, if present, would be capable of growing in the food under defined storage conditions. Milk technology affords good examples of their use. Liquid milk for domestic consumption is distributed frequently and a short storage life can be accepted. A pasteurisation process can destroy pathogens in the milk while leaving its organoleptic properties effectively unimpaired. The pasteurisation of milk for cheese-making destroys organisms that would compete with the desired fermentation.

Nicholas Appert (1750–1840), the inventor of the process of preservation by heating in sealed containers, recommended the heating of containers of food in boiling water in a bain-marie and holding them there for prescribed periods of time. Such processes belong to the second class above (heating to a temperature of 100°C) and are still in use for home bottling and for the commercial canning of acid products such as fruit (say in the pH range 3·7–4·5). For products of less acidity the holding times at 100°C required to produce a microbiologically acceptable pack are very long and it is desirable to heat to temperatures above 100°C to achieve a shorter process with improved product quality (see Section 11.1.4). This third class of heat process was developed in the mid-nineteenth century; first baths of boiling salt solution and then steam under pressure in a retort being used as the heating medium.

As may be seen from the above, the pH of the material strongly influences the nature of the heat process required to produce an acceptable product. Preserved foods range in pH from neutrality to about pH 3·0. The inhibiting effect of acids on spoilage organisms starts to become apparent at pH 5·3, whilst *Clostridium botulinum* and other food-poisoning organisms are inhibited at pH 4·5. Below pH 3·7 only fungi are likely to grow. The important demarcation point occurs at pH 4·5. For low acid foods (pH ≥ 4·5) the requirement to destroy food poisoning organisms such as *C. botulinum* leads to the use of the severest class of heat processing, treatment above 100°C; such processes are frequently described as 'sterilisation'—a term to which some objection can be raised, since it implies complete absence of viable microflora. A better term is 'commercial sterilisation' (see Section 11.1.2) which may be defined as heat processing designed to inactivate substantially all micro-organisms and spores which, if present, would be capable of growing in the food under defined storage conditions.

The pH is not the only factor which influences the nature of the heat process required for the product. The presence of osmotically active ingredients like salt or sugar will affect the growth properties of the microflora. Again, the organoleptic properties of large cans of ham would be impaired by normal heat processing; the use of refrigerated post-processing storage enables a sound product to be marketed following a mild heat process. Products with a very low pH, such as acid pickles, or with low water activity, such as sweetened condensed milk or dried foods, provide environments so hostile to spoilage micro-organisms that no heat processing is needed for their preservation. In such cases, however, it is possible that a mild pasteurisation process might be needed to inactivate enzymes.

11.1.2. THE THERMAL DESTRUCTION OF SPOILAGE MICROORGANISMS

The microbiological stability and eating quality of heat processed foods are affected both by the temperature and duration of the thermal process. Under-processed food will be liable to bacterial spoilage, and over-processed food will be nutritionally and organoleptically inferior. The parameters of a suitable thermal process may be estimated on the basis of assumptions regarding the heat resistance of the spoilage micro-organisms, the kinetics of quality loss and a knowledge of the temperature history of the food during processing.

It is customary to assume that bacterial spores (as also vegetative cells) have a logarithmic order of death,[2] i.e. when a given spore preparation is held at a constant temperature sufficiently high for thermal destruction to occur, the number of spores per unit volume decreases as shown in Fig. 11.1. Clearly, from Fig. 11.1, if the spore concentration is N_1 spores ml^{-1} of suspension at time $t = 0$ and N spores ml^{-1} at time $t = t$:

$$\log \frac{N}{N_1} = -\frac{t}{D} \tag{11.1}$$

where D is a constant known as the 'Decimal Reduction Time' and is the time over which the spore concentration is reduced tenfold ($\log 10 = 1$). For the purposes of heat process calculations the decimal reduction time is assumed to be independent of the initial spore concentration but a function of temperature. It is also dependent not only on the strain of the species of bacterial spore and the medium in which the spores are heated, but also on

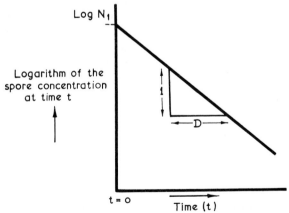

FIG. 11.1. The relationship between the spore concentration and the time of heating at a constant temperature.

the previous history of the spores and the techniques used for detecting survivors (what is always measured is the number of surviving spores that grow under the experimental conditions, which is not necessarily an absolute measure of the 'number of survivors').

Experimental determinations of spore survival characteristics do not always yield the straight line relationship shown in Fig. 11.1. The most commonly observed variation is a sigmoidal curve with a shoulder and tail, i.e. with lower gradients at high and low values of the time, t, than at intermediate t-values. While, in some instances, this may be generated by features of the microbiological technique (e.g. clumping of cells or the presence of two or more spore types with differing heat characteristics[1]), it may also be a consequence of the kinetics of spore inactivation.

Let us assume that all spores present are equally susceptible to heat inactivation and that the inactivation event takes place randomly with the probability of it occurring in any one spore in time dt being $p\,dt$, where p is a constant. If the spore concentration at time t is N per ml, the change in spore concentration dN in time dt will be $-Np\,dt$ so

$$\frac{dN}{N} = -p\,dt \tag{11.2}$$

which, on integration, leads directly to equation (11.1).

However, if the spores do not have a uniform resistance, p will vary from spore to spore about a mean value, according to some distribution function. The more rapid inactivation of spores with high values of p will lead to the development of a population with a mean resistance to thermal inactivation that will increase as heating progresses.

The position is by no means clear and, for practical purposes, it seems reasonable to retain the concept of a straight line relationship, as shown in Fig. 11.1, but to interpret experimental data conservatively, giving more weight to any 'tail' when determining the value of D since, in practice, the validity of any experimentally determined relationship must be assumed to hold down to spore concentrations far lower than can be experimentally investigated (see below), requiring the extrapolation of the line in Fig. 11.1 to a very considerable distance to the right.

An immediate result of equation (11.1) is that since N can become equal to zero only when t becomes infinite, it would appear to be impossible to sterilise a spore concentration with absolute certainty. From this the concept of 'commercial sterility' has arisen. If the concentration of a given strain of bacteria or bacterial spores in a batch of food product is reduced to below a certain value ($N_0\,ml^{-1}$), just low enough to present a commercially acceptable spoilage hazard, the product is said to be 'commercially sterile' with respect to that organism. If N_1 is taken to be the initial concentration of a particular bacterial spore in a certain food material before heat processing, then we may write:

$$m = \log\left(\frac{N_1}{N_0}\right) \tag{11.3}$$

This has been termed the 'reduction exponent'[1] since, e.g. for $m = 5$ the process reduces the spore concentration by a factor of 10^5. Table 11.1 gives frequently adopted values of m for different spoilage organisms. It should be noted that these figures are based on a value of N_1 resulting from good hygienic practice in the preparation of the product. If a higher than normal initial spore level is expected for any reason, the value of the reduction exponent must be correspondingly higher if commercial sterility is to be achieved. Furthermore the value of m adopted, particularly in the case of *C. botulinum*, is such that the validity of equation (11.1) is assumed far outside the range for which it has been experimentally verified. For instance, it is unlikely that equation (11.1) would be testable, experimentally, below a level of 10^{-2} spores ml^{-1} because of practical difficulties. The spore concentration of this organism in a can of unprocessed low-acid food might be only 100 times this level. The use of $m = 12$ therefore implies extrapolation

TABLE 11.1
Approximate heat processing data for some important spoilage organisms[a]

Organism	θ (°C)	D_θ (Min)	z (°C)	m	Type of product needing protection against spoilage by this organism
C. botulinum		0·1–0·3	8–11	12	Low acid foods (pH > 4·5)
C. sporogenes		0·8–1·5	9–11	5	Meats
B. stearothermophilis		4–5	9·5–10	5	Vegetables and milk
C. thermosaccarolyticum	121·11	3–4	7–10·5	5	Vegetables
B. subtilis		∼0·4	6·5	6	Milk products
B. coagulans		0·01–0·07	10	5	Foods of pH 4·2–4·5, e.g. tomatoes
C. pasteurianum	100	0·1–0·5	8	5	Foods of pH 4·2–4·5, e.g. pears

[a] These figures are intended to be indicative only. The nature of the foodstuff affects the thermal resistance of spoilage organisms, so the specialist literature should be consulted for more precise information on particular products.

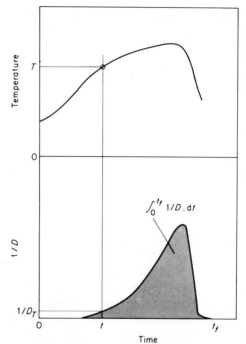

FIG. 11.2. The evaluation of the integral in equation (11.6).

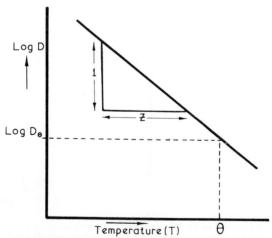

FIG. 11.3. The variation of the decimal reduction time with temperature.

by a factor of 10^{10} beyond the experimental data. Thus it may be seen that the methods of thermal process calculation described subsequently are justified mainly by their success in practice; elaboration of theory and results stated to several significant figures are out of place when the fundamental ground of the calculation is so lacking in precision.

11.1.3. THE EFFECT OF VARYING TEMPERATURES

Consider a suspension of bacterial spores of equal heat resistance held at a temperature which is uniform but varies with time. Suppose that at the start of the process ($t = 0$) the spore concentration is N_1 and at the end of the process ($t = t_f$) it has been reduced to N_f. From equation (11.1):

$$\log \frac{N_f}{N_1} = - \int_0^{t_f} \frac{dt}{D} \qquad (11.4)$$

For commercial sterility to be achieved N_f must be no greater than N_0 or in other words:

$$\log \frac{N_f}{N_1} \leq \log \frac{N_0}{N_1} \qquad (11.5)$$

So that, from equations (11.3), (11.4) and (11.5)

$$\int_0^{t_f} \frac{dt}{D} \geq m \qquad (11.6)$$

Referring to Fig. 11.2, suppose the upper graph represents the temperature-history of the spore suspension. At any arbitrary time t, let the temperature of the suspension be T. If the variation of the decimal reduction time with temperature is known from experimental data, the decimal reduction time, D_T, at temperature T can be determined (say from a graph of experimental results) and the point (t, $1/D_T$) plotted on the lower axes as shown. Repeating this operation for a number of different values of t will enable the graph of $1/D$ against t to be drawn. The area under this graph (shown shaded) will then be equal to the left hand side of the inequality (11.6). This area can then be compared with m, as indicated by the inequality, to see if commercial sterility has been achieved with respect to this organism.

If we can express the decimal reduction time as an explicit function of temperature, the inequality (11.6) can be developed further. One approach, following a suggestion of Bigelow[3] is to assume an empirical relationship in which the logarithm of the decimal reduction time is a linear function of temperature (Fig. 11.3). Thus if the decimal reduction time at some reference temperature, θ, is equal to D_θ, the decimal reduction time, D, at temperature T is given by:

$$\log \frac{D}{D_\theta} = -\frac{T-\theta}{z} \qquad (11.7)$$

where z is the temperature range over which the decimal reduction time changes tenfold. Thus equation (11.4) may be re-written:

$$\frac{1}{D_\theta} \int_0^{t_f} 10^{(T-\theta)/z} \, dt \geq m \qquad (11.8)$$

or, putting $L = 10^{(T-\theta)/z}$, as:

$$\int_0^{t_f} L \, dt \geq mD_\theta \qquad (11.9)$$

The inequalities of equations (11.6) and (11.9) offer alternative, though related, ways of assessing the severity of a thermal process since, if the inequality is satisfied, commercial sterility of the suspension has been achieved. In both cases the left hand side may be evaluated by graphical integration.

An alternative approach, advocated by some workers is to assume an Arrhenius-type relationship between the decimal reduction time and temperature, the logarithm of the decimal reduction time being a linear function of the reciprocal of the absolute temperature. Although this relationship is quite different to that assumed in Fig. 11.3, over a limited range of temperature both assumptions lead to predictions in reasonable agreement with each other. It can be seen from Fig. 11.2 that, in practice, the majority of the sterilising effect accrues over a narrow temperature range near the maximum temperature experienced by the suspension. The most accurate values of D will be required over the range where the temperature, and therefore the rate of spore inactivation, is highest. In the case of Fig. 11.3, if the reference temperature is chosen so that it falls at the upper end of the temperature range experienced by the material under process, and if the line from which D and z are determined is drawn so that it has the best fit to the experimental data in the temperature range close to this reference temperature, then divergences between the line and the experimental data at lower temperatures will be of lesser importance since the contribution being made to the overall sterilising effect will be much less at those temperatures. Correspondingly, an Arrhenius relationship may be modelled to give the best fit to the experimental data in the higher temperature range, leading to similar and equally acceptable results. In the treatment given below equations (11.7)–(11.9) are used, rather than those derived from an Arrhenius-type relationship, since the former have achieved wide currency in canning technology.

To make use of equation (11.9), it is necessary to assume a certain z-value for the organism and a suitable reference temperature. From what has been said before, it is clear that this last should be approximately equal to the maximum temperature experienced by the suspension. For suspensions processed at 100°C, the reference temperature should be taken as that. For pasteurisation processes, reference temperatures below 100°C may be used.[4] For products processed in a retort it has, in the past, been a general convention to take 250°F as a reference temperature. In terms of the Celsius scale this is 121·11°C. Although inconvenient when expressed on the Celsius scale, this standard is now too well established to be abandoned in favour of a round number such as 120°C.[4] Because of its present currency it has been retained in Table 11.1, where a selection of the thermo-bacteriological constants of important food spoilage organisms are listed.

After selecting z and θ, L can quickly be determined for any set of temperatures, T, using a pocket calculator. However, for convenience, two tables of such results (Lethal Rate Tables) are given below. Tables 11.2 and 11.3 have been constructed assuming $z = 10°C$, which is an average value

TABLE 11.2

L values for $z = 10°C$ and $\theta = 121 \cdot 11°C$ ($= 250°F$) (from 100°C to 110°C in increments of 1°C and to 121·9°C in increments of 0·1°C)

°C	0	1	2	3	4	5	6	7	8	9
100	0·01	0·01	0·01	0·02	0·02	0·02	0·03	0·04	0·05	0·06

°C	0·0	0·1	0·2	0·3	0·4	0·5	0·6	0·7	0·8	0·9
110	0·08	0·08	0·08	0·08	0·08	0·09	0·09	0·09	0·09	0·10
111	0·10	0·10	0·10	0·10	0·11	0·11	0·11	0·11	0·12	0·12
112	0·12	0·13	0·13	0·13	0·13	0·14	0·14	0·14	0·15	0·15
113	0·15	0·16	0·16	0·17	0·17	0·17	0·18	0·18	0·19	0·19
114	0·19	0·20	0·20	0·21	0·21	0·22	0·22	0·23	0·23	0·24
115	0·24	0·25	0·26	0·26	0·27	0·27	0·28	0·29	0·29	0·30
116	0·31	0·32	0·32	0·33	0·34	0·35	0·35	0·36	0·37	0·38
117	0·39	0·40	0·41	0·42	0·43	0·44	0·45	0·46	0·47	0·48
118	0·49	0·50	0·51	0·52	0·54	0·55	0·56	0·57	0·59	0·60
119	0·62	0·63	0·64	0·66	0·67	0·69	0·71	0·72	0·74	0·76
120	0·77	0·79	0·81	0·83	0·85	0·87	0·89	0·91	0·93	0·95
121	0·97	1·00	1·02	1·04	1·07	1·09	1·12	1·15	1·17	1·20

TABLE 11.3

L values for $z = 10°C$ and any Reference Temperature (from $(\theta - 20)°C$ to $(\theta - 10)°C$ in increments of $1°C$ and to $(\theta + 1\cdot9)°C$ in increments of $0\cdot1°C$)

°C	0	1	2	3	4	5	6	7	8	9
$(\theta - 20)$	0·1	0·01	0·02	0·02	0·03	0·03	0·04	0·05	0·06	0·08

°C	0·0	0·1	0·2	0·3	0·4	0·5	0·6	0·7	0·8	0·9
$(\theta - 10)$	0·10	0·10	0·10	0·11	0·11	0·11	0·11	0·12	0·12	0·12
$(\theta - 9)$	0·13	0·13	0·13	0·13	0·14	0·14	0·14	0·15	0·15	0·15
$(\theta - 8)$	0·16	0·16	0·17	0·17	0·17	0·18	0·18	0·19	0·19	0·19
$(\theta - 7)$	0·20	0·20	0·21	0·21	0·22	0·22	0·23	0·23	0·24	0·25
$(\theta - 6)$	0·25	0·26	0·26	0·27	0·28	0·28	0·29	0·30	0·30	0·31
$(\theta - 5)$	0·32	0·32	0·33	0·34	0·35	0·35	0·36	0·37	0·38	0·39
$(\theta - 4)$	0·40	0·41	0·42	0·43	0·44	0·45	0·46	0·47	0·48	0·49
$(\theta - 3)$	0·50	0·51	0·52	0·54	0·55	0·56	0·58	0·59	0·60	0·62
$(\theta - 2)$	0·63	0·65	0·66	0·68	0·69	0·71	0·72	0·74	0·76	0·78
$(\theta - 1)$	0·79	0·81	0·83	0·85	0·87	0·89	0·91	0·93	0·95	0·98
θ	1·00	1·02	1·05	1·07	1·10	1·12	1·15	1·17	1·20	1·23
$(\theta + 1)$	1·26	1·29	1·32	1·35	1·38	1·41	1·45	1·48	1·51	1·55

among those listed in Table 11.1. Table 11.2 assumes the traditional reference temperature of $121\cdot11°C$ ($250°F$) while Table 11.3 is applicable to any reference temperature and is convenient to use when the reference temperature is an integral number of Celsius degrees. In such a case, the quantities in the left-hand column of the table can swiftly be interpreted as a set of temperatures, T, and these temperatures entered, temporarily, by the side of the table in such a way that they may be changed if subsequently it is desired to use a different reference temperature.

The integral on the left hand side of equation (11.9) has the dimensions of time, and has been called the 'equivalent time' of the process and denoted by the symbol F. Since this time is calculated with respect to a particular value of z and a particular reference temperature θ, these values are often used respectively as superscripts and subscripts to the symbol for equivalent time, thus: F^{10}_{120}.

In the particular case of equivalent times calculated with respect to $z = 10°C$ and $\theta = 121\cdot11°C$, important for reasons which are discussed in the following subsection, the symbol F_0 is used.

The evaluation of the equivalent time, F, follows the same course as that of the evaluation of $\int_0^{t_f} \dfrac{dt}{D}$ (see Fig. 11.2). First a graph of L against time is

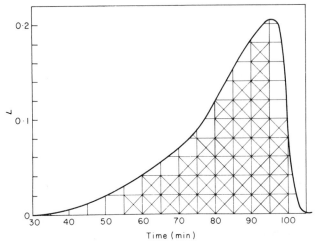

Fig. 11.4. Graph of L versus time showing how the integral is evaluated.

drawn up, using the temperature history of the suspension and a suitable lethal rate table, to give a curve as shown in Fig. 11.4. Next the area beneath that curve is measured. An easy way of measuring such areas is by counting squares. For instance, using the squares ruled in Fig. 11.4, the area beneath the curve amounts to 39 whole squares (marked by crosses) and parts of squares which have a total area amounting approximately to 15 squares more. Each square represents an area 5 min wide by 0·02 units high (i.e. of 5 × 0·02 min), so the total area beneath the curve is approximately

$$5 \times 0·02 \times (39 + 15) = 5·4 \text{ min}$$

11.1.4. THE PRACTICAL APPLICATION OF THE THEORY TO THERMAL PROCESS CALCULATIONS

The theory given in Section 11.1.3 relates only to a spore suspension in which the temperature varies with time but not location. Where material is sterilised in a continuous process outside the container (say, by Ohmic heating or in a plate heat exchanger) and subsequently filled aseptically into containers (see Section 11.4), it may sometimes be possible to regard the material as divided into elementary volumes each of which experiences a substantially identical temperature history as it flows through the apparatus. Nevertheless for food in containers such as cans, heated and cooled by external agencies, the temperature in the food during the process varies from point to point. Some writers have suggested that in this situation the probability of spore survival should be integrated over the contents of the can.[2] Such a procedure is possible only if the temperature history of every particle of food in the can can be inferred.

A common practice is to assume that the can is a homogeneous right-circular cylinder of material heating and cooling purely by conduction. This is to ignore the enormous variety of heating regimes that occur in real packs of canned foods. There is likely to be at least a limited convective product movement, which may change as heating progresses due to the reduction of density gradients and/or the gelatinisation of the contents of the can. Packs will be non-homogeneous (fluid–solid mixtures, often non-uniform throughout due to settlement of the contents). The headspace gases (see Section 11.2.2.1) will locally reduce heat transfer to the contents, and so on. Although a substantial literature has built up around the concept of integrating the heat sterilising effect throughout the can, it is difficult to see that it could be practically applied except in a minority of cases.

An alternative approach—simple, practical, though less logical—is to base calculations on a single temperature history determined at the slowest heating point within the can. In the case of pure conduction heating and cooling, the F-value calculated for temperature histories measured at locations in the vicinity of this point will probably show relatively little spatial variation. Towards the outside of the can F-values increase considerably. Thus, it is reasonable to assume that if the material at the slowest heating point is adequately processed, overall the material has, on average, received a more severe and, therefore, safer process. For cans where free convection prevails, temperatures are more uniform throughout and the question of product location is of less relevance.

In packs where conduction heating prevails, the slowest heating point is at, or slightly above, the geometric centre of a can retorted in an upright position. In other cases its location is best determined experimentally. Where solid particles are present in the can contents, consideration must be given to whether spores are likely to be distributed throughout the piece or only near its surface. This will determine whether the temperature history should be measured at the centre or near the surface of a solid piece located at the slowest heating point. If dry ingredients form part of the can fill to be rehydrated during the sterilising process by absorption of water from the surroundings, it must be remembered that heat inactivation of spores can be a slower process in a dry environment than in a moist one.

So far, attention has been given only to suspensions containing organisms of identical thermal resistance. While unprocessed cans contain a varied microflora, certain spoilage organisms are of particular importance either because they are the most heat resistant present or because, for safety reasons, their final concentration must be reduced to an exceptionally low level. Thus it is possible to restrict attention to one of the organisms present in the pack, this organism being the critical one for the particular foodstuff involved. For instance, while all packs with a pH above 4·5 must be processed sufficiently to protect them against *C. botulinum*, meat packs, in which *C. sporogenes* may prove a problem, will require a more severe heat process to protect them from spoilage by the latter organism. Furthermore, since many of the important spoilage organisms have a *z*-value of about 10°C, the commercial process for many canned foods can be conveniently specified by giving the F_0 value (see Section 11.1.3) which should be achieved over the process. A number of these values are listed in Table 11.4.

Thus, if it is desired to establish a satisfactory thermal process for a new product, a decision is first made as to the probable value of F_0 required to achieve commercial sterility, having regard to established practice with other packs and the nature and composition of the pack in question. Next, a process has to be designed to achieve this F_0 value. A specific F_0 value can be achieved by any number of temperature/time combinations. The availability of equipment will place some constraints on the process adopted, but a major consideration will be the nutritional and sensory quality of the finished product brought about by chemical activity during the heating process. The rate of, say, vitamin loss may be represented as a function of temperature by a curve such as in Fig. 11.3 and, on the basis that the rate of a chemical reaction is, roughly, doubled by a 10°C increase in temperature, a *z*-value of about 33°C might be expected for such a change. Ohlsson[5] determined the rate of loss of sensory quality in a number of products as a function of heating temperature using a panel of assessors and found *z*-values were generally in the range 20–30°C. These values are substantially higher than the value $z = 10$°C conventionally adopted for spore inactivation so, clearly, quality loss is a less temperature-dependent process than spore inactivation. Thus, it might be concluded that to achieve the required F_0 value by heating to a high temperature for a short time will give a better quality retention. While this is true in many cases and forms the rationale for the processing methods discussed below in Section 11.4, theoretical calculations based on a pure conduction model[5] indicate that, for such products heated in sealed containers, an optimum process temperature exists for maximal quality retention at a specific F_0 value.

To assess the F_0 value achieved in any specific set of processing conditions, temperature history measurements at the thermal centre of test cans are required. In making these measurements, special consideration is required in three areas. Firstly, the can contents must be those which will be encountered in a normal production run of the product. The ingredients

TABLE 11.4

F_0 values that have been successfully used commercially for products on the UK market

Product	Can sizes	F_0 values
Babyfoods	babyfood	3–5
Beans in tomato sauce	All	4–6
Peas in brine	up to A2	6
	A2 to A10	6–8
Carrots	All	3–4
Green beans in brine	up to A2	4–6
	A2 to A10	6–8
Celery	A2	3–4
Mushrooms in brine	A1	8–10
Mushrooms in butter	up to A1	6–8
Meats in gravy	All	12–15
Sliced meat in gravy	Ovals	10
Meat pies	Tapered, flat	10
Sausages in fat	up to 1 lb	4–6
Frankfurters in brine	up to 16Z	3–4
Curried meats and vegetables	up to 16Z	8–12
Poultry and Game, whole in brine	A2½ to A10	15–18
Chicken fillets in jelly	up to 16 oz	6–10
'Sterile' ham	1 and 2 lb	3–4
Herrings in tomato	Ovals	6–8
Meat soups	up to 16Z	10
Tomato soup, not cream of	All	3
Cream soups	A1 to 16Z	4–5
	up to A10	6–10
Milk puddings	up to 16Z	4–10
Cream	4/6 oz	3–4
	16Z	6
Evaporated milk	up to 16 oz	5
Petfoods	up to 16Z	15–18

(Reproduced by courtesy of *Food Manufacture*, London.)

and the way that they are prepared must be correct, the initial temperature of the contents at the start of the process and the delays between formulation and can filling and can filling and retorting must be matched to the production schedules as all these factors can influence product viscosity, the mobility of the product within the can and hence the F_0 value. Even if all precautions are taken there will still be can-to-can variability. Secondly, the headspace conditions (see Section 11.2.2.1) must match those in a production can (in particular, the can vacuum). Temperature probes that make the achievement of this criterion difficult because they are incompatible with the filling and closing procedures to be adopted in production runs should best be avoided. Finally, it must be appreciated that some variation of F_0 value will be observable between cans in different parts of any retort—batch or continuous—due to the dynamics of heating and cooling. In a badly designed retort these variations can be very substantial and, obviously, it is a requirement that the least-well-processed can is adequately treated. A discussion of these sources of variability has been given by Cleland and Robertson.[6]

Experimental determinations of temperature histories (or 'heat penetration' experiments, as they are termed) are most conveniently made with thermoelectric thermometers. Several thermocouples specifically designed for this purpose are available commercially. Temperature probes are even available which link to a special computing device which displays the accumulated F-value as processing proceeds. While it is desirable to use a thermocouple which is robust, mounts conveniently in the test can and allows the can to be filled and closed conventionally, nevertheless it is essential that the presence of the thermocouple and its mounting should not disturb significantly the temperature distribution within the can. Heavy metal fittings and the use of heavy-gauge copper wires are therefore to be avoided.[7,8] Where cans are agitated in a rotary batch retort (see Section 11.3.1) consideration must be given to the possibility that the stirring effect of the thermocouple probe appreciably enhances heat transfer in the test can. Additionally, in such a situation, the thermocouple head will be rotating with the can so an assembly with sliding contacts is required to link the probe and the electrical meter. This assembly must be specifically designed to avoid the generation of parasitic thermoelectric voltages that would cause errors in the indicated temperature. In continuous retorts the problems of measuring temperature histories are even more acute. In hydrostatic retorts (see Section 11.3.3.1) temperature sensors linked to radio transmitters have been used. An aerial array installed within the retort picks up the transmitted temperature signal. Alternatively, electronic devices which can be sealed within the container and which measure and store information during the processing operation have been produced. The devices can subsequently be interrogated after removal from the container and the information passed to a computer. Although modern microelectronics has enabled these devices to be relatively small, their size is not negligible and it is wise to validate that the indicated temperature history is not an artifact of the presence of the device. A final approach to the problem of obtaining temperature histories for products processed in continuous retorts is to use a specially-built process simulator which mimics the movements of the can in the continuous retort and subjects the can to the same temperature environment. The simulator is built on the lines of a rotary batch retort so that the temperature signal may be more easily accessed.

Once a process has been developed by these techniques, it should be further validated by a carefully planned programme of incubation testing of canned product produced first in pilot scale and, subsequently, in production runs. After this validation, routine testing should be instituted to give assurance that the required F_0 value is maintained in subsequent production.

11.1.5. INOCULATED PACKS

It may be deduced from equation (11.2) that a thermal process will reduce the spore concentration of a given bacterial species by a fixed factor. For normal levels of initial infection, a process giving commercial sterility will reduce the normal initial spore concentration of, for example, *C. botulinum* in a low-acid food by such a factor that survivors will, to all intents and purposes, no longer be found. If, however, the initial concentration is increased artificially to such a level that a measurable fraction of the processed cans spoil on subsequent incubation, a direct measure of the actual reduction exponent of the *process* (call this m') becomes possible. The initial concentration must be determined and the final concentration may be inferred either from the fraction of spoiled cans or by microbiological examination of the contents of the cans immediately after processing, depending on the survivor level. For safety reasons, rather than using *C. botulinum* spores, those of strains of *Bacillus steareothermophilus* or *Clostridium sporogenes* PA 3679—a putrefactive anaerobe isolated by the National Food Processors Association Laboratory—are widely used. The z-value of PA 3679 is about $10°C$, similar to that for *C. botulinum*, and the value of $D_{121.1}$ for this organism can be up to 1.5 min, depending upon the substrate. If, using PA 3679, m' for the process is measured with respect to the substrate in question (i.e. the material the spores were suspended in during the heating process) then $m'D_{121.1}$ will give an estimate of F_0 for the process.

Two strategies are possible. Firstly, the spores, suspended in an appropriate buffer, are encapsulated in small glass spheres that can be located at the slowest heating point of the can. This allows easy recovery for determination of the final spore count and produces an estimate of the equivalent time, F_0, which is directly comparable to that obtained by calculation from a temperature history determined at the slowest heating point as in Section 11.1.4. However, a support must be provided to locate the spore spheres and in packs heating by natural or forced convection the presence of this support can disturb the pattern of movement in the same way as the shaft of a thermocouple sensor. Secondly, the spores may be mixed uniformly with the can contents. The value of F_0 then derived relates to the integrated effect of lethal heat throughout the whole can (sometimes represented by the symbol F_s). While this overcomes the logical objection mentioned at the commencement of Section 11.1.4, F_s will have a higher numerical value than an F_0 derived from the slowest heating point; the two quantities are different and must not be confused.

Where temperature history measurements are difficult to obtain (e.g. in continuous sterilisers) or unreliable (e.g. because of the stirring effect of probes in agitated retorting) and where adequate microbiological facilities exist, the use of these methods has attractions. However, they are relatively expensive and, because of the requirements of isolation and incubation, slow in giving results.

11.1.6. FORMULA METHODS OF THERMAL PROCESS EVALUATION

Consider a can of food heated by a medium at a constant temperature T_r. If the initial temperature at the slowest heating point within the can is T_0 and the temperature at this point at any given time is T, then a dimensionless temperature (see Appendix II) can be defined as:

$$V = \frac{T_r - T}{T_r - T_0}$$

If log V is plotted against time, the resulting curve is often found to become asymptotic to a straight line (see Fig. 11.5). Further, it is often the case that thermal destruction of the spores of the critical bacterial species occurs substantially during the period when the linear asymptote forms a good approximation to the true heating curve. This asymptote can be specified by the 'lag factor', j, and the 'slope', f (see Fig. 11.5). The equation to the asymptote provides a relationship between T and t to substitute into equation (11.9). If the equivalent time of the heating phase of the process is denoted by F_h and the value of $T_r - T$ at the end of the heating phase is denoted by g, the left hand side of equation (11.7) can be integrated to give:

$$F_h = Mf \exp\left(\frac{T_r - \theta}{Mz}\right)\left\{-Ei\left(-\frac{g}{Mz}\right)\right\} \tag{11.10}$$

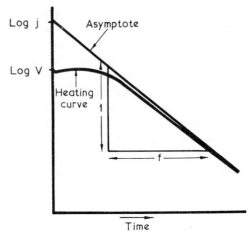

FIG. 11.5. The linear asymptote to the heating curve and its parameters.

where $M = \log e = 0\cdot4343$ and the exponential integral

$$- Ei(-x) = \int_{x}^{\infty} \frac{e^{-t}}{t}\, dt$$

In deriving equation (11.10) it has been assumed that the lower limit of integration (corresponding to the early stages of the heating process) can be ignored as having a negligible value—an approximation which is generally satisfactory.

Values of the exponential integral can be calculated from

$$- Ei(-x) = -\gamma - \ln(x) - \sum_{n=1}^{n=\infty} \frac{(-1)^n x^n}{n.n!} \qquad (11.11)$$

or, in other words

$$- Ei(-x) = -\gamma - \ln(x) + x - \frac{x^2}{4} + \frac{x^3}{18} - \frac{x^4}{96} + \cdots \qquad (11.12)$$

where $\gamma = $ Euler's constant $(0\cdot5772)$.

A simple computer program can easily be developed to evaluate the series in equation (11.11) to any desired accuracy and the terms set down in equation (11.12) will provide values to an accuracy of 1% or better for $x \le 1$ (which are quite likely to be the values sought).

One problem with equation (11.10) is that the quantity g (or $T_r - T$) can be expected to be small and therefore not susceptible to accurate direct measurement. It is wiser to use the eye-fit linear asymptote drawn to the experimental data in order to estimate f (see Fig. 11.5). Knowing the time at the end of the heating phase, a value of V at that instant can be derived from the asymptote and used to determine the value of g.

Since in many instances the majority of the F-value of the overall process is accumulated during the heating phase, the contribution due to the cooling phase is sometimes treated as a safety margin and F_h taken as the total equivalent time. This is an appropriate approach for products which heat and cool mainly by convection, for which the cooling phase contributes little to the overall F-value. However, where conduction is the major mode of heat transfer both during heating and cooling and when the value of g is relatively large, the can-centre temperature will continue to *rise* in the early part of the cooling phase ('overshoot'). The contribution of the cooling phase to the overall F-value can then be considerable.[9] Starting with Ball,[10] many workers have attempted to extend equation (11.10) to cover the cooling phase. Such extensions introduce complexity into the calculation and must, of necessity, be based on assumptions concerning the mode of heat transfer during that phase (e.g. that it is by conduction). However, it should not be assumed that because a can heats by conduction it will cool by conduction. When headspace air pressure is sufficiently low, boiling, with mass movement of the contents and erratic variation of centre temperature, can be observed during the cooling of conduction heating packs and wide variations in F-values can result.[9]

Thus while these 'formula' methods of calculation may offer some advantages when changes of can size or retort temperature are being considered for existing products, the assumptions made concerning the physics of heating restrict their usefulness.

11.2. PRELIMINARY OPERATIONS FOR STERILISATION IN CONTAINERS

'Commercial sterilisation', as defined in Section 11.1.1, is heat processing designed to inactivate all micro-organisms and spores which, if present, would be capable of growing in the food under defined storage conditions. Two general methods of sterilisation are used: (i) sterilising in containers, and (ii) sterilisation of the food before placing in the containers (see Fig. 11.6). All these procedures involve temperatures in excess of 100°C, hence pressures above atmospheric are generated.

The containers used are cans, glass jars and film pouches. Considerable

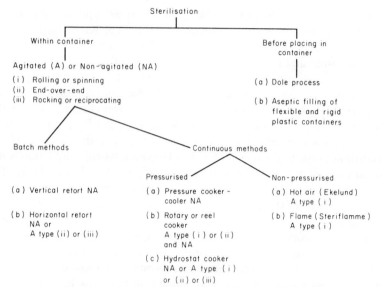

FIG. 11.6.   Categorisation of sterilising methods.

development of sterilisable containers has taken place in recent years. Cans are now available with easy-open ends and with 'necked-in' flanges (to control post-process infection). The use of tin-free steel cans is also of interest. Sterilisable plastic containers are obtainable in rigid, semi-rigid and flexible forms in wide material varieties and combinations (see Section 21.2). Heat penetration in these packs is controlled by the geometry of the pack and by the thermal properties of the food, the container and the heating medium. For these reasons, in-pack sterilisation, particularly where conduction heating foods are involved, is slow compared with external sterilisation where high-speed heat exchangers may be used.

Irrespective of the type of container used, heat processing is preceded by filling, exhausting and closing, and these operations exert considerable influence over the rate of heat penetration and the effectiveness of the heat process. The methods of carrying out these preliminary stages and their effect on the process and on the food are considered, briefly, in the following sections. These refer, specifically, to canned foods, but the underlying principles are applicable to other types of container.

11.2.1. FILLING INTO CONTAINERS

Containers and lids are supplied in a 'commercially clean' condition. This guarantees nothing and it is vital, therefore, to ensure that containers are cleaned before filling. Cans and glass containers are washed by inversion over hot water sprays or by rotary brushing. They are then conveyed upside down for draining and, to limit recontamination, should remain inverted until just before filling.

Filling machines vary, depending on whether the material filled be a liquid, a paste, or a solid (see Section 21.3), but all fillers must:

(i) ensure accurate fill,
(ii) avoid slopping even at maximum fill-rate,
(iii) include a 'no can—no fill' device,
(iv) be flexible for different size and fill-rates, and
(v) be of good sanitary design.

Liquid components include brines (i.e. salt solutions) and syrups, or sugar solutions. Syrup strengths in canned and bottled fruits are controlled either by Codes of Practice[11] or by legislation. Sugars are relatively expensive so that, apart from specification considerations, it is important to control syrup strengths within narrow limits. The hardness of the water used to make syrups and brines is often an important factor controlling the texture of canned fruits and vegetables (see Chapter 18).

Syrups and brines have the following desirable attributes:

(i) they improve heat transfer to food packed with them;
(ii) being osmotically active, they help to preserve the food;
(iii) they displace air and gases from solid or paste ingredients, assisting heat transfer within them and reducing pressure strain in containers during processing;
(iv) they improve flavour and acceptability;
(v) they provide a convenient means of incorporating small-quantity ingredients such as flavours and colours;
(vi) in some foods (e.g. apples, pears, potatoes) they inhibit browning.

Viscous ingredients, such as fish and meat pastes, purees, etc., pose special filling problems in canning since they tend to carry entrapped air into the container reducing heat transfer, increasing internal pressure and causing uneven filling. These difficulties may be alleviated by pre-vacuumising the food before filling.

Solid ingredients of a delicate nature, such as strawberries or sliced beetroot or components where orientation affects heat transfer within the container (e.g. rhubarb sticks, asparagus spears), are filled by hand. Other solid components may be filled by volumetric devices described in Section 21.3.

It is important that filling of containers ensures correct headspacing (see Section 11.2.2.1) and also leaves the container flanges in a clean condition. Food trapped between the body of the container and its closure may lead to post-process infection.

11.2.2. EXHAUSTING OF CONTAINERS

11.2.2.1. The development of internal pressure during heat processing

When a closed container (e.g. a can of food) is heated, internal pressure is generated owing to the following effects:

(i)   the can contents expanding,
(ii) the water vapour pressure increasing, and
(iii) the air and other gases, in the headspace and in the food, expanding.

This internal pressure is partially balanced by the expansion of the can and by the outwards movement of the can ends, which are provided with expansion rings for this purpose. However, a completely filled can would be subjected to excessive strain when sterilised and, to obviate this, a free space (headspace) must be established above the food in the can. The headspace, apart from accommodating liquid and gaseous expansion, facilitates heat transfer during agitated processing. For glass containers processed at 115–121°C it is recommended that the headspace should occupy not less than 6% of the container volume measured at normal sealing temperature (55°C).[12] This recommendation would also appear to be an appropriate lower limit for sterilisation in other rigid containers. As a general rule, the headspace should not exceed 10% of the container volume.

11.2.2.2. The control of internal pressure during heat processing

The vapour pressure within the container is determined by the processing temperature, but the partial pressure of the air in the can during processing may be reduced: (i) by ensuring that the food is freed from entrapped gases (by blanching or pre-vacuumising), and (ii) by producing a partial vacuum in the headspace (exhausting) before closing. In addition to reducing pressure strain (Fig. 11.7) de-gassing and exhausting lowers the oxygen tension within the can, thus reducing can corrosion, limiting oxidation of the food and inhibiting the growth of aerobic organisms. Four methods of exhausting are in general use: mechanical exhausting, hot filling, hot exhausting and steam flow closing.

Mechanical exhausting is applied to heat-sensitive or dry foods, and comprises closing of the cold-filled container under mechanically produced vacuum (e.g. using a pump). Both batch and continuous vacuum seamers are in use and, to ensure adequate degassing of liquid foods, vacuum filling

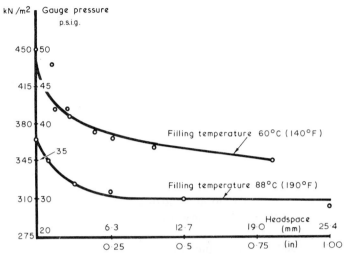

FIG. 11.7. The effect of headspace and filling temperature on the internal pressure in cans during processing. The curves are drawn from measured values of pressure generated in 16Z cans (300 × 410) filled with water to the headspace indicated and processed at 127°C (260°F). (By courtesy of The Metal Box Co. Ltd, London.)

should precede mechanical exhausting wherever practicable. This method is not suitable for viscous foods which tend to froth when vacuumised, and should not be used for foods which liberate gas on heating (e.g. strawberries in syrup).

Hot filling depends on the fact that an aqueous food, hot filled near the boiling point of water, generates about one atmosphere of water vapour pressure in the can headspace so that, on closing without delay and cooling, a vacuum is produced within the can. This method effectively removes gases—in the headspace and trapped in the food—and provides useful preheating which reduces processing time. Disadvantageously, unless the can and its lid are heated before filling, localised cooling and loss of vacuum results on closing. Any delay between filling and closing also causes loss of vacuum.

In *hot exhausting*, the filled cans, either open or with their lids clinched on (Section 11.2.3), are conveyed through a thermostatically controlled water bath or steam chamber where they are heated to 80–95°C. The exhausted cans are then double seamed immediately after leaving the exhauster. The method gives reproducible results because there is no local condensation, as occurs with hot filling. Exhausting time may be excessive with conduction-heating foods, and there is a considerable risk of contamination through the open top or, to a lesser extent, through the clinched lid. Hot exhausting is often used in conjunction with hot filling.

Steam-flow closing involves displacing the headspace gases by jetting steam into the top of the filled container. After a pre-set time the lid, which may also be heated by steam, is automatically positioned and the container is closed.[13] This method of exhausting is applied to slow heating or gassy foods. Obviously removal of entrapped gases by this method is minimal so pre-vacuumising of the food or hot filling should precede steam-flow closure.

11.2.3. CLOSING OF CONTAINERS

Clearly, the storage life of foods preserved in containers is dependent on the protection provided by the closures and on the integrity of any seams which may be present in the containers (e.g. in cans, retort pouches, etc.). Container evaluation is a vital part of quality and safety assurance and reference should be made to specialist literature.[14,15]

Clinching of can lids, as employed in hot exhausting, involves attaching the lid by a first-operation roller. The lids should be just loose enough to allow gases to be vented whilst limiting contamination by exhauster water or condensate. After exhausting, double seaming is completed. Clinching must be carried out so that the final seam is of the correct dimensions.

Types of closure for sterilisable containers and methods of closing are described in Sections 21.2 and 21.3.

11.3. METHODS OF HEAT STERILISATION IN CONTAINERS

Heat processing of food in containers may be effected: by indirect heating by saturated steam; by hot air under forced convection; or by direct flame contact (cans only). Of these, heating in saturated steam is the most commonly used method.

11.3.1. GENERAL CONSIDERATIONS

Low-acid foods (Section 11.1.1) are sterilised at temperatures above 100°C (usually 115–127°C), and this requires the use of pressurised sterilisers. As with any other type of process using steam, it is important to ensure adequate venting of air and condensate from the retort and from the container surfaces.[16] This is particularly important in the case of food sterilisation where any reduction in heat transfer rate could result in under-processing.

Retorting in steam, under pressure, must be carried out so as to minimise thermal shock to the food and to limit pressure strain on the containers. The internal pressure developed on heating, when the food approaches retort temperature, is partly balanced by the pressure of the steam surrounding the containers. However, during the heating-up stage the food is below retort pressure and the containers are under compression, whereas during sterilising and cooling the food is above retort pressure and the containers are under tension. This pressure strain is reduced by controlling the heat-up and cool-down rates and by applying a balancing air pressure to the retort during the cooling stage (pressure cooling).

Thermal shock to glass containers is controlled by processing under water. The application of a superimposed air pressure during heating and cooling is used to counteract pressure strain.[12] This method is also applied to cans which have large areas of flat surface (e.g. rectangular corned-beef cans) and to foods packaged in flexible pouches.[17]

In many conduction heating packs, agitation of the container is used to produce movement of the food and, hence, accelerate the rate of heat transfer. Agitation may be produced by any of the following methods:

(i)   Rotation about the long axes of the cans by rolling them along tracks.

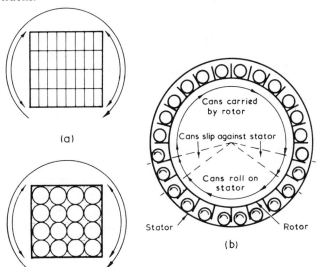

FIG. 11.8.   Common methods of agitating cans during processing. (a) Rotary or oscillatory, axial or end-over-end movement of crated cans in a batch retort. (b) Axial rotary movement of cans in a continuous steriliser.

(ii) End-over-end rotation, the cans being rotated with their long axes aligned as the spokes of a wheel.

(iii) Imparting a reciprocating or rocking motion to the containers (Fig. 11.8).

In order to minimise the risk of infection of the sterilised food after processing, stringent hygiene precautions are necessary. These include: the use of chlorinated cooling water; effective and frequent sanitisation of can runways and conveyors; warm air drying of the containers immediately after discharge from the retort; and strict avoidance of manual handling of the containers whilst they are wet or still warm.

11.3.2. BATCH STERILISERS

Non-agitating batch retorts are used extensively in spite of their high labour requirements. They can accommodate containers of different sizes and are suitable for different types of process but steam and water consumptions are high compared with modern continuous retorts. The vertical (top loading) types (Fig. 11.9) require less floor-space than horizontal (side loading) retorts, but the latter are more convenient to charge and discharge. The design and operation of batch sterilisers are considered in the specialist literature.[18]

Batch sterilisers equipped for end-over-end rotation, for reciprocating and for rocking action of the containers are available.

The Orbitort steriliser (FMC Corp., San Jose, Calif., USA) is an automatic, batch-type cooker-cooler operating at steam pressures of 340–415 kN m^{-2} (25–45 psig). Cans are charged, with their long axes horizontal, at 45 cans min^{-1} via an air-operated gate valve, into the annular space between two concentric reels equipped with spiral guides. The reels are housed in a cylindrical pressure-shell about 1·5 m diameter and 8 m long. When charging is complete (around 600 cans depending on size), the retort is closed automatically, the reels are clamped together to hold the cans and the assembly is rotated within the shell at a controlled speed so that the headspace bubble passes through the can contents once each revolution, inducing stirring. The cooking and pressure-cooling is then controlled by a programmer, the cooled cans being discharged through an air-operated gate valve at the outlet end as a fresh charge is introduced at the inlet valve. The complete cycle, charge to discharge, is automatic.[17]

Reduced operating costs, better space utilisation and better processing of viscous foods compared with other batch retorts are claimed for the Orbitort which is widely used in the USA and in many other parts of the world.

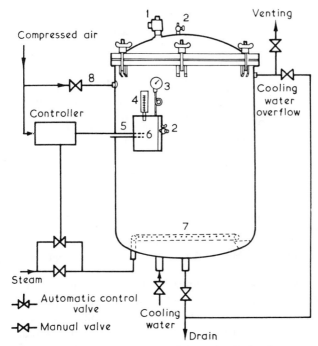

FIG. 11.9. A vertical batch retort equipped for cooling under air pressure. 1, safety valve; 2, petcocks to maintain a steam bleed from retort during processing; 3, pressure gauge; 4, thermometer; 5, sensing element for controller; 6, thermo-box; 7, steam spreader; 8, air inlet for pressure cooling.

11.3.3. CONTINUOUS STERILISERS

Continuous sterilisation may be effected under pressure (using steam) or at atmospheric pressure (using hot air or direct flame heating). This latter method is restricted to use for small cans capable of withstanding the considerable pressure developed.

11.3.3.1. Continuous pressure sterilisers

The main types of continuous pressure sterilisers are: (i) the continuous pressure cooker-cooler, (ii) the continuous rotary steriliser, and (iii) the hydrostatic steriliser. The Hydrolock continuous cooker-cooler (Ateliers et Chantiers de Bretagne, Paris, France) is a recent addition to this class of steriliser.

The continuous pressure cooker-cooler is a non-agitating steriliser. The containers are carried on a roller track or chain conveyor through the

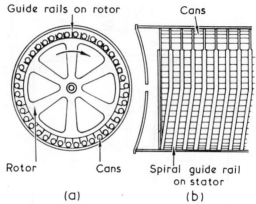

FIG. 11.10. The Mather & Platt Automatic Continuous Rotary Steriliser. (a) End view of rotor. (b) Side view, showing how the lead is confined to the lower part of the spiral so that the cans move forward only when they are in the rolling position. (By courtesy of Mather & Platt Ltd., Manchester, England.)

preheating, sterilising and cooling sections. Transfer between the sections, which are at different pressure, is effected by means of pressure locks.

In the *rotary (or reel) steriliser* (Fig. 11.10) the containers are carried in a helical track affixed to the inner walls of each of three horizontal cylinders. Flanges, attached to the periphery of a slowly rotating hollow drum, convey the containers around and along each cylinder. Pressure locks effect transfer into and out of the machine and between the three sections. Agitation occurs by a combined rolling and sliding action as the containers travel around the helix (Fig. 11.10).

Continuous sterilisers of these types have good capacity (up to 500 cans min^{-1}) and give excellent uniformity of process, providing special care is taken in controlling product viscosity and can head-space conditions.[19] Disadvantageously, a large number of cans are undergoing processing at any one time so that a breakdown, such as may occur at the transfer locks, is serious. Pressure strain and thermal shock, particularly at the transfer valves, may also be considerable in these sterilisers.

In the *hydrostatic steriliser*[17,18] (Fig. 11.11), the containers are conveyed through a steam tower, pressurised by means of water columns. The conveyor consists of slowly moving (~ 2 m min^{-1}) twin roller-chains to which are attached transverse carriers of various types (e.g. 'I' or 'C' section channels or perforated tubes). Containers are normally carried with their long axes horizontal, thus assisting convective heat transfer within the can. Although, primarily, the hydrostatic cooker is a non-agitating steriliser,

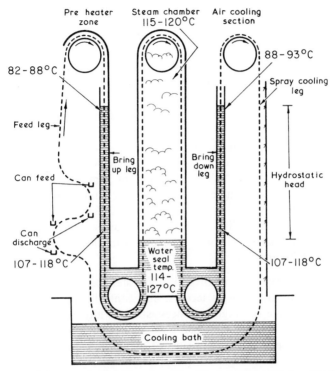

Fig. 11.11. Diagram showing the operating principle of the 'Hydron' hydrostatic steriliser. (By courtesy of Chisholm-Ryder International Ltd., Middlesex, England.)

a degreee of agitation may be imparted. Devices for affecting this include:

(i) Cans conveyed in carriers equipped with sprockets which mesh with a separate chain running parallel with the main conveying chains. This causes the carriers to rotate, inducing end-over-end or axial can motion depending on the orientation of the cans in the carriers.

(ii) Mechanical vibration of the chains carrying the cans.

(iii) Permanent magnets set along the carrier-tube guides cause the tubes to rotate as they adhere to the guides during conveyance.

Other facilities include can-driers and the provision of over-riding air pressure to allow effective processing of foods packaged in plastic pouches and glass containers.

The expanding use of this type of steriliser, since its introduction into Europe in 1936 (there are now several hundred in use throughout the world), is due to its numerous advantages which are as follows:

(i) Its minimisation of thermal and pressure shock to the food and container.

(ii) Its suitability for all types of sterilisable containers.

(iii) Its amenability to a high degree of automation.

(iv) Its efficient use of steam and water.

(v) The excellent uniformity and control of processing of which it is capable.

(vi) Its mechanical reliability.

(vii) Its economic use of floor space (about $40\,m^2$ for an output of $1000\,cans\,min^{-1}$). Although a height of 20 m is necessary, only the bottom section, where charging and discharging takes place, needs to be enclosed.

(viii) Its relative flexibility for different container sizes.

(ix) Its availability in a wide range of capacities (within the range 60–$1000\,cans\,min^{-1}$).

The capital investment involved in these sterilisers, together with their ancillary equipment such as feeders, and control gear, is considerable. Additionally, there is a high in-process stock at any one time. For these reasons, the hydrostatic steriliser is of particular application in high-capacity plants processing long runs of materials requiring similar heat processes.

The Hydrolock steriliser[17,20] (Fig. 11.12), introduced around 1966 comprises a horizontal, cylindrical pressure vessel into which 'sticks' of cans or glass jars, contained in chain-driven carriers, are conveyed via a rotary valve. This valve is sealed partly mechanically and partly by the water in which it is submerged. The containers are preheated as they pass through the valve and then ascend into the top of the pressure cylinder where they are conveyed horizontally, back and forth, under pressure in saturated steam for the required sterilising time. The cans are then pre-cooled as they pass through a slot in a hollow, insulating partition into a water layer in the base of the retort. After pre-cooling the cans are discharged by the rotary valve to final, atmospheric cooling and are then unloaded.

Axial rotation of the cans is effected by rolling them along tracks located below the carriers. Alternatively, these tracks may be disengaged to give non-agitated cooking. Sterilising temperatures up to 143°C are possible (allowing shorter processing times) and the retort may be used with an air-overpressure for processing glass or plastic containers. In this case a fan,

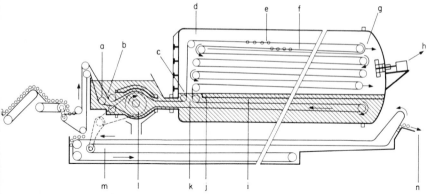

FIG. 11.12. The Hydrolock steriliser: (a) water seal; (b) carrier chain; (c) retort water-level; (d) steam space; (e) cans in carriers; (f) can track; (g) direction-changer; (h) steam–air mixing fan; (i) insulating partition separation steam space from water space; (j) pre-cooling water; (k) transfer slot; (l) water-sealed rotary valve; (m) air cooling; (n) discharge. (By courtesy of Ateliers et Chantiers de Bretagne, Paris, France.)

mounted in the pressure shell, is used to promote intimate mixing of the steam and air to offset, partly, the poor thermal properties of the latter.

Advantages claimed for this machine are economic use of steam, water, labour and space. Disadvantageously, it is to be expected that pressure strains at the rotary valve during charging and discharging would be appreciable.

11.3.3.2. Continuous atmospheric-pressure sterilisers

The Ekelund hot-air steriliser has been used successfully in Sweden for the sterilisation of canned milk. The milk is preheated and is then filled into sterilised cans. The cans are closed and are then conveyed into the top of a hot-air chamber where they roll down tracks (9 passes at 10 m each). The chamber is heated by forced convection with air at 145°C and at a flow-rate of 10 m s^{-1}. Sterilising time is about 15 min, after which the cans are water cooled. The steriliser has a capacity of 3200 cans per hour.[21] Pressure strain is considerable and the process would appear to be limited to small cans for this reason. Successful trials on the canning of fruits and vegetables using this method have also been reported.[22]

Flame sterilisation (the Steriflamme Process) has been used for canned milk, peas, beans, carrots and mushrooms. The cans are preheated in a steam chamber whence they are conveyed into a sterilising chamber where the cans are spun (120 rpm) over gas flames at 1300°C. Thus the can contents are heated rapidly to sterilising temperature (97–125°C in 45 s) after which they are conveyed to a steam-heated holding chamber and finally through a water cooler. Recent equipment modifications include improved agitation using 'shuttle-bar' movement of the cans and pulsing of the heating cycle to allow equilibration of temperatures within the can. The steriliser is uncomplicated in concept and operation and the fast, high temperature process gives high-quality products. Problems exist in can temperature measurement and in the absence of pressure-balancing, this restricting the method to small cans. The heat transfer, thermal processing and quality aspects of Steriflamme processing have been the subject of detailed study.[23]

Flame sterilisation is of particular application in the processing of vacuum packs such as canned corn. In this process, particulate foods are packed with minimal amounts of liquid (typically, 15 parts liquid: 85 parts solid) and the cans are then sealed under high vacuum ($10–30 \, kN \, m^{-2}$ abs.) and are retorted conventionally. Unfortunately, the use of pressurised steam causes a high level of stress failure of the vacuumised cans. This is much reduced if the vacuum packs are flame sterilised, with the added bonus that high-temperature short-time sterilisation is possible, giving improved quality.[24]

11.4. STERILISATION OF THE FOOD OUTSIDE THE CONTAINER

Sterilising methods of this type take advantage of the fact that high temperature processing (up to 150°C) by means of high-speed heat exchangers may be used. This results in a substantial reduction in processing time with consequent general improvement in product quality. Processes using rapid sterilising at these high temperatures are referred to as high-short processes and should not be confused with the HTST process used for milk pasteurisation.

11.4.1. THE EFFECTS OF HIGH-SHORT PROCESSES ON FOOD QUALITY

What little information there is suggests that the destruction of vitamins and food colours or the inactivation of enzymes in foods follows much the same course as the destruction of bacterial spores, but with a z-value considerably higher.[2] This has important consequences. Consider a food that requires an equivalent time.

$$F_{120}^{10} = 10 \, min \text{ for commercial sterilisation}$$

This could be provided by heating the food instantaneously to 120°C, holding it at that temperature for 10 min and instantaneously cooling it again. Alternatively the food could be heated instantaneously to 140°C and instantaneously cooled after a holding time of only 0·1 min.

Suppose that this food contains an enzyme with a z-value of 50°C which requires holding for 4 min at 120°C for inactivation. Clearly the 10 min process at 120°C will both sterilise the food and inactivate the enzyme. However, at 140°C (by adapting equation 11.7) the enzyme can be calculated to require

$$4 \times 10^{(120 - 140)/50} = 1.6 \text{ min for inactivation}$$

Thus the process of 0·1 min at 140°C will produce a commercially sterile product, but not inactivate the enzyme. This simple illustration demonstrates why high temperature-short time processing, while giving acceptably sterile products of high organoleptic quality and with good vitamin retention, can experience enzyme regeneration problems.

In general, therefore, high-short processing gives improved quality products. Exceptions to this include meat based products in which flavour and colour development are the results of extended cooking (as in conventional canning) and canned pulses which are tenderised by lengthy in-container cooking. In such cases it is possible to 'build in' some degree of cooking by inserting a sterile holding tube or buffer vessel between the heating and cooling sections of the equipment.

11.4.2. METHODS OF STERILISING OUTSIDE THE CONTAINER

In processes of this type, the preheated food is rapidly heated in a high-speed heat exchanger to about 140°C and is then passed to a holding section. After the requisite holding time, which is only a matter of seconds with the high 'L values' (Section 11.1.3) obtaining at this temperature, the food is rapidly cooled and is then sealed in sterile containers. This process, which is completed in a few minutes when carried out under aseptic conditions, is known as 'aseptic processing'.

Various types of heat exchanger are used depending on the nature of the food. Low-viscosity foods may be heated indirectly, using steam heated, spiral-tube, or plate-type heat exchangers (Fig. 12.10), or, directly, using in-line injection of 'live' steam. High-viscosity foods are best heated by scraped-surface heat exchangers (Fig. 9.6). Cooling, after holding, may be effected by passage through a vacuumised flash-chamber (which also de-aerates the product), or a continuous cooler of suitable design may be used.

The sterilised food may then be submitted to other processes such as straining or homogenisation before being filled aseptically into sterile containers.

Aseptic processes are now well established and their application is expanding.[25] The more important industrial methods are described below.

11.4.2.1. The Dole Process (The James Dole Engineering Co., San Francisco, USA)

This process has been in use, mainly in the USA, since 1951, and has been applied to milk products, purées, some soups and to yoghourt and sour cream.[17] This process is applied in a closed, inter-connecting system which carries out the sequence of operations described in Section 11.4.2 and provides an uninterrupted passage of the food through the steriliser. The plant is pre-sterilised with superheated steam at about 300°C and a slight positive pressure is maintained during operation to retain sterility. The cans and ends are sterilised with superheated steam at 225°C, briefly cooled by spraying the can-bottoms with sterile water and are then filled through a slit-filler with the cooled, aseptically-sterilised food. Fill-in weights are controlled by using a positive displacement pump to feed the slit-filler. The filled cans are then double seamed using seamers of standard design modified to allow shrouding for sterilisation and to withstand the high temperatures involved. Containers may be handled at 450–500 min^{-1} in retail sizes and packs ranging from 125 ml cans to 22·5 litre drums can be processed. Development of a Dole Aseptic Steriliser for glass containers has reached an advanced stage.

11.4.2.2. Aseptic filling of bulk containers

In the USA pumpable food products such as fruit purées and tomato concentrates are now filled aseptically into specially designed large cans and drums.[17] In one such system, two retorts are used alternately. A drum and its cover, which is fitted with a small filling hole, are placed in the retort, sterilised with steam at 800 kN m^{-2} (~100 psig) and is filled, under vacuum, with cooled aseptically-sterilised food. The filling hole is then closed, with the filled drum still in the retort, the vacuum is released and the sealed drum is removed. The two retorts are operated in sequence and the system can fill 24–55 gallon (US) drums h^{-1}.

Another bulk filler sterilises the drum and lid by jetting with steam at 207 kN m^{-2} (15 psig) for $1\frac{1}{2}$ min with venting followed by a further 1 min with the vent closed. The sterilising jet is then retracted and replaced by a filling tube through which cool, sterilised food is introduced. At the completion of filling, the tube is withdrawn and the filling hole is automatically closed in an aseptic manner.

The advantages claimed for bulk packs are: reduced handling, labour and transportation costs; reduced product hold-up in empty packages and better space utilisation in storage.

11.4.2.3. Aseptic filling of plastic containers

Aseptic filling of rigid and flexible plastic containers is the subject of intensive investigation.[26] Rigorous control is necessary in forming seams and monitoring their integrity. Meticulous attention must be given to the sterilisation of the containers, which, in general, are not amenable to heat treatment. Treatments with ethylene oxide, hot and cold hydrogen peroxide, ionising radiation and sterile air are advocated. Aseptic filling procedures using form-fill-seal equipment, glove-boxes and/or 'clean-room' techniques have been reported (see Section 21.3.4).

11.4.2.4. Aseptic processing of particulate materials

Aseptic processing of foods containing solids in equipment described in Section 11.4.2 is limited to particulates only a few millimetres in size. A number of systems are now available in which pieces of meat, fruit, vegetables, etc., or whole units, such as peas, beans or fruits, may be batch sterilised aseptically. The cooled sterilised pieces are then combined, in a sterile manner, with aseptically processed sauce or other liquid ingredients.

Typical of such equipment is the APV Jupiter System (APV Company Ltd, Crawley, West Sussex, England)[27] depicted in Fig. 11.13. This comprises a double-cone pressure vessel which is fitted with a jacket and carried on a horizontal axle about which it rotates at 2–20 rpm. Steam, air and liquids may be charged via an inlet trunnion whilst the outlet trunnion houses the product delivery pipe which connects the vessel outlet to the filler reservoir. Product heating is effected by live steam injection and/or steam jacketing. The jacket may be used for cooling. Plant pre-sterilisation, process sequencing and in-place cleaning are all microprocessor controlled.

Two new devices for aseptic sterilisation of pumpable (up to custard consistency) foods containing particulates are reported by Stork (Amsterdam).[28] These systems pump a mixture of liquid and particulates (up to 25 mm) at rates of 500–1000 litres h^{-1} through a tubular heat exchanger into a specially designed holding unit which allows the liquid to flow through whilst the solids are retained longer in order to experience an appropriate heat process. The solids are then released and are accumulated together with the sterile liquid in an aseptic buffer/delivery tank after being

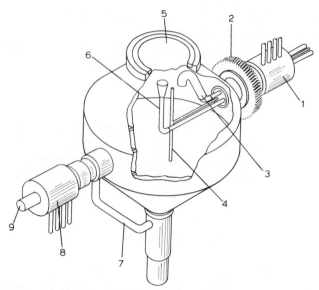

FIG. 11.13. The APV Jupiter double-cone aseptic processing vessel. 1, Services and liquids inlet manifold; 2, rotary drive; 3, steam inlet; 4, temperature transducer; 5, charging port; 6, adjustable drain pipe; 7, product pipe; 8, outlet manifold; 9, product outlet. (By permission of the APV Company Ltd, Crawley, West Sussex, England.)

cooled in a tubular heat exchanger. The cooled, sterile liquid/solid mix is then pumped, aseptically, to the filling unit, the solid/liquid ratio being controlled by metering pumps. Thus the two components of the mixed food are subjected to adjustable and different heat processes in a single pass ('single pass fraction-specific thermal processing'). All stages from plant sterilisation through production to in-place cleaning (CIP) are controlled automatically.

The innovatory part of this process is the design of the holding section and the Stork equipment takes two forms. In the first of these the mix is pumped tangentially into a vessel of circular cross-section in which rotates an assembly like a revolving door, turnstile or rotary valve (see Section 19.6.3.3) which extends from a central axis to the cylindrical walls and rotates at a controlled speed. The individual leaves of this assembly are fabricated from a series of strips to form multipronged forks which sweep through the volume of the vessel. The prongs of these forks are spaced in such a way that the particulate matter is held on the leaf as it rotates. The large particles that cannot pass the fork gaps are retained for attainment of appropriate F_0 value (controlled by the adjustable rotor speed) being heated by the flow of hot liquid through the fork gaps. After the appropriate holding time the solids are released to the buffer/delivery tank. The second type of holding vessel comprises a tubular chamber through which the mixture is pumped axially. The vessel is fitted with a shaft driven slowly at a speed which is adjustable and which is equipped with radial spokes spirally located along it, the pitch of this spoke-spiral decreasing from the inlet to the outlet end of the tube. Adjustment of the shaft speed controls the residence time of the particles retained by the spokes, the sterilised particulates being discharged and recombined with the liquid in metered proportions as described above.

This process is reported to be applicable to a wide range of foods, including dairy, fruit and petfood products.

11.4.2.5. Milk sterilisation

In-pack sterilisation of milk is widely practised but the colour, flavour and sterility of the product leave much to be desired. High-short aseptic processes give much improved quality and extended storage life and numerous processes have been developed. These differ in the method of heating (e.g. 'live' steam injection or indirect plate heating, etc.) and in the times and temperatures used for sterilisation. Cooling and filling are carried out aseptically, the containers being cans, bottles and cartons of various types. The 'Tetra-Pak' and 'Tetra-Brik' Systems (AB Lund, Sweden) have achieved considerable use in the production of long-life milk and coffee whiteners. Composite packs made from laminates of polythene/paperboard/aluminium foil/polythene are used in a process which forms the container, fills it aseptically and seals it in a continuous manner in a single piece of equipment. This is known as 'form-fill-seal' packaging (see Section 21.3.4).

11.5. PASTEURISATION BY HEAT PROCESSING

11.5.1. GENERAL CONSIDERATIONS

This heat process (Section 11.1.1) was developed by Pasteur in 1864 for preventing abnormal fermentations in wine. Pasteurisation is now applied to a wide range of foods: milk, cream, ice-cream, canned and bottled fruits, fruit juices, pickles, beers, wines, and canned liquid egg. In some countries, and for some foods, pasteurising procedures are specified in legislation.

Where legal standards do not exist, suitable pasteurisation processes may be calculated using the principles set out in Section 11.1.

Sterilisation is concerned with spore destruction, whereas in pasteurising the major concern is with the destruction of vegetative organisms and yeast and mould spores. Owing to the relatively low temperatures used (< 100°C) in pasteurisation, foods preserved by this method suffer less heat damage than foods preserved by sterilisation. However, processing at these lower temperatures for times adequate for pasteurisation may leave the food with residual enzyme activity. This may cause spoilage of the food during storage (e.g. in pickles and fruit juice). The oxygen concentration within the food, apart from determining the extent of oxidative deterioration, also controls the growth of some micro-organisms (particularly moulds) in pasteurised foods. For these reasons, pasteurisation processes should be such as to ensure: (i) adequate microbiological control, (ii) destruction of undesired enzymes and (iii) low oxygen tension in the food.

11.5.2. PASTEURISING METHODS
Both batch and continuous methods are used and pasteurisation may take place before or after placing in the container. In all cases the equipment is less complex than that used for sterilisation since pasteurisation is carried out at atmospheric pressure.

11.5.2.1. Batch pasteurisation
Bulk foods such as milk and fruit juices may be pasteurised in individual batches in stirred, jacketed, stainless steel vessels. The jacket may be used both for heating (using steam or hot water) and cooling (using chilled water or brine). Very often, since rapid cooling is advisable in order to limit the growth of thermophilic organisms, the pasteurised food is passed through a separate cooler. Foods sealed in containers may be batch pasteurised in water or steam baths followed by water-spray cooling.

11.5.2.2. Continuous pasteurisatiom
Bulk liquid foods may be pasteurised by passage through plate heat exchangers which usually comprise four stages—preheating (regeneration), heating, holding and cooling (Fig. 11.14). Pasteurisers of this type are available with capacities up to 35 000 litres h^{-1}. Ancillary equipment may include flash-vacuum deodorisers for cream and de-aerators for fruit juices.

Continuous, non-agitating pasteurisation of food in containers is carried out by conveying them through an atmospheric pressure cooker-cooler. The containers may be heated by immersion in hot water, or by spraying

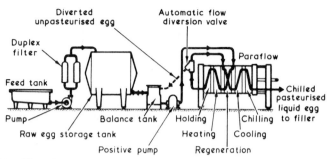

FIG. 11.14.   Flow diagram of a typical APV Paraflow liquid egg pasteurising plant.
(By courtesy of The APV Company Ltd., Crawley, England.)

with hot water, or by exposure to steam at atmospheric pressure. The pasteuriser is usually divided into sections which are heated and thermostatically controlled individually. This minimises thermal shock and improves thermal efficiency since countercurrent heating may be used. The hydrostatic cooker (Fig. 11.11) may also be used for the continuous pasteurisation of foods in containers.

The rotary, atmospheric pressure cooker-cooler is used for the continuous, agitating pasteurisation of canned foods. This is of similar design to the pressure steriliser illustrated in Fig. 11.10 but is of simpler construction since pressurisation is unnecessary.

Microwave heating (Chapter 10) is finding some application as a continuous pasteurisation method for packaged foods such as bread and cakes, and has been studied as a possible method for continuous sterilisation of foods.[29] Industrial hot-air/microwave units are now available for continuous in-pack pasteurisation of prepared meals. These units achieve a minimum of $80 \pm 2°C$ in 8–12 min (depending on the pack geometry and the contents) compared with times of an hour or so which are necessary with conventional hot air or steam pasteurisers. One such system comprises a 7 kW, 896 MHz, continuous microwave oven controlled by a programmable logic controller (PLC). This is fed from an automatic packaging line, the pasteurised packs being cooled, after treatment, by a refrigerated air cooler.[30]

REFERENCES

1. Hersom, A. C. and Hulland, E. D., *Canned Foods—An Introduction to their Microbiology*, 7th edn. Churchill, Edinburgh, Scotland, 1980.

2. Stumbo, C. R., *Thermobacteriology in Food Processing*, 2nd edn. Academic Press, New York, 1973.
3. Bigelow, W. D., The logarithmic nature of thermal death time curves. *J. Infectious Dis.*, **29**(5) (1921) 528–36.
4. Shapton, D. A., Lovelock, D. W. and Laurita-Longo, R., The evaluation of sterilisation and pasteurisation processes from temperature measurements in degrees Celsius. *J. Applied Bacteriology*, **34**(2) (1971) 491–500.
5. Ohlsson, T., Optimisation of heat sterilisation using C-values. In *Food Process Engineering. Vol. 1*, ed. P. Linko, Y. Mälkki, J. Olkku and J. Larinkari. Applied Science Publishers, London, 1980, pp. 137–45.
6. Cleland, A. C. and Robertson, G. L., Determination of thermal processes to ensure commercial sterility of foods in cans. In *Developments in Food Preservation—3*, ed. S. Thorne. Elsevier Applied Science Publishers, London, 1985, pp. 1–43.
7. Cowell, N. D., Evans, H. L., Hicks, E. W. and Mellor, J. D., Conduction errors in thermocouples used for heat penetration measurements on foods which heat by conduction. *Food Technology*, **13** (1959) 425–9.
8. Beverloo, W. A. and Weldring, J. A. G., Temperature measurements in cans and the consequences of errors for the process calculation. *Lebensmittel Wissenschaft und Technologie*, **2** (1969) 9–14.
9. Board, P. W., Cowell, N. D. and Hicks, E. W., Studies in canning processes. III— The cooling phase of processes for products heating by conduction. *Food Research*, **25** (1960) 449–59.
10. Ball, C. O. and Olson, F. C. W., *Sterilization in Food Technology*. McGraw Hill, New York, 1957.
11. Anon., Canning of low acid foods. Food hygiene code of practice. Department of Health and Social Security, HMSO, London, 1981.
12. Anon., Processes for low acid canned foods in glass containers. *Bull. Nat. Food Process. Assoc. No. 30L*, 5th edn. National Food Processors Association, Washington, D.C., USA, 1984.
13. Coleman, G., Steam flow closure, a re-examination. Technical memo. No. 73, Campden Food Preservation Research Association, Gloucestershire, England, 1967.
14. Anon., *Metal Box Double Seam Manual*. C.M.B. Technology, Wantage, England, 1978.
15. Anon., *Canned Foods*. Food Processors Institute, Washington, D.C., USA, 1982.
16. Smith, T., Tung, M. A., Bennett, L. V. and Cummings, D. B., Importance of removing condensate from vertical retorts. *Food Technology*, **39**(6) (1985) 53–6.
17. Lopez, A., *A Complete Course in Canning*, 11th edn. The Canning Trade, Md., USA, 1981.
18. Thorpe, R. H., Atherton, D. and Steele, D. A., Canning retorts and their operation. Technical manual No. 2, Campden Food Preservation Research Association, Gloucestershire, England, 1975.
19. Hersom, A. C., Sterility problems associated with rotary cooker-coolers. In *Proc. 2nd Int. Food Industries Congress*. Grampian Press, London, 1964, pp. 63–6.
20. Lawler, F. K., New sterilizer made in France. *Food Engineering*, **39**(7) (1967) 73–5.

21. Sporle, C. H., Sterilising milk by hot air. *Food Processing and Packaging*, **24** (1955) 232–3.
22. Gillespie, T. G., Ekelund hot air cooker. Heat penetration and canning trials. Technical Memo. No. 28, Fruit and Vegetable Canning and Freezing Research Association, Chipping Campden, England, 1958.
23. Leonard, S., Merson, R. L., Marsh, G. L., York, G. K., Heel, J. R. and Walcott, T., Flame sterilisation of canned foods: An overview. *J. Food Sci.*, **40**(2) (1975) 246–9.
24. Anon., New approach to open-flame sterilisation. *Food Production/Management*, **107**(1) (1984) 10, 12.
25. Kirtley, N., Emerging developments in aseptic processing. *Food Processing*, **56**(3) (1987) 35–40.
26. Guise, B., Aseptics set to clean up the market. *Food Processing*, **54**(7) (1985) 33–6.
27. Manvell, C., Sterilisation of food particulates—An investigation of the APV Jupiter system. *Food Science and Technology Today*, **1**(2) (1987) 106–9.
28. Anon., Stork innovation ready for market. *Food Processing*, **58**(6) (1989) 41–2.
29. Kenyon, E. M., The Feasibility of continuous heat sterilisation using microwave power. Technical Report 71-8-FL, US Army Natick Laboratories, Mass., USA, 1970.
30. Guise, B., Microwave pasteurisation. *Food Processing*, **58**(6) (1989) 37–8.

CHAPTER 12

EVAPORATION

12.1. USES OF EVAPORATION

Evaporation—the concentration of a solution by boiling off solvent—has four major applications in the food industry:

(i)   Pre-concentration of a liquid prior to further processing, e.g. before spray drying, drum drying, crystallisation, etc.

(ii) Reduction of liquid volume to reduce storage, packaging and transport costs.

(iii) To reduce 'water activity', by increasing the concentration of soluble solids in food materials, as an aid to preservation, e.g. in sweetened condensed milk manufacture.

(iv) For the utilisation and reduction of effluents, e.g. fodder production from vinasse.[1]

12.2. BASIC EVAPORATOR CONSTRUCTION

Industrial evaporator systems normally consist of:

(i)   A heat exchanger to supply sensible heat and latent heat of evaporation to the feed. In the food industry saturated steam is usually used as the heating medium.

(ii) A separator in which the vapour is separated from the concentrated liquid phase.

(iii) A condenser to effect condensation of the vapour and its removal from the system. This may be omitted if the system is working at atmospheric pressure.

In the food industry, risk of heat damage to the concentrating liquid often arises if evaporation is carried out at atmospheric pressure. It is usual to evaporate food liquids at reduced pressures. In this case ancillary equipment—vacuum pump or steam jet-ejector and extraction pumps and/or barometric legs—will be required (Section 12.7).

Items of evaporator plant must function well and must be accurately matched to each other.[1]

12.3. FACTORS INFLUENCING LIQUID BOILING POINT

The driving force for heat transfer in the heat exchanger of an evaporator is the temperature difference between the heating medium and the liquid being heated. The temperature of the latter is influenced by several factors including the following.

12.3.1. EXTERNAL PRESSURE

A liquid boils when the vapour pressure it exerts equals the external pressure to which it is subjected. In the case of food materials the solvent is usually water—a substance for which vapour pressure-temperature relationships are readily available.

For the evaporation of non-aqueous solvents, recourse can be made to the Clausius–Clapeyron equation of physical chemistry.[2] This gives the relationship between vapour pressure and temperature for pure solvents as

$$\log_{10} P = -\frac{\Delta H_v}{2\cdot303R}\left(\frac{1}{T}\right) + C \tag{12.1}$$

where P = the vapour pressure, T = corresponding temperature in degrees absolute, ΔH_v = the latent heat of vaporisation and R = universal gas constant in appropriate units. Plots, which give values of $\log_{10} P$ versus $1/T$, are available in the literature for a number of common organic solvents. The equation predicts that the logarithm of the vapour pressure should be a function of the reciprocal of the absolute temperature and, when ΔH_v and the constant, C, are known, it may be used to calculate the boiling point at a particular applied pressure.

12.3.2. DISSOLVED SOLUTE—BOILING POINT RISE (BPR)

The boiling point of a solution is higher than that of the pure solvent at the same pressure. The more concentrated the solution, the higher the boiling point. As evaporation proceeds the liquid concentration increases and the boiling point rises. This change leads to a progressively decreasing

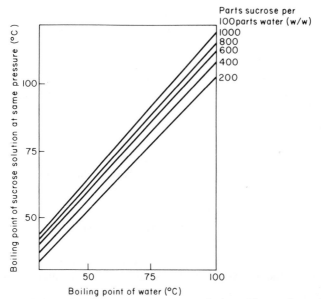

Parts sucrose per
100 parts water (w/w)
1000
800
600
400
200

FIG. 12.1. Dühring plot for aqueous sucrose solutions (drawn from data in Honig[3]).

temperature difference and hence rate of heat transfer. This decrease in rate of heat transfer must be taken into account in the design of commercial evaporators. The value of the BPR must be subtracted from any value of the temperature difference based on the boiling point of pure solvent. The actual elevation of the boiling point with change in concentration can often be obtained from Dühring's rule. This empirical rule states that the boiling point of a solution is a linear function of the boiling point of the pure solvent at the same pressure. Dühring plots show the boiling points of the solution at various concentrations, plotted against the boiling point of pure solvent at the same pressures. Differing concentrations are represented as a family of curves, and the boiling points of solutions of various concentrations are obtained by interpolation. A Dühring plot for sucrose solutions is shown in Fig. 12.1. The rule is not exact over wide ranges of pressures although it finds wide application in industrial calculations. Dühring plots for food materials are not readily available.

12.3.3. HYDROSTATIC HEAD

At any level beneath its free surface, liquid is subjected to a pressure equal to the sum of the pressure on the surface and the pressure corresponding to the hydrostatic head—the vertical distance from the free surface to the level in question. Thus the boiling temperature of the liquid in an evaporator varies with depth. This increase in boiling temperature with increasing depth lowers the temperature difference between the heating medium and the boiling liquid and may lead to overheating of the process liquid, which can become superheated. Overheating can give rise to heat damage in a unit designed to operate at a specific temperature which is unknowingly exceeded. The influence of hydrostatic head becomes more pronounced in vacuum evaporation and can be a problem in long-tube evaporators (Section 12.6.3). Commonly the average boiling temperature for liquid, based on the pressure at a liquid level halfway up the evaporator, is used in design calculations.

12.4. THE HEAT LOAD

The overall rate of heat transfer, Q, from the heating medium to the boiling liquid across the intervening wall and surface films, is often known as the 'heat load' and is given by

$$Q = UA\Delta T \tag{12.2}$$

U is the overall heat transfer coefficient, based on the outside or inside surface area, A, and ΔT is the temperature difference between the heating medium and boiling liquid. The values of U depends on a number of factors and cannot be predicted with any accuracy (see Section 12.4.3).

In the design, selection and operation of evaporators, an important requirement is a knowledge of the heat load. This may be obtained from heat and material balances.

12.4.1. HEAT BALANCE

Ideally a heat balance should be constructed on the basis of enthalpy-concentration data.[4] Such data is not readily available for food materials and a modified heat balance using mean specific heats of the materials is often used.

Referring to Fig. 12.2:

L_i is the feed liquor flow rate in $kg\,s^{-1}$, the liquors containing a mass fraction x_f of solids.

L_0 is the product liquor flow rate in $kg\,s^{-1}$, the liquors containing a mass fraction x_p of solids.

V_i is the mass of steam ($kg\,s^{-1}$) condensed in the steam chest.

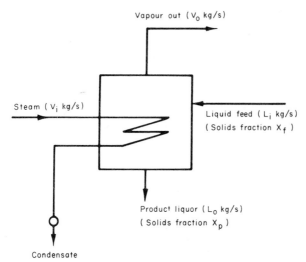

FIG. 12.2. A simple mass balance diagram for one effect of an evaporator.

V_0 is the mass of solvent ($kg\,s^{-1}$) vaporised in the evaporator (the 'evaporative capacity').
λ_s is the latent heat of condensation of the inlet steam ($J\,kg^{-1}$).
C_p is the mean specific heat of the feed stream ($J\,kg^{-1}\,°C^{-1}$).
λ_v is the latent heat of vaporisation of the vapours produced ($J\,kg^{-1}$).

Heat losses from the system are omitted from Fig. 12.2. These losses are due almost entirely to convection and radiation from hot surfaces. For efficient operation, heat losses should be minimised by lagging exposed surfaces and by avoiding steam leaks. The cost of such losses is discussed by Goodhall.[5] Neglecting heat losses, so that all the heat given up by the condensing steam is transferred to the process liquors, the heat balance becomes:

Heat given up by condensing steam

$$= \frac{\text{sensible heat gained}}{\text{by liquid feed}} + \frac{\text{latent heat of vapour}}{\text{produced}}$$

or

$$V_i\lambda_s = L_iC_p(T_b - T_f) + V_0\lambda_v \qquad (12.3)$$

T_b is the boiling point of the liquid and in general rises with increasing concentration (Section 12.3.2).
T_i is the temperature of the feed stream.

No account has been taken of the heat in the condensate leaving the steam chest. This is only a very small fraction of the total heat transferred. The heat given up by the condensing steam is transferred to the liquid, i.e.

$$V_i \lambda_s = Q = UA\Delta T \tag{12.4}$$

12.4.2. MATERIAL BALANCES

The rate of vapour production, V_0, during evaporation is obtained from a material balance.

Two equations are required which may be solved for V_0.

The overall material balance:

$$L_i = V_0 + L_0 \tag{12.5}$$

The material balance on the liquid:

$$L_i(1 - x_f) = L_0(1 - x_p) + V_0 \tag{12.6}$$

12.4.3. FACTORS INFLUENCING THE OVERALL HEAT TRANSFER COEFFICIENT

The value of U may be calculated (see Appendix II) knowing:

(a) The condensing film heat transfer coefficient on the steam side of the heat exchanger.
(b) The boiling liquid film coefficient on the liquid side of the heat exchanger.
(c) The scale or fouling factors on both inner and outer walls bounding the heat transfer surfaces.
(d) The thermal resistance of the wall material.

Film coefficients for steam condensing both inside tubes and on tube banks are well known and fall in the range $5\text{--}15\,\text{kW}\,\text{m}^{-2}\,{}^{\circ}\text{C}^{-1}$ ($1000\text{--}3000\,\text{Btu}\,\text{h}^{-1}\,\text{ft}^{-2}\,{}^{\circ}\text{F}^{-1}$).

Boiling film heat transfer coefficients tend to be higher in forced circulation, as opposed to natural circulation systems (see Appendix II). However, as yet, general methods for calculating boiling film coefficients are unreliable. In a well-designed natural circulation evaporator, flows of $1\text{--}2\,\text{m}\,\text{s}^{-1}$ of liquid through the heat exchanger are developed, while for forced circulation units, where the flow velocity is increased by means of some mechanical agency such as a circulation pump or an impeller, velocities of $3\text{--}5\,\text{m}\,\text{s}^{-1}$ are commonly quoted. A number of workers have shown that the boiling film heat transfer coefficient, h, is critically dependent

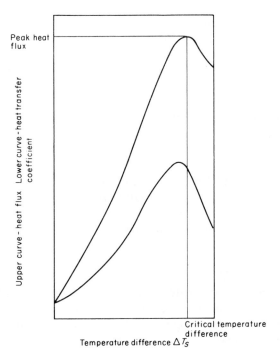

FIG. 12.3. Heat flux and heat transfer coefficient—variation with temperature difference. For water boiling at 100°C on submerged surfaces.

on the temperature difference, ΔT_s, between the submerged heating surface and the liquid. As the temperature difference increases, the heat transfer coefficient initially increases (Fig. 12.3). In this region of the curve, superheated liquid rises to the liquid–vapour interface by natural convection, where gentle boiling takes place. At somewhat higher values of ΔT_s, bubbles of vapour form at projections on the submerged surface. The bubbles break away, agitating the liquid as they rise to the surface. The number of these 'active nuclei' increases rapidly with increasing ΔT_s and an appreciable increase in heat transfer results. The promotion of this vigorous 'nucleate boiling' is important in industrial applications. At still higher values of ΔT_s, the heat flux passes through a maximum, corresponding to a 'critical temperature difference' and then starts to fall. This fall off in heat transfer is due to blanketing of the heating surface by vapour.

In industrial evaporation the aim is to achieve a value of ΔT_s just below the critical value. For many applications it appears that this corresponds to an overall temperature difference, 'ΔT', of about 25–30°C. To achieve energy conservation in evaporation systems it is frequently necessary to operate at temperature differences considerably less than these (see Section 12.8).

In summary, it may be said that the calculation of U-values is difficult if not impossible. Pilot plant studies give valuable information, but the process engineer leans heavily on experience when selecting a value of U for use in design studies.

12.5.　THE INFLUENCE OF FEED LIQUOR PROPERTIES ON EVAPORATION

The choice of evaporator type for a given process duty is greatly influenced by the properties of the feed liquor and those of the product desired.

12.5.1.　VISCOSITY

Higher viscosities lead to reduced circulation rates and lower heat transfer coefficients. Since, in general, the viscosity of a solution undergoing evaporation increases with concentration, a fall-off in heat transfer rate is to be expected as evaporation proceeds.

In recent years, the use of high capacity, falling-film evaporators (Section 12.6.3.2) has proved increasingly popular in the concentration of more viscous products. For the very high viscosities encountered with some products, falling-film type, mechanically-wiped surface evaporators (Section 12.6.6) are used as 'finishing' evaporators.

12.5.2.　FOULING–SCALING

As in other heat exchange processes in the food industry, fouling of heat transfer surfaces can be a major cause of declining efficiency in evaporation systems. Deposition of scale on evaporator heat transfer surfaces lowers the U-value and, if sufficiently severe, can also lead to high pressure drops and reduced flow rates necessitating shutdown and cleaning. The design engineer incorporates a 'fouling factor' into the overall heat transfer coefficient (OHTC) to take into account the additional resistance to heat transfer offered by a layer of scale but over-allowances can lead to large increases in capital cost.

Though still relatively little understood, the phenomenon of fouling on heat transfer surfaces has been receiving increasing attention.[6] The fouling may be due to the adhesion of suspended solids present in the feed liquor.

More usually the scale is deposited from solution on heating. Proteins are denatured on heating and polysaccharides may be deposited leading to burn-on. The chemical composition of the food liquid is obviously an important factor. In the case of milk the composition of the scale varies at different temperatures and even with the milking season.[7] Experience shows that fouling is less pronounced at high liquid velocities. This is possibly due to the scouring action of the fast-flowing liquid stream. For this reason, liquids likely to result in severe scaling are best processed in forced circulation or mechanically-wiped surface evaporators. The bulk liquid temperature, the temperature of the surface on which decomposition occurs and the nature of the surface also influence fouling. There is some evidence that high-finish heat transfer surfaces result in reduced deposition in some evaporation processes[8] but the cost of producing these highly polished surfaces is considerable.

Magnetic scale prevention devices are said to be capable of reducing cleaning down-time very significantly in some evaporator applications. Passage of feed liquor through a strong magnetic field prior to entering the evaporator is thought to lead to modifications in the physical characteristics of the deposited solids. Instead of a difficult to remove scale, solids are deposited in a form which is easy to remove. The scouring effect of the boiling liquid can then keep heat transfer surfaces cleaner for longer periods. According to Diamant,[9] the interval between 'shut-downs' for the descaling of sugar evaporators was increased from 6 to 52 days after magnetic treatment had been introduced. Nevertheless, although the use of magnetic descaling units is now widely accepted in some areas of processing, e.g. water treatment, the scientific basis for their use gives rise to continuing disagreement.[10]

In order to reduce labour costs, scale-forming liquids should always be processed in evaporators designed for ease of cleaning. Formerly this meant incorporating man-holes for easy access. Food engineers now regard 'clean in place' (CIP) methods, incorporated into hygienically designed plants, as the modern answer to the clean-down problem (Chapter 17).

12.5.3. ENTRAINMENT AND FOAMING

The rapid production of vapour under conditions of vigorous boiling frequently causes entrainment of droplets of liquid in the vapour leaving the evaporator. In some circumstances with food liquids, e.g. milk, the boiling leads to the formation of a stable foam. This is particularly the case where pool boiling takes place under reduced pressure and the hydrostatic head is large. Pure liquids rarely foam but solutions or suspensions containing surface-active agents which reduce the surface tension—usually organic compounds such as higher fatty acids, alcohols, vegetable gums, proteins, etc. often present in food liquids—can induce foaming. This is particularly the case under nucleate boiling conditions when bubbles of super-heated vapour agitate the liquid in older 'standard-type' batch evaporators. Interfacial forces arising between vapour, superheated liquid and suspended solids, are thought to play a part, the solids being capable of acting as nuclei for bubble formation.

Entrainment and foaming not only result in loss of product but, in the case of aqueous feeds where direct contact spray condensers are often used, contamination of the cooling water leading to increased effluent loading. Kouloheris[11] discusses methods for the break-down of foams, and a number of mechanical devices for minimising carry-over from evaporators are in common use (see Section 12.7.3).

12.5.4. TEMPERATURE SENSITIVITY

To reduce the risk of heat damage to heat-sensitive materials during evaporation, boiling temperatures should be kept low and residence times of the liquid in the heating zone short.

Boiling temperatures are lowered by reducing the operating pressure of the evaporator. Satisfactory temperature differences can then be achieved with heating media at correspondingly lower temperatures. Depending on the heat sensitivity of the product, boiling temperatures in the range 40–90°C are commonly used.[1]

It is now generally accepted that somewhat higher temperatures than those previously regarded as a safe working maxima can be tolerated if residence times at these elevated temperatures are kept very short. Falling-film evaporators (Section 12.6.3.2) are widely used for concentrating heat-sensitive food liquids[12] and in the dairy industry they have almost replaced recirculation type units.[13] In these evaporators very low liquid hold-up volumes and high flow velocities give short residence times in the range 10–30 s, even with quite viscous products. For heat-sensitive liquids with even higher viscosities the mechanically-wiped film evaporator (Section 12.6.6), giving very short residence times of 2–5 s for most materials,[14] is now well established.

12.5.5. AROMA LOSS

The organic aroma and flavour components in many liquid foods, fruit-juices, etc., are more volatile than water. When such liquids are evaporated these components can be removed with the water vapour causing a deterioration in the sensory attributes of the resulting concentrate. Volatile constituents are commonly recovered from the vapour as an 'essence' by fractional distillation.[15,16] The 'stripped' liquor is concentrated separately and reblended with the essence.

A more recent development in flavour recovery is a molecular distillation process incorporating a modified spinning-cone column. This device is being used for fruit-juice concentration. The unit is said to give better stripping and, since residence times are low, reduced heat damage.[17]

12.5.6. CORROSION CHARACTERISTICS

In process design studies, the corrosive nature of the materials handled must be considered. Materials of construction compatible with the food material must be selected. With foodstuffs, even traces of contamination can lead to infringement of the regulations prescribing maximum levels of trace metals in foods.[18] In the UK a Working Party of the Ministry of Agriculture, Fisheries and Food's Steering Group on Food Surveillance now determine and report on the amounts of certain heavy metals in foods—e.g. Food Surveillance Paper No. 15.[19] Process engineers selecting materials of construction that come into contact with foodstuffs should be aware of the Working Party's findings.

Stainless steel is the favoured material of construction for use in food evaporators.[12]

12.6. EVAPORATION EQUIPMENT

A number of evaporator types are available. The essential features of the more important types are discussed below.

12.6.1. NATURAL CIRCULATION EVAPORATORS

12.6.1.1. Open pan evaporator

These are the simplest commercial evaporators available and their cheapness makes them popular. The pans can be directly heated. More often they are fitted with either an outer jacket, or with internal coils through which a heat transfer medium passes. In these units evaporation rates are low and heat economy is poor. The pans may be closed to permit vacuum operation. Stirring increases the rate of heat transfer and reduces the risk of 'burn-on'. These simple evaporators are used in tomato pulp concentration, soup and sauce preparations and in jam and confectionery boilings. Small, jacketed pans are very useful, but with larger

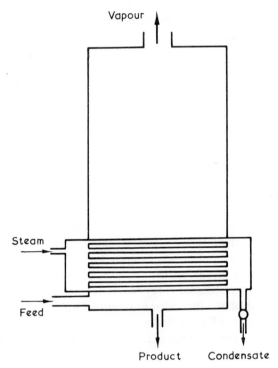

FIG. 12.4.   Diagram of a horizontal short tube evaporator.

capacities the ratio of heat transfer surface to liquid volume falls and the heating becomes less effective. Internal heating coils fitted in larger units can interfere with the liquid circulation, so affecting the heat transfer rate. In general, when larger capacities are required, other types of evaporator offer greater advantages.

12.6.1.2. Horizontal short tube evaporator
The shell carries a bundle of internally steam heated, horizontal tubes (Fig. 12.4). The purpose of the disengagement space above the heater is to permit a gravity separation of liquid droplets carried off with the vapour from the bulk of the liquid. To reduce entrainment still further, impingement baffles are usually fitted. The horizontal tube bundle interferes with the circulation so the overall heat transfer coefficients are low.

   This type of unit was originally intended for the evaporation of non-scaling, non-foaming, low viscosity liquids.

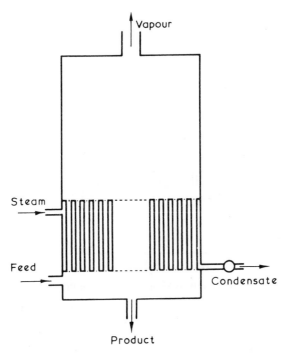

FIG. 12.5. Diagram of a vertical short tube evaporator.

12.6.1.3. Vertical short tube evaporator

This type of unit (Fig. 12.5) is still used in the process industries and has become known as the 'standard evaporator'. Here steam condenses on the outside of tubes which are mounted vertically. The 'calandria'—the assembly of tubes built into a steam chest—often has a central downcomer which normally occupies at least 40% of the flow area of the riser tubes. Since liquid in the downcomer is cooler than that in the heated risers, natural circulation currents are set up. Tube lengths are from 0·5 to 2 m (2–6 ft) and tube diameters 25–75 mm (1–3 in).

With scale-forming liquors, the tubes should be kept covered with liquor to minimise fouling. Units can be fitted with 'basket calandrias' (Fig. 12.6) which can be easily removed for maintenance.

This evaporator gives good rates of evaporation with non-corrosive, mildly scaling liquors of moderate viscosity. Typical applications include the concentration of solutions of cane sugar, beet sugar, glucose, malt extract, salt and fruit juices.

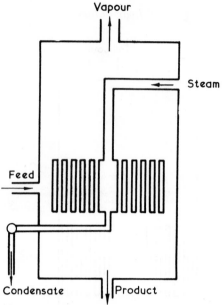

FIG. 12.6. Diagram of a vertical short tube evaporator using a basket type calandria.

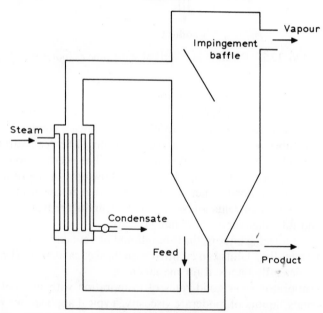

FIG. 12.7. Natural circulation evaporator with external calandria and cyclone separator for vapour disengagement.

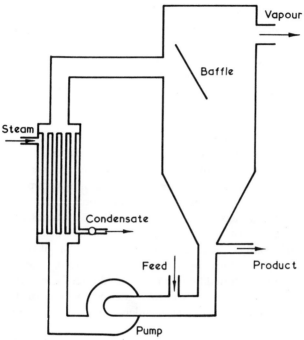

Fɪɢ. 12.8. Diagram of a forced circulation evaporator with an external calandria.

12.6.1.4. Natural circulation evaporator with external calandria
In this unit the calandria is outside the vapour disengagement space (Fig. 12.7). Construction is simple and permits easy access to the tube bundle. The tube and shell assembly is often replaced by a plate heat exchanger. This is particularly useful if scale formation or product degradation is likely, since the unit can be quickly opened for cleaning. Despite the recirculation of large volumes of liquid, evaporators of this type working at reduced pressures are still used for the concentration of heat sensitive food materials including milk, meat extracts and fruit juices.

12.6.2. FORCED CIRCULATION EVAPORATORS
Evaporators with external calandrias are often operated as forced circulation units (Fig. 12.8). Such units are capable of concentrating viscous liquids, adequate circulation rates being maintained by use of a suitable pump. Centrifugal pumps are used with lower viscosity liquids. Positive displacement pumps—gear or lobe type—can be used with more viscous materials.

With some crystallising evaporators, the circulation is increased by means of an impeller mounted inside the central downcomer.

12.6.3. LONG TUBE EVAPORATORS

These evaporators may be regarded as vertical shell and tube heat exchangers. The heating medium is usually steam, condensing inside the shell.

12.6.3.1. Climbing film evaporator

Typical evaporators of this type (Fig. 12.9(b)) have tubes 3–12 m in length with diameters of 25–50 mm. Liquid, pre-heated to near boiling, is introduced at the bottom of the tube assembly. Boiling commences a short distance up the tubes. Expansion on vaporisation causes high velocity vapour bubbles and slugs of liquid to rise rapidly up the tubes. Evaporation proceeds as the liquid ascends. Under optimum conditions the vapour lifts a thin film of rapidly concentrating liquid up the walls of the tubes. The vapour–liquid mixture leaving, passes into a separator where vapour is removed. The concentrated liquid may be used directly, mixed with fresh feed and recirculated, or passed to a second evaporator for further concentration (see Section 12.8.1). Residence time in the heating zone is

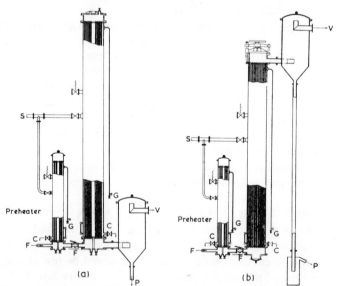

FIG. 12.9.   Long tube evaporators. (a) Climbing and falling film evaporator. (b) A climbing film evaporator with a barometric leg for product removal.

short and U-values high, making the climbing film evaporator useful for concentrating heat-sensitive materials.

12.6.3.2. Falling film evaporator

This is similar to the climbing film evaporator but in this case pre-heated feed liquid is pumped to the top of the tube bundle which may be up to 15 m long. Liquid is then distributed to the tubes so as to flow down over the internal heating surfaces in the form of a boiling film. According to Wiegand,[12] 'the most critical component of a falling film evaporator is the distribution device since the quality of its operation is vital to the performance of the entire installation'. It is imperative that the surface of each tube is completely and evenly wetted, otherwise dry spots will lead to deposition of solids, rapid decrease in heat transfer performance and even blockage of the tubes.

Since no thermosyphon effect is required to lift the liquid upwards over the heating surface and with correct operation there is no hydrostatic liquid head in the tubes, a uniform, low boiling temperature can be maintained. Used in conjunction with carefully designed steam side conditions, the low pressure drop/constant temperature system on the product side enables this type of evaporator to be used with temperature differences as low as 2°C. At low-temperature differences, scaling is reduced so cleaning is easier but, in addition, the opportunity for energy conservation using multiple effect evaporation (Section 12.8) becomes much greater. The high-velocity vapour core and the very small quantity of liquid wetting the tube surfaces lead to low residence times (10–30 s) depending on the length of the tubes and the viscosity of the concentrate.[12] These units are excellent for the concentration of heat sensitive materials. They are used with citrus fruit-juices and in recent years have gained wide use in other areas of the food industry, particularly in the dairy field where they have virtually replaced circulation-type evaporators.[20]

12.6.3.3. Climbing–falling film evaporator

A climbing film–falling film combination (Fig. 12.9(a)) is often used. The dilute feed is partially concentrated in the climbing film section and the more viscous material then encounters the falling film region. High rates of evaporation can be achieved in such combinations.

12.6.4. PLATE EVAPORATORS

Though the modern plate evaporator, so popular in the process industries, has only been commercially available since the 1950s, the first evaporator

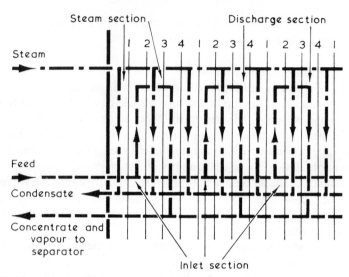

Fig. 12.10. Arrangements of plates in an APV plate evaporator showing how the steam, inlet climbing film and discharge falling film sections are repeated. (By courtesy of APV–Baker.)

based on the principles used in the plate heat-exchanger was first installed for the concentration of a clear marmalade as long ago as 1928.[21]

The conventional plate evaporator utilises the climbing–falling film principle within a plate heat exchanger although wider plate spaces are required to accommodate the vapour produced without excessive pressure drop. The plates are commonly arranged in units of four (Fig. 12.10). Steam condenses in plate spaces 4–1 and 2–3. Pre-heated liquid boils at the plate surfaces, rising as a film in plate space 1–2 and falling in 3–4. The number of such units can be varied to suit the plant capacity required. The vapour–liquid mixture leaving the plate assembly passes into a centrifugal separator. High liquid velocities lead to good heat transfer with short residence times, making this evaporator useful for the concentration of heat-sensitive materials. This, together with its facility for rapid dismantling and its small floor space requirement, makes the evaporator a very popular unit.

In another type of plate evaporator, developed by APV–Baker, the climbing film sections have been discarded. Liquid flows entirely in the form of a falling-film over plates larger than those in the conventional plate evaporator. Internal recirculation is said to be avoided and very short residence times are claimed for the unit which is being used for citrus juice concentration.[22] In another type of evaporator, designed for larger evaporative capacities, the heating surface—in the form of a pack of vertical plates—is suspended inside a cylindrical vessel which acts as a vapour–liquid disengagement space. Pre-heated feed liquor is sprayed onto the top of the heated plate assembly again flowing downwards over the heating surface in the form of a thin film.

Yet another recent development in evaporator design combines features of both the tube and the plate type evaporator. In the Alfa-Laval Cassette Evaporator (Middlesex, England), the flow path on the product side is designed to give an increasing area for vapour flow while the wetted perimeter for the concentrating liquid decreases. Constant liquid velocity, film thickness and also vapour velocity are said to be maintained as the vapour/liquid properties change. This reduces pressure drop, permitting the use of lower temperature ranges than in many other evaporators. The absence of contact points on the heat transfer surfaces in the product space, which is formed by clamping together a number of gasketed cassettes, makes the unit far less prone to fouling and blockages so easier and faster to clean.[23]

12.6.5. EXPANDING FLOW EVAPORATOR

In this device for the concentration of dairy products, fruit juices etc.,[24,25] liquid and steam flow through alternate passages in a manner similar to that in the plate evaporator (Fig. 12.11). The plates, however, are replaced by thin, inverted stainless steel cones, gasketed to prevent leakage. Feed enters through a central spindle at the base of the cone assembly and is fed, via nozzles, to the heated cone spaces. Flowing upwards and outwards over the steam-heated surfaces, under vacuum operation, liquid rapidly attains boiling point. A high velocity vapour–liquid stream leaves the cone assembly tangentially, ensuring a good separation. Vapour passes upwards to leave via a concentric baffle separating the inner and outer shells. The high velocity in the cone spaces promotes thin, turbulent films of evaporating liquid giving high rates of heat transfer and short residence times. The unit has been designed for 'in-place cleaning'.

12.6.6. MECHANICAL THIN FILM EVAPORATORS

These evaporators usually consist of a cylindrical, steam jacketed shell which carries an axially mounted multi-bladed rotor. The units may be mounted vertically or horizontally. Horizontal units are often tapered (Fig. 12.12). With cross-sectional area decreasing in the direction of flow, adequate wetting of the walls is possible, even at low flow rates, thus

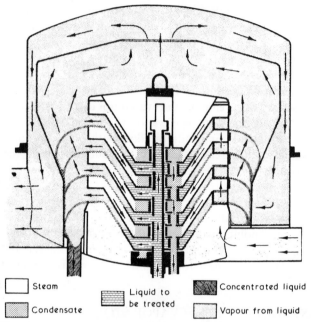

| | Steam | | Liquid to | | Concentrated liquid |
| | Condensate | | be treated | | Vapour from liquid |

FIG. 12.11. A cross-section of the Alfa-Laval expanding flow evaporator shows the method of operation in diagrammatic form. (By courtesy of Alfa-Laval Co. Ltd., Brentford, Middlesex.)

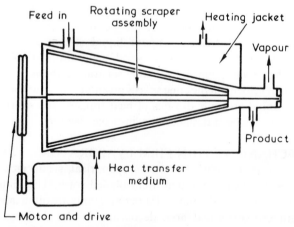

FIG. 12.12. Horizontal mechanical thin-film evaporator.

minimising the risk of scale formation and burn-on. Rotor blades may be fixed clearance or floating.

With fixed-blade mechanically-wiped surface evaporators the blades do not come into contact with the inside wall, the clearance between the rotor-blade tip and heat transfer surface falling in the range 0·5–2 mm. The blades normally run the full length of the heating jacket.

In the centrifugally-agitated wiped film evaporator, floating blades are incorporated.[26] These shorter blades are fitted in sections at intervals along the length of the jacket and the number fitted at any level varies. As the rotor turns the blades swing out towards the wetted heating surface under the influence of centrifugal force. With some units springs are fitted to help the centrifugal force generated balance the fluid forces developed in the film. This type of 'wiped film' evaporator has smaller clearances giving film thicknesses as low as 0·25 mm. The actual thickness varies with the type of feed and the operating conditions. The blades ride on the surface of the film and a bow wave is generated immediately in front of the blade. Most of the evaporation occurs in the thin film formed behind the blade. The bow wave plays an important part in the vertical and angular distribution of the concentrating liquid over the hot surface and the flow pattern developed ensures that each element of the concentrate is uniformly heated. This, together with an ability to handle highly viscous liquids prone to foaming and to scale formation, while maintaining high rates of heat transfer, makes these evaporators very useful for the concentration of heat-sensitive materials.

The advantages of mechanically-wiped film evaporators are, to some extent, offset by their relatively high capital costs and small capacities ($50–3000 \, kg \, h^{-1}$)[26] and for these reasons they are usually employed as 'finishing evaporators' where smaller capacities and higher viscosities are usually encountered.

Mechanically-wiped surface evaporators are now being recommended because of their wide operational versatility. For a particular evaporator, operating parameters, such as pressures and temperatures, hydraulic loadings, evaporative capacities, etc., can be varied within very wide limits, making them very suitable for multi-product application.[27] In the food industry they find wide use in the concentration of tomato pastes, coffee, milk, whey, malt and sugar products.

Another mechanical thin-film evaporator developed for heat-sensitive materials is similar to the expanding-flow unit. The stack of cones rotates at high speed, and liquid droplets and steam condensate are thrown off the heating surfaces under the action of centrifugal force. Good separations and high rates of heat transfer with extremely short residence times are reported with the 'Centritherm' evaporator.[24,28]

12.6.7. LOW TEMPERATURE EVAPORATORS—HEAT PUMP OR REFRIGERATION CYCLE EVAPORATORS

For vacuum concentration of highly heat-sensitive materials at low pressures, correspondingly low temperatures are required for vapour condensation. Evaporators using 'heat pumps' have been used for this purpose (Fig. 12.13). A refrigerant gas condenses on the calandria tubes to supply the necessary latent heat of vaporisation for boiling and evaporates in the condenser to condense the vapour produced on the product side.[29] In evaporators of this type boiling temperatures as low as 20°C can be used to avoid heat damage.

It has been long recognised that quite heat-sensitive materials, e.g. citrus fruit-juices, can withstand much higher temperatures than had previously been thought possible provided that contact times at higher temperatures

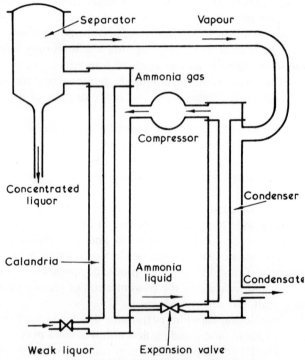

FIG. 12.13.   Refrigeration cycle evaporator.

are kept short.[22] A variety of short residence-time thin film evaporators, capable of handling very heat-sensitive materials at higher boiling temperatures (hence affording better energy economy), are now available and since their advent the use of low temperature evaporators has declined.[30] Nevertheless, their use is still reported in the literature.[31]

12.7. EVAPORATOR ANCILLARY PLANT

Since most evaporator systems processing food materials operate below atmospheric pressure, vapour condensers and vacuum pumps or ejectors are usually required.

The atmosphere in an evaporator consists of:

(i) Condensable vapour.
(ii) Incondensable gases—air from leaks into the system and from degassing of the feed liquors.

In vacuum evaporation the partial pressure of the vapour is kept low by condensing the water vapour, and the incondensables are removed by pump or ejector.

12.7.1. CONDENSERS

Surface condensers (e.g. shell and tube condensers) are used when the condensed vapour cannot be mixed with cooling water. These units have both a high capital cost and cooling water requirement as compared to the jet condenser commonly used in food applications.

In the latter unit the vapour mixes directly with a spray of cooling water. Jet condensers are simpler, smaller and cheaper than surface condensers. Condensate and the cooling water from the jet condensers are removed using either a condensate pump or a barometric leg. The latter is a vertical pipe about 11 m (34 ft) long. At the top it is connected to the discharge from the condenser while its lower end is immersed in a small seal pot (Fig. 12.9b).

The difference in head between the liquid level in the pipe and in the seal pot automatically adjusts so as to correspond to the difference in pressure between the evacuated equipment and that of the atmosphere. Under these conditions liquid can be removed without breaking the vacuum.

12.7.2. VACUUM PUMPS

Positive displacement pumps and steam jet-ejectors are commonly used. In the jet-ejector (Fig. 12.14) high-pressure steam is fed through a nozzle into a chamber where it entrains surrounding vapour or gases. The steam and

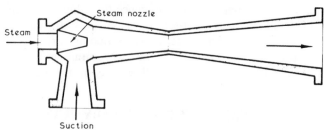

Fig. 12.14. Diagram of a single stage steam jet-ejector.

entrained fluids pass, at high velocity, into a convergent–divergent nozzle where velocity energy is converted into pressure energy. A single-stage ejector will produce a vacuum of about $16.7\,kN\,m^{-2}$ (25 in Hg), a two-stage unit one of about $3.4\,kN\,m^{-2}$ (29 in), and a three-stage ejector a vacuum of less than $1\,kN\,m^{-2}$ (30 in). It is important to appreciate that the vacuum equipment is responsible for removing non-condensable gases from the system. It is not responsible for maintaining boiling at the desired temperature, this being the duty of the condenser. With either type of condenser overall performance is greatly influenced by both cooling water flow rate and temperature. Many operating difficulties in evaporator systems can arise through inadequate cooling water conditions.

12.7.3. ENTRAINMENT SEPARATORS

At higher evaporation rates liquid droplets are carried from the boiling liquid by the vapour. To reduce the loss of concentrated liquor entrained in the vapour, entrainment separators are used.

They may consist of a single baffle plate (Fig. 12.8) or an inclined plate assembly (louvre-baffle) positioned near the vapour off-take. Close-woven knitmesh packs of stainless steel or other material are also popular.[32]

The centrifugal separator is widely used. Here the vapour–liquid mixture is introduced tangentially into a cylindrical vessel (Fig. 12.7). Under the influence of centrifugal force the heavier, liquid droplets are thrown to the wall where, on collision, they lose kinetic energy and drain away, the vapour passing out of the unit at a separate take-off. In principle, these simple 'momentum separators' arrest the heavier liquid droplets but permit the passage of vapour. In practice, much depends on liquid level, boil-off rate and overall operator efficiency.

12.7.4. STEAM TRAPS AND VENTS

It must be stressed that for maximum steam economy and heat transfer, any equipment using steam as a process heating medium must be fitted with adequate condensate removal and inert gas-venting systems. Inadequately vented and partially water-logged heat exchangers are causes of a great deal of inefficiency in the operation of evaporation plant and should not be tolerated. For a comprehensive account of these important ancillary systems, see Goodhall.[5]

12.8. HEAT CONSERVATION IN EVAPORATOR SYSTEMS

As with all process plants, capital, operating and maintenance costs for evaporator systems are all very important. In these energy-conscious days, however, energy-accounting studies have shown evaporators to be '.... prime candidates for possible modification to reduce energy consumption'.[33] To keep costs low every effort must be made to keep the steam usage to a minimum and this is accomplished by recovering and re-using as much of the latent heat in the vapour produced as possible. This is wasted if the vapour is discarded. In addition, more cooling water is required to effect the condensation of larger quantities of vapour, so the reduction in water requirement through re-use of the heat in the vapour reduces the operating costs of the plant still further.

Several methods are available for heat conservation in evaporation systems.

12.8.1. FEED PRE-HEATING

A simple method, sometimes used for the conservation of heat, is to use hot vapours from an evaporator to pre-heat the incoming cold feed liquid. Steam temperatures are likely to be low, so large heat transfer surface areas may be required for the pre-heater.

12.8.2. MULTIPLE-EFFECT EVAPORATION (MEE)

The exhaust vapour from an evaporator can be used in the calandria of a second evaporator provided that the boiling temperature of the liquid in this unit is suffciently low to maintain an adequate temperature difference for the transfer of heat. This is achieved by operating the second 'effect' at a lower pressure, hence boiling point. The re-use of the heat in the vapour in this way can be extended to a number of effects and is called multiple-effect evaporation. Exhaust vapour from the final effect passes to a condenser before removal from the system.

The first operational multiple-effect evaporator was built by Rillieux in 1844 and installed in a cane-sugar factory in Louisiana. Multiple-effect

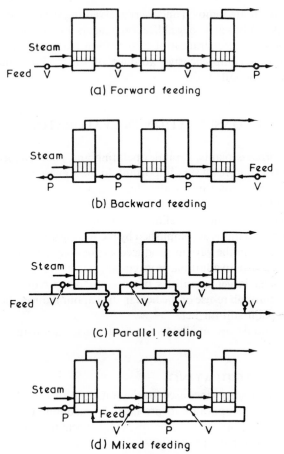

FIG. 12.15. Methods of feeding a triple-effect evaporator. P, extraction pump; V, control valve.

operation arrived in Europe in about 1850 and quickly found extensive use in the sugar-beet industry.[34] Triple effect systems are shown in Fig. 12.15.

A single-effect evaporator requires 1·10–1·30 kg of steam to evaporate 1 kg of water, where kg steam per kg vapour is known as the specific steam consumption. However a double-effect evaporator only needs 0·55–0·70 kg kg^{-1} vapour and a triple-effect 0·37–0·45 kg kg^{-1} vapour.[35]

In general, the greater the number of effects, the better the steam economy.

The price of this steam economy is an increase in capital cost of the installation as the number of effects increases. The cost of *n* effects in a multiple-effect evaporation system is approximately *n* times the cost of a single effect, so the capital cost of the plant rises rapidly as the number of effects rises. To arrive at the optimum number of effects the decreasing operating costs must be balanced against the increased capital charges.[36] The number of effects is also limited by the available overall temperature difference between the steam in the first effect and the condenser cooling water temperature. With larger numbers of effects the available temperature difference across individual effects becomes correspondingly smaller. This means that for a given capacity, the heat transfer surface area must be greater, again increasing capital costs.[37]

Though optimisation studies show that larger capacity plants justify the use of more effects than do smaller, it should be remembered that multiple-effect evaporation does not lead to larger throughputs than those obtainable with single-effect systems with comparable heat exchange surface. The purpose of multiple-effect operation is to achieve an improvement in overall steam economy for the process, not to increase plant capacity. No more than five or six effect units are normally encountered though economic conditions can influence the optimum number of effects. In larger capacity dairy plants in the USA, five to seven effects are said to be optimum and even more effects are sometimes used in Europe.

12.8.3. THE OPERATION OF MULTIPLE-EFFECT EVAPORATOR SYSTEMS

12.8.3.1. Forward feeding (Fig. 12.15(a))

This is the simplest, hence most common method of feeding. Feed passes forward in the same direction as the vapours, namely from the first effect to the second, hence to the third effect, etc. An extraction pump only is required, the final effect being operated at low pressure. With this feed arrangement the viscosity of the process liquor increases during passage through the plant owing to both an increase in concentration and decrease in temperature in each effect. Thus the overall heat transfer coefficient is low in the later effects. However, the lower temperature in these effects is less likely to produce heat damage in the more viscous liquors. High quality raw steam condenses in the first effect calandria. If the initial feed is below its boiling point some of the heat transferred must be used for pre-heating the feedstock. Since less heat is available for vaporisation, less vapour condenses in the second effect and this pattern is repeated in later effects. The overall result is a loss in steam economy.

12.8.3.2. Backward feeding (Fig. 12.15(b))
Interstage pumps are required for this arrangement. Dilute, cooler feed liquor meets poorer quality steam since steam and liquor flows are counter-current. An improved steam economy results. The increase in viscosity on concentration is off-set by the higher temperatures experienced, since the more viscous material meets increasingly hotter surfaces in going from effect to effect. However, care must be taken to avoid localised overheating.

12.8.3.3. Parallel feeding (Fig. 12.15(c))
This is commonly used with crystallising evaporators. This mode of operation leads to better control over the crystallisation operation and also avoids the pumping of dense slurries—with all the attendant flow problems—between effects.

12.8.3.4. Mixed feeding (Fig. 12.15(d))
This method is common with a larger number of effects. It represents a compromise between the simplicity of 'forward feeding' and the greater economy of 'backward feeding'. The method is useful with very viscous liquids and is recommended when large increases in viscosity with concentration are likely.

12.8.4. VAPOUR RECOMPRESSION
In this method of energy conservation, water vapour from an evaporator is compressed and returned to the calandria at a pressure which makes it suitable for reuse as a heating medium.

The use of vapour recompression for improving the economy of an evaporation process has been practiced for many years although its use has grown significantly since the steep increase in energy prices in 1973. These systems can result in considerable savings in overall energy requirements when compared with multiple-effect evaporation. A single-effect evaporator with a thermal vapour recompression system has a steam usage comparable to that of a double-effect evaporator operating under the same conditions without vapour recompression but the cost of the recompression system is far less than the extra evaporator effect.

Two methods of recompression are available:

(i) Thermal vapour recompression (TVR), in which a steam jet compressor is used to compress the vapour.
(ii) Mechanical vapour recompression (MVR), where a mechanical pump is employed.

According to Schwartzberg,[30] thermal recompression is the much more commonly used of the two alternatives.

(i) Thermal vapour recompression. With this method only part of the vapour from the separator of the evaporator is exhausted to the condenser (or passed to a second effect in the case of multiple-effect operation with vapour recompression at the first effect). The other part enters a steam jet compressor fed with boilerhouse steam at a pressure of about 10 bar $(1\,\text{MN}\,\text{m}^{-2})$ (Fig. 12.16(a)). In passing through the inlet nozzle in the jet compressor, the pressure of this fresh steam falls to that of the vapour with which it mixes, its pressure energy being converted into velocity energy. The high velocity, mixed stream then flows through a second converging–diverging nozzle where velocity energy is again converted into pressure energy. The upgraded higher pressure steam then passes back to the steam side of the calandria. The thermocompressor is specifically designed so that the resulting steam mixture leaves at the pressure–temperature conditions required on the steam side of the calandria. This means that thermal vapour recompression systems lack flexibility though they are quite efficient when working at, or very near, their specific design condition. For maximum economy they require low temperature differences across the calandria. For variable production demands, Wiegand[12] recommends the use of two vapour compressors designed for one- and two-thirds of the total evaporative capacity and which can be switched in or out to accommodate changes in evaporation requirements.

Thermal recompression systems (Fig. 12.16(a)) can handle large volumes of vapour. They are relatively simple and are cheap compared to mech-

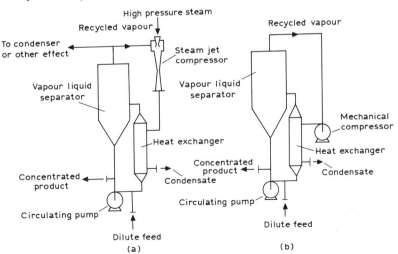

FIG. 12.16. Vapour recompression methods. (a) Thermal recompression, (b) mechanical recompression.

anical vapour recompression systems. Since they contain no moving parts they give long service life when fabricated in erosion-resistant materials.

(ii) Mechanical vapour recompression. With mechanical recompression (Fig. 12.16(b)), all the vapour produced in the evaporator is compressed and recycled to the steam side of the calandria. For initial start-up an auxiliary steam supply or electric heater is required, but no on-site high pressure steam source is needed. Also, since all the vapour is condensed in the calandria, no external condenser is needed and cooling water costs are also saved. These are important advantages when compared to TVR.

Mechanical compressors[12] are much more expensive than steam jet compressors. This limits their use to large capacity plants (45 000 kg h^{-1}).[38]

As with TVR, the use of MVR is only viable when process conditions allow the evaporator to operate with lower temperature differences (10–15°C is common) between the steam and product side. Only then will the amount of energy required to compress the vapour to the required degree be economically advantageous in comparison to other heating methods. This means that large evaporator heat transfer areas are required when overall heat transfer coefficients are low, which increases the capital cost of the evaporator system.

Mechanical vapour recompression is best suited for the evaporation of dilute solutions that give lower viscosity products.[39] Since low temperature differences are a necessity, boiling point rise or hydrostatic head effects should be avoided as both will reduce the temperature difference still further.

Mechanical compressors for MVR can be driven by electric motors, gas engines or steam turbines. In areas where fossil fuel costs are high and electrical power is cheap, electrically-driven mechanical recompression systems do have economic advantages despite the high cost of turbocompressors.

If a supply of high pressure steam is available then the use of a steam turbine to drive a mechanical compressor can be considered. This may give significant reduction in operating costs when compared to an electrical drive system. The low pressure exhaust steam may be used to heat further effects of a multiple-effect system.

More recently, electrically operated, direct drive fans, which are simpler and much cheaper than turbocompressors, have been specially designed for vapour recompression application. They give lower compression ratios and correspondingly lower temperature elevations than turbocompressors (4–5°C as compared to 10–15°C) but are finding increasing use in applications requiring lower evaporation rates.[12,40]

Comparative energy savings of MVR systems are greatest at highest throughputs. In one study, manufacturing costs for MVR were 10% less than MEE at $450 \, \text{kg} \, \text{h}^{-1}$ but 50% less at $45\,000 \, \text{kg} \, \text{h}^{-1}$.[41]

Falling film evaporators (Section 12.6.3.2) are widely used in conjunction with both mechanical and thermal vapour recompression systems since they are capable of working with low temperature differences, give high overall heat transfer coefficients, and generate minimal hydrostatic heads.[12]

To maximise energy utilisation in high capacity evaporation plants it is now common practice to use MEE systems incorporating vapour recompression systems on one or more effects. In the dairy industry, using the most advanced techniques of evaporation, it is now possible to get specific steam consumptions of 0.08–$0.13 \, \text{kg steam} \, \text{kg}^{-1}$ water.[38]

REFERENCES

1. Burkart, A. and Wiegand, B., Quality and economy in evaporator technology. In *Food Technology International Europe 1987*, ed. A. Turner. Sterling, London, 1987, pp. 35–9.
2. Maron, S. H. and Prutton, C. F., *Principles of Physical Chemistry*, 4th edn. Macmillan, New York, 1965.
3. Honig, P., *Principles of Sugar Technology*. Vol. 2. Elsevier, Amsterdam, 1959.
4. Lewis, M. J., *Physical Properties of Foods and Food Processing Systems*. Ellis Horwood, Chichester, England, 1987.
5. Goodhall, P. M., *Efficient Use of Steam*. IPC Science and Technology Press, Guildford, Surrey, England, 1979.
6. Lund, D. and Sandu, C., State-of-the-art of fouling: Heat transfer surfaces. In *Fundamentals and Applications of Surface Phenomena Associated with Fouling and Cleaning in Food Processing*, ed. B. Hallstrom, D. B. Lund and Ch. Tragardh. Lund, Sweden, 1981, pp. 27–56.
7. Grandison, A., UHT processing of milk: Seasonal variation in deposit formation in heat exchangers. *J. Soc. Dairy Technol.*, **41**(2) (May 1988) 43–9.
8. Nordin, S. and Westergren, L., Practical experiences of prevention of scaling by means of high-finish surfaces in evaporator tubes. In *Fundamentals and Applications of Surface Phenomena Associated with Fouling and Cleaning in Food Processing*, ed. B. Hallstrom, D. B. Lund and Ch. Tragardh. Lund, Sweden, 1981, pp. 356–64.
9. Diamant, R. M. E., The use of magnetic water treatment. *Chemical Processing*, (November 1970) 31–5.
10. Sohnel, O. and Mullin, J., Some comments on the influence of a magnetic field on crystalline scale formation. *Chemistry and Industry*, **11** (6 June 1988) 356–8.
11. Kouloheris, A. P., Foam phenomena. In *Encyclopedia of Food Engineering*, 2nd edn, ed. C. W. Hall, A. W. Farrall and A. L. Rippen. AVI, Westport, Conn., USA, 1986.

12. Wiegand, B., Evaporation. In *Evaporation, Membrane Filtration and Spray Drying in Milk Powder and Cheese Products*, ed. R. Hanson. North European Dairy Journal, Copenhagen, 1985.
13. Kutcher, P. A. and Cox, G. C., Evaporation and drying of heat sensitive products. *Food Technology in Australia*, **38**(8) (August 1986) 326–30.
14. Arlidge, D. B., Wiped film evaporators on pilot plants. *Chemical Engineering Progress*, **79**(7) (1983) 35–40.
15. Robbins, R. H. and Greswell, D. M., The evaporation of fruit juices. *J. Appl. Chem. Biotechnol.*, **21**(12) (1971) 363–5.
16. Shore, D. T., Essence recovery on citrus evaporators. In *Advances in Preconcentration and Dehydration of Foods*, ed. A. Spicer. Applied Science Publishers, London, 1974, pp. 95–9.
17. McCraig, A. J., Flavour recovery by the flavourtech recovery system. *Food Technology in Australia*, **39**(3) (1987) 102–4.
18. Davis, M. S., UK regulations on trace elements in foods. *Food Trade Rev.*, **36**(3) (1966) 55–6.
19. Ministry of Agriculture, Fisheries and Food. Food Surveillance Paper No. 15, London, 1985.
20. Gray, R. M., Technology of skimmed milk evaporation. *J. Dairy Technol.*, **34** (April 1981) 2.
21. Gray, R. M., The plate evaporator. *J. Appl. Chem. Biotechnol.*, **21**(12) (1971) 359–62.
22. Mannheim, C. H. and Passy, N., Non-membrane concentration. In *Advances in Preconcentration and Dehydration of Foods*, ed. A. Spicer. Applied Science Publishers, London, 1974, pp. 151–91.
23. Olsson, B., Recent advances in evaporation technology. In *Food Technology International Europe 1988*. Sterling, London, 1988, pp. 55–8.
24. Halstrom, B., The use of the centri-therm, expanding flow and forced circulation plate evaporators in the food and biochemical industries. Food Industry Studies No. 1, United Nations Industrial Development Organisation, Vienna, 1969.
25. Shinn, B. E., Evaporators utilising stationary or rotating conical heating surfaces. *Food Process. Market.*, **34**(410) (November 1965) 434–7.
26. Burrows, M. J. and Beveridge, G. S. G., The centrifugally agitated wiped film evaporator. *The Chemical Engineer*, **343**(4) (1979) 229–32.
27. Salden, M. D., Agitated thin film evaporators. *The Chemical Engineer*, **404** (suppl.) (September 1987) 17–19.
28. Shinn, B. E., The centri-therm evaporator and its application to heat sensitive foods. *J. Appl. Chem. Biotechnol.*, **21**(12) (1971) 366–71.
29. Armerding, G. D. In *Advances in Food Research. Vol. 15*, ed. C. O. Chichester, E. M. Mrak and G. F. Stewart. Academic Press, New York, 1966, pp. 303–58.
30. Schwartzberg, H. G., Energy requirements for liquid food concentration. *Food Technol.*, **31**(3) (1977) 67–76.
31. Mehra, D. K., Selecting evaporators. *Chemical Engineering*, **93**(3) (3 February 1986) 56–72.
32. Pryce Bayley, D. and Davies, G. A., Process applications of knitted mesh mist eliminators. *Chemical Processing* (May 1973) 33–9.
33. Singh, R. P., Energy management in the food industry. In *Engineering and Food*,

Engineering Science in the Food Industry. Vol. II, ed. B. M. McKenna. Elsevier Applied Science Publishers, London, 1984, pp. 901–15.

34. Taylor, D. C., The history of evaporation. *The Chemical Engineer,* **380**(5) (1982) 187–90.

35. Cole, J., A guide to the selection of evaporation plant. *The Chemical Engineer,* **404** (June 1984) 20–3.

36. Lambert, R. N., Joye, D. D. and Koko, F. W., Design calculations for multiple effect evaporators. *Ind. Eng. Chem. Res.,* **26** (1987) 100–4.

37. Loncin, M. and Merson, R. L., *Food Engineering—Principles and Selected Applications.* Academic Press, New York, 1979.

38. Darlington, R., Energy use and conservation in concentrated and dried milk production. *J. Dairy Technol.,* **35**(3) (July 1982) 82–6.

39. Dinnage, D. F., How to design for economic evaporation. *Food Engng,* **47**(12) (1975) 51–4.

40. Knipschildt, M. E., Drying of milk and milk products. In *Modern Dairy Technology. Vol. I: Advances in Milk Processing,* ed. R. K. Robinson. Elsevier Applied Science Publishers, London, 1986.

41. Renshaw, T. A., Sapakie, S. F. and Hanson, M. C., Concentration economics in the food industry. *Chem. Engng Prog.,* **78**(5) (1982) 33–40.

CHAPTER 13

DEHYDRATION

13.1. WATER IN FOODS

Water is an important contributor to the organoleptic quality of foods. A loss of water from high moisture content foods or a gain in water by low moisture content foods can lead to a reduction in the organoleptic quality and hence the acceptability of said foods. On the other hand, the presence of moisture at certain levels in foods enables spoilage to occur due to the activity of micro-organisms and enzymes or through non-enzymic chemical changes. Thus, removing moisture from foods or making it less available can lead to an extension of the shelf life of these foodstuffs.

13.1.1. MOISTURE CONTENT

The moisture content of a material may be expressed on a *wet-weight basis* (WWB), i.e. mass of water per unit mass of wet material, or on a *dry-weight basis* (DWB), i.e. mass of water per unit mass of dry solids. The latter method is commonly used in connection with drying calculations.

13.1.2. WATER ACTIVITY

When considering the influence of moisture on the stability of foods it is not just the total moisture content that is of interest but also the moisture which is available for microbial growth and chemical activity. There is considerable evidence that a proportion of the total moisture present in food is strongly bound to individual sites on the solid components and an additional amount is less firmly bound, but is still not readily available as a solvent for various soluble food components. In studying the availability of water in food, a fundamental property known as water activity (a_w) is

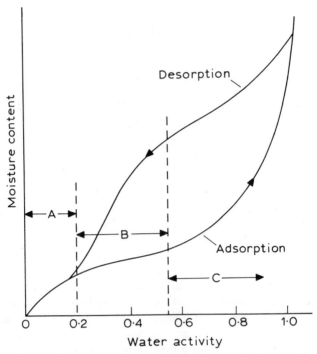

Fig. 13.1.   Adsorption and desorption isotherms showing hysteresis.

measured. This property is defined by the expression

$$a_w = \frac{p_v}{p_w} \tag{13.1}$$

where p_v is the water vapour pressure exerted by a solution or wet solid and p_w is the vapour pressure of pure water at the same temperature. This expression also describes the relative humidity of an air–water vapour mixture (equation III.4 in Appendix III). Thus, if a solution or wet solid is in equilibrium with its surrounding atmosphere then the water activity of the solution or wet solid will be numerically equal to the relative humidity of the atmosphere and the latter will be known as the equilibrium relative humidity of the solution or wet solid. A plot of moisture content as a function of water activity is known as a *sorption isotherm*. Many such plots can be found in the literature.[1] Isotherms may be prepared by adsorption, i.e. placing a dry material in contact with atmospheres of increasing relative humidity, or desorption, i.e. placing a wet material in contact with

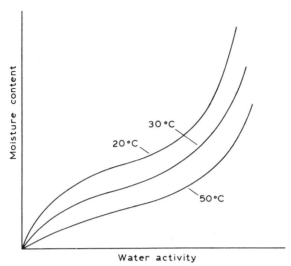

FIG. 13.2. Effect of temperature on sorption behaviour.

atmospheres of decreasing relative humidity. Thus two different curves may be obtained for the same material (Fig. 13.1). This hysteresis effect is typical of many foods. Food isotherms are often divided into three regions, denoted by A, B and C in Fig. 13.1. In region A, water molecules are strongly bound to specific sites on the solid. Such sites may be hydroxyl groups in polysaccharides, carbonyl and amino groups in proteins and others on which water is held by hydrogen bonding, ion–dipole bonds or other strong interactions. This bound water is regarded as being unavailable as a solvent and hence does not contribute to microbial or chemical activity. It is often referred to as the monomolecular or monolayer value and is found in the a_w range 0–0·35. Monolayer values for foods reported in the literature are typically in the range 0·05–0·11 (DWB).

Above region A, water may still be bound to the solid but less strongly than in region A. It has been the practice to distinguish region B as consisting of a multilayer region and region C as one in which structural and solution effects account for a lowering of the water vapour pressure. However, this distinction is dubious as these effects can occur over the whole isotherm. Thus, above region A, weak bonding, the influence of capillary forces in the solid structure and the presence of soluble solids in solutions all have the effect of lowering the water vapour pressure of the wet solid. All these effects occur at low moisture contents, < 1·0 (DWB). Most foods exhibit a water vapour pressure close to that of pure water when the

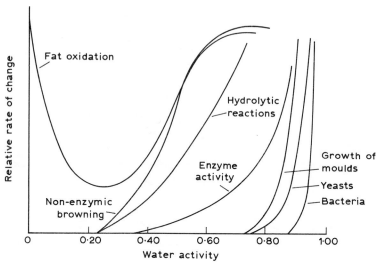

FIG. 13.3.   Influence of water activity on the stability of foods. (Adapted from Labuza.[5])

moisture content is above 1·0 (DWB). Temperature affects the sorption behaviour of foods. The amount of adsorbed water at any given value of a_w decreases with increase in temperature (Fig. 13.2).

Numerous attempts have been made to represent sorption isotherms by means of mathematical expressions. The earliest and most widely quoted expression is known as the BET isotherm.[2] This takes the form

$$\frac{a_w}{(1 - a_w)W} = \frac{1}{W_m C} + \frac{a_w(C - 1)}{W_m C}$$ (13.2)

where $W =$ the total moisture content (DWB); $W_m =$ the monolayer moisture content (DWB); $C =$ a constant. It is applicable in the a_w range 0·05–0·45. More than thirty other expressions can be found in the literature and many of them have been reviewed by Chiriffe and Iglesias.[3] In recent years the GAB equation, which is an extension of the BET model, seems to have found favour and was used and recommended by the European project group COST 90 on physical properties of food.[4] This expression is reported to be applicable up to an a_w value of 0·9 in many cases.

A knowledge of the sorption characteristics of a food is useful in facilitating the prediction of its shelf life. In many cases the most stable moisture content corresponds to the monolayer value (Fig. 13·3). Such information also helps in the prediction of drying times and energy

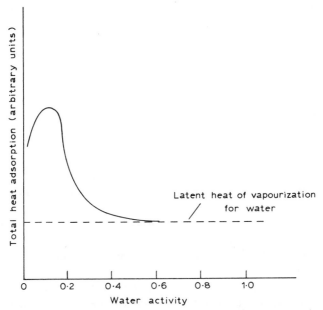

FIG. 13.4. Dependence of the total heat of adsorption (latent heat plus heat of adsorption) on water activity. (Adapted from Karel.[6])

requirements for dehydration processes. In hot-air drying systems the moisture content which is in equilibrium with the drying air at a specified temperature and humidity is the lowest value attainable under these conditions. When drying to very low moisture contents, i.e. in the monolayer region, energy additional to the latent heat of evaporation must be supplied to overcome the bonding of the water (Fig. 13.4).[7-9]

13.2. INTRODUCTION TO DEHYDRATION

Dehydration is a common method used to reduce water activity and hence extend the shelf life of foods. In addition to preservation of the product, dehydration reduces the weight and, usually, the bulk to be carried per unit food value.

In this chapter the terms 'food dehydration' and 'food drying' are used interchangeably to describe the unit operation in which nearly all the water normally present in a foodstuff is removed by evaporation or sublimation, as a result of the application of heat under controlled conditions. By this definition, therefore, these terms do not include alternative methods of moisture removal such as Filtration and Membrane Separation (Chapter 6), Centrifugation (Chapter 7), Solid–Liquid Extraction and Expression (Chapter 8). Sun-drying is also excluded because of the lack of control over the drying conditions. Evaporation or concentration of liquid foods is dealt with elsewhere in the text (Chapter 12) and is omitted by definition from this chapter because the extent to which moisture is removed is usually much less than during drying.

The methods used for the drying of foodstuffs may be conveniently classified as follows:

(i) *Drying by heated air:* The food is placed in contact with a moving stream of heated air. Heat is supplied to the product mainly by convection.

(ii) *Drying by direct contact with a heated surface:* Heat is supplied to the product mainly by conduction.

(iii) *Drying by the application of energy* from a *radiating, microwave* or *dielectric source.*

(iv) *Freeze-drying:* The moisture in the food is frozen and then sublimed to vapour, usually by the application of heat under very low-pressure conditions.

13.3. DRYING BY HEATED AIR

13.3.1. THEORETICAL CONSIDERATIONS

During the drying of a wet solid in heated air, the air supplies the necessary sensible and latent heat of evaporation to the moisture and also acts as a carrier gas for the removal of the water vapour formed from the vicinity of the evaporating surface.

Consider the situation where an inert solid, wetted with pure water, is being dried in a current of heated air flowing parallel to the drying surface. Assume that the temperature, humidity and velocity of the air above the drying surface remain constant throughout the drying cycle and that all the necessary heat is supplied to the material by convection. If the change in moisture content of the material is recorded throughout drying, the data can be presented in the form of curves as shown in Fig. 13.5. A study of these curves shows that the drying cycle can be considered to consist of a number of stages.

Stage A–B. This stage represents a 'settling down' period during which the solid surface conditions come into equilibrium with the drying air. It is

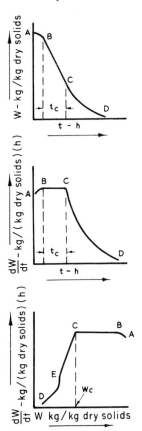

FIG. 13.5. Drying curves for a wet solid in heated air at constant temperature and humidity.

often a negligible proportion of the overall drying cycle but in some cases it may be significant.

Stage B–C. This stage is known as the *constant rate period* of drying. During this period the surface of the solid remains saturated with liquid water by virtue of the fact that movement of water within the solid to the surfaces takes place at a rate as great as the rate of evaporation from the surface. Drying takes place by movement of water vapour from the saturated surface through a stagnant air film into the main stream of the drying air. The rate of drying is dependent on the rate of heat transfer to the drying surface. The rate of mass transfer balances the rate of heat transfer, and so the temperature of the drying surface remains constant. The surface of the solid can be compared to the wick of a wet-bulb thermometer (see Appendix III) and, under the conditions specified, the constant surface temperature will correspond to the wet-bulb temperature of the drying air. The 'driving-force' causing vapour movement through the stagnant air film is the water vapour pressure gradient between the drying surface and the main stream of the drying air. The rate of mass transfer can be expressed in the form of an equation as follows:

$$\left(\frac{dw}{dt}\right)_c = -K_g A(p_s - p_a) \qquad (13.3)$$

where $-(dw/dt)_c$ = drying rate; K_g = mass transfer coefficient; A = drying surface area; p_s = water vapour pressure at surface (i.e. vapour pressure of water at surface temperature); p_a = partial pressure of water vapour in air.

Equation (13.3) may also be written in the form

$$\left(\frac{dw}{dt}\right)_c = -K_g^1 A(H_s - H_a) \qquad (13.4)$$

where K_g^1 = mass transfer coefficient; H_s = humidity at surface (i.e. saturation humidity of the air at surface temperature); H_a = humidity of air. The rate of heat transfer to the drying surface may be expressed thus:

$$\left(\frac{dQ}{dt}\right)_c = h_c A(\theta_a - \theta_s) \qquad (13.5)$$

where $(dQ/dt)_c$ = rate of heat transfer; h_c = heat transfer coefficient for convection heating; A = area for heat transfer (i.e. drying surface area); θ_a = dry-bulb temperature of air; θ_s = temperature of drying surface.

In the situation being considered here, i.e. convection heating only, θ_s is the wet-bulb temperature of the air.

Since a state of equilibrium exists between the rate of heat transfer to the body and the rate of mass transfer from it these two rates may be related simply as follows:

$$\left(\frac{dw}{dt}\right)_c L = -\left(\frac{dQ}{dt}\right)_c \qquad (13.6)$$

where L = latent heat of evaporation at θ_s.

Combining equations (13.5) and (13.6) gives

$$\left(\frac{dw}{dt}\right)_c = -\frac{h_c A}{L}(\theta_a - \theta_s) \qquad (13.7)$$

If the drying rate is expressed in terms of the rate of change of moisture content W (DWB), equation (13.7) may be written

$$\left(\frac{dW}{dt}\right)_c = -\frac{h_c A^1}{L}(\theta_a - \theta_s) \qquad (13.8)$$

where $-(dW/dt)_c = $ drying rate; $A^1 = $ effective drying surface per unit mass of dry solids.

For a tray of wet material of depth d, evaporating only from its upper surface, assuming no shrinkage during drying:

$$\left(\frac{dW}{dt}\right)_c = -\frac{h_c}{\rho_s L d}(\theta_a - \theta_s) \qquad (13.9)$$

where $\rho_s = $ bulk density of the dry material. The drying time in the constant rate period can be obtained by the integration of equation (13.9) thus

$$t_c = \frac{(W_o - W_c)\rho_s L d}{h_c(\theta_a - \theta_s)} \qquad (13.10)$$

where $t_c = $ constant rate drying time; $W_o = $ initial moisture content of solid; $W_c = $ moisture content at end of constant rate period.

The rate controlling factors during the constant rate period are, therefore: (1) the drying surface area, (2) the difference in temperature or humidity between the air and the drying surface, (3) the heat or mass transfer coefficients.

Perry[10] states that in estimating drying rates, the use of heat transfer coefficients is more reliable than mass transfer coefficients and suggest that for many cases the heat transfer coefficient can be expressed as:

$$h_c = \frac{aG^n}{D_c^m} \qquad (13.11)$$

where $G = $ mass velocity of air; $D_c = $ characteristic dimension of the system; a, n and m are empirical constants.

Thus the air velocity and system dimensions influence drying rates in the constant rate period.

Alternative expressions for h_c are used where the air flow is not parallel to the drying surface or for through-flow situations.[10]

Where heat is supplied to the material by radiation and/or conduction, in addition to convection, then an overall heat-transfer coefficient, taking this into account, must be substituted for h_c in equation (13.9). Under these circumstances the surface temperature during the constant rate period of drying remains constant, but at some value above the wet-bulb temperature of the air and below the boiling point of water.

Stage C–D (Fig. 13.5). As drying proceeds, a point is reached at which the rate of movement of moisture within the material to the surface is reduced to the extent that the surface begins to dry out. At this point, C, the rate of drying begins to fall and the *falling rate period* commences. The moisture content of the material at point C is known as the *critical moisture content* (W_c). From point C onwards the surface temperature begins to rise and continues to do so as drying proceeds, approaching the dry-bulb temperature of the air as the material approaches dryness. Often the falling rate period consists of two parts known as the first and second falling rate periods, C–E and E–D respectively. In the first falling rate period the surface is drying out and the drying rate falls. At point E the plane of evaporation moves into the solid and the drying rate falls further. In the falling rate periods the rate of drying is mainly influenced by the rate of movement of moisture within the solid and the effects of external factors, in particular air velocity, are reduced, especially in the latter stage. Usually the falling rate periods represent the major proportion of the overall drying time.

The nature of the mechanism of moisture movement within the solid has received much attention in the literature.[10–12] There appear to be four probable major modes of transfer: liquid movement caused by capillary forces, liquid diffusion resulting from concentration gradients, vapour diffusion due to partial pressure gradients, and diffusion in liquid layers adsorbed at solid interfaces. The mechanisms of capillarity and liquid diffusion have received the most detailed treatment. In general the former is most applicable to coarse granular materials and the latter to single-phase solids with colloidal or gel-like structures. In many cases it appears that the two mechanisms may be applicable to a single drying operation, i.e. capillarity accounting for the moisture movement in the early stages of drying while a diffusional mechanism applies at lower moisture contents.

Perry[10] suggests that for systems where a capillary flow mechanism applies, the rate of drying can often be expressed with reasonable accuracy by an equation of the type:

$$\left(\frac{dW}{dt}\right)_f = -K(W - W_e) \qquad (13.12)$$

where $-(dW/dt)_f$ = rate of drying at time t from the start of the falling rate period; W = moisture content of the material at time t; W_e = the moisture content of the material when in equilibrium with the drying air (equilibrium moisture content). This represents the lowest moisture content attainable, theoretically, in air at the temperature (θ_a) and humidity (H_a) specified; K is a constant and is related to the constant rate period thus:

$$K = \frac{-\left(\dfrac{\mathrm{d}W}{\mathrm{d}t}\right)_c}{W_c - W_e} \qquad (13.13)$$

Combining equations (13.9), (13.12) and (13.13) gives

$$\left(\frac{\mathrm{d}W}{\mathrm{d}t}\right)_f = \frac{-h_c(\theta_a - \theta_s)}{\rho_s L d} \frac{(W - W_e)}{(W_c - W_e)} \qquad (13.14)$$

Integration of this expression within limits $t = 0$, $W = W_c$; $t = t$, $W = W$, gives the drying time in the falling rate period thus:

$$t = \frac{\rho_s L d(W_c - W_e)}{h_c(\theta_a - \theta_s)} \ln \frac{(W_c - W_e)}{(W - W_e)} \qquad (13.15)$$

For slab-shaped solids, drying from one large face only, where liquid diffusion controls the internal movement of moisture, Perry[10] suggests the following type of expression:

$$\frac{W - W_e}{W_c - W_e} = \frac{8}{\pi^2} \left\{ \exp\left[-Dt\left(\frac{\pi}{2d}\right)^2 \right] + \frac{1}{9} \exp\left[-9Dt\left(\frac{\pi}{2d}\right)^2 \right] + \cdots \right\} \qquad (13.16)$$

where W = average moisture content, at time t, of an infinite slab of thickness d; W_c = initial moisture content, assumed to be uniform throughout the slab; D = liquid diffusivity.

For large values of t, equation (13.16) may be reduced to:

$$\frac{W - W_e}{W_c - W_e} \simeq \frac{8}{\pi^2} \left\{ \exp\left[-Dt\left(\frac{\pi}{2d}\right)^2 \right] \right\}$$

or

$$t = -\frac{4d^2}{\pi^2 D}\left(\ln \frac{W - W_e}{W_e - W_e} - \ln \frac{8}{\pi^2} \right) \qquad (13.17)$$

Equation (13.17) holds for values of $(W - W_e)/(W_c - W_e) < 0.06$. By differentiating equation (13.17), a rate equation similar in form to equation (13.14) is obtained

$$\left(\frac{\mathrm{d}W}{\mathrm{d}t}\right)_f = -\frac{D\pi^2}{4d^2}(W - W_e) \qquad (13.18)$$

The rate equations (13.9), (13.14) and (13.18) apply when drying takes place from one side only. For situations where drying occurs from both large faces, then d = half the thickness of the slab.

To establish whether or not a simple relationship exists during the falling rate period, $(W - W_e)/(W_c - W_e)$ may be plotted against t on semilogarithmic paper. If a uniform straight line results (13.14) applies and the slope of the curve should relate to the drying rate during the constant rate period as in equation (13.13). If the plot becomes asymptotic to a straight line as t increases, equation (13.18) may apply and D can be calculated from the slope of the asymptote. The effect of thickness d on the drying rate may be determined experimentally and used to distinguish between the two mechanisms.[10,12]

Some data is available on the critical moisture content of non-food materials[10] but very little relating to foodstuffs.[13] The critical moisture content generally depends on the drying rate, dimensions of the material and moisture movement mechanisms. Normally it increases with drying rate and material thickness.

13.3.2. DRYING OF FOODSTUFFS

The theoretical considerations given in Section 13.3.1 apply only to the simple system defined therein. Foodstuffs, however, are far more complex and heterogeneous than this system. The components of foods include proteins, fats, carbohydrates, vitamins, enzymes and inorganic salts, many of which are strongly hydrated. The water present is not pure but may be in the form of a solution of solids, a gel, an emulsion or bound in various ways with the solid constituents. In addition, both plant and animal tissue are cellular. This further affects their drying behaviour.[6,11]

Movement of solubles. One particular feature of the drying foodstuffs that is of interest is the movement of soluble solids which occurs during drying. If there is a flow of liquid water to the surface during drying, the water carries with it various soluble materials. The movement of some soluble compounds may be hindered by cell walls acting as semi-permeable membranes. Shrinkage of the material, setting up pressures in the interior of the pieces, may also contribute to the migration of solids. The net result may be a build-up of such soluble materials at the surface as the water evaporates.

As Van Arsdel *et al.*[11] points out, migration of soluble solids in the opposite direction, towards the centre of the pieces, can also occur. As the surface dries out, a concentration gradient is set up between it and the wet centre of the piece which could result in the diffusion of soluble material to the centre. Which of these two phenomena predominates depends on the characteristics of the material and the drying conditions. Both mechanisms have been demonstrated as occurring in foods during drying.

Shrinkage. Animal and vegetable tissue undergo some degree of shrinkage during drying by all the drying methods, with the possible exception of freeze-drying. Colloidal materials also shrink. In the early stages of drying, at low rates, the amount of shrinkage bears a simple relationship to the amount of moisture removed. Towards the end of drying, shrinkage is reduced so that the final size and shape of the material is fixed before drying is completed.

The bulk density and porosity of dried vegetable pieces depends to a large extent on the drying conditions. At high initial drying rates the outer layers of the pieces become rigid and their final volume is fixed early in the drying. As drying proceeds, the tissues split and rupture internally forming an open structure. The product in this case has a low bulk density and rapid rehydration characteristics. At low initial drying rates the pieces will shrink inwards to give a product of high bulk density. Shrinkage of foodstuffs during drying may influence their drying rates because of the changes in drying surface area and the setting up of pressure gradients within the material.[11,12,14] Some work done indicates that shrinkage does not affect drying behaviour.[15]

Case hardening. It has been observed that during the drying of some fruits, meat and fish, a hard impermeable skin often forms at the surface. This usually results in a reduction in drying rate, and the phenomenon is usually known as case hardening. The exact mechanism of case hardening is far from fully understood but is probably influenced by a number of factors, including migration of soluble solids to the surface and high surface temperature towards the end of drying resulting in complex physical and chemical changes in the surface layer.[11,16]

13.3.2.1. Studies of drying mechanisms

Following are some examples of studies made of the drying behaviour of foodstuffs. These indicate the complexity of food dehydration as compared with the simple model system for which the theory in Section 13.3.1 was developed.

Jason[14] studied the drying of fish muscle under carefully controlled conditions. Figure 13.6 is a typical example of the behaviour of a cod fillet dried in heated air flowing parallel to the longest edge. He concludes that there are at least two periods during the initial stages of drying during which the drying rates remain relatively constant. The end of the first period

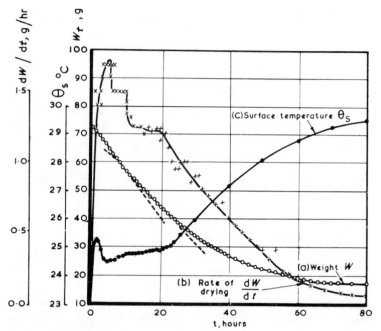

Fig. 13.6.   Initial drying behaviour of single fillet piece $10 \times 5 \times 1.5$ cm exposed to air stream of velocity 30 cm s^{-1} parallel to 10 cm edges. Dry-bulb temperature 30°C; wet-bulb temperature 18°C. Curve A: weight as a function of time; Curve B, rate of drying as a function of time; Curve C: temperature at centre of surface as a function of time. (From Jason,[14] by courtesy of the Society of Chemical Industry.)

occurs when the surface near the leading edge of the piece has dried out. The second period ends when the rest of the surface begins to dry out. Otherwise he concludes that in the early stages of drying the cod muscle behaves as though the surface was saturated with water. Jason presented the falling rate period results in the form of the curve shown in Fig. 13.7. Here the difference between the equilibrium weight (W_e) and the weight (W_t) at time t after the commencement of drying is plotted on a logarithmic scale as a function of time. The results may be seen to fall on two straight lines LL and MM over most of the curve. The drying behaviour in the first of these falling rate phases can be explained by the solution of a diffusion equation based on Fick's Law. The results indicate that the diffusion coefficient is constant and that its effective value is not dependent on the shrinkage of the muscle. In the second phase a similar explanation applies, but the effective diffusion constant assumes a value less than that of the first phase.

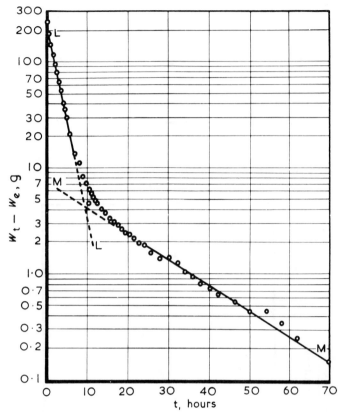

FIG. 13.7. Amount of free water remaining in fillet piece $10 \times 5 \times 0.60$ cm as function of time. Dry-bulb temperature 35°C; wet-bulb temperature 20.3°C; air velocity 366 cm s⁻¹. (From Jason,[14] by courtesy of the Society of Chemical Industry.)

Gorling[15] presented the results obtained by one-sided drying of a potato slice in the form of a curve, as shown in Fig. 13.8. The ratio X_m/X_o, where X_o = initial moisture content and X_m = average moisture content at any given time, is plotted against the product of the drying rate and sample thickness (to allow for shrinkage). There are three stages evident in the drying. From the results of systematic tests Gorling concluded that, with vegetable products, moisture is transferred to the surface during the first stage only by a capillary mechanism. Due to shrinkage, the rate of drying is not constant.

Saravacos and Charm[13] studied the drying of fruits and vegetables in

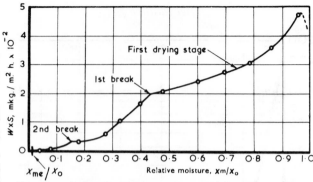

FIG. 13.8. Complete drying-rate curve for one-sided drying of potato slices in an air current at 60°C. (From Gorling,[15] by courtesy of the Society of Chemical Industry.)

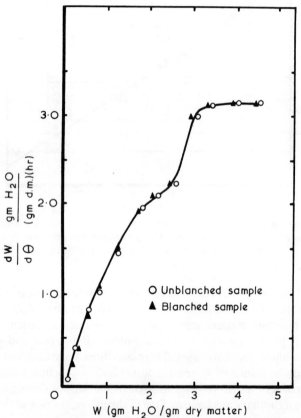

FIG. 13.9. Effect of blanching on the drying rate of potato. Drying conditions: potato dice, $\frac{1}{2} \times \frac{1}{2} \times \frac{1}{4}$ in; air velocity, 400 fpm; dbt, 150°F: wbt, 92°F. (From Saravacos and Charm.[13])

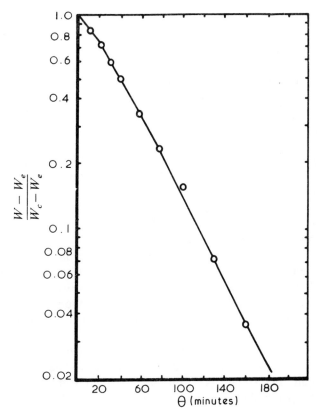

FIG. 13.10. Falling-rate period of blanched potato dice. Drying conditions; air velocity, 400 fpm; dbt, 150°F; wbt, 90°F. (From Saravacos and Charm.[13])

single layers. Constant rate periods were found with most materials, followed by falling rate periods of a sigmoid form. Figure 13.9 shows a typical drying curve. The drying of potato was studied in detail and, when tests of the type referred to in Section 13.3.1 were applied to the data, i.e. when $(W - W_e)/(W_c - W_e)$ was plotted on semi-logarithmic paper against time, a curve of the form shown in Fig. 13.10 was obtained.

The drying time in the falling rate period was found to be proportional to the square of the sample thickness. It was concluded from this work that moisture is transferred by a diffusion-type mechanism. No evidence of a capillary mechanism was found.

The application of simple theoretical expressions, such as those discussed in Section 13.3.1, to the drying of foodstuffs, suffers from serious limitations due to the complexity of such materials. In particular, there is considerable evidence to show that, in many materials undergoing drying, diffusivity, D, is not constant throughout the drying cycle but, in fact, changes as the moisture content changes. Many, more sophisticated, mathematical expressions have been proposed to represent drying behaviour in the falling rate period. Brennan[17] discussed some of these. However, the lack of data on the drying characteristics of specific foods, e.g. critical and equilibrium moisture contents, diffusivities and thermal properties, limits the application of such relationships in practice. Where simple relationships are found to be valid and data is available drying times may be estimated by calculation. Alternatively accumulated data obtained by workers in this field and/or data obtained by pilot scale experimentation may be used to estimate drying times.[11]

13.3.3. HOT-AIR DRYING EQUIPMENT
13.3.3.1. Cabinet, tray or compartment drier
This consists essentially of an insulated cabinet containing an air circulating fan which moves the air through a heater and then through adjustable baffles which direct it either horizontally between the trays of food material or vertically through the trays and food. Dampers are provided to control the rate of fresh air intake and the amount of air recirculation as required. Air heaters may be direct gas burners, steam coil exchangers or electrical resistance heaters in smaller models. In cross-flow systems, air velocities of the order of $2\text{--}5\,\text{m s}^{-1}$ are used while through-flow systems require $0\text{·}5\text{--}1\text{·}25\,\text{m}^3$ (s^{-1}) (m^2 of tray area). Cabinet driers are relatively cheap to build and maintain, and are very flexible. They are used singly or in groups, mainly for drying fruits and vegetables at throughputs of $1\text{--}20\,\text{tons day}^{-1}$ ($1000\text{--}20\,000\,\text{kg day}^{-1}$). They are also useful for pilot scale work.

13.3.3.2. Tunnel drier
This type of equipment provides a means of drying fruits and vegetables in piece form on a semi-continuous basis at high throughputs. It consists of a tunnel, which may be up to 24 m long with a square or rectangular cross-section of the order of 2 m by 2 m. The wet food material is spread in even layers on trays of slatted wood or metal mesh. The trays are assembled in stacks on trucks, clear spaces being provided between the trays to permit passage of the drying air. The loaded trucks are fed one by one, at suitable intervals, into the tunnel. As one truck enters the 'wet end' of the tunnel a truck of dry product is removed from the other, 'dry end'. Air is moved by fans through heaters and horizontally between the trays, although some

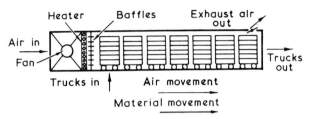

FIG. 13.11. Principle of concurrent drier.

through-flow does occur. Air velocities of the order of $2 \cdot 5 - 6 \cdot 0 \, \text{m s}^{-1}$ are normally employed.

Tunnel driers are usually classified in terms of the relative direction of movement of the material and the air. In one class of tunnel drier a *concurrent system* of material/air flow is employed as illustrated in Fig. 13.11. The characteristic features of this class of tunnel are high initial rate of drying at relatively low product temperature and low rate near 'dry end' of tunnel.

In another class of tunnel drier a *countercurrent system* of material/air flow is maintained as illustrated in Fig. 13.12.

The characteristic features of this class are relatively low initial rate of drying with severe drying conditions at the 'dry end'. There is a danger of heat damaging the product.

Two or more tunnels may be used in series in order to give more flexibility of control of the drying conditions at various stages of the cycle. The most common combination, however, consists of a concurrent primary tunnel followed by a countercurrent secondary tunnel. In this system advantage may be taken of the characteristic high initial drying rate in the concurrent tunnel while the good drying conditions in the secondary countercurrent tunnel permit more rapid finishing and lower final moisture contents in the product.

Single tunnels are also in use which provide for two-stage drying in one

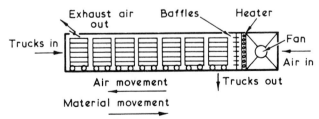

FIG. 13.12. Principle of countercurrent tunnel drier.

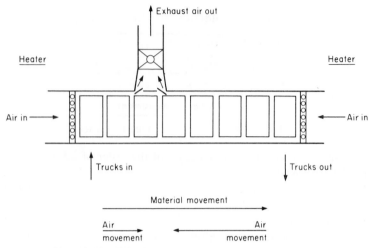

FIG. 13.13. Principle of centre-exhaust tunnel drier.

unit. The *centre-exhaust* tunnel has a single fan which draws heated air into the system from both ends. The air, after contacting the food, is partly exhausted or recirculated as required (Fig. 13.13). Relatively high air temperatures are used in the concurrent section while fresh, dry but cooler air is used in the countercurrent section.

In yet another class of tunnel drier a *cross-flow system* of air/product movement may be employed. The principle of such a unit is illustrated in Fig. 13.14. Such tunnels permit good control over the drying conditions and moisture content of the end product.

From the point of view of economy of heat usage and control of air humidity, recirculation of part of the exhaust air from tunnel driers would

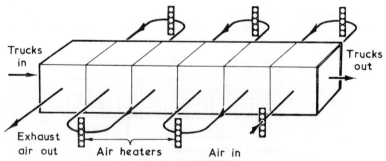

FIG. 13.14. Principle of cross-flow tunnel drier.

appear beneficial. However, as Van Arsdel *et al.*[11] point out, each drying operation should be evaluated for overall cost as recirculation inevitably results in a decrease in throughput of wet material. Up to 75% of the exhaust air can be recirculated under certain circumstances but there are situations where little or no recirculation may be the most economic procedure. Many modern commercial tunnel driers are constructed on simple lines with straight-through air flow.

13.3.3.3. Conveyor drier

This type of drier is similar in principle to a tunnel drier, but the wet material is conveyed through the system on a moving belt rather than on trucks. Any of the systems of material/air movement referred to in Section 13.3.3.2 may be used, but the most common system used in practice is a *through-flow* one in which the air is directed through the belt and layer of material. Often upward air movement is employed in the first sections, i.e. at the 'wet end' of the tunnel, and downward air movement at the 'dry end' to avoid lifting of the low density dry material. Some models consist of two or more belts working in series. Such driers are limited to solid particles that form a porous bed. Drying times are relatively short. To reduce costs, the product may be removed at a relatively high moisture content and finished in a less expensive drier.[17-20]

13.3.3.4. Bin drier

In its simple form this type of drier consists of a box with a false bottom or wire mesh base. A fan moves air over a heater and up through the material at relatively low speed, not greater than $0.5 \, m^3 \, (s^{-1})(m^{-2})$. Stationary bins of large capacity are fitted with their own fans and heaters. Portable bins are fitted with wheels and can be 'plugged in' to a stationary air supply system. Drying rates and costs are relatively low.

The main application for this type of drier is in 'finishing' vegetable products dried in other types of drier from moisture contents of about 15% down to about 3%.

13.3.3.5. Fluidised bed drier

The principle of this type of drier is that heated air is forced up through a bed of solids under such conditions that the solids are suspended in the air. The heated air acts both as the fluidising and drying medium. Detailed treatment of the principles of solids fluidisation may be found elsewhere (Appendix I).[12,21]

Fluidised bed driers may be operated as batch units, or on a continuous

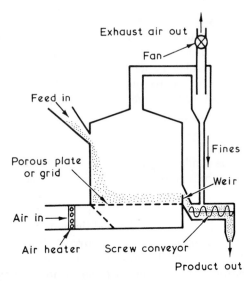

Fig. 13.15.   Principle of continuous fluidised bed drier.

basis. Figure 13.15 illustrates a simple continuous unit. The grid supporting the bed may be a simple perforated plate, but very complex designs incorporating jets, bubble caps, etc., are also employed. Some units have vibrating bases to assist movement of the product. Dust separators, usually cyclones, are included in the exhaust air line to remove fines. Driers may be operated under applied overhead pressure or reduced pressure by suitable siting of the fans. Such driers are limited to particles that will fluidise. Drying rates are relatively high.

A novel type of fluidised-bed drier, known as the *toroidal fluidised-bed*, has become available recently. A high-velocity stream of heated air enters the base of the process chamber, through blades or louvres. This creates a rotating bed of particles. A high rate of heat transfer and hence rapid drying is a feature of this design.[17]

Fluidised bed drying has been applied on either a commercial or experimental scale to a wide variety of products with varying success. These include peas, beans, carrots, onions, potato granules, meat cubes, flour, cocoa, coffee, salt and sugar. Beds are also used for agglomeration and coating of dried powders.[17,21]

13.3.3.6. Pneumatic drier

In this type of drier the wet material is suspended in a moving stream of heated air which conveys it through the drying system. It can be looked on as an extension of fluidised bed drying where higher air velocities are used. The principles of pneumatic conveying are dealt with in Chapter 19.

In a simple drier of this type the feed material is introduced into the moving stream of heated air. The solids are then carried in the air stream through ducts of sufficient length to give the required residence time. The air is exhausted from the system through a solids/gas separator, usually a cyclone, and the dried product collected.

The drying ducts may be arranged vertically, as in 'Air Lift Driers', or horizontally. In single pass systems relatively high air temperatures need to be used to avoid excessively long lengths of ducting. Better control of air temperatures at different stages can be exercised by introducing expansion chambers into the system. Alternatively, two or more such driers may be used in series with fresh air supplies to each.

In a pneumatic ring drier the ducting is in the form of an endless ring. The material can be directed around this ring continuously for several minutes while the drying air is constantly renewed, fresh material introduced and dried product removed continuously. In such units drying times can be varied over a wide range.

Pneumatic driers will only handle small particles, such as grains, flour, granulated potato and meat cubes. They may also be used as secondary driers for spray-dried milk and egg products.[17,22]

13.3.3.7. Spray drier

This type of drier is used extensively in the food industry for drying solutions and slurries. The food material is introduced into the drying chamber in the form of a fine spray where is is brought into intimate contact with a stream of heated air. Thus very rapid drying occurs and a dry powder is produced. The very short drying times, of the order of 1–20 s, and the relatively low product temperatures are the main features of this type of drying. The droplets of the spray usually have diameters of the order of 10–200 μm thus presenting a very large surface area per unit volume of material to the drying air, resulting in rapid drying. Most of the drying occurs under conditions which promote constant rate drying so that the solids temperature does not rise much above the wet-bulb temperature of the drying air until drying nears completion. If operating conditions are correct and equipment design is good, the residence time of the particles in the drying chamber can be controlled so that the time the dry particles remain in contact with the heated air is kept to a minimum, thus, their temperature is kept low.

The theory of evaporation from droplets in spray drying is treated elsewhere in the literature.[23-25]

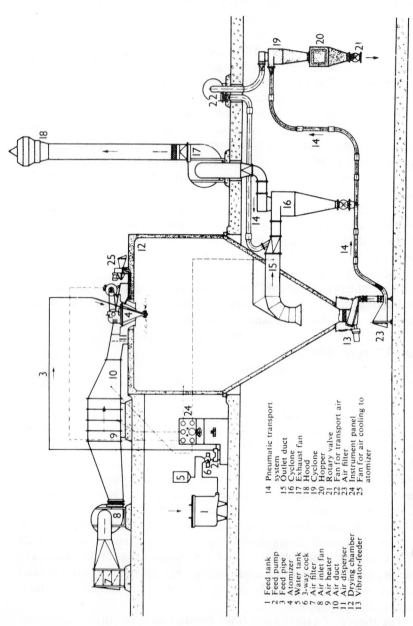

1 Feed tank
2 Feed pump
3 Feed pipe
4 Atomizer
5 Water tank
6 3-way cock
7 Air filter
8 Air inlet fan
9 Air heater
10 Air duct
11 Air disperser
12 Drying chamber
13 Vibrator-feeder

14 Pneumatic transport
   system
15 Outlet duct
16 Cyclone
17 Exhaust fan
18 Hood
19 Cyclone
20 Hopper
21 Rotary valve
22 Fan for transport air
23 Air filter
24 Instrument panel
25 Fan for air cooling to
   atomizer

Fig. 13.16.   A typical spray drying system. (By courtesy of Niro Atomizer Ltd, Denmark.)

The essential components of a spray drier include:

(i) An air heating and circulating system.
(ii) A spray-forming device.
(iii) A drying chamber.
(iv) A product recovery system.

A typical spray drier is illustrated in Fig. 13.16.

(i) *Air heating and circulating systems.* Steam heaters are commonly used, either on their own or to complement indirect gas or oil heaters. In recent years the use of direct heating, using natural gas, has increased. Electric heating is only used on pilot scale plant.

Centrifugal fans or blowers are usually used for moving the air through the system. Some spray driers have a single exhaust fan while others employ both an inlet and outlet fan. Thus many drying chambers operate under a very slight negative pressure. Dampers are normally provided in air inlet and outlet ducts to control air flow. Filters are also provided to clean the inlet air.

(ii) *Spray forming devices.* The formation of a spray of the feed material, with uniform droplets of the desired dimensions, and the distribution of this spray throughout the heated air is of utmost importance for successful spray drying. The term usually employed to describe the formation of the spray is atomisation. There are three main types of atomising devices used in spray driers, namely: *Pressure nozzles, centrifugal atomisers* and *two-fluid nozzles.*

The principle of the *pressure nozzle* is that the feed material is pumped at relatively high pressure, usually in the range 500–7000 psig (3·6–48·4 MN m^{-2}), through a small orifice. Thus the energy in the high pressure liquid is used to form the spray. A grooved core insert, sited before the orifice, imparts a spinning motion to the liquid and a cone of spray is formed. Hollow cone sprays are commonly employed in food spray driers. A typical nozzle is shown in Fig. 13.17. Various other designs are available. Pressure nozzles, if fed at a uniform pressure, recommended for the particular design, can produce fine, uniform sprays. Blockage of the orifice by particulate matter and widening of the orifice, particularly if the feed contains abrasive solid, are limitations.

A *centrifugal atomiser* usually consists of a disc or bowl rotating on the end of a shaft. The liquid feed is introduced near the centre of rotation of the atomiser, accelerated to the linear velocity of the periphery of the head and spun off in the form of a spray into the drying chamber. The rotating head can take various forms including: inverted bowls, rimless wheels with

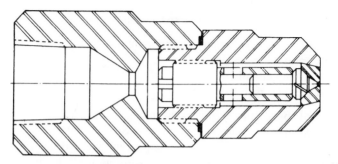

FIG. 13.17.   A pressure nozzle. (By courtesy of Niro Atomizer Ltd, Denmark.)

hollow spokes, discs with holes at the periphery and turbine type impellers. A typical design is shown in Fig. 13.18. Sizes and speeds vary from say a 2 in (5·08 cm) disc rotating at 50 000 rpm to a 30 in (76·2 cm) spoked wheel rotating at 3450 rpm. Provided they are correctly operated, centrifugal atomisers can produce fine uniform sprays. They are not very subject to blockage or abrasion due to solids in the feed and can handle viscous materials at relatively low pumping pressures. Special wear-resistant designs are available and also some suited to the production of relatively large particles, 0·5–1·0 mm diameter. The latter are applicable to spray congealing of melted products.[26]

The *two-fluid nozzle* depends on the energy in a high velocity stream of gas to atomise the feed material. The principle of this type of nozzle is shown in Fig. 13.19. The feed pressures used are less than those necessary

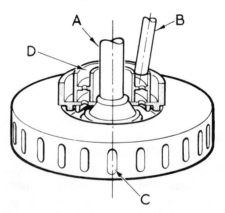

FIG. 13.18.   A centrifugal atomiser head. A, shaft; B, feed pipe; C, radial channel; D, dispenser. (By courtesy of Niro Atomizer Ltd, Denmark.)

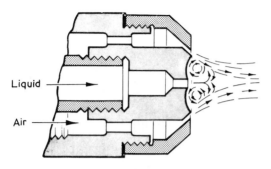

Liquid

Air

Fig. 13.19. The principle of the two-fluid nozzle. (By courtesy of Niro Atomizer Ltd, Denmark.)

for pressure nozzles. They suffer from orifice widening and blockage as do the latter type. They are generally of comparatively low capacity and a wide variation in droplet size very often occurs. Mainly for these latter reasons they are seldom used for the spray drying of foods.

(iii) *Drying chambers.* The drying chamber is that part of the spray drier where the hot air and spray of feed meet. Some of the many chamber designs are shown in Fig. 13.20.

Pilot plant experimentation or trial runs on industrial scale plant are the only reliable methods for selecting a drier for a particular duty. Due to the dangers of damaging heat-sensitive materials, countercurrent spray driers are seldom used for food drying.

(iv) *Product recovery systems.* In some spray driers the major proportion of the dry product falls to the bottom of the chamber and is removed with the aid of rakes, screw conveyors and rotary valves. When the dried product is thermoplastic and/or hygroscopic, special chamber designs involving cooled walls, air brooms and similar features may be necessary to facilitate product discharge.[25]

In other driers all the dried product leaves the drying chamber in the outgoing air. In all driers it is necessary to clean the outgoing air and recover the product therein. The methods commonly employed for this purpose are *dry cyclone separators, wet scrubbers, bag filters* and *electrostatic precipitators.*

The principle of the cyclone separator is the same as that of the centrifugal entrainment separator (Section 12.7.3, Fig. 12.7). Large cyclones, e.g. 10 ft (3·05 m) in diameter, are often used singly, or in pairs in series. Alternatively, banks of smaller cyclones in parallel may be employed. The latter tend to be more effective in removing light products of small

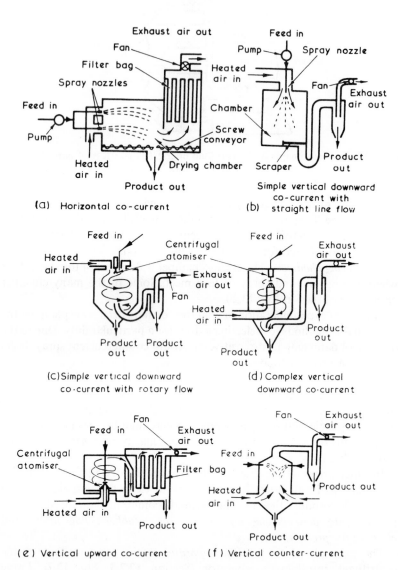

FIG. 13.20. Schematic drawings of various spray drying systems.

particle size, e.g. less than 50 μm in diameter. Cyclones generally give recoveries of the order of 90–97%. They are simple to operate and maintain.

The principle of the *wet scrubber* is to draw the exhaust air from the drying chamber through a vessel where it is washed with a liquid, usually the incoming feed to the atomiser. In some plants this system is employed not only to scrub the exhaust air but also to preheat or preconcentrate the incoming feed, thus improving the overall efficiency of the system. Growth of micro-organisms in wet scrubbers can be difficult to control and recirculation of some of the product can lead to heat damage. Recovery is usually of the order of 95–98%.

Drawing the exhaust air from the chamber through *cloth filters* is another technique employed for air cleaning and product recovery. Filters may be tubular or flat screen types. Such filters need to be mechanically shaken at intervals to loosen the product. Unless the temperature and humidity in the bag house is carefully controlled during shut-down, plugging can occur. Recovery is of the same order as wet scrubbers.

In an *electrostatic precipitator* the powder-laden air flows into a strong electric field formed between discharge electrodes and earthed plates. The plates are mounted in series with the electrodes suspended between them. Discharge of air ions from the electrodes combines with the powder particles. These obtain a negative polarity and move towards the earthed plates. When they contact the plates the particles lose their charge. They are removed from the plates by a tapping device and fall into a hopper. Precipitators are effective over a wide particle size range and can have an efficiency of up to 99%. They are not widely used in food applications.

In some spray driers a combination of methods is employed for product recovery, e.g. cyclones followed by bag filters.

It is not uncommon for liquid foods to be dried in two or more stages, e.g. in a spray drier followed by one or more secondary driers, very often vibrating fluidised bed driers. This is said to give more control over product quality and to improve thermal efficiency as compared with straight spray drying. One spray drier design features a built-in fluidised bed so that two-stage drying can be carried out in one unit.[17,25,27] Systems are also available which enable spray drying to be carried out under aseptic conditions. These are used mainly in the pharmaceutical industry. Closed cycle spray driers are also in use, mainly in the chemical industry.[25,26,28]

Spray driers are used extensively in the food industry. Examples of food products which are spray dried are: milk (skim and whole), whey, ice cream mix, butter, cheese, milk based baby foods, coffee and tea whiteners, eggs (whole, yolk and white), coffee, tea, fruit and vegetable juices, edible proteins, meat and yeast extracts, wheat and corn products.[19,20,25,27]

13.4. DRYING BY CONTACT WITH A HEATED SURFACE

13.4.1. GENERAL PRINCIPLES

As an alternative to the use of hot air as a drying medium, water may be removed by placing the wet material in contact with a heated surface. In such systems the necessary sensible, and latent heat of evaporation is supplied to the material by conduction. The drying pattern is similar to that of hot air drying to the extent that drying occurs mainly in two stages. During the initial constant rate period the material temperature approximates its boiling point at the prevailing pressure. The drying rates during this period are higher than those attained by drying in air at the same temperature as the heated surface. When the rate of movement of liquid to the evaporating surface falls below the rate of evaporation, the falling rate period commences and the material temperature rises and approaches that of the heated surface. If drying is carried out at atmospheric pressure, the material temperature, during the initial drying stage, is in excess of 100°C. In order to achieve reasonable drying times and to dry to low moisture contents, the heated surface temperature needs to be appreciably higher than this and, therefore, as drying nears completion the material temperature rises quite high. Thus the danger of heat damage to sensitive food materials is comparatively high. To reduce this hazard, drying by contact is often carried out under reduced pressure so that lower surface and material temperatures may be employed.

Assuming that drying is taking place from one face only and that shrinkage is negligible, the overall drying rate for a complete cycle may be expressed as follows

$$\frac{dw}{dt} = \frac{(W_o - W_f)M}{t} = \frac{K_c A(\theta_w - \theta_e)}{L} \tag{13.19}$$

where dw/dt = rate of change of weight; W_o = initial moisture content (DWB); W_f = final moisture content (DWB); M = mass of dry solids; t = total drying time; A = drying surface area; θ_w = temperature of heated surface; θ_e = temperature of the evaporating surface; L = latent heat of evaporation at θ_e; K_c = overall heat transfer coefficient (allowing for a reduction in $(\theta_w - \theta_e)$ as drying proceeds).

13.4.2. EQUIPMENT FOR DIRECT CONTACT DRYING
13.4.2.1. Drum drier (film drier, roller drier)
This type of drier consists essentially of one or more hollow metal cylinders, revolving on horizontal axes and heated internally by steam, water or other liquid heating medium. A film of the wet material, of uniform thickness, is applied to the drum surface. As the drum rotates drying takes place and the dried material is removed from the drum surface by a scraping device located usually $\frac{1}{2}-\frac{3}{4}$ of a revolution from the point of application of the feed. Drum driers are often classified into three types namely: *single drum, double drum* and *twin drum*. These are illustrated in Fig. 13.21. Drums have to be carefully machined to true cylindrical forms. Scraper knives need to be very sharp and to touch the drum surface uniformly, along its length. Adjusting screws are provided for this purpose.

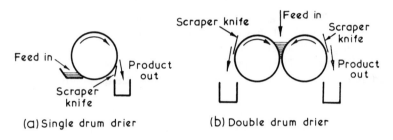

(a) Single drum drier (b) Double drum drier

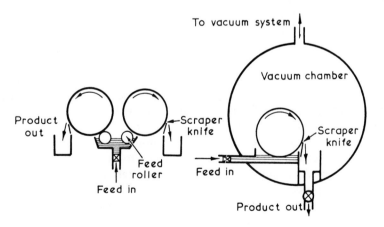

(C) Twin drum drier (d) Vacuum drum drier

FIG. 13.21. Schematic drawings of various types of drum drier.

It is essential, to ensure good performance, that the film of feed material applied to the drum surface should be as uniform as possible in depth. Single drums are fed by the use of feed vessels into which the drum dips, by the use of rotating devices to spray or splash the feed on and spreading knives or rollers to even out the film, or by the use of unheated feed rollers. The feed to the double drum drier is introduced into the trough between the drums.

For handling heat-sensitive materials, drums enclosed in a vacuum-tight chamber may be employed so that drying can be carried out at pressures less than atmospheric. Such a drier is also shown in Fig. 13.21. Vacuum, steam or heated water is usually used as a heating medium. The product is discharged into receivers, and adjustments to feeders, scrapers, etc., are made from outside the chamber. Such driers have relatively high capital cost and are normally used only for very heat-sensitive materials.

The factors affecting the drying rate and final moisture content of a particular material on a drum drier are: speed of rotation of drum (controlling dwell time), steam pressure or heating medium temperature and film thickness. The latter parameter depends on the feeding mechanism used and the solids content, rheological and surface tension properties of the feed.

The advantages of drum drying are high rates of drying and economic use of heat. The main limitations are that it can only be applied to foods in a liquid or slurry form and which can withstand relatively high temperatures for short periods of time (2–30 s). Drum driers have been applied to the drying of milk, soup mixes, ingredients for baby foods (meat, fruit and vegetables), potato slurries and instant breakfast cereals.[17,19,20,29,30]

13.4.2.2. Vacuum shelf drier

This is another method for drying heat-sensitive foods in the solid or liquid state by the application of heat by conduction. Such a drier consists of a vacuum tight chamber of heavy construction, with one or more access doors and an outlet for vapours and gases. Hollow shelves, through which the heating medium is circulated, are fitted inside the chamber. The feed material is spread in fairly thin layers on metal trays which rest on these hollow shelves. A vacuum is drawn on the chamber via the vapour outlet and drying proceeds at pressures in the range 1–70 torr (0·134–9·43 kN m^{-2}). Shelves and trays need to be as flat as possible to ensure good thermal contact. Initial drying rates are high but as the food dries and shrinks, contact with the tray becomes less effective and heat transfer declines. The shelf temperature requires very careful control to avoid

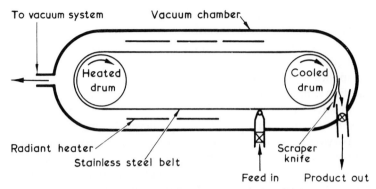

FIG. 13.22. Principle of the vacuum band drier.

overheating the dried portions of the food in contact with the trays. Vacuum shelf driers and their ancillaries incur high capital cost, and are normally only used for very heat-sensitive foods, for example fruit juice concentrates.

13.4.2.3. The vacuum band drier

This is mainly applicable to the drying of liquids and slurries. The principle of one such drier is shown in Fig. 13.22. It consists of a continuous stainless steel belt which passes over a heating and cooling drum inside a vacuum chamber. The feed is applied to the underside of this belt and heat is supplied both via the heated drum and radiant heaters. The dried product is cooled as the belt passes over the cooled drum and is removed by means of a scraper blade. Other band driers of this type have belts made up of stainless steel plates. Other heat sources may be used, such as steam coils and heated platens. Applications include fruit-juice concentrates, egg yolk and white, coffee extract and malt beverages.[11,12,17,30]

13.5. DRYING BY THE APPLICATION OF ENERGY FROM A RADIATING, MICROWAVE OR DIELECTRIC SOURCE

13.5.1. RADIANT HEATING

This has been applied to a limited extent to food dehydration. The characteristics of radiant heating and the methods of generating such radiation are dealt with in Chapter 10, Section 10.4.3.1. The basic equations governing heat transfer by radiation are given in Appendix II.

It must be realised that radiant heat plays a part in supplying the necessary sensible and latent heat of evaporation in both hot air drying and direct contact drying. Taking the cabinet drier as an example, the walls of the cabinet, the trays and other metal parts of the cabinet will radiate heat to the food.

The application of radiant heat as the major source of heat for food dehydration is limited because of its limited penetration into foods except at certain wavelengths. The heterogeneous nature of foods both in surface and absorptive characteristics can lead to uneven heating and hence non-uniform drying. Careful control of high temperature sources is necessary to avoid overheating. On the other hand, radiant heaters do not suffer from the disadvantages of poor contact and sluggish response to changes in temperature, experienced with most conduction sources.[17]

13.5.1.1. The continuous infra-red drier

This has found some application to food dehydration. In this type of equipment the food material is carried on a conveyor belt or vibrating deck beneath infra-red sources for the required drying times. The sources used for heat sensitive food materials are usually short-wave lamps while long-wave bar generators may be used for less sensitive materials. Some applications quoted by the manufacturers include drying of bread crumbs, starches, custard powders, cake mixtures, tea, almonds and spices.

The vacuum band drier discussed in Section 13.4.2.3 also employs radiant heating.

13.5.2. MICROWAVE AND DIELECTRIC HEATING

This has so far had little commercial application to food dehydration. The characteristics of this type of heating and the types of generating equipment are dealt with in Chapter 10, Sections 10.4.3.2 and 10.4.3.3. While at this stage of its development this type of heating appears to be uneconomic for removing moisture in bulk, some of the duties to which it is put are essentially dehydration processes. The drying of starch-reduced rolls in dielectric ovens at 35 MHz and the finishing of biscuits are examples. To date, dielectric heating seems to have wider commercial application than microwave mainly due to the comparative simplicity of the equipment available. Microwave systems would appear potentially better because of the greater dissipation of heat in foods and the higher power potential of the generators. Some encouraging results have been obtained in studies on the application of microwave heating in vacuum drying.[17,31,32]

A fully automated microwave plant for heat treatment and partial dehydration of cereals, peas and beans in bulk, has been reported.[33]

13.6. FREEZE-DRYING (SUBLIMATION DRYING; LYOPHILISATION)

13.6.1. GENERAL PRINCIPLES

This method of drying involves freezing the material followed by sublimation of the ice from the frozen state to produce a dried product. Sublimation is brought about by maintaining a water vapour pressure gradient between the immediate surroundings of the material and the ice front within the material. Complete drying could be said to take place in three stages. Initially, by freezing, water is withdrawn from the hydrated components of the food by the formation of crystals of ice or eutectic mixtures. By subsequent sublimation of these crystals, water is removed from the body of the material. When all the ice has been removed the solid remaining will still have a small amount of water absorbed within the structure of its components. This may be removed by evaporation in the freeze-drying equipment, usually by raising the material temperature, or alternatively the 'finishing' of the material may be carried out in another form of drier, such as a bin drier.

The removal of the major portion of the water by sublimation results in a product with a light porous structure, retaining the shape and size of the original material. Many of the disadvantages associated with other drying methods as discussed in Section 13.3.2 are avoided or minimised. Shrinkage is almost negligible, movement of soluble solids is limited and heat damage is minimised. The reconstitution characteristics of the product are good both in terms of rate and extent of reconstitution. The retention of volatile odour and flavour compounds is also high. On the other hand cell structure may be damaged during freezing, giving poor texture in the reconstituted product, and the dried product itself is very brittle and susceptible to mechanical damage.

In most conventional freeze-drying systems the vapour pressure gradient necessary for sublimation is attained by maintaining the total pressure in the drying chamber at a low level of the order of 0.1–2.0 torr (13.5–270.0 N m^{-2}). A condensing system is provided to remove the water vapour formed and a heating system to supply the necessary latent heat of sublimation to the frozen material. Such a system is shown schematically in Fig. 13.23. In such a system the two main factors affecting the rate of drying are the rate of movement of water vapour from the ice surface through the porous layer of dry material and the rate of transfer of heat to the ice front.

The movement of water vapour through the porous layer of dried material has been discussed by various authors.[6,11,34-37] Karel[6] used a general equation to represent the rate of flow of vapour through the solid layer

$$\frac{dw}{dt} = \frac{Ab(p_i - p_D)}{l} \qquad (13.20)$$

where dw/dt = mass flow rate of vapour through dry layer, A = drying area normal to the direction of flow of vapour, b = permeability of of the dry layer, p_i = vapour pressure of ice at specified temperature, p_D = partial pressure of water vapour at surface of dry layer, l = thickness of dry layer.

In order to achieve the maximum rate of drying, the ice temperature should be as high as possible consistent with product quality. Unless the heat of sublimation is supplied to the ice at a sufficient rate, the ice temperature will fall and, consequently, so will the drying rate. In a system where the heat is transferred to the ice through the dried layer only and where drying takes place only from the heated surface (as would happen, theoretically, if the heat supply to the lower plate in Fig. 13.23 were cut off), then the rate of heat input, dQ/dt, is given by the equation:

$$\frac{dQ}{dt} = \frac{k_D A(\theta_D - \theta_i)}{l} \qquad (13.21)$$

where k_D = thermal conductivity of dried layer, θ_D = temperature of dried surface, θ_i = temperature of ice surface.

An energy balance combining equations (13.20) and (13.21) gives:

$$\frac{k_D A(\theta_D - \theta_i)}{l} = -\frac{L_s Ab(p_i - p_D)}{l} \qquad (13.22)$$

where L_s = latent heat of sublimation at θ_i.

Note that l cancels out so that the relationship is independent of the extent of drying. If the dried surface temperature and chamber pressure are fixed then the ice surface temperature is also fixed (since θ_i and p_i are thermodynamically related).

If a slab-shaped solid is being freeze-dried from one or both large faces, i.e. end effects are ignored, if the moisture content of the dry layer formed is W_e, *dry-weight basis*, and if the ice front recedes in a uniform plane then the rate of drying, dw/dt, may be described by an equation thus:

$$\frac{dw}{dt} = A\rho_m(W_0 - W_e)\frac{dl}{dt} \qquad (13.23)$$

where ρ_m = the density of the dried solid, W_0 = initial moisture content of the material, *dry-weight basis*.

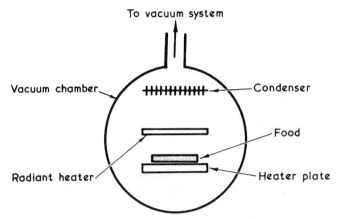

FIG. 13.23.   The basic elements of a freeze-drying system.

From (13.22) and (13.23) one can deduce the relationship:

$$\frac{dw}{dt} = -\frac{Ak_D(\theta_D - \theta_i)}{L_s l} = \frac{Ab(p_i - p_D)}{l} = A\rho_m(W_0 - W_e)\frac{dl}{dt} \quad (13.24)$$

Integrating within the limits: $t = 0$, $l = 0$; $t = t_t$, $l = l_t$:

$$t_t = \frac{\rho_m(W_0 - W_e)}{b(p_i - p_D)}\frac{l_t^2}{2} = \frac{L_s\rho_m(W_0 - W_e)}{k_D(\theta_D - \theta_i)}\frac{l_t^2}{2} \quad (13.25)$$

where t_t = total drying time to W_e, l_t = total thickness of slab for one-sided drying = half the slab thickness for two-sided drying. Note that t_t is proportional to l_t^2, hence the drying of thick slabs is prolonged. Both the permeability and thermal conductivity of the dry layer are dependent on pressure and the nature of the gases in the pores. Some values of these properties for meat, fish, coffee and apple are reported by Karel.[6] This author also presents expressions relating heater plate temperature to dry surface temperature and discusses the situation when heat is conducted through the ice layer to the subliming surface.

13.6.2.   FREEZE-DRYING EQUIPMENT
13.6.2.1.   The freezing stage
Ideally, to carry out the freeze-drying process correctly, all the liquid present in the food should be frozen. However, in practice this is not feasible, and provided the amount of unfrozen liquid remaining is small the product quality is not seriously affected.[38]
     The optimum rate of freezing for freeze-drying depends largely on the

nature of the product. Variation in rate of freezing affects ice crystal size and hence pore size in the dried product, and so can be expected to influence the rate of drying and the characteristics of the product, particularly its reconstitutability. Optimum rates of freezing should be determined experimentally. Freezing may be carried out by any of the methods discussed in Chapter 14.

13.6.2.2. Batch freeze-driers
The essential components of a batch freeze-drier are a vacuum cabinet, a vacuum system and a heating system. Freeze-drier cabinets are essentially similar to the vacuum shelf driers described in Section 13.4.2.2. Parts in direct contact with the food are usually of stainless steel and other internal surfaces are suitably coated.

The *vacuum system* must be capable of pumping down the cabinet initially in a short time to prevent melting of the frozen product. In practice this usually entails lowering the cabinet pressure to between 5 and 1 torr (675 and 135 N m^{-2}) within 10 min. The cabinet pressure then needs to be lowered to the required level for drying, usually well below 1 torr (135 N m^{-2}), and held at that pressure during the drying. The vacuum system has to cope with the vapour produced during drying, gases evolved from the food and leakage into the chamber. It is usual to provide 'roughing pumps' for the initial pump down and smaller capacity, holding pumps for use during drying.

Refrigerated condensers, backed by a mechanical pumping system, are commonly used, commercially, for producing and maintaining chamber vacuum. Most of the water vapour is condensed as ice onto the refrigerated plates or coils and the pumps remove the non-condensable gases and residual vapour. Location of two or more condensers in separate chambers (traps), connected to the drying chamber through sliding gates or valves, facilitates deicing during operation of the drier. Multistage steam ejector systems may be used instead of the condenser-pump systems but are less effective at very low chamber pressures.

Heat may be supplied to the frozen material by conduction or radiation. Most modern plants use a combination of these mechanisms. The trays of frozen food are placed between heated plates with a fixed spacing, greater than the depth of the trays plus the food. Heat is transferred to the food by conduction from below and by radiation to its top surface from the plate above. Careful design of plates and trays facilitates rapid heat transfer. Microwave heating, for this purpose, has also been investigated with some promising results.[17]

A typical batch freeze-drier would have a capacity of 900 lb (408·6 kg) of prepared food and a drying cycle of the order of 7–8 h, with most materials.

13.6.2.3. Multicabinet units

These are widely used for freeze-drying of foods at larger throughputs of the order of 5 tons day^{-1} (5080 kg day^{-1}) material. A typical unit consists of four batch cabinets each fitted with its own heater plates but all four connected to two vacuum manifolds. One manifold is used for pump down and roughing duties and the other for maintaining the appropriate pressure during drying. The cabinets are loaded sequentially at appropriate intervals, depending on the food, but usually 2–3 h, and the vacuum system controlled to maintain appropriate pressures in each cabinet at all times.

13.6.2.4. Tunnel freeze-driers

These are available for very high throughput operations. Such a unit consists of a cylindrical tunnel 6–8 ft (1·8–2·4 m) in diameter fitted with

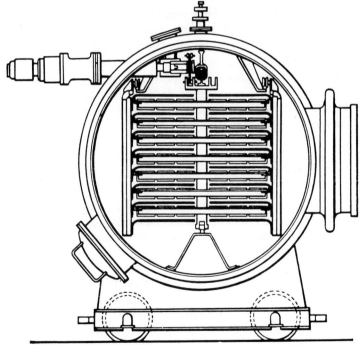

FIG. 13.24. Typical cross-section through the tunnel. (Reproduced from *Freeze-drying of Foodstuffs*,[38] by courtesy of Columbine Press (Publishers) Ltd.)

heater plates with fixed spacing. The food material in trays or ribbed dishes is carried, either on a trolley running on ground rails or suspended from an overhead rail so that the trays fit between the heater plates in the tunnel (Fig. 13.24). In some units the trays can be lowered as required into direct contact with the heater shelves. The tunnel has a length dependent largely on the throughput required and is generally made up of a number of standard sections. The complete tunnel is fitted with entry and delivery locks at the ends. The batches of food are fed into the tunnel at suitable intervals through the entry lock, the latter being pumped down rapidly after each entry. As the batch passes from the lock into the tunnel proper a sliding pressure gate closes off the lock, the vacuum therein is broken and it is ready to receive the next batch. Dried product is removed similarly from the exit lock and here the vacuum may be broken by the introduction of inert gas.

For efficient operation the vacuum and heating systems should be designed to suit the loads at the various stages in the tunnel. Both the vapour and heat loads decrease as drying proceeds. Other designs of continuous freeze-driers have been described in the lierature. In these particulate solids are conveyed through vacuum chambers by screws, belts or vibrating decks. A vacuum spray freeze-drier has also been described.

Because of the high capital and running costs associated with freeze-drying and the stringent packaging requirements of the product, it is an expensive method of food preservation. Industrial applications for freeze-drying include coffee and tea extracts, meat and fish (e.g. shrimp and prawn) and some vegetable and fruit products.[6,11,17,34−36,39]

13.7. RECONSTITUTABILITY OF DRIED FOODS

Reconstitutability, as applied to dehydrated foods, is the term used to describe the rate at and extent to which dried foods pick up, absorb water and revert to a condition resembling the undried material, when put in contact with a surplus of water.

13.7.1. FACTORS INFLUENCING RECONSTITUTION

In the case of dried foods in piece form such as sliced or diced vegetables or diced meat products, the reconstitutability largely depends on the structure of the dried pieces and the extent to which the water holding components, mainly proteins and starch, have been affected by the drying operation. For example, the rate at which air dried vegetables reconstitute can depend on the initial rates of drying (see Section 13.2.3.2). Freeze dried foods often reconstitute rapidly because of the porous structure, which is a feature of this method of drying (see Section 13.3.4). On the other hand, excessive heat damage during drying, or freezing damage in the case of freeze dried foods, can result in a reduction in the water holding capacity of the reconstituted material and hence a poor appearance and texture.

In the case of dried powders a number of properties may influence the overall reconstitution characteristics of the material. These include:

Wettability. This term describes the ability of the powder particle to adsorb water on its surface, thus initiating reconstitution. This property largely depends on particle size. Small particles, representing a large surface area: mass ratio, may not be wetted individually, but clump together, sharing a wetted surface layer. This layer reduces the rate at which water penetrates into the clump of particles. Increasing the particle size and/or agglomerating particles can reduce the incidence of clumping. The nature of the surface of the particles can also affect wettability. For example the presence of free fat at the surface reduces wettability. The selective use of surface active agents such as lecithin can sometimes improve wettability in dried powders containing fat.

Sinkability. This term describes the ability of the powder particles to sink quickly into the water. It depends mainly on the size and density of the particles. Larger, more dense particles sink more rapidly than fine, lighter particles. Particles with a high content of occluded air may be relatively large but exhibit poor sinkability because of their low density.

Dispersability. This term describes the ease with which the powder may be distributed, as single particles, over the surface and throughout the bulk of the reconstituting water. Dispersability is reduced by clump formation and is improved when the sinkability is high.

Solubility. This term describes the rate and extent to which the components of the powder particles dissolve in the water. It depends mainly on the chemical composition of the powder and its physical state, e.g. degree and type of crystallinity.

For a powder to exhibit good reconstitution characteristics, i.e. a so-called 'instant' powder, there needs to be a correct balance between the individual properties discussed above. In many cases alteration of one or two of these properties can markedly change the behaviour of the powder on reconstitution. In addition to their influence on the reconstitution of dried powders, properties such as particle size, density and bulk density can affect the handling characteristics and appearance of such products.

13.7.2. PROCEDURES FOR IMPROVING RECONSTITUTABILITY

13.7.2.1. Adjustment of drying conditions

Variations in the feed (solids content, viscosity, temperature), atomisation (type of atomiser and operating pressure or speed) and drying air (inlet and outlet temperatures) can result in changes in the particle size, density and bulk density of the product. Adjustment of conditions can sometimes lead to an improvement in reconstitution characteristics. The introduction of additional steps in the process may also help. An example of the latter remedy is the inclusion of crystallisation stages in the spray drying of whey.

13.7.2.2. Recycling of fines

The fine particles produced in a spray drier may be recycled to the wet zone of the drying chamber, near the atomiser. Dried particles from the chamber are cooled on a vibrating, fluidised-bed cooler. The fines from this cooler, together with those in the exhaust air from the drying chamber, are recycled and form agglomerates with the spray. Thus the fine particles are eliminated from the product and the reconstitutability, mainly in terms of wettability and dispersability, may be improved.

13.7.2.3. Straight-through instantiser

The product leaves the drying chamber at a relatively high moisture content, 6–8% (WWB). In this condition the particles may be thermoplastic and tacky at the surface and agglomeration may occur. On leaving the chamber, the agglomerates, now 300–400 μm in diameter, are dried further and cooled on a two-stage vibrating, fluidised-bed unit. Fines are also recycled to the drying chamber.

13.7.2.4. Rewetting

This is probably the most effective and widely used method of improving the reconstitution characteristics of dried powders. Spray dried powder, produced in a conventional plant, is treated with steam or warm, humid air such that condensation occurs on the surface of the particles. Inter-particle contact is promoted, often by swirling the wetted powder in a vortex. Agglomerates are formed. The agglomerates are dried in a chamber, then cooled on a vibrating fluidised-bed. Fines from the bed and chamber are recycled to the agglomeration zone. This procedure is known as surface

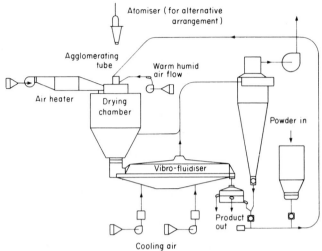

FIG. 13.25. Rewet instantiser. (Reproduced from *Spray Drying Handbook*,[25] by courtesy of the author.)

agglomeration. An alternative procedure, known as droplet agglomeration, involves contacting the dried powder with a fine mist or spray of water or a solution of some or all of the components of the powder. The mist may be formed by spray jets or an atomiser wheel (see Fig. 13.25). The agglomerates formed are dried and cooled as in surface agglomeration.

Agglomeration results in an increase in interstitial air between the particles. On reconstitution this air is replaced rapidly by water and rapid wetting and disersion of the particles occurs.[25,40,41]

REFERENCES

1. Iglesias, H. A. and Chiriffe, J., *Handbook of Food Isotherms*. Academic Press, New York, 1982.
2. Brunauer, S., Emmett, P. H. and Teller, E., Adsorption of gases in multimolecular layers. *J. Am. Chem. Soc.*, **60** (1938) 309–19.
3. Chiriffe, F. and Iglesias, H. A., Equations for fitting sorption isotherms of foods. *J. Food Technol.*, **13** (1978) 159–74.
4. Jowitt, R., Escher, F., Hallstrom, B., Meffert, H. W., Spiess, W. E. L. and Vos, G., *Physical Properties of Foods*. Applied Science Publishers, London, 1983.
5. Labuza, T. P., The properties of water in relationship to water binding in foods. A review. *J. Food Process. Preserve.*, **1** (1977) 167–90.
6. Karel. M., Fundamentals of dehydration processes. In *Advances in Preconcentration and Dehydration of Foods*, ed. A. Spicer. Applied Science Publishers, London, 1974, pp. 45–94.

7. Rockland, L. B. and Stewart, G. F. (ed), *Water Activity: Influences on Food Quality*. Academic Press, New York, 1981.

8. Duckworth, R. G. (ed.), *Water Relations in Foods*. Academic Press, New York, 1975.

9. Troller, J. A. and Christian, J. H. B., *Water Activity and Food*. Academic Press, New York, 1978.

10. Green, D. W. (ed.), *Perry's Chemical Engineers' Handbook*, 6th edn. McGraw-Hill, New York, 1984.

11. Van Arsdel, W. B., Copley, M. J. and Morgan, A. I., Jr, (ed.), *Food Dehydration. Vol. I: Drying Methods and Phenomena*. 2nd edn. AVI, Westport, Conn., USA, 1973.

12. Charm, S. E., *The Fundamentals of Food Engineering*, 3rd edn. AVI, Westport, Conn., USA, 1978.

13. Saravacos, G. D. and Charm, S. E., A study of the mechanisms of fruit and vegetable dehydration. *Food Technol., Champaign*, **16**(1) (1962) 78–81.

14. Jason, A. C., A study of evaporation and diffusion processes in the drying of fish muscle. In *Conf. on the Fundamental Aspects of the Dehydration of Foodstuffs, Aberdeen, March 1958*. SCI, London, 1958, pp. 103–34.

15. Gorling, P., Physical phenomena during the drying of foodstuffs. In *Conf. on the Fundamental Aspects of the Dehydration of Foodstuffs, Aberdeen, March 1958*. SCI, London, 1958, pp. 42–53.

16. Crank, J., Some mathematical diffusion studies relevant to dehydration. In *Conf. on the Fundamental Aspects of the Dehydration of Foodstuffs, Aberdeen, March 1958*. SCI, London, 1958, pp. 37–41.

17. Brennan, J. G., Dehydration of foods. In *Water and Food Quality*, ed. T. Hardman. Elsevier Applied Science Publishers, London, 1989.

18. Sturgeon, L. F., Conveyor driers. In *Handbook of Industrial Drying*, ed., A. S. Mujumdar. Marcel Dekker, New York, 1987, pp. 501–13.

19. Van Arsdel, W. B., Copley, M. J. and Morgan, Jr, A. I. (ed.), *Food Dehydration. Vol. II. Practices and Applications*, 2nd edn. AVI, Westport, Conn., USA, 1973.

20. Sokhansanj, S. and Jayas, D. S., Drying of foodstuffs. In *Handbook of Industrial Drying*, ed. A. S. Mujumdar. Marcel Dekker, New York, 1987, pp. 517–54.

21. Hovmand, S., Fluidized bed drying. In *Handbook of Industrial Drying*, ed. A. S. Mujumdar. Marcel Dekker, New York, 1987, pp. 165–225.

22. Kisakurek, B., Flashdrying. In *Handbook of Industrial Drying*, ed. A. S. Mujumdar. Marcel Dekker, New York, 1987, pp. 475–99.

23. Kerkhof, P. J. A. M. and Schoeber, W. J. A. H., Theoretical modelling of the drying behaviour of droplets in spray driers. In *Advances in Preconcentration and Dehydration of Foods*, ed. A. Spicer. Applied Science Publishers, London, 1974, pp. 349–97.

24. Filkova, I. and Mujumdar, A. S., Industrial spray drying systems. In *Handbook of Industrial Drying*, ed., A. S. Mujumdar. Marcel Dekker, New York, 1987, pp. 243–93.

25. Masters, K., *Spray Drying Handbook*, 4th edn. George Godwin, London, 1985.

26. Kjaergaard, O. G., Effects of the latest developments on design and practice of spray drying. In *Advances in Reconcentration and Dehydration of Foods*, ed. A. Spicer. Applied Science Publishers, London, 1974, pp. 321–48.

27. Pisecky, J., Evaporation and spray drying in the dairy industry. In *Handbook of*

Industrial Drying, ed. A. S., Mujumdar. Marcel Dekker, New York, 1987, pp. 571–603.

28. Brennan, J. G., Developments in food dehydration. *Process Chem. Engng.*, **31**(9) (1978) 11–12, 14, 16–17, 20, 24.

29. Moore, J. G., Drum dryers. In *Handbook of Industrial Drying*, ed. A. S. Mujumdar. Marcel Dekker, New York, 1987, pp. 227–42.

30. Williams-Gardner, A., *Industrial Drying*. George Godwin, London, 1976.

31. Meisel, N., Microwave heating in vacuum drying. In *Advances in Preconcentration and Dehydration of Foods*, ed. A. Spicer. Applied Science Publishers, London, 1974.

32. Schiffmann, R. F., Microwave and dielectric drying. In *Handbook of Industrial Drying*, ed. A. S. Mujumdar. Marcel Dekker, New York, 1987, pp. 327–56.

33. Anon., Continuous drying microwaves. *Food Processing*, **54**(12) (1985) 13.

34. Mellor, J. D., Cyclic-pressure freeze-drying. In *Advances in Preconcentration and Dehydration of Foods*, ed. A. Spicer. Applied Science Publishers, London, 1974, pp. 503–9.

35. Mellor, J. D., *Fundamentals of Freeze-Drying*. Academic Press, New York, 1978.

36. Judson King, C., *Freeze-Drying of Foods*. Butterworths, London, 1971.

37. Lorentzen, J., New directions in freeze drying. In *Advances in Preconcentration and Dehydration of Foods*, ed. A. Spicer. Applied Science Publishers, London, 1974, pp. 413–33.

38. Cotson, S. and Smith, D. B. (ed.), *Freeze-Drying of Foodstuffs—A Symposium*. Columbine Press, Manchester, England, 1963.

39. Liapis, A. I., Freeze drying. In *Handbook of Industrial Drying*, ed. A. S. Mujumdar. Marcel Dekker, New York, 1987, pp. 295–326.

40. Jensen, J. D., Methods of instantizing powders for the preparation of food and drinks. *Manufacturing Confect.*, **53**(10) (1973) 47–56.

41. Jensen, J. D., Agglomerating, instantizing and spray drying. *Food Technol.*, *Champaign*, **29**(6) (1975) 60–71.

CHAPTER 14

FREEZING

14.1. INTRODUCTION AND DEFINITIONS

From time immemorial food has been preserved by freezing in localities which have a sufficiently low ambient temperature (weather freezing). Iced confections, produced from naturally occurring snow and ice, have been available from antiquity and, in the Andes of South America, potato tubers were weather frozen as a preparatory operation in the traditional manufacture of a dried potato product. The second half of the nineteenth century saw the development of reliable mechanical refrigeration equipment and the foundation of the present day cold storage and frozen food industries. The increasing impact of the freezing industry on United Kingdom eating habits can be clearly seen in Table 14.1. The UK is one of the world's highest *per capita* consumers of frozen foods (21 kg per person per year in 1986) and expectations are that the frozen food industry will continue to expand, though perhaps less rapidly, into the 1990s.

The earliest freezing processes, known as 'sharp freezing', involved placing food in refrigerated rooms, usually with natural air circulation. Fish, meat, poultry, eggs and fruit for jam manufacture were frozen in this way. Vegetable freezing developed after 1930, following the work of, among others, Clarence Birdseye. This indicated that the rate of freezing influenced the quality of the thawed product and led to rapid freezing to attain a high quality product and to the use of the term 'quick freezing'. More recent work has indicated that food quality is not always improved by an increase in freezing rate.[3,4] After freezing and thawing, fluid may escape from materials with a higher water content. This fluid is called 'drip' and there is evidence that drip losses are increased when freezing is slow in the case of beef and strawberries. Spiess[4] has divided foods into four groups

417

TABLE 14.1
Frozen food in relation to total food
expenditure[1,2]

Year	Percentage
1975	3·1
1976	3·4
1977	3·4
1978	3·4
1979	3·5
1980	3·8
1981	4·1
1982	4·5
1983	4·6
1984	4·9
1985	5·2
1986	5·4

depending on their sensitivity to rate of freezing as measured by the rate of fall of temperature over the range 0 to $-20°C$ (see Table 14.2).

High rates of freezing lead to the production of very small ice crystals. In part, quality improvements at high rates of freezing with Spiess' Group 4 materials may be attributed to the formation of such crystals. However, on storage and distribution, temperature fluctuations can lead to the development of fewer and larger crystals in the produce (see Chapter 9) and

TABLE 14.2
Products grouped according to their sensitivity to rate of freezing (after Spiess[4])

Group 1	Products with a high content of dry matter, e.g. peas, high fat meats, some ready-to-serve meals.	Freezing rate has no influence on final quality.
Group 2	Fish, lean meat, starch-containing ready-to-serve foods.	Freezing rate should be $>0·5–1°C\,min^{-1}$.
Group 3	Strawberries, carrots, beans, gelatinous materials, such as egg products and sauces with a flour base.	Freezing rate should be $>3–6°C\,min^{-1}$.
Group 4	Materials with relatively little dry matter, e.g. raspberries, tomatoes, cucumbers.	High rates of freezing advantageous.

the quality advantage can be lost. Small crystals formed in rapid freezing are also more reflective than larger crystals formed at lower freezing rates, so frozen red meats appear paler and poultry flesh whiter. The latter effect may be desirable from the point of view of consumer acceptability without necessarily enhancing the quality of the flesh of the thawed bird. Very rapid freezing (say, by immersion in liquid nitrogen) can set up disruptive stresses in the frozen material which may break apart.

Whether it affects quality or not, the freezing time remains a matter of importance as it influences the economics of the freezing process. Though freezing is less thermodynamically efficient when low temperatures are used to obtain high freezing rates, energy costs are only a fraction of the total. The plant throughput per unit area of factory floor space and the throughput per unit labour cost can be of much greater importance.

The definition of the term 'freezing time' presents some difficulty. Two instants need to be defined, the instant that the freezing time starts and the instant that it stops. Unfortunately freezing will occur at different rates at different points in the piece or package of food. Freezing will be faster at some point on the surface. In the body of the piece or package will be located a point which cools the slowest. This is known as the thermal centre and measurements of temperature histories during freezing are normally made at this point. The highest temperature at which ice crystals have a stable existence in a food material is conventionally known as the 'freezing point' of that material and the formation of the first ice crystals at the surface of the body being frozen can be utilised as signalling the start of the 'freezing time'. However, because of the nature of foodstuffs and the presence of water-soluble constituents, all of the water present does not solidify at this temperature. Under equilibrium conditions and at a temperature just below the freezing point, a certain fraction of the water present remains in a fluid phase. This fraction falls when the temperature is lowered and eutectic mixtures may separate from the unfrozen fluid, but unfrozen water is still present even at comparatively low temperatures. Thus it is not possible to define a clear endpoint to the freezing process. There are two approaches to a practical definition of freezing time, one relevant to the quality of the product and the other to the throughput of the freezing plant.

First, the freezing time may be defined as that time during which the majority of the ice is formed in the body. Thus the International Institute of Refrigeration[5] defines the 'nominal freezing time' to be the time elapsing from the instant the surface of a body reaches 0°C to the instant that the thermal centre reaches a temperature 10°C colder than the temperature of initial ice formation at that point. While it might be objected that ice formation will not occur until the surface temperature of the body has fallen below 0°C, the difference in time involved is probably too small to be of importance. The significance of taking the end point of the freezing process as the achievement of a temperature ten degrees below the freezing point at the thermal centre is clear from Fig. 14.1, which shows that for a typical food product, virtually the whole of the ice formation will have occurred by that time. Because we are considering here the time during which the majority of the ice is formed, this definition may be used in circumstances where the influence of freezing rate on quality is under consideration.

On the other hand, the processor will require to know the total time that an item will remain in the freezing plant. For this reason the 'effective freezing time' (t_e) has been defined[5] as the time to lower the temperature of the product from its initial average value to a given value at the thermal centre. The final centre temperature taken will, of course, be that at which it is desired to remove the product from the freezer and statements of the effective freezing time are meaningless unless the initial and final conditions are clearly specified.

There are alternative, though unsatisfactory, definitions of freezing time. If a temperature history is measured at the thermal centre of a body cooling from above its freezing point to below, a curve as in Fig. 14.2 results. There

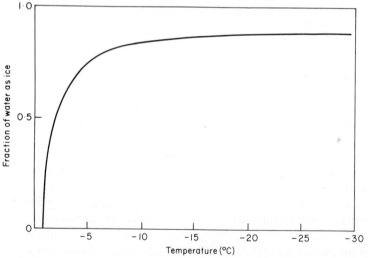

FIG. 14.1. The ice content of beef muscle (74·5% water) (after Riedel[6]).

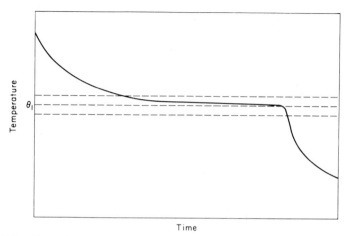

FIG. 14.2. Typical temperature history at the thermal centre during the freezing of a food body (diagrammatic).

is quite a sharp 'knee' in the vicinity of the freezing point (θ_1) of the body and while before this point the temperature changes slowly, afterwards there is a rapid fall. Many workers have taken two arbitary temperatures, one slightly above and the other below the freezing point, and treated the time to cool through this temperature range at the thermal centre as a measure of the freezing time of the body. The term 'period of thermal arrest' has been used for this time, since the temperature changes only slowly with time during the period. Such a definition is unsatisfactory for a number of reasons. First the temperature limits are specified arbitrarily and a wide variety of intervals have been chosen by different workers.[7] Secondly, as Long[8] has shown, the period of thermal arrest, in any instance, is a function of the initial temperature of the body, reducing with rise of initial temperature. And finally, as may be seen by reference to Fig. 14.14 later, by the time the temperature at the thermal centre approaches anywhere near the freezing point, ice formation can have advanced well into the body.

14.2. THE ESTIMATION OF FREEZING TIMES

Calculations involving unsteady state conduction heat transfer with change of phase are not easy. However, if it is desired to estimate a freezing time from physical data, rather than determine it experimentally, two approaches are possible. In the first case, with the advent of modern computer technology, a realistic, and consequently complicated, mathematical model may be set up and the differential equations for heat flow solved by numerical methods. While such an approach can be accurate, the results obtained relate only to the data included in the calculation and so will be of specific, rather than general, applicability. Additionally, for accuracy in such calculations, accurate data are required on the variation of the enthalpy and thermal conductivity of the product with temperature, and the heat transfer coefficient and cooling medium temperature at the surface of the product body, together with its variation over the surface and with time. Considering the lack of homogeneity of many foods, the variations likely to exist between different packs and the difficulties of measuring heat transfer coefficients under these circumstances, it would seem easier to determine accurate freezing times for any particular circumstances by experimental measurement than from calculations based on such a mathematical model.

The alternative approach is to assume a highly simplified mathematical model such that the basic differential equations can be solved analytically to yield simple formulae giving crude estimates of freezing times in a wide variety of situations. While such equations may not give that reliable an estimate of a freezing time, they can usefully serve to indicate by what factor the freezing time would change as a consequence of a given change to the parameters of the process.

Formulae for estimating freezing times are usually based on the assumption that the body to be frozen is initially at a uniform temperature and is cooled by a constant temperature medium, there being a uniform and constant heat transfer coefficient between the surface of the body and the cooling medium. It is also assumed that the material of the body has a constant thermal conductivity and specific heat (different for the frozen and unfrozen states), a density which does not vary with temperature or alter during the freezing process and a definite freezing point at which all the latent heat of fusion is liberated. This last assumption enables freezing to be divided into three processes: *precooling* of the unfrozen material, *freezing* proper and cooling the frozen material to its final state (*tempering*). If the body to be frozen is initially at its freezing point there is no pre-cooling period, hence no heat flow in the unfrozen material, and calculation of its freezing time is comparatively simple. To make such an assumption is not unreasonable as products are often chilled before entering the freezer. Further simplification occurs if the material at the thermal centre at the end of the freezing process is assumed to be frozen, but still at its freezing point. The freezing time calculated on these assumptions may be termed the 'calculated freezing time' (t_f). The effective freezing time can be estimated from the calculated freezing time by applying corrections to allow for the precooling and tempering periods.

Formulae for the calculated freezing time can be simplified by making use of dimensionless groups. Two of these, the Biot (Bi) and Fourier (Fo) Numbers, are commonly used for unsteady state heat transfer involving thermal conduction (see Appendix II). The third group is:

$$\frac{c\,\Delta\theta}{L}$$

where L = the latent heat of fusion of the material, c = its specific heat in the frozen state, $\Delta\theta$ = the difference between the freezing point of the material and the temperature of the cooling medium. This has been termed the Stefan Number (Ste),[9] although some Russian workers use the Kossovitch Number, which is the reciprocal of the Stefan Number.

In calculating the Biot and Fourier numbers, in this instance, the characteristic dimension (l) is the shortest distance from the thermal centre to the surface of the body being frozen, the time is the calculated freezing time and the thermal constants used are those for the frozen material.

The freezing of an infinite slab of material initially at its freezing point (i.e. a block of infinite length, breadth and uniform thickness $2l$) by cooling its exposed surfaces, there being an infinite surface heat transfer coefficient, is one of the few cases for which, making the assumptions outlined above, an exact formal closed solution to the equation of conduction of heat has been obtained. This solution, due to Stefan,[10] yields the relationship:

$$\left(\frac{\pi}{4Fo}\right)^{1/2} \exp\left\{\frac{1}{4Fo}\right\} \mathrm{erf}\left\{\frac{1}{(4Fo)^{1/2}}\right\} = Ste \qquad (14.1)$$

where $\mathrm{erf}(x) = (2/(\pi)^{1/2}) \int_0^x \exp(-x^2)\,\mathrm{d}x$ and is known as the error function.

Expanding the reciprocal of the left hand side of equation (14.1) as a power series:

$$2Fo\left\{1 - \frac{1}{6Fo} + \frac{1}{90Fo^2} - \cdots\right\} = \frac{1}{Ste} \qquad (14.2)$$

so for large values of Fo

$$Fo.Ste = \tfrac{1}{2} \qquad (14.3)$$

This approximation is often acceptable, having regard to the simplifying

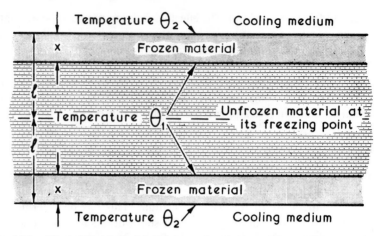

FIG. 14.3.   The infinite slab with infinite surface heat transfer coefficient at time t after the commencement of freezing.

assumptions previously made. For instance, the values of the Fourier numbers calculated from equations (14.1) and (14.3) for peas frozen by a medium at $-32°C$ differ by 7%. If the cooling medium temperature or the moisture content of the food (on which the value of the ratio L/c largely depends) is lower, the error in this approximation will be larger, and vice versa.

Equation (14.3) can also be deduced by making an interesting physical approximation. Let the freezing point of the material be θ_1 and the temperature of the cooling medium θ_2. At time t, let the thickness of frozen material at each face of the slab be x (see Fig. 14.3). Assume the heat transfer through the frozen material to be the same as would occur if the frozen material were conducting heat in the steady state between static plane surfaces at temperatures θ_1 and θ_2 separated by a distance x. This assumption, known as the quasistatic assumption, should be noted carefully. It implies that the dynamic process of freezing can be approximated by a sequence of instantaneous thermal equilibrium states. With this assumption it is obvious that the heat transferred, per unit area, to one face of the slab in time dt at time t

$$= \frac{k(\theta_1 - \theta_2)\,dt}{x}$$

where k is the thermal conductivity of the frozen material.

This abstraction of heat will freeze a thickness dx of the material given by:

$$\frac{k(\theta_1 - \theta_2)\,dt}{x} = L\rho\,dx \tag{14.4}$$

where L is the latent heat of the material and ρ its density.

Integrating equation (14.4) and substituting the boundary conditions:

$$x = 0 \quad \text{at} \quad t = 0$$
$$x = l \quad \text{at} \quad t = t_f$$

one obtains:

$$k(\theta_1 - \theta_2)t_f = \frac{L\rho l^2}{2} \tag{14.5}$$

When equation (14.5) is expressed in dimensionless form it reduces at once to equation (14.3).

The above discussion shows that, in the particular case investigated, the quasistatic assumption leads to a simple and reasonably accurate formula for the calculated freezing time. The quasistatic assumption has been used by Plank[11-13] to obtain similar approximate formulae in the case of freezing infinite slabs, infinitely long cylinders and spheres when there is a finite surface heat transfer coefficient (h) and, making still further approximations, infinite rods of rectangular cross-section and rectangular parallelepipeds ('bricks') have been treated.

Plank's work may be summarised in the formula

$$t_f = \frac{DL\rho}{\Delta\theta}\left\{\frac{l}{h} + \frac{Gl^2}{k}\right\} \tag{14.6}$$

or in the dimensionless form:

$$Fo\,.\,Ste = D\left\{\frac{1}{Bi} + G\right\} \tag{14.7}$$

where the constants D and G are determined by the geometry of the body being frozen and the other symbols are as previously defined. G takes the value $\frac{1}{2}$ for the infinite slab, infinite cylinder and sphere. The values of G calculated from Plank's expressions for an infinite rod of rectangular section and a brick can be read from Figs. 14.4 and 14.5 respectively.

The constant D is given by

$$D = \frac{v}{al} \tag{14.8}$$

where $v =$ the volume of the body, and $a =$ the area of its cooled surface.

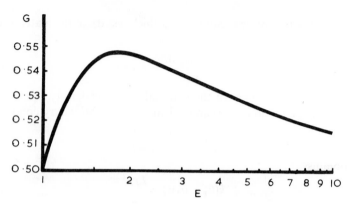

FIG. 14.4.   The values of the constant G for a rod of infinite length with rectangular cross-section $2l \times 2El$.[14]

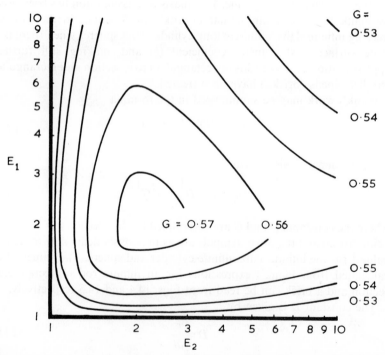

FIG. 14.5.   The values of the constant G for a brick-shaped body $2l \times 2E_1l \times 2E_2l$.[14]

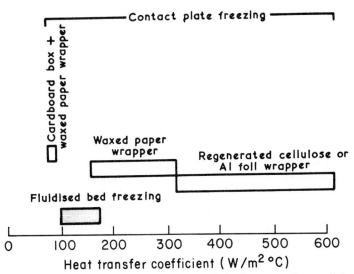

Fig. 14.6. Chart indicating the magnitude of the heat transfer coefficients in contact plate and fluidised bed freezing and the effect of the packaging material.[15,16]

For the infinite slab, infinite cylinder and sphere respectively, D takes the values 1, $\frac{1}{2}$ and $\frac{1}{3}$.

In the practical application of equation (14.6) it is often difficult to decide on an appropriate value for the heat transfer coeffcient h. An indication of the size of this coefficient may be obtained from Fig. 14.6. To measure a heat transfer coefficient directly, the rate of heat loss per unit area of a surface (dq/dt), the surface temperature (θ_s) and the temperature of the cooling medium (θ_m) must be known, when the heat transfer coefficient (h) can be calculated from

$$h = \frac{1}{(\theta_s - \theta_m)} \cdot \frac{dq}{dt} \qquad (14.9)$$

One method[17] of obtaining dq/dt is to insert a block of high conductivity metal (i.e. with negligible internal resistance to heat conduction) into the surface whose heat transfer is being measured. The exposed surface of this block must match the original surface in contour and finish and have all other faces thermally insulated so that its rate of fall of temperature is simply related to the rate of heat loss from the exposed face by

$$\frac{dq}{dt} = \frac{mc_b}{A} \cdot \frac{d\theta}{dt} \qquad (14.10)$$

where m, c_b and A are the mass, specific heat and exposed surface area of the block respectively. An alternative approach[18] is to derive h from the variation of surface temperature with time for a block of material of known thermal properties. For the blast freezing of unpackaged food, heat transfer coefficients can be calculated from standard formulae (see Appendix II).

It is also necessary to select average values of the specific heat and thermal conductivity of the frozen material, as well as adopting a value for the latent heat of fusion to be used in equation (14.6). While data for the enthalpy of foods in the freezing zone is available (e.g. Riedel[6]), the simple model assumed here for calculation divides the enthalpy change experienced by a food in cooling from marginally above its freezing point to some arbitrary lower temperature into a latent heat of fusion given out at the freezing point and a loss of sensible heat proportional to the temperature drop thereafter. This division, and the latent and specific heats that result from it, must be somewhat arbitrary. For rough work, a latent heat equal to

$$3 \cdot 3\, M \,\text{kJ}\,\text{kg}^{-1}$$

and a specific heat capacity equal to

$$\frac{M}{80} + 0 \cdot 84\,\text{kJ}\,\text{kg}^{-1}\,\text{k}^{-1}$$

may be adopted, where M is the percentage by weight of water in the foodstuff (wet weight basis).

While the formulae derived by Plank and discussed above are undeniably simple, the crudity of the assumptions used in deriving them, and so the very approximate nature of the results obtained from using them, has encouraged much activity directed to obtaining better estimates of freezing time without adding too much to the complexity of calculation. Cleland, Earle and their co-workers have recently been in the forefront of this activity.

The approach of these workers[9] was to consider homogeneous bodies at an initial uniform temperature $\theta'^\circ\text{C}$ (which is above the freezing point of the material, $\theta_0\,^\circ\text{C}$) being cooled by a medium at a constant temperature of $\theta_1\,^\circ\text{C}$ ($\theta_1 < -10$). They defined the freezing time as the period from the commencement of cooling until the instant the thermal centre reaches -10°C, thus this is a specific example of the 'effective freezing time' (t_e) defined earlier (Section 14.1). This freezing time is, as before, expressed in dimensionless form by the Fourier Number (*Fo*). The Stefan number was modified to

$$Ste' = \frac{c\,\Delta\theta}{\Delta H} \qquad (14.11)$$

where c and $\Delta\theta$ have the same significance as in the previous definition of the Stefan Number, but ΔH is the total enthalpy change of the material over the temperature range θ_0 to $-10°C$.

A number, analogous to the Stefan Number and called by these workers the Plank Number (*Pk*), was defined as a measure of the requirement for pre-cooling, i.e.

$$Pk = \frac{c_u(\theta' - \theta_0)}{\Delta H} \qquad (14.12)$$

where c_u is the specific heat of the unfrozen material and the other quantities have already been defined.

Using both experimental data derived from the freezing of fairly high water content homogeneous materials by cooling media ranging in temperature from -20 to $-40°C$, and also numerical calculations of freezing times using finite difference methods, the freezing time of a wide variety of bodies was related[19] to the freezing time of an infinite plane slab of the same material with the same characteristic dimension (l) frozen under the same conditions of heat transfer coefficient and cooling medium temperature, i.e.

$$Fo_{\text{body}} = \frac{Fo_{\text{slab}}}{H} \qquad (14.13)$$

where the quanitity H was called the 'equivalent heat transfer dimensionality'.

A number of different modifications of the Plank equation were developed which gave reliable predictions of Fo_{slab}, e.g.

$$Fo_{\text{slab}} = \frac{(1 + 0.057\sqrt{Bi.Ste'} + 1.27\sqrt{Pk.Ste'})}{Ste'} \cdot \left(\frac{1}{Bi} + \frac{1}{2}\right) \qquad (14.14)$$

This equation, the charts in Figs 14.7 and 14.8 and Table 14.3 have been modified from the original published form since there the characteristic dimension was taken to be the *total* thickness of a slab and the diameter of a cylinder, etc., rather than the *half-thickness* and radius as has been used in this chapter. The original nomenclature has also been changed to avoid confusion. Equation (14.14) (due originally to Pham) may be compared with the Plank equation (14.7) when the constants for the infinite slab are entered into it;

$$Fo = \frac{1}{Ste}\left(\frac{1}{Bi} + \frac{1}{2}\right) \tag{14.15}$$

When considering the freezing of bodies other than the infinite slab, the value of the equivalent heat transfer dimensionality (H) can be determined from the equation

$$H = M_1 + M_2 N_1 + M_3 N_2 \tag{14.16}$$

where the values of M_1, M_2 and M_3 may be read from Table 14.3 and the values of N_1 and N_2 from Figs 14.7 and 14.8, respectively, using the values of β_1 and β_2 specified in Table 14.3.

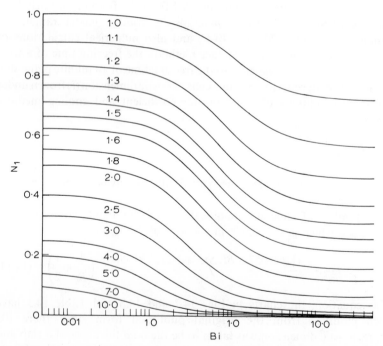

FIG. 14.7. Chart showing N_1 as a function of Bi for different values of β_1. (Adapted from Cleland *et al.*[19])

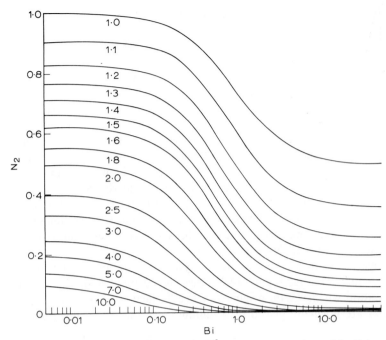

FIG. 14.8. Chart showing N_2 as a function of Bi for different values of β_2. (Adapted from Cleland *et al.*[19])

TABLE 14.3

Definitions of β_1 and β_2 and the values of M_1, M_2 and M_3 for bodies of different shape (after Cleland *et al.*[19])

Body	Specification of body shape	M_1	$M_2{}^a$	$M_3{}^a$
Infinite plane slab	Thickness $2l$	1	—	—
Infinitely long circular cylinder	Radius l	2	—	—
Sphere	Radius l	3	—	—
Finite cylinder (shorter than its diameter)	{ Height $2l$ { Radius $\beta_1 l$	1	2	—
Finite cylinder (longer than its diameter)	{ Radius l { Length $2\beta_2 l$	2	—	1
Infinite rod of rectangular section	{ Cross-section { $2l \times 2\beta_1 l$	1	1	—
Rectangular parallelepiped (brick)	$2l \times 2\beta_1 l \times 2\beta_2 l$	1	1	1

β_1 and β_2 are always larger than or equal to unity.
^{a} When the entry under these columns is a dash (—) the term containing that factor should be omitted from equation (14.16).

14.3. FREEZING EQUIPMENT

14.3.1. FREEZING BY CONTACT WITH A COOLED SOLID

The plate contact freezer invented by Birdseye is, with some modification, still used extensively today. Freezers of this type consist of a series of flat hollow refrigerated metal plates. The plates are mounted parallel to each other and may be either horizontal or vertical. The spaces between the plates are variable, the plates being opened out for loading and, prior to the freezing operation, closed so that the surface of the plates is in intimate contact with the packaged or unpackaged food. Clearly the frozen product is in the form of parallel sided blocks and, during the freezing process, heat flow is perpendicular to the faces of the plates. Thus freezing times can be calculated assuming that the material between the plates forms part of an infinite slab with cooled faces.

Freezers with horizontal plates may be used for processing foods in rectangular cartons. Figure 14.9 shows such a plant designed for batch operation, which was the original practice. To facilitate batch loading, these packs are normally placed in aluminium freezing trays dimensioned to

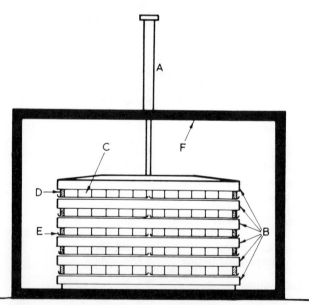

Fig. 14.9.   Diagrammatic view of a horizontal plate freezer. A, ram for raising and lowering the freezer plates; B, hollow refrigerated freezer plates; C, food packages; D, spacer bar; E, freezing tray; F, insulated enclosure.

utilise the plate area efficiently. After loading, the plates are closed by an hydraulic ram operating either on the top (as shown) or on the base of the stack of plates. A moderate pressure (of the order of 10–$30\,kN\,m^{-2}$) is maintained between the plates and the package surfaces during freezing to promote good face to face contact. A simple relief valve in the hydraulic circuit could be used to maintain this pressure constant against any expansion of the product on freezing. Spacers, fractionally thinner than the cartons, are often set between the plates to prevent packages being crushed should the plates close unevenly.

Where horizontal plate freezers are used today they are almost always adapted to semi-continuous operation where the entire plate stack is indexed, layer by layer, past loading and unloading devices which accept packages off a conveyor from a continuous filling line and reject them, when frozen, to an output conveyor. Only two plates are separated at a time, while the packages between them are level with the loading/unloading devices. Machines of this type are used, for instance, in the hardening of ice cream blocks. Ice cream is initially frozen in a scraped surface heat exchanger (see Fig. 9.6), which itself constitutes another class of continuous freezer where heat is transferred by contact with a cooled solid (the heat transfer tube). The vigorous mixing of the fluid being frozen allows rapid heat removal, but the final product must be sufficiently plastic to flow from the machine and be formed into the required product shapes. Freezing then continues to harden these products, either in a plate freezer as described above or in an air blast freezer (see Section 14.3.3).

For efficient operation, the heat transfer coefficient between the surface of the food and the cooling medium in a plate freezer must be both high and uniform. These conditions will be achieved if packages are completely filled with food (so that the latter is in good contact with the inner faces of the packaging material through which heat transfer takes place), if the packages are in uniform contact with plates which are free from any ice or other deposit and if the plates themselves are designed for a rapid and uniform exchange of heat. The introduction of plates made from aluminium alloy extrusions has considerably improved the performance of plate contact freezers in this last respect.

Vertical plate freezers are well suited to freezing unpackaged deformable materials such as fish, meat and offal. The product is fed directly between the vertical plates (see Fig. 14.10) to form blocks which may be compacted further by closing the plates a little on to limit stops prior to freezing. At the end of the freezing process the plates are heated both to release the frozen block and to defrost and clean the plate surfaces before the next freezing

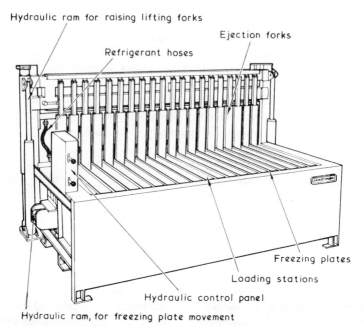

Hydraulic ram for raising lifting forks

Ejection forks

Refrigerant hoses

Freezing plates

Loading stations

Hydraulic control panel

Hydraulic ram, for freezing plate movement

FIG. 14.10. A 'Jackstone' vertical plate-contact freezer. (Courtesy of Jackstone Froster Ltd.)

cycle. It is important that the refrigeration circuit be designed to give a quick defrost, say within $1\frac{1}{2}$ min, to minimise reheating of the frozen product. There should be minimal surface thawing of these blocks on removal not only to prevent product loss and difficulties of handling, but also because unpackaged blocks with thawed surfaces will refreeze and weld together into one mass when stacked together in frozen storage.

Plate freezers of this type were used extensively during the 1960s and 1970s for freezing whole fish at sea in distant water operations. The extension of territorial waters that subsequently took place destroyed much of this activity but, more recently, interest has revived in freezing gutted fish and fish fillets at sea as fishing has now become more difficult in near-water fisheries and the technique allows voyage times to be increased.

Apart from plate-contact freezers, there are a number of other systems that fall under the heading of freezing by contact with a cooled solid. The scraped surface heat exchanger used in ice cream freezing has already been mentioned. Also in the ice cream industry, products (particularly ice lollies) may be frozen in metal moulds which dip into a refrigerated brine. The mould assemblies are mounted on conveying systems located above the brine bath. The moulds are moved from an initial location where they are filled with the unfrozen material to an intermediate position where the lolly-stick is inserted into the still-unfrozen centre of the partly frozen item and then on to a final location where the lolly, in its mould, is removed from the brine and subjected to a brief heating to release it from the mould, which then returns to the filling position.

Other freezing systems have been developed in which refrigerated brines are sprayed onto one side of flexible stainless steel bands which are in contact with the product on their other face. For instance, thin products such as meat patties may be deposited onto a continuous horizontal travelling band, the under side of which is sprayed with refrigerated brine. As the band and the product frozen to it emerge from the freezing zone, the band flexes over a roller at the discharge point to break free from the product, which then passes out down a chute.

14.3.2. FREEZING BY CONTACT WITH A COOLED LIQUID

In theory, the freezing of solid foods by immersion in a cooled liquid has three advantages over plate contact freezing. High heat transfer coefficients can be developed between the solid and liquid, bodies of irregular shape can be frozen as easily as rectangular blocks and individual food items can be frozen separately rather than compacted together in a block. The production of individually quick frozen (IQF) food materials is advantageous since it enables individual items or portions of food to be dispensed from a pack, the remaining material being retained in the package and stored until required. If unpackaged foods are to be frozen by immersion, the heat transfer fluid must be edible and acceptable as a contaminant to the product.

In the early days of freezing, salt brines and syrups were used for immersion freezing, or such materials were sprayed directly on to the foods to freeze them. There are considerable difficulties with such a process. The coolant contaminates the food and must, therefore, be an acceptable additive—hence the use of salt brines and sugar syrups. More seriously, there is contamination of the coolant by fluids and soluble matter from the food. This can dilute the coolant, increasing its freezing point and can deteriorate in the coolant causing off-flavours, etc. This makes long-term re-use of the coolant difficult and so affects the economics of the process. However, with the recent development of a much wider range of packaging materials, there has been a re-awakened interest in the method, since the problems of cross contamination of food and coolant are overcome and also both solid and liquid foods can be processed. Of course, there is the problem of coolant remaining on the package after the process is over (unless the coolant is volatile—alcohol was used in one process), but this can usually be overcome satisfactorily by rinsing the package.

Poultry carcases may be closely wrapped in plastic film and frozen in brine or glycol to achieve rapid freezing of their surface flesh.[20] This produces a crust of small, highly reflective ice crystals (see Section 14.1) which give that white appearance to the frozen carcase which is desired by the consumer. After this process the remainder of the freezing process is usually conducted in a blast freezer.

14.3.3. FREEZING BY CONTACT WITH A COOLED GAS

Freezing food in cold air, a technique practised from the earliest days of food freezing, has many of the advantages of immersion freezing. Foods of irregular shape can be frozen and IQF products produced. In addition the problem of transfer of material between the fluid cooling medium and the food is limited to the evaporation of moisture from unpackaged products. However, the heat transfer coefficients developed at the surface of foods in forced air circulation freezers ('blast freezers') are lower than can be obtained in liquid immersion freezing. Nevertheless, because of their other advantages, blast freezers are extensively used in the food freezing industry.

Blast freezers may operate either batchwise or continuously with air temperatures generally in the region -20 to $-40°C$. The higher the air velocity, of course, the greater is the heat transfer coefficient between the moving air and the solid body (see Appendix II). However, an increase in this heat transfer coefficient does not result in a proportional decrease in freezing time owing to the thermal resistance of any packaging materials and the effect of heat transfer by conduction within the freezing food. Additionally, at the higher velocities, the energy dissipation of the fans moving the air provides a not inconsiderable fraction of the load on the refrigerator. Therefore the cost of providing air circulation above a certain velocity in any given instance will not be economically justifiable. There is also a possibility that, at high air velocities, product may be displaced from its position on a belt or tray by the force of the air stream. For the freezing of fish on a continuous belt freezer a velocity of $10\,\mathrm{m\,s^{-1}}$ was regarded as optimal.[21]

Batch blast freezers are only used where the throughput of material is low. Such a unit would consist of a well-insulated chamber equipped with an air cooler and suitable fans. The product is usually loaded by hand on to trolley mounted trays, and guide rails are provided within the chamber to locate the trolley in the air stream and facilitate loading the chamber. To obtain uniform cooling, the air is ducted so that it flows evenly over all the food items. It is therefore most undesirable to load a partially filled trolley into the freezer, since this could lead to a redistribution of the air flow, with air bypassing the material to be frozen by flowing preferentially through the empty spaces in the trolley. Similarly, if the trolley used is too small and does not fill the space available in the chamber, air will again bypass the load, this time by flowing round the trolley.

Continuous air blast freezers are either (a) built on the principle of a tunnel through which the food is transported, either on trolleys, on trays, by conveyor or, in the case of carcase meat, on hooks suspended from a track, or (b) utilise the fluidised bed principle. The air in tunnel freezers using trolleys can either flow parallel to the direction of product movement or perpendicular to it ('cross flow'). The second system is perhaps more frequently used today. In this system a series of unit coolers, comprising refrigerated air coolers, fans and associated duct-work, are mounted side-by-side along the length of the tunnel. The unit coolers provide a blast of cold air through adjacent sections of the tunnel and perpendicular to the direction of product movement. This arrangement has a number of advantages. For instance, to load and unload the tunnel, openings must be provided at either end. The cross flow system allows the pressures to be balanced at these points to minimise air exchange between inside and outside the tunnel. Again, the thermal conditions can be controlled in each zone to maintain a high humidity in the circulating air to minimise evaporation from the product. Such evaporation, if excessive, can lead to a condition of surface dehydration known as 'freezer burn'.

Clearly, if food is to be frozen on a travelling conveyor belt, rather than on trays stacked in trolleys, a considerable length of conveyor must be accommodated within the insulated enclosure. Figure 14.11 shows a unit where a very economical use of factory floor-space is achieved by employing a flexible stainless steel link conveyor belt wound in vertical helices.

Indeed, the design of continuous air-blast freezers largely reduces to a problem of materials handling, i.e. principally, packing the product-supporting conveyors or trays in such a way that a high product throughput can be achieved for a modest utilisation of factory floor space. Plant designers continually offer more elegant solutions to this practical problem. Another problem in blast freezers where, for instance, unpackaged sliced vegetables are being frozen on a moving conveyor is that items will freeze both to each other and to the conveyor. They must be

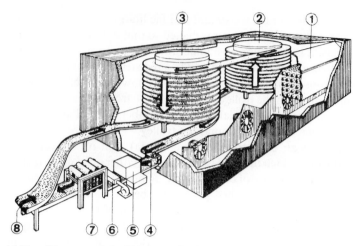

FIG. 14.11. Diagram of the Frigoscandia GyroFreeze system showing the main features: (1) cooling coil with cover in open position with fans below; (2) first drum where the belt runs upwards; (3) second drum with belt running downwards; (4) discharge; (5) automatic belt washing station; (6) dryer fan; (7) belt tension control and take-up; (8) turn roller. Products are loaded onto the belt on the free run after this roller.

broken apart to produce an IQF product and the conveyor must be cleaned before reloading, as in Fig. 14.11. This difficulty is overcome in the fluidised bed freezer.

Fluidised bed freezers consist of a trough with a perforated bottom through which refrigerated air is blown vertically upwards (see Fig. 14.12). The air velocity is such that when small particulate food bodies of fairly uniform size, e.g. peas, Brussels sprouts, berry fruits or even chips (French fried potatoes), are fed into the trough they form a fluidised bed (see Section 13.3.3.5). Froude numbers (see Appendix I) between about 65 and 180 are developed in commercial units, though 100–120 is the normal range. The feed is at one end of the trough and the product is discharged over a weir at the other end to give a bed depth of the order of 15 cm. The feed rate is adjusted so that the dwell time of individual pieces in the fluidised bed is sufficient to allow proper freezing. In cases where the product to be frozen is not of ideal shape for fluidisation, i.e. deviates widely from that of a small sphere, the bed may be operated at the state of incipient fluidisation with only slight bed expansion (see Appendix I.2) and in place of a stationary perforated base to the fluidising trough, a travelling perforated belt is used, thus imparting forward motion to the product above. The base of the

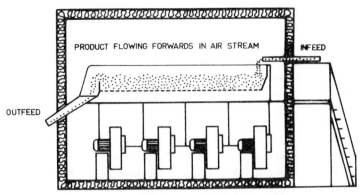

FIG. 14.12. Diagrammatic longitudinal section of a fluidised bed freezer. (By courtesy of Frigoscandia Ltd.)

fluidising trough may also be inclined so that forward movement is assisted by gravity.

One of the major advantages of fluidised bed freezers is their compact size. This compactness is possible since the surface heat transfer coefficient developed in them is comparatively high and a large total surface of particles exists in the bed. For instance, in a fluidised bed of peas 14 cm deep, the product surface is 60–70 times the superficial area of the freezing trough. Since the food items are in constant motion and are surrounded and supported by air, they freeze separately to give a free-flowing product. In addition, any water remaining on the items from earlier preparative and cleaning processes is spread over their surfaces by the air stream and gives a glazing of ice, protecting the food itself from 'freezer burn'.

In continuous blast freezers, since water will evaporate from unpackaged food and deposit as frost on the refrigeration units, the latter must be defrosted periodically if their efficiency is to be maintained. The unit may be designed to accommodate the frost build-up in the course of one shift of operation and be defrosted in the cleaning period between shifts. Alternatively, since the cooling/air circulating system is frequently split into a number of parallel units (see Fig. 14.12), these may be so sized that one unit can be taken out of operation and defrosted while the cooling duty is shared between the others. This sequential defrosting permits the cooling efficiency to be maintained indefinitely. Of course, in fluidised bed freezers, the fluidising air supply must be maintained during this process. With either method of defrosting, the frost-loaded cooling surface may be heated (a) electrically, (b) by water sprays or (c) in the case of those units cooled by direct expansion of liquid refrigerant, by discharging the hot refrigerant gases from the refrigeration compressor through the cooling coils.

14.3.4. TWO-PHASE FREEZING SYSTEMS

A variety of freezing systems have been designed in which the cooling medium is a subliming solid (e.g. solid carbon dioxide) or a boiling liquid (e.g. liquid nitrogen). In the majority of such systems the refrigerating effect is not provided by an on-site refrigerator, but by the heat transfer agent itself as a consequence of its phase change. The gases resulting from this phase change are vented to the atmosphere. These systems are known as cryogenic freezers and the materials providing the refrigeration as cryogens.

Carbon dioxide is most conveniently handled as a liquid under pressure. Sprayed through nozzles to atmospheric pressure it gives a mixture of cold gaseous carbon dioxide and carbon dioxide snow (solid) which can be contacted with the food to be frozen. The system can either be used to boost the capacity of conventional blast freezing lines at peak processing periods or provide the sole cooling for a freezing plant.

The boiling point of liquid nitrogen ($-196°C$ at atmospheric pressure) is such that food may be frozen at very high rates. This in turn has made possible improvements in the quality of products which did not freeze well by conventional methods (e.g. mushrooms and many sea-foods) and, coupled with the low water holding capacity of the very cold gas, to a reduction in loss of product weight by evaporation of water during freezing. However, as is shown below, the economics of liquid nitrogen freezing are, to a degree, dependent on the discharge temperature of the spent gas so the advantage of low moisture loss is obtained at the cost of a limitation on the efficiency of cryogen use. The cost of liquid nitrogen freezing is very dependent on the cost of the gas itself, since the capital cost of the equipment used is comparatively low. The price paid for liquid nitrogen is in turn dependent on the quantity used and the expense of bringing it from the liquefaction plant to the food factory. In the UK the fraction of in-line freezing operations using liquid nitrogen had risen to 10–15% by 1986 as a consequence of the locally favourable price structure for the cryogen.

The use of liquid nitrogen simply as an immersion medium is disadvantageous from two points of view. The rate of cooling of a body plunged into the liquid cannot be controlled, and efficient use is not made of the refrigerating capacity of the medium. The latent heat of evaporation of liquid nitrogen at $-196°C$ is $200\,kJ\,kg^{-1}$. Gaseous nitrogen warming at

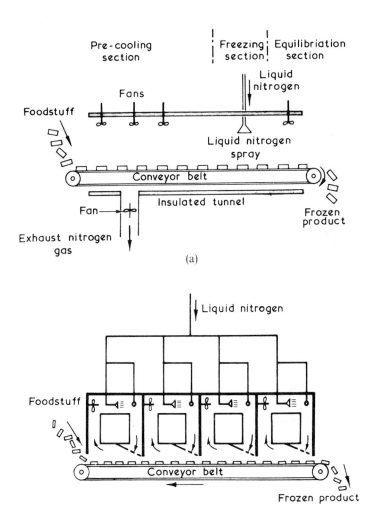

FIG. 14.13. Two methods of efficiently using the refrigerating power of liquid nitrogen. In method (a) liquid nitrogen is sprayed directly onto the food and evaporates, the resultant cold gas moving to left and right to effect further cooling. Method (b) uses the liquid nitrogen to cool down one or more chambers in which the temperature is thermostatically controlled, but the liquid nitrogen does not contact the food. (By courtesy of BOC.)

constant pressure from this temperature to $-18°C$ absorbs a further 209 kJ kg^{-1}. Commercial plant, as shown diagrammatically in Fig. 14.13, therefore makes extensive use of the refrigerating capacity of the nitrogen gas. The liquid nitrogen, if applied directly to the food, is sprayed on at a controlled rate to control the rate of freezing. In Fig. 14.13(a), while the supply of liquid nitrogen may be controlled to avoid gross excess, any cryogen not vaporised after spraying can be collected in the base of the tunnel and either re-circulated to the spray head or vaporised by gas returned from the 'warm' end of the tunnel to provide a further source of cold gas to effect freezing away from the spray zone. In Fig. 14.13(b) the system is essentially a blast freezer such as described in Section 14.3.3. As well as the tunnel types illustrated, cabinet freezers for batch operation (say, in cook/freeze catering) and spiral freezers have been marketed.

In 1967, the Du Pont company developed a freezing technique based on 'R12' (dichlorodifluoromethane). This material boils at $-30°C$ at atmospheric pressure and is an excellent heat transfer medium. Food could be frozen by immersion in the liquid or by having the liquid sprayed onto its surface. Since the gas is expensive, it must be recovered. It was therefore recondensed on a refrigerated surface below its boiling point and re-cycled. Because the gas has a high density, the input conveyor, which has closed sides, was angled steeply down into the enclosed freezing zone and the output conveyor, similarly, mounted upwards. Thus the heavy vapours were retained in the unit and R12 losses were reduced to a few percent of the product weight. In 1973, 150 000 tons of food were frozen by this method. However, in the 1980s the environmental consequences of the emission of R12 into the atmosphere became apparent and the process can no longer be regarded as acceptable.

14.4. THAWING

While the process of thawing is the converse of that of freezing, there are important differences. If a body is to be thawed as a piece, the heat of fusion must be conducted in through a layer of unfrozen material, whilst in freezing it was conducted out through a frozen layer. The thermal conductivity of water is about a quarter that of ice, the thermal diffusivity as low as one eighth. Again the temperature difference between the heating medium and product freezing point is much restricted in thawing because of the requirement not to heat damage the product.

In Fig. 14.14, computed temperature profiles are compared for the

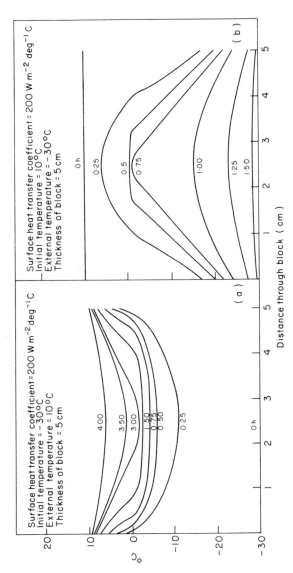

Fig. 14.14. A comparison of the freezing and thawing processes. (a) Computed temperature profiles in a 50 mm thick slab of fish fillets during thawing at various times after commencement of operation. (b) Computed temperature profiles in a 50 mm thick slab of fish fillets during freezing at various times after commencement of operation. h and $|\theta_e - \theta_s|$ are the same as in (a). (After Jason[22])

freezing and thawing of a 5 cm thick block of fish fillets. Not only should the considerable difference in processing time be observed but also that during freezing the bulk of the material spends about a quarter of an hour in the region of $-5°C$ to $-1°C$ (where the material is most at risk from damage by freeze-concentrated solutes) while in thawing this time extends to something over 2 h. Thus thawing presents its special problems.

Thawing on an industrial scale is necessary where bulk-frozen foods (e.g. cartons of boneless beef or frozen eviscerated whole fish) are to be thawed for subsequent manufacturing operations. Sometimes complete thawing is unnecessary, since all that is required is to soften the frozen material so that it can be cut with a guillotine. In this case the problems encountered are less severe since the process can be conducted in a temperature range where there is sufficient ice remaining in the material to give it a comparatively high thermal diffusivity. Thawing is also of interest in the field of catering, where the freezing of cooked meals and meal components and their thawing and reheating for serving is being developed. This system is particularly suitable for institutional or hospital use and differs from industrial thawing in that small scale rapid versatile units are required which will raise the temperature of the food to that required for serving.

Thawing equipment has been constructed using warm air blasts, immersion of the frozen product in water or treatment of its surface with vacuum steam (a saturated steam treatment carried out in a vacuum chamber maintained at, say, 3 kN m^{-2} so that the saturation temperature of the steam is only 20°C). Dielectric, microwave and resistance heating (see Chapter 10) are also used.[5]

Since the thawing process is the converse of freezing, the time required to effect thawing can be calculated by methods analogous to those discussed for freezing in Section 14.2.

In the approach of Cleland, Earle and their co-workers,[19,23] the thawing of a homogeneous body from an initial uniform temperature θ_{in} by an external heated medium at a constant temperature of θ_a until the centre temperature reached 0°C was considered. The thawing time was defined as the period required for this change (this time being expressed dimensionlessly, as before, in a Fourier number). Equations (14.11), (14.13) and (14.16) still apply, as do Table 14.3 and Figs 14.7 and 14.8. The Plank Number for thawing (Pk') is defined by

$$Pk' = \frac{c(\theta_0 - \theta_{in})}{\Delta H}$$

and the Stefan Number for thawing (Ste'') by

$$Ste'' = \frac{c_u(\theta_a - \theta_0)}{\Delta H}$$

The thawing time of the infinite slab is given by the relationship

$$Fo_{slab} = \frac{P}{Ste''}\left(\frac{1}{Bi} + \frac{R}{P}\right)$$

where

$$P = 0.775 + 2.28 \; (Ste'')(Pk')$$

and

$$R = 0.214 + 2.12 \; (Ste'') - 1.48 \; (Ste'')^2$$

REFERENCES

1. Jeffries, D., New products with microwave potential. *Food Science and Technology Today*, **1**(4) (1987) 212–7.
2. Anon., Frozen foods up…again. *Food Engineering International*, **13** (March 1988) 21–2.
3. Ästrom, S., How quick should freezing be? In *Frozen and Quick Frozen Food, Proc. Symposium on New Agricultural Production and Marketing Aspects*, United Nations Economic Commission for Europe and the Food and Agriculture Organisation of the United Nations, Budapest, Hungary, 25–28 April 1977. Pergamon Press, Oxford, England, 1977, pp. 111–21.
4. Spiess, W. E. L., Impact of freezing rates on product quality of deep-frozen foods. In *Food Process Engineering, Vol. 1*, ed. P. Linko, Y. Mälkki, J. Olkku and J. Larinkari. Applied Science Publishers, London, 1980, pp. 689–94.
5. Anon., *Recommendations for the Processing and Handling of Frozen Foods*, 3rd edn. IIF/IIR, Paris, 1986.
6. Riedel, K., DKV Arbeitsblatt 8–11. *Kältetechnik*, **9**(2) (1957) 38.
7. Cowell, N. D., The definition of the term 'Freezing Time'. In *Meat Freezing—Why and How?*, ed. C. L. Cutting. MRI Symposium No. 3. Agricultural Research Council, Meat Research Institute, Bristol, 1974, pp. 14.1–8.
8. Long, R. A. K., Some thermodynamic properties of fish and their effect on the rate of freezing. *J. Sci. Food Agric.*, **6** (1955) 621–33.
9. Cleland, A. C. and Earle, R. L., A comparison of freezing calculations including modifications to take into account initial superheat. In *Towards an Ideal Refrigerated Food Chain*. IIF/IIR, Paris, 1976, pp. 369–76.
10. Carslaw, H. S. and Jaeger, J. C., *Conduction of Heat in Solids*, 2nd edn. Oxford University Press, Oxford, England, 1959.
11. Plank, R., Die Gefrierdauer von Eisblöcken. *Zeitschrift für die gesamte Kälte-Industrie*, **H6** (1913) 109–14.

12. Plank, R., Über die Gefrierzeit von Eis und wasserhaltigen Lebensmitteln. *Zeitschrift für die gesamte Kälte-Industrie,* **H4**(39) (1932) 56–8.

13. Plank, R., Beiträge zur Berechnung und Bewerbung der Gefriergeschwindigkeit von Lebensmitteln. *Zeitschrift für gesamte Kälte-Industrie. Reihe* 3, **H10** (1941) 1–24.

14. Cowell, N. D., The calculation of food freezing times. In *Proc. 12th Int. Congress Refrigeration. Vol. 2.* L'Institut International du Froid, 1969, pp. 667–76.

15. Persson, P-O., The fluidising technique in food freezing. *ASHRAE J.,* **9**(6) (1967) 42–4.

16. Watzinger, A., Gefrierdauer und Kältebedarf bei zweizeitigen Gefrieren von Fischfilet. *Kältetechnik,* **1** (1949) 189–94.

17. Cowell, N. D. and Namor, M. S. S., Heat transfer coefficients in plate freezing— Effect of packaging materials. IIF/IIR Meeting of Commissions B1, C1 and C2, Bressanone, 17–20 September 1974.

18. Cleland, A. C. and Earle, R. L., A new method for prediction of surface heat transfer coefficients in freezing. In *Towards an Ideal Refrigerated Food Chain.* IIF/IIR, Paris, 1976.

19. Cleland, D. J., Cleland, A. C. and Earle, R. L., Prediction of freezing and thawing times for multi-dimensional shapes by simple formulae. Part I: Regular shapes. *Int. J. Refrig.,* **10** (1987) 156–64.

20. Anon., *ASHRAE Handbook, Applications Volume.* ASHRAE, Atlanta, Ga., USA, 1982, Chapter 28.

21. Graham, J. and Mair, S., The design and performance of a continuous air blast freezer. *Refrig. & Air Conditioning,* **82** (1979) 61, 64, 66.

22. Jason, A. C., Rapid thawing of foodstuffs. *Proc. of the IFST,* **7**(3) (1974) 146–57.

23. Cleland, D. J., Cleland, A. C., Earle, R. L. and Bryne, S. J., Prediction of thawing times for foods of simple shape. *Int. J. Refrig.,* **9** (1986) 220–8.

CHAPTER 15

IRRADIATION

15.1. INTRODUCTION

15.1.1. HISTORICAL

In 1896, a year after Roentgen discovered X-rays and the same year that Becquerel discovered radioactivity, a paper was published 'On the Question of the Effect of Roentgen Rays on Bacteria and the Possibility of their Eventual Application'.[1] Radiation processing of strawberries was investigated in Sweden in 1916 and a patent for food preservation using ionising radiation was issued in France in 1930.[2] However, early work in this field was handicapped by the sources of radiation available and it was not until the mid-1940s that high energy, high intensity irradiation sources were sufficiently developed to make the irradiation preservation of foods a feasible industrial process.

The introduction of a novel preservation process is more difficult today than it was in times past due to the legislative framework within which the food industry now operates. Governments required extensive testing before permitting irradiation of any specific product. Commercial irradiation of food therefore made a slow start compared with the irradiation of disposable medical supplies. Dressings, gloves, syringes and catheters are widely sterilised by ionising radiation and it was estimated in 1987[3] that 85% of irradiation use worldwide was for such products and only 5% for food. Of the approximately 150 γ-radiation plants then operating, a total of 24 commercial plants within 11 countries irradiated food as some part of their throughput.

Further commercialisation of food irradiation requires international agreement on legislative controls and widespread acceptance of the process

447

by the consuming public. In respect of the first point there has been some progress. Following extensive studies by the Joint FAO/IAEA/WHO Expert committee, the FAO/WHO Codex Alimentarius Commission issued a Recommended International General Standard for Irradiated Food in 1979,[4] setting out a number of irradiation processes which it considered should be permitted. Subsequently the Joint FAO/IAEA/WHO Expert Committee reviewed the state of knowledge again[5] and concluded that radiation of food by electrons of up to 10 MeV (see Section 15.2) or X- or γ-rays of up to 5 MeV to an average dose in both cases of 10 kGy (see Section 15.4) presented no toxicological hazard or special nutritional or microbiological problem. They also held out the possibility that, with further study, these limits might be relaxed. These conclusions were adopted by the Codex Alimentarius Commission in 1983[6] and following this the UK Government Advisory Committee on Irradiated and Novel Foods reported favourably on food irradiation up to the proposed limits, though also supporting the view that irradiated food should be so labelled for information of the user,[7] and, in 1989, the UK government announced their intention of legalising food irradiation—a step which had already been taken by the governments of a number of other nations.

In respect of the second impediment to the commercialisation of food irradiation—acceptance by the consumer—studies in the late 1980s[8] indicated a low level of understanding and a high level of apprehension among consumers at large concerning food irradiation. It is, presumably, these consumer attitudes that give rise to the proposals for labelling products which have an appreciable proportion of irradiated ingredients in their composition when similar products made from, say, canned, dried or frozen ingredients would not be required to be labelled as such. It has been suggested that acceptance by consumers might be made easier if tests were available to detect whether a product had been irradiated or not (cf. the phosphatase test for pasteurised milk). Investigations are currently in progress on a number of systems,[9] though the task of identifying changes which are specific to the irradiation process, convenient to detect and occur in a wide range of products is somewhat daunting.[10] Electron spin resonance spectroscopy to measure trapped free radicals in products containing bone and thermoluminescence from the small amounts of mineral dust still adhering to vegetable matter even after washing appear the most promising techniques.

It is not unusual for several decades to elapse before full commercialisation of a novel food preservation process is achieved[11] and food irradiation is proving no exception.

15.1.2. IRRADIATION PROCESSES

Most of the irradiation processes for foods can be classed under one of five headings:

(i) Radappertisation—in which a commercially sterile product (see Section 11.1) is produced.

(ii) Radicidation—in which the treatment is intended to destroy organisms of public health significance, say salmonellae, while not achieving radappertisation.

(iii) Radurisation—in which the treatment is aimed simply at the prolongation of storage life by a general reduction in the level of vegetative bacteria.

(iv) Radiation disinfestation—where the targets are insect pests.

(v) Sprout inhibition in stored vegetables and growth inhibition in mushrooms.

Current interest in irradiation processes is concentrated on categories (ii)–(v) since the limit of 10 kGy is rather low for radappertisation.

Additional to these processes, which are aimed at preservation, radiation processing could be used as an aid in processing, e.g. to improve rehydration of dried vegetables or the yield of sugar from beet. The stimulation of bakers' yeast with radiation resulted in faster breadmaking and the ability of ionising radiation to depolymerise large molecules such as carbohydrates and proteins enables radiation to be used to alter the functional properties of such materials.[2]

All foods exhibit a certain amount of radioactivity. The principal cause of this is the presence of naturally occurring radionuclides, such as ^{40}K, ^{14}C and ^{3}H. The extent to which any plant, or plant-derived, food contains radioactive nuclides is largely dependent on the naturally occurring nuclides in the soil on which the plants were grown and therefore on the local geology. However, atmospheric nuclear weapons testing and emissions from nuclear accidents have added to this natural background through widespread distribution of ^{131}I, ^{134}Cs and ^{137}Cs.

The unit of radioactivity is the Becquerel (Bq). A quantity of material exhibits one Becquerel of radioactivity when there is one nuclear distintegration per second within it. The specific activity of a food material may therefore be expressed as Becquerels per kg (Bq kg^{-1}) or Becquerels per litre. The natural activity in meat might, for instance, be about 100 Bq kg^{-1}. The risk of contamination following an accidental release of radioactive material has led to the establishment of minimum limits for food. Currently, in the European Economic Community, these are

600 Bq kg^{-1} for all foods, except milk and baby foods for which a limit of 370 Bq kg^{-1} is set.

It is a clear requirement of any irradiation process that it should not add appreciably to the levels of radioactivity in foods. Fortunately, this requirement is easily satisfied.

15.2. ENERGY OF RADIATION

To minimise the incidence of induced radioactivity, food irradiation processes have been restricted to those using electromagnetic waves (X-rays and γ-rays) of limited frequency and beams of electrons (cathode rays and β-rays) of limited energy. High frequency electromagnetic waves, high energy electrons and beams of the heavier atomic particles (such as neutrons) are capable of inducing nuclear transformations in the atoms of the target food, rendering them radioactive.

The energy associated with electrons is measured in electron volts. An electron volt (eV) is the energy acquired by an electron in falling through a potential difference of one volt and

$$1\,eV \simeq 1{\cdot}6 \times 10^{-19}\,J$$

The electron volt is small and in practice multiples of the unit are used:

$$1\,keV = 10^3\,eV$$
$$1\,MeV = 10^6\,eV$$
$$1\,GeV = 10^9\,eV$$

The energy of the quantum of electromagnetic energy, i.e. a photon, is a function of its frequency. It is also measured in electron volts and is given by the equation

$$E = h\nu$$

where E = photon energy (eV), h = Planck's constant = 4·13 eV s, ν = frequency (Hertz).

15.3. EFFECTS OF RADIATION

The interactions between an electron and an atom of the target material can differ, depending on the energy exchanged in the event. In low energy encounters, the electron may become captured in the orbital electron shell of the atom, giving a negative ion. Alternatively it may impart some of its energy to the orbital electrons, leaving them in higher energy orbits; the atom is then said to be in an excited state. With higher energy exchange an orbital electron may be ejected from the atom. With higher energies still, the interactions may involve the nucleus and result in the conversion of energy supplied by the electrons into photons (bremsstrahlung).

Photons interact with the target material with similar results. Photons of ultraviolet light are only sufficiently energetic to excite the molecules of foodstuffs. Somewhat higher frequency radiation, with its higher energy photons, can cause ionisation. Photons can be absorbed by an atom, almost all the energy reappearing in the kinetic energy of an ejected electron (the photoelectric effect). With photons of higher energy still the interaction results in both an ejected electron and a photon of lower energy (the Compton effect). Finally, with the highest energies, interactions may take place with the nucleus. Such interactions can take three forms:

(i)   A proton or neutron can be ejected from the nucleus, normally giving rise to induced radioactivity in the target material.

(ii) The photon is absorbed and an electron-positron pair created. The positron member of this pair is short lived and rapidly interacts with an electron, both particles disappearing and a further photon, or photons, being emitted.

(iii) The nucleus remains in an excited state after the interaction, subsequently releasing its excess energy by the emission of further photons. This type of interaction does not occur with the atoms forming the common constituents of foods.

From the above discussion it can be seen that irradiation with electrons, *or* photons, sufficiently energetic to cause ionisation but not induced radioactivity, gives rise to a chain of interactions resulting in the creation of chemically reactive ions, excited molecules and free radicals in the target food. The extra energy possessed by the food by virtue of the irradiation can therefore either be absorbed in chemical changes, lost in subsequent radiation from the system or appear as heat energy when the ions are neutralised and excited molecules decay to their ground states.

As many foods have a high water content, it is the interaction of radiation with that molecule, giving rise to, for example, hydrogen, hydrogen peroxide and hydroperoxy radicals, that leads to a spectrum of chemical activity and so to the effects of importance in food technology. Such effects may be advantageous to the preservation of the material; vital processes leading to deterioration in the food itself may be inhibited, contaminating organisms such as bacteria or insects may either be destroyed, or have their reproductive systems impaired. At the same time disadvantageous changes may result. Vitamins may be destroyed or off-flavours develop. Irradiation, as a process, is not unique in producing such a broad spectrum of chemical change. The heating of foods also leads to substantial chemical activity and the presence of naturally occurring enzymes can catalyse reactions involving the same reactive species as are formed during irradiation.[12] It is through understanding the chemical processes resulting from treatment with ionising radiation that it became possible to recommend the acceptance of the process for use with any food material, subject to the limitations mentioned in Section 15.1.1.

Although 10 MeV radiation does not produce induced radioactivity in the common atoms present in food, trace elements and rare isotopes can be affected by such radiation. Of those nuclides likely to occur in foods, three (^2H, ^{17}O and ^{13}C) have energy thresholds for nuclear transformation below 5 MeV. However, all the products of these reactions are stable nuclides (^1H, ^{16}O and ^{12}C) and the neutrons produced do not induce other reactions of importance in the food. Becker[13] calculated that the activity induced in meat by irradiation with 10 MeV electrons would be of the order of 10^{-6} Bq kg^{-1}, i.e. a factor about 10^8 below the natural background activity. Becker concluded that irradiated food was likely to be *less* radioactive than the original fresh material because irradiated products were more likely to undergo storage and the decay of natural radioactivity during such storage would exceed any activity induced by the irradiation treatment.

15.4. DOSIMETRY

The biological effects of ionising radiation depend not only on the energy of the incident radiation but also on the quantity which interacts with unit mass, or volume, of the target material. A unit of quantity, or 'dose', is thus required. The unit currently used for this is the Gray (Gy). When one Gray of radiation has fallen on a body, that body has absorbed energy from the radiation amounting to 1 J kg^{-1}. Large doses are expressed in kiloGray (1 kGy = 10^3 Gy).

The following show, roughly, the range of dose requirement for different processes:[2]

Radappertisation	10–50 kGy
Radicidation	
—of non-spore-forming micro-organisms	2–8 kGy
—of tape worms and trichina	0·1–1 kGy

Radurisation	0·4–4 kGy
Radiation disinfestation	0·3–1 kGy
Control of ripening processes	0·1–1 kGy
Sprout inhibition	20–150 Gy

These may be compared with the dose of 5 Gray, which is sufficient to kill a man. Enzyme systems are even more resistant to radiation than bacterial spores, so enzyme preparations can be irradiation sterilised (i.e. radappertised) without being rendered inactive.

Dose measurements can be made directly in terms of the Gray by calorimetric methods. Such methods, however, must be highly sensitive because of the small thermal energies involved (10 kGy raises the temperature of water by only about 2°C—the low heat dissipation during processing is one of the attractive features of irradiation processing since thermal damage to the foods is avoided). Therefore, calorimetric methods are suitable only as primary standards. Secondary standards, normally involving measurements of some chemical change brought about by irradiation, are more simple to operate. The oxidation of ferrous ions to ferric in a defined acid aqueous solution (the Fricke dosimeter)[14] is widely used as a reference system. The method can be used for accurate determination of doses from 40 to 400 Gy. As this range is somewhat limited it is most likely to be used for the determination of dose rate (in $Gy\,s^{-1}$). Other systems, suitable for measuring higher total doses, can then be calibrated against the Fricke dosimeter by irradiating them for longer periods. The accuracy of the measurements is unaffected by dose rate in the range $0·2–2 \times 10^7\,Gy\,s^{-1}$ and the chemical system can be modified to allow accurate measurements at somewhat higher dose rates. The system is also substantially independent of temperature in the range 1–60°C and of the spectral energy of the radiation in the range 0·5–16 MeV. The ferric ion concentration, which is proportional to the adsorbed dose, is measured spectrophotometrically by the absorption at a wavelength of 305 nm. For higher doses than can be handled by the Fricke dosimeter, other chemical systems are available.[14] The addition of cupric sulphate to the ferrous sulphate of the Fricke dosimeter reduces the sensitivity of the system and permits dose measurements in the range 2–8 kGy and the reduction of ceric to cerous sulphate has been used over the range 1–500 kGy, though care is required since trace impurities in the solutions can make the results unreliable.

Routine industrial measurements require simpler devices which can be bought as stable systems, stored until required and allow relatively simple evaluation. Certain dye solutions, coloured plastics and glasses change colour on irradiation and have been used as the basis of routine dosimeter systems. Small slips of polymethylmethacrylate sheet, either clear or coloured with red or yellow radiochromic dyes, are frequently used—the dose being determined by subsequent spectrophotometry. Precautions must be observed if reliable results are to be obtained from these systems since, for instance, the temperatures both during irradiation and during the period between irradiation and assessment can affect the relationship between dose and absorptivity at the test wavelength. Dyed self-adhesive PVC film labels have been marketed as a 'go/no-go' device for checking that containers have been irradiated, the film changing colour after a certain dose has been received due to the release of hydrochloric acid from the plastic base.

Personnel operating irradiation facilities must be protected from absorbing any harmful dose of radiation and, while industrial irradiation plants should be built to a standard acceptable as intrinsically safe in this respect, it is normal practice to check this by equipping such personnel with dose measuring devices. The dose rates and adsorbed doses will, of course, be extremely low. The effect of radiation on the human body is measured in Sieverts. The Sievert and the Gray differ by a 'harmfulness factor' which depends on the radiation involved. For the radiations under consideration here, this factor is unity so that the dose in Sieverts is numerically equal to that in Gray. A member of the general public in the UK might receive about 1·3 milliSieverts a year from natural background and other forms of radiation. In Bolivia and parts of India this could rise as high as 10–50 milliSieverts a year.[15] The International Commission on Radiological Protection has set the permissible dose for industrial workers at 5 milliSieverts a year, though higher levels are permitted for some specialised workers. The design of industrial irradiation facilities would be such that operatives should experience levels well below the 5 milliSievert limit. The monitoring of such minute doses is achieved using small sachets of lithium fluoride powder mounted in plastic badge-holders giving the name of the worker involved. The badge is worn, typically throughout a working month, and then sent to a laboratory where the dose experienced in that time is assessed.[16] Lithium fluoride exhibits thermoluminescence, that is, irradiation of the material with X- or γ-rays stores energy in the crystal lattice which can subsequently be released as visible light by heating the material, the light emission being a measure of the dose received.

A beam of ionising radiation is attenuated in its passage through material so the dose given to the irradiated food will differ from point to

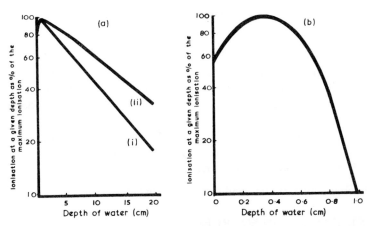

FIG. 15.1. The relative penetrating powers of (a) cobalt-60 γ-rays (from the data of Jones *et al.*, *Brit. J. Radiol.*, **25**, 302) and (b) 2 MeV electrons (from the data of Trump *et al.*, *J. Appl. Phys.*, **21**, 345).

point. Measurements of the spatial distribution of radiation dose are simple if the food irradiated is a fluid or a particulate assembly, but dosimetry in a solid body, such as a joint of meat, presents greater problems. In such cases a model may be made in the form of a hollow shell filled with a fluid, the whole designed to have absorption characteristics equivalent to those of the original body, and measurements are carried out within the fluid in this replica.

Using the techniques of dosimetry outlined above, the relative penetrating power of various radiations can be investigated. This, of course, increases with increasing particle energy, but as may be seen in Fig. 15.1, compared with photons, electrons dissipate their energy in a thin layer of the target material. Thus electron irradiation is only suitable for treating small objects or the surface layers of larger ones. It is also clear that the dose-rate is not strictly exponentially attenuated. It rises from its surface value to a maximum before starting to fall. This maximum is the result both of the incident radiation being scattered through its interaction with the target material and of the production of secondary radiation in these interactions. The curve (i) in Fig. 15.1(a) is drawn from data on the variation in dose along the path of a narrow pencil of radiation. A broad beam of radiation may be regarded as a bundle of such pencils, in which case radiation scattered from one pencil reinforces the ionisation in those which lie near by. This gives rise to the rather less rapid attenuation in dose rate observed in broad beam irradiation, as shown by curve (ii) in Fig. 15.1(a).

15.5. IRRADIATION PLANT

In the design of a food irradiation plant, it is necessary to ensure that:

(i)   suitable radiation will be produced at the lowest cost,
(ii)   economic use is made of this radiation in treating the food so that a suitable dose distribution and total dose is given to each food item, and
(iii) operating personnel will not be subjected to harmful radiation either during normal operation of the plant or in the event of accidents and breakdowns.

Each of these matters will now be discussed in turn.

15.5.1. RADIATION SOURCES

Sources suitable for irradiating foods are either made of radioactive materials which in decay emit suitable radiation or they take the form of electron accelerating machines. The accelerated electrons may be used directly or can interact with a suitable target to produce a beam of high-energy photons. Such photons are generally termed X-rays to distinguish them from the photon radiation of radioactive decay (γ-rays). An essential difference between radioactive and machine sources is that a machine can be switched off when not required, while the process of radioactive decay cannot be so arrested. Continuous operation of a radioactive source radiation facility is therefore indicated if the process is to be carried out relatively cheaply. On the other hand, the capital investment in a machine source is such that it will be uneconomic to have it out of use, and so producing no income, for any length of time.

15.5.1.1. Radioactive sources

The Becquerel, as a unit of quantity of radioactivity (Section 15.1.2) is extremely small and the petaBequerel ($1\,\text{PBq} = 10^{15}\,\text{Bq}$) is now used to describe the quantity of radioactive material in an industrial irradiation plant. This unit has replaced the earlier unit of the Curie (Ci), which was defined to be approximately the number of disintegrations occurring in one gram of pure radium per second ($1\,\text{Ci} = 3\cdot7 \times 10^{10}\,\text{Bq}$). Clearly, the effectiveness of a radioactive source depends not only on the number of disintegrations occurring, but also on the energy and nature of the particles produced in those disintegrations. Nevertheless, the quantity of radio-activity, as defined, does offer a means of comparing the size of sources constructed using the same radioactive nuclide (e.g. ^{60}Co). A source of

37 PBq (or 10^6 Ci) would be required, roughly speaking, to treat 10 tonnes of food per hour with a dose of 2·5 kGy.

The instability of the radioactive nucleus results in a steady decline in source activity, i.e. the quantity of radiation (in Bq) within a particular body of radioactive material will decrease with time. It is convenient to specify the rate of decay of a nuclide (that is of a single atom species characterised by specific atomic and mass numbers) by its 'half-life', i.e. the period during which one half of the atoms in a given amount of the nuclide undergo radioactive disintegration. Clearly, when a radioactive source is used in irradiation equipment, the source must be progressively renewed if its activity is to be maintained at a reasonably constant level. This renewal is simplified if the source is subdivided into a number of self-contained interchangeable units. If the plant is initially equipped with a set of such units in which the intensity increases in a planned progression from the least to the most active, and if, at set intervals, the currently least active unit is removed and replaced by a unit of high activity, the total activity of the whole source assembly can be kept reasonably uniform. The frequency of renewal will depend on the half-life of the material. Source material with a short half-life will be highly active, so a relatively small mass would be all that would be required to provide the desired quantity of radioactivity, but such a source would require frequent renewal if anything like a constant activity is to be maintained. Spent fuel rods removed from power reactors have provided the radiation source for experimental work, but their limited availability and the instability of their activity, due to many of the nuclides present having short half-lives, limits their usefulness. On the other hand, material with a long half-life, having less radioactivity per unit mass, though more stable, will be more massive and problems of self-adsorption of the radiation by the source itself will build up. A compromise between these extremes is required in a practical system.

Cobalt-60 (^{60}Co), which is generally used, is an artificial isotope produced in relatively large amounts by neutron irradiation of ^{59}Co in a nuclear reactor which provides a flux of slow neutrons. The extent of the nuclear change and its rate are related to the intensity of the neutron flux and more than a year of exposure is required to reach useful levels. ^{60}Co has a half-life of 5·3 years; sources constructed from this material lose activity at the rate of 1% per month. In its decay, 1·17 and 1·33 MeV γ-rays and electrons of up to 0·31 MeV are emitted. The latter do not penetrate the protective stainless steel sheath enclosing the material. The γ-rays only, which are little attenuated by the sheath, are thus available for irradiation. ^{60}Co has provided the source of radiation for almost all the large irradiation plants constructed to date. Another radioactive source material, occasionally used, is caesium-137 (^{137}Cs). This can be separated from the fission products of power reactor fuel rods and has a half-life of 30 years, emitting γ-rays of 0·66 MeV. The longer half-life of ^{137}Cs leads to greater self-absorption of the emitted radiation than experienced with ^{60}Co sources (about 55% self-absorption compared with 10–30%). The lower energy of the γ-radiation makes the achievement of a satisfactory level of dose uniformity more difficult as the radiation is less penetrating than that from ^{60}Co. The high radiotoxicity of ^{137}Cs requires the installation of more sophisticated control systems.[15] However, the material is currently cheaper than ^{60}Co.[17]

15.5.1.2. Machine sources

As mentioned earlier, electron accelerating machines can be used as sources of ionising radiation. Such machines consist of two major components, an evacuated accelerating tube and a suitable source of electrical power. There are two main classes of machine.[18] In one a high voltage electrostatic field applied to the accelerating tube accelerates to high energy the low energy electrons from a heated cathode. A variety of methods have been used for producing the accelerating voltage and these devices are under continuous development to reduce costs. In the second class of machine, linear accelerators, the accelerating tube forms a waveguide along which radio frequency electromagnetic radiation (of, say, 10 cm wavelength) passes. By suitably designing the waveguide, it is possible to accelerate the electrons from a cathode axially along the tube in the direction of motion of the travelling waves.

The accelerated electrons may either be used directly for irradiation or converted to the more penetrating X-radiation by interaction with a suitable target. In X-ray machines of a conventional design only a small fraction of energy incident in the electron beam is converted into X-ray energy. The efficiency of conversion rises with the energy of the incident electrons.

15.5.2. APPLICATION OF THE RADIATION

Electron beams are only capable of limited penetration into foods, so the material must be presented to the beam in a thin layer if it is to be treated in bulk, or all surfaces must be presented if a surface treatment is desired. Since electrons are charged particles, an electron beam can be deflected by an oscillating magnetic field to scan the material in a direction perpendicular to the direction of motion of the conveyor.

Because of the more penetrating nature of X- or γ-radiation and its progressive absorption throughout items or packages of the target material it is necessary to present this material in different orientations at various stages of the irradiation process to give a reasonably uniform dose distribution throughout the package. All parts of the material being treated must receive the minimum dose necessary to achieve the desired effect. Doses higher than this will probably lead to unwanted product deterioration and are, in any case, unnecessary and wasteful. There will always be dose differences but, by appropriate design of the source and the materials handling system for moving the material past the source, these can be held to acceptable levels. The ratio of the maximum dose

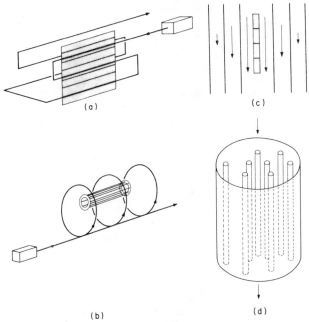

(a)

(c)

(b)

(d)

FIG. 15.2. Source disposition and product movement patterns. (a) A plate source with packages passing on both sides. A second layer of packages may be used to absorb the radiation which has penetrated through the inner layer. This second layer may either form a separate circuit or be an extension of the one flow path. (b) A cage source with containers moving about it on a 'Ferris Wheel' system. (c) A rod source with particulate or fluid material flowing past it in annular channels. The rate of flow in each channel is controlled to regulate the dose given to the material passing through. (d) An array of rod sources through which particulate or fluid material flows. The strength and disposition of each rod is so fixed that the dose rate over the cross-section is reasonably uniform.

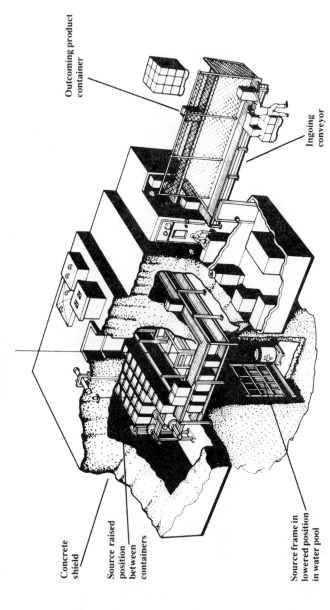

Outcoming product container

Ingoing conveyor

Concrete shield

Source raised position between containers

Source frame in lowered position in water pool

Fig. 15.3. Diagrammatic view of a typical radiation plant. (Reproduced by permission of Isotron plc, Swindon, Wiltshire, England.)

experienced by any part of the product to the minimum dose experienced is the 'uniformity ratio'. Currently operating commercial irradiation plants have uniformity ratios of about 1·3–2·5. The actual values achieved in any instance will depend on the product. Boxes of particulate items can exhibit varying bulk densities depending on the way the items pack. This will influence the dose distribution and so the uniformity ratio. In setting up a process, point measurements of absorbed dose are required to substantiate that all the material has been adequately processed and that legal requirements in respect of average or maximum doses have been met. Continued monitoring of production is advisable to ensure that this situation is maintained.

In order to make the maximum use of the continuous emission from radioactive sources, it is necessary to box the source in with target material. Figure 15.2 shows possible product movement and source disposition patterns to achieve adequate uniformity of dose and a satisfactory level of radiation utilisation. Figure 15.3 shows a cut-away view of a typical irradiation facility using a ^{60}Co radioactive source. The layout is a modification of that in Fig. 15.2(a), with product containers making two passes (an inner and an outer) on either side of a rectangular source plaque. The containers, when in the outer passes, absorb radiation which has penetrated the containers in the inner passes, making more efficient use of the radiation provided by the source.

Another consequence of the continuous activity of radioactive sources is that input and output storage facilities may have to be provided so that irradiation can continue when the production and distribution lines serving the plant are idle (overnight for instance) (see Fig. 15.3). Thus to satisfy the technical requirements of the process an elaborate materials handling system is required, the reliability of which will influence the efficiency of the whole plant. With machine sources, the need for input and output storage is not so great since the source can be switched off.

Finally, if a plant is not completely loaded the distribution of radiation, and therefore the local dose rate, will differ from that in normal operation. Higher intensities of radiation falling on the walls of the plant will result in a greater leakage of radiation into surrounding areas and, on start up and shut down, packages will not receive the normal dose. To obviate these difficulties, the plant can be loaded initially with dummy material having similar absorption characteristics to the process material. This dummy material will then be progressively displaced as process material enters and will follow the process material back into the plant at the end of a processing run.

15.5.3. SAFETY

It is clear from a comparison of the lethal dose for a man and the doses required for various processing operations that operating personnel must be protected from the radiation generated in the plant they tend. The chief protective agent is an envelope of radiation-absorbing shielding surrounding the plant. Lead, concrete and purified water are the chief shielding materials in use. A sufficient thickness of material is required to reduce the dose rate outside the plant to an acceptable level (see Section 15.4). This thickness is roughly inversely proportional to the density of the shielding material. Lead shielding is used in the transport of radioactive source rods or in transportable demonstration irradiators because its high density reduces the thickness of shielding required and allows such units to be as compact as possible. High density concrete is used for permanent installations (Figs 15.3 and 15.4). Figure 15.4 shows a plant constructed in 1973. The concrete shielding can clearly be seen in the diagram and some idea of its thickness can be gained from the fact that the circular turntable in the irradiation chamber is 5 m in radius. Finally, a 5·5 m deep tank of purified water is used, as in the plant illustrated in Fig. 15.4, to provide a safe location into which radioactive sources can be retracted when maintenance must be carried out in the irradiation zone. An alternative to this is 'dry pit' storage, where the source is lowered into a concrete lined pit and covered with a lead or concrete lid to prevent escape of radiation. The mechanisms for moving the source into and out of the storage location must be of exceptional reliability since a mechanical failure leaving the

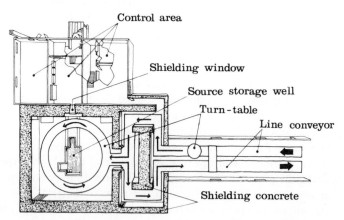

Fig. 15.4. A plan view of the irradiation cell of the potato irradiation plant at Hokkaido, Japan. (From *Food Irradiation Information*, No. 3 (June 1974) 79.)

source jammed wholly or partly in the operating position would be disastrous.

Some access points must be provided through the shielding material, but these should not lead to an escape of radiation. Conveyors handling the product pass through maze-like passages in the shielding (see Fig. 15.4). Access points are also required so as to obtain admittance to the interior for maintenance, e.g. of the product transport system and to allow the exchange of radioactive source units. Figure 15.3 shows this last operation with the access point through the roof of the plant in the open position, and with a lead transport container holding the replacement source unit lowered to the bottom of the storage pool ready for the remotely controlled exchange to be effected. Such access points are also constructed so that there is no direct path for radiation to escape round their edges. Stringent safety precautions are necessary to ensure that the source cannot be moved to the operating position when an access point is open or when personnel are present within the irradiation zone. Such controls imply the presence of electrical equipment and wiring in the irradiation zone and consideration must be given to the effect of the radiation on such equipment, e.g. the possibility of deterioration of insulation under the influence of radiation.

Finally, where electron beams from machine sources are being used, adequate ventilation of the area is essential since the ozone generated by the passage of electrons through air must be diluted to an acceptable and safe concentration.[18]

REFERENCES

1. Goldblith, S. R., Historical development of food irradiation. In *Food Irradiation*. IAEA, Vienna, 1966.
2. Ehlermann, D. A. E., Future prospects for radiation processing of food. In *Recent Advances in Food Irradiation*, ed. P. S. Elias & A. J. Cohen. Elsevier Biomedical Press, Amsterdam, 1983, pp. 331–54.
3. Ley, F. J., Applying radiation technology to food. In *Food Technology International Europe 1987*, ed. A. Turner. Sterling Publications, London, 1987, pp. 72–5.
4. Anon., Recommended international general standard for irradiated foods, CAC/RS 106—1979. FAO/WHO, Rome, 1980.
5. Anon., Wholesomeness of irradiated food—Report of a Joint FAO/IAEA/WHO Expert Committee. WHO Technical Report Series No. 659. WHO, Geneva, 1981.
6. Codex Alimentarious. Vol. XV, Codex general standard for irradiated foods. CODEX STAN 106—1983, FAO, Rome, Italy.

7. Advisory Committee on Irradiated and Novel Foods, Report on the safety and wholesomeness of irradiated foods. HMSO, London, 1986.
8. Woollen, A., Consumer mistrust. *Food Processing*, **56**(4) (1987) 12.
9. Parsons, B. J., Prospective methods for testing the irradiation of foods. *Food Sci. Technol. Today*, **1**(3) (1987) 148–50.
10. Goodburn, K., Detecting the undetectable? *Food Sci. Technol. Today*, **1**(3) (1987) 145–8.
11. Diehl, F. F., Food irradiation—worldwide activity. *Food Eng. Int.*, **4**(1) (1979) 34–6.
12. Robinson, D. S., Irradiation of foods. *IFST Proceedings*, **19**(4) (1986) 165–8.
13. Becker, R. L., Absence of induced radioactivity in irradiated foods. In *Recent Advances in Food Irradiation*, ed. P. S. Elias & A. J. Cohen. Elsevier Biomedical Press, Amsterdam, 1983.
14. IAEA, Manual of food irradiation dosimetry. Technical Reports Series No. 178. IAEA, Vienna, 1977.
15. Etienne, J. C. and Buyle, R., Electromechanical engineering aspects of irradiator design. *J. Food Engng*, **3** (1984) 265–84.
16. The Ionising Radiations Regulations, Approved code of practice—The protection of persons against ionising radiation arising from any work activity. HMSO, London, 1985.
17. Urbain, W. M., *Food Irradiation*. Academic Press, New York, 1986.
18. Boaler, V. J., Electron accelerator facilities for food processing. *J. Food Engng*, **3** (1984) 285–94.

CHAPTER 16

FOOD STORAGE

16.1. INFLUENCE OF STORAGE CONDITIONS ON THE PRODUCT

16.1.1. INTRODUCTION

Food being stored may become spoiled by three mechanisms:

(i) living organisms (e.g. vermin, insects, fungi or bacteria) may feed on the food and contaminate it,

(ii) biochemical activity within the food itself (e.g. respiration, staling, browning and rancidity development) may in time diminish its quality and usefulness, and

(iii) physical processes (e.g. bursting and spillage of the contents of packages or recrystallisation phenomena in sugar confectionery, fats and frozen products) may have the same effect.

The primary production of foods may be seasonal, with a specific harvest season (e.g. cereals and fruits), while consumption is spread over a longer period. Thus there must be storage of such products between harvest and use. To extend the availability of such products in the market place they may be transported over considerable distances (say, from the southern hemisphere to the northern) to take advantage of differing harvest seasons. Even for fresh meats, for example, where there is no harvest season, the produce must be transported from producer to consumer and buffer stocks must be held in storage to allow for variations in demand. Where primary products are used in the formulation of manufactured foods, storage will be required both for the raw materials and the finished products. The differing nature of these two classes of material will almost certainly lead to differing storage requirements.

It is useful to consider the link between primary production and manufacture, between manufacture and final consumption, or between primary production and final consumption (where there is no manufacturing stage) as a distribution chain. Within this chain there may be pre-treatments (say, to hold back mould growth or bacterial decay), packaging, storage in one or more fixed locations and one or more transportation operations. The conditions under which products are held by the final purchaser, either in the home or in some catering operation, are all part of this distribution chain and each link of the chain will contribute to the final perceived quality—and to the cost to the final consumer. Indeed, it has been estimated[1] that distribution costs account for up to 25% of the purchase price of food items.

The three main factors of the storage environment which influence the storage life of a particular commodity are the temperature, humidity and the composition of the store atmosphere. In addition, rough handling, careless packing or unsuitable packaging can reduce storage life, but these matters are outside the scope of the present chapter.

16.1.2. STORE TEMPERATURE

The rate at which biochemical reactions occur in food increases with increasing temperature.

The relationship frequently observed between reaction rate and temperature is similar to that already noted in connection with the thermal inactivation of bacterial spores by moist heat in Chapter 11. As with that case, the range of absolute temperatures involved in the storage of any particular commodity is fairly small compared with the numerical values of the absolute temperatures themselves and so, just as the logarithm of the decimal reduction time could be reasonably represented either as a linear function of the reciprocal of the absolute temperature (an Arrhenius relationship) or as a linear function of the temperature itself, the same might be expected of the logarithm of the storage life of foods.

In the present instance, however, the rate of change of the reaction rate is more frequently measured in terms of Q_{10} (the ratio of the rate at one temperature to that at a temperature $10°C$ lower) than by z (the temperature range over which the rate changes 10-fold). The gradient of the plot of the logarithm of the reaction rate against temperature is expressible in terms of both quantities, i.e.

$$\text{gradient} = \frac{1}{z} = \frac{\log Q_{10}}{10}$$

whence

$$z = \frac{10}{\log Q_{10}}$$

The concept of Q_{10} values was introduced by vant' Hoff, who found that the Q_{10} for many chemical reactions was about 2, i.e. the reaction rate approximately doubled for each 10°C temperature rise. The rate of respiration of harvested fruit, however, has a Q_{10} of about 2·5 and that for vegetables is of the same order[2] while the quality deterioration of frozen strawberries has a Q_{10} about ten times greater again than this.[3]

The concept of a specific Q_{10} value to relate the storage life of a food product to the temperature of its storage, all other parameters being kept constant, is somewhat flawed since published information[4] often shows relationships between the logarithm of the storage life and the temperature which are not linear. For example, the Q_{10} value might be observed to fall from about 5 to about 1·3 as the temperature falls from -10 to -30°C.

This reduction in Q_{10} is important, indicating how the improvement in storage life for a given reduction in temperature becomes less marked as the temperature falls while the costs of providing such lower temperatures will be escalating. The utility of ultra-low temperatures for frozen food storage in any instance must be questioned.[5] Indeed, there is evidence that, for some frozen cured meats at least, product deterioration rates *increase* as the temperature drops.

In general, the lower the storage temperature, the more slowly do foods suffer degradation by those biochemical spoilage reactions that are operative under normal ambient conditions. In addition, the rate of growth of bacteria is reduced as the temperature falls and low temperature storage—particularly frozen storage—has some bactericidal effect. Fungi, like bacteria, have a temperature range over which growth is possible at a given water activity (see Section 16.1.3) and an optimum growth temperature within this range. This optimum is nearer the upper end of the range and at, or above, normal ambient temperatures. Near the limiting temperatures, growth takes place only very slowly, so again it may be said that lowering the temperature of the product will reduce its rate of deterioration. Most insect activity is inhibited below about 4°C, although some insect species and insect eggs are capable of surviving long exposures to these temperatures. Flour and grain mites are active near 0°C, breeding at temperatures which render other insects inactive from cold.[6,7]

From all this it might be inferred that a reduction in storage temperature inevitably results in an extension of storage life. This is, however, by no means the case. Foods containing water will freeze if their temperature is lowered much below 0°C, the actual freezing temperature depending on the nature of the aqueous solutions in the food. The act of freezing and thawing alters the food, sometimes very extensively, and the properties of 'fresh' produce such as fruits and vegetables are adversely affected should they freeze during storage. For fresh meat stored in the frozen state there is the problem of 'drip'. This is a red fluid which exudes from muscle cells damaged by the freezing and thawing process and which, if extensive, spoils the appearance of the meat and results in loss of weight. If canned foods are allowed to freeze, the cans may burst, and in goods which contain gels or emulsions these may break down.

Even if held above the freezing temperature, deleterious physiological changes can result in the spoilage of fresh fruits and vegetables. Pears may be stored close to their freezing point at temperatures of about −1°C. However, apples stored close to their freezing point can exhibit forms of injury not observed at slightly higher temperatures. Soggy or Low Temperature breakdown (where a clearly defined moist breakdown of the tissues midway between the core and surface develops), Internal Browning (where a browning occurs radiating out from the core area while the tissues remain firm) and Brown Core or Core Flush (where the flesh around the seed cavity browns) result from storage at 0°C and are not a problem at 3–4°C.[2]

Apples are not alone in suffering from this sort of injury. Table 16.1 shows the temperatures below which chilling injury can be observed in a variety of tropical fruits and vegetables.

The limitation of storage life resulting from the restriction of storage temperature in chill-sensitive tropical products can be overcome, to a

TABLE 16.1
The susceptibility of various tropical fruits and vegetables to chilling injury

Product	Approximate temperature below which chilling injury may be observed (°C)
Avocado (other than West Indian), Cucumber and Lime	5
Papaya and Pineapple	6
Avocado (West Indian)	10
Lemon	11
Banana	13

Based on data from Pantastico.[8]

certain degree, by various chemical and heat pre-treatments and/or the control of the gaseous environment in which the material is held.[9] A longer term strategy is to develop chill-resistant cultivars by cross-breeding commercial varieties with related chill-resistant species where such species exist and will hybridise. On the other hand, because a commodity is chill-sensitive it does not mean that it necessarily has an inconveniently short storage life; sweet potato will keep for up to 16 weeks at 12°C.

There is evidence that ripe tomatoes can be stored at a lower temperature than green tomatoes, which can suffer cold injury below 7°C resulting in abnormal ripening and susceptibility to rots.[8] Storage of potatoes below 3°C is undesirable as they are susceptible to chilling injury. However, even above this temperature there can be a change in the starch–sugar balance leading to the accumulation of sugar in the tissues making the tubers unsuitable for processing into chips or crisps. Storage at 10°C or higher is recommended to avoid this.[10]

Another factor to be taken into consideration, even when low temperature storage will increase the storage life of a commodity, is the cost of such storage. To the prime cost of foods put into storage must be added the cost of maintaining them under the chosen storage conditions. Thus stored foods appreciate in cost even if they do not in value. Refrigerated storage is more expensive than unrefrigerated storage, and the lower the storage temperature the higher the cost. Clearly storage conditions need be no more elaborate than those required to maintain the stored commodity in good condition up to the time of use. The maintenance of conditions sufficient to provide a shelf life for the material in excess of that required will usually be economically disadvantageous.

This concept has been applied, particularly, to the storage and distribution of frozen food products. Here, provided the products are suitably packaged, the deterioration is almost entirely a function of temperature. By using organoleptic testing procedures, the duration of storage at a given temperature before some specified degree of quality loss is observed can be determined.

Two measures are used, the 'High Quality Life' and the 'Practical Storage Life'.[4] A batch of frozen product is properly prepared from quality ingredients. Immediately, samples are put into store at a variety of different, but constantly maintained, temperatures—one of which is at or below −40°C. The material stored at this, the lowest, temperature is taken to be the control and assumed not to deteriorate in comparison to the others. Material from the various samples is submitted to a panel of experienced sensory assessors using triangle or duo-trio tests[11] at regular intervals. The

High Quality Life of the material is regarded as over when 70% of the assessors successfully distinguish it from the control. The Practical Storage Life is similar but extends from the start of the storage period at a given temperature to the instant when quality loss has become sufficiently marked to render the product unsuitable for sale or use as intended. In other words, the Practical Storage Life of a product depends on the marketing policy as well as the rate of product deterioration. Practical storage lives may exceed the corresponding high quality lives by a factor of some 3–5.

The High Quality Life is used principally in research or product development as it offers a means of comparing the rates of deterioration of different products or formulations. The Practical Storage Life is of more use in evaluating a distribution chain. If the variation of temperature with time throughout the chain is known, if the variation of Practical Storage Life (P) with temperature (T) has been determined for the product, and if the rate of deterioration at any instant can be assumed to be determined by the temperature at that instant alone and uninfluenced by the previous history of the product, then the fraction of the Practical Storage Life expended by storage for time dt at temperature T is

$$\frac{dt}{P}$$

and the total expenditure of practical storage life over the whole distribution chain is the integrated value of this

$$\int_i^f \frac{dt}{P}$$

The integration may be effected graphically by the same method as is employed in Fig. 11.2. If this integral exceeds unity, the distribution chain is unable to deliver the product to the end user at the quality proposed. If the integral is much below unity the conditions maintained during distribution are unnecessarily stringent. It might be possible to reduce costs by using a cruder distribution system or, alternatively, the marketing strategy for the product might be reviewed.

As an alternative to the above procedure, temperature sensitive indicators of varying degrees of sophistication have been developed. These are normally self-adhesive devices which can be attached to food packages at the start of the distribution chain and inspected at the end of it. Since only temperature is monitored, product deterioration must be a function of temperature only. The product must either be insensitive to, e.g., ambient humidity (Section 16.1.3) or the composition of the atmosphere in which it is held (Section 16.1.4) or such parameters must be under control. The simplest device exhibits a colour change when a predetermined temperature has been exceeded. It would therefore show if the temperature had risen to a level where the practical storage life was short, but would give no indication of how long it remained at that temperature. Other devices attempt an integrated estimate of the loss of storage life by incorporating systems whose rate of change with temperature is selected to be similar to the change of product deterioration rate with temperature, e.g. systems involving an enzyme reaction or which use the progress of a dye along a wick. Such devices are known as time/temperature monitors.

It may now be seen that three main factors influence the choice of the storage temperature for a particular commodity: the temperature dependence of the rate at which spoilage processes occur, the risk of cold injury to the commodity, and the economic balance between storage costs and the maintenance of product quality. Recommended conditions for the refrigerated storage of perishable produce have been published.[2,10] Recommended temperatures for land transport[12] and sea transport[13] of perishable foods are also available. Transport conditions may be less stringent than storage conditions. This is because the provision of refrigeration and the control of product temperature during transport present more problems and are relatively more costly than in stationary storage. Since the duration of land transportation, in particular, is often relatively short, the fraction of the high quality life expended during transportation at temperatures rather above those recommended for storage is comparatively small. It is of greater importance, if a further storage period is to follow transportation, to ensure that, subsequently, the goods are rapidly cooled to the new storage temperature since the persistence of the higher transport temperature during the subsequent storage period may well lead to loss of quality. This problem is intensified since the heat gain will most likely take place when the bulk of the product is broken down into smaller units for loading and unloading transport vehicles. Heat penetration will then be rapid, due to the more extended surfaces and smaller product depths involved. However, if the product is subsequently returned to bulk storage the re-cooling can be much slower since it must take place from a large body of material. Reducing the temperature rises during handling to a minimum is desirable.

The temperature conditions for storage of less perishable items are by implication less rigorous. The keeping qualities of sugar are independent of

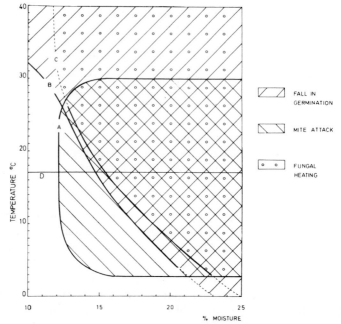

FALL IN GERMINATION

MITE ATTACK

FUNGAL HEATING

FIG. 16.1. Effect of grain moisture content and temperature on insect heating (above line D), fall in germination to 95% in 35 weeks storage (to right of line B), damp grain heating (to right of line C) and mite attack (shaded area within line A).[6] (Originated by the Pest Infestation Control Laboratory. Reproduced by permission of Controller, HM Stationery Office.)

temperature between 10 and 30°C.[14] Canned goods must, of course, be protected from frost damage. Figure 16.1 shows that dry grain can be safely stored at temperatures up to 17°C, while with increasing moisture content storage at reduced temperatures becomes more necessary. In general terms, the cooler and drier seeds can be stored, the longer their storage life. Some nuts will store quite well at 20°C, though longer storage periods are possible at reduced temperatures. For instance, shelled peanuts will store for 4 months at 20°C, 2 years at 1°C and 5 years at −4°C.[7]

16.1.3. STORE HUMIDITY

If the humidity of a store atmosphere is below the equilibrium relative humidity (or ERH—see Chapter 21) of the food being stored, that food will lose moisture to the atmosphere. Conversely if it is above the ERH of the food, the latter will absorb water. Thus, ideally, the relative humidity of the store atmosphere should be adjusted to the ERH of the stored product. For

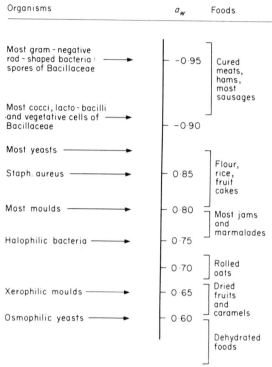

Organisms		a_w	Foods

Most gram-negative rod-shaped bacteria : spores of Bacillaceae ⟶ -0.95 — Cured meats, hams, most sausages

Most cocci, lacto-bacilli and vegetative cells of ⟶ -0.90 Bacillaceae

Most yeasts ⟶

Staph. aureus ⟶ 0.85 — Flour, rice, fruit cakes

Most moulds ⟶ 0.80 — Most jams and marmalades

Halophilic bacteria ⟶ 0.75

0.70 — Rolled oats

Xerophilic moulds ⟶ 0.65 — Dried fruits and caramels

Osmophilic yeasts ⟶ 0.60

Dehydrated foods

FIG. 16.2. Diagram showing the approximate limiting water activities for various classes of micro-organism and the water activities of various classes of foods. At the a_w indicated, the micro-organisms listed will just be inhibited. Marginally above these a_w values, their growth will be very slow.

instance, granulated white sugar has a moisture content of about 0·02% and an ERH of about 60%. If the moisture content rises to 0·06%, the sugar is in danger of caking. Therefore storage relative humidities below 60% are recommended for this product. Conversely brown sugar has a moisture content of 4% which must be maintained if the product is to retain a workable texture, so relative humidities of 60–70% are recommended for long term storage.[15] Again, peanuts become brittle and may split due to dehydration if the storage relative humidity is below 70% RH and are liable to mould spoilage above this ERH.[7] Thus, as with temperature, there is often an optimum condition for storage.

The ERH of a product has a considerable bearing on its vulnerability to microbial attack. When expressed as a fraction, instead of a percentage, the ERH is known as the water activity (a_w) of the material. Figure 16.2 shows the a_w limits below which various classes of organism are inhibited and also indicates the a_w of various classes of food. As may be seen, bacterial growth may be a major problem in foods with a high a_w—for instance fresh fruits and vegetables, meats and fish—but in materials with a lower a_w it is the fungi that cause the most trouble. Insects can also flourish in foods of comparatively low a_w.

In the case of fresh fruits and vegetables, mould growth is a risk at high store humidities. A compromise relative humidity may therefore be adopted for storage, in which some wilting is accepted as the price for reducing microbial attack. A certain drying of the surface of meat also slows the development of bacterial slime and is sometimes required in the case of long distance transport. In these cases there is no equilibrium between the store atmosphere and the material in store and the effective a_w at the surface is below that in the bulk of the produce.

Packaging can be used to isolate the environment of the food from the store air and so allow foods to be held at the ERH in storage atmospheres of undetermined relative humidity. Occasionally treatment of the surface of foods achieves the same purpose. Thus shell eggs lose water freely and require high humidity environments if they are not to experience excessive weight loss. This may lead to microbial growth on the egg shell and consequent tainting of the egg. Treating the shell with oil improves its water vapour barrier properties and allows the humidity of the store to be lowered, so avoiding mould growth.

As with storage temperature, recommended levels of store relative humidity have been published for many products.

16.1.4. COMPOSITION OF STORE ATMOSPHERE

A variety of food materials are advantageously stored in atmospheres different from normal air. A noteworthy example of this occurs in the refrigerated storage of fruit. Fresh fruit respires, taking up oxygen and evolving carbon dioxide. The rate of respiration can be reduced by cooling, so extending storage life, but can be further reduced by storing the fruit in an atmosphere richer in carbon dioxide and poorer in oxygen than normal air. In the case of apples, particularly, worthwhile increases in storage life are possible and this technique, which is known as 'controlled atmosphere' storage, is in extensive commercial use. In 1984 there was a controlled atmosphere storage capacity of some 140 000 tonnes on the fruit farms of England alone. The oxygen and CO_2 levels used vary markedly between varieties and are controlled to optimum values, since too great a modification of the storage atmosphere can lead to secondary spoilage. For

Bramley's Seedling an atmosphere of 8% CO_2 + 13% O_2 + 79% N_2 is satisfactory. Cox's Orange Pippin on the other hand, which have a storage life at 3·5°C of 3 months in normal air, will keep for about 5 months when the atmosphere is changed to 5% CO_2 + 3% O_2 + 92% N_2. Even lower levels of oxygen (*c.* 1%), coupled with less than 1% CO_2, are now recommended for storing this variety, so achieving a storage life of about 8 months. However, such a low oxygen level is close to the threshold at which the fruit will respire anaerobically, generating 'alcoholic' off-flavours. Close and accurate control is required if such levels are to be used.[16]

More recently, controlled atmosphere storage has been applied to winter white cabbage, which is harvested in the late autumn and maintained in refrigerated storage up to the following summer. An atmosphere of 5% CO_2 + 3% O_2 + 92% N_2 is found to reduce fungal spoilage by *Botrytis cinerea*, reduce wastage (together with the cost of trimming prior to marketing) and to extend storage life. The technique is finding application to other leafy vegetables, though root vegetables seem to store more efficiently simply with low temperature and high humidity.

The examples so far given involve substantial quantities of product stored for extended periods. Specially-built storage chambers (typically holding 25–200 tonnes) are used, often with elaborate control systems.

However, there are many other products for which storage life can be extended usefully by holding in atmospheres other than air, but where the quantities involved are more modest and the overall storage periods are much less. For such products transportation will take up an appreciable fraction of the refrigerated storage life. The unit quantity to be considered is, therefore, that which will fill a road, rail or sea transport container or that which is held in an individual pallet. This concept of modifying the atmosphere around more limited quantities of a product has developed rapidly into the marketing of sealed retail packages of a variety of foods to achieve extended shelf lives. Table 16.2 gives examples of the conditions used and Goodburn and Halligan[17] have reviewed the microbiology and technology of this rapidly growing method of preparing products for market.

Food materials sufficiently dry to be protected from microbial deterioration, e.g. ground coffee, can still spoil in the presence of oxygen. To prevent this, the air in a container or package may be replaced by an inert gas, such as nitrogen or carbon dioxide, or by a vacuum. To prevent oxidative changes in beer and wines the containers in which they are to be marketed may, again, be flushed out with nitrogen before the filling operation takes place.

TABLE 16.2
Examples of temperatures and atmospheres for various products (from Smith, Simpson and Lambert[18])

Product	Temperature (°C)	O_2 (%)	CO_2 (%)	N_2 (%)
Fresh meat	0–2	70	20	10
Cured meat	1–3	0	50	50
Poultry	0–2	60–80	20–40	0
Cheese	1–3	0	60	40
Baked goods and pizza	Room temperature	0	60	40
Dry snacks		0	20–30	70–80

16.1.5. ODOURS AND TAINTS

Stored produce may pick up foreign odours and flavours from other foodstuffs stored with it,[19] from inappropriate packaging materials[20] or from the storage chamber and environment. Foods with strong odours— spiced meats, smoked fish, citrus fruit, etc., and spoiled meat and fish are likely to cause tainting. Packaging materials may either themselves contribute odours or be contaminated during production. Adhesives and printing materials may also cause trouble. Finally the constructional materials of the store may become contaminated or taints may be absorbed from vapours entering the store from outside. While such taints do not alter the nutritional status of the food, its commercial value can be seriously affected.

Fatty foods are particularly liable to absorb odours. Butter is very subject to tainting, and meat shipped to England has, on occasions, been found to be tainted by diesel and fuel oil fumes, smoke and fruit (particularly oranges). Eggs will also pick up taints fairly easily. Tables have been prepared indicating commodity combinations which are liable to cause tainting problems in refrigerated shipping space.[21,22]

The most satisfactory method of avoiding problems of tainting during storage is to avoid storing taint-absorbing foods in the presence of odorous materials. Suitable packaging can help to preserve food untainted, and both activated charcoal and ozone have been used for removing odorous volatiles from food stores. Unfortunately the concentrations of ozone for efficient action are toxic and so require special care, both in their use and in the purification of the air in the chamber afterwards. To be efficient, after these treatments the surfaces of the chamber and refrigerator should be thoroughly cleaned, treating all surfaces with a disinfectant. It is worth remembering that these processes are all more effective the higher the temperature of the chamber when they are carried out.

16.1.6. LIGHT

The ultra-violet light in the sun's rays will quickly impart a taint to butter and milk by oxidising their fats. Potatoes exposed to light will turn green due to the formation of chlorophyll. While this is in itself harmless, a parallel production of the toxic substance, solanine, often takes place. In storage buildings the effect of light on produce is normally unimportant since daylight does not penetrate into them and only a low level of artificial light is provided. Where problems have recently arisen is in supermarkets, where high intensity lighting from fluorescent tubes is used to display foods. The ultra-violet rays from such lights are more intense than those from tungsten filament lighting and have been shown to be sufficient to oxidise fats, bleach colours and to green potatoes. Coloured or opaque packages may be used, but are not necessarily satisfactory from a commercial point of view.

16.2. VARIABILITY IN STORAGE CONDITIONS

Both spatial and temporal variations may be found in the conditions in a food store. Temporal variations may either be transient—resulting, say, from recently introduced material coming to an equilibrium state in the store—or they may be periodic in nature and a permanent feature of the storage situation. The main causes of variability in storage conditions are:

(i)   the equilibration of products to storage conditions,
(ii) respiratory activity (either of the food, in the case of fruits and vegetables, or due to insect infestation or spoilage micro-organisms),
(iii) variation of climatic conditions (e.g. temperature, pressure, insolation and wind force) external to the store,
(iv) fluctuations in the performance of refrigeration and other equipment designed to maintain the storage conditions at the desired levels, and
(v)   the activities of operating personnel (e.g. in loading or unloading the store).

The effects of such variations are often complex, inter-related changes occurring in the temperature, humidity and atmosphere composition throughout the store. As an example of this, consider a bin of wheat, a small volume within which is infested with insects. These insects, in respiring, will absorb oxygen and generate heat and carbon dioxide. The local temperature will therefore rise. The higher temperature at the site of insect activity will result in the grain in that place drying, the moisture being transferred to the surrounding grain, particularly that above the area of infestation. The conditions at the original site of infestation are now less favourable to insect growth; the grain is drier and the oxygen tension low. Thus infestation will spread away from this site, although it will remain warm by being surrounded by a zone of heat generation. The rise of temperature and humidity in the region surrounding the zone of infestation may, if sufficient, cause wheat germination and mould growth (see Fig. 16.1) which in its turn can result in sufficient heat generation to initiate a fire.

In refrigerated storage the magnitude of spatial variations in storage conditions is considerably influenced by the mode of transfer of heat and gases within the stack of stored material. Temperature differences of no more than 1°C in the circulating air should be aimed at and short period fluctuations due to the operation of the temperature control system should be limited to less than 0·5°C.[10] The location of the sensing element for temperature control should be such that it contacts air representative of the average temperature within the chamber. If the store air does not move through the stack, diffusional mechanisms and thermal conduction predominate and larger variations will be observable than when the store air moves and promotes additional convective transfer. Thus in order to maintain uniform conditions throughout the store, such air movement is desirable. The produce must therefore be so stacked in the store that air flow through the stack is facilitated, particular care being taken with items such as rectangular cartons, which can be stacked in a solid block. The pallets in a palletised stack will serve as ducts to circulate air round the stack providing they are aligned both with each other and with the direction of air movement. Care must be taken to ensure air flow between the stack and the walls and the stack and the floor if local warm spots are to be avoided.

Air circulation through the stack may either be fan assisted (forced convection) or due solely to the thermally generated density gradients in the air (natural convection). The former system is almost universally used today because the cooling systems are less bulky and cheaper. The most frequently used forced convection systems use a cooling system and fan located in a separate enclosure connected to the store by delivery and return air ducts (Fig. 16.3), located in a floor mounted vertical duct (Fig. 16.4) or built into a compact unit which may be suspended from the ceiling of the

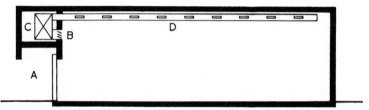

FIG. 16.3. A forced convection store using a ducted air supply (longitudinal section). A, loading area; B, air inlet to cooler; C, air cooler; D, cool air delivery duct.

store. Maintenance work is somewhat less convenient in the last two of these systems since the cooling unit is located entirely within the low temperature region and cannot be brought to ambient temperature without raising the temperature of the whole chamber.

In order to maintain quality, it is frequently desirable to reduce the temperature of, for example, freshly harvested vegetable material, freshly caught fish or freshly killed poultry rapidly. One exception is carcass meat, such as beef and lamb, where freezing before rigor has passed can lead to toughening of the muscle ('cold shortening') on thawing. Introducing material ready pre-cooled into a store also helps maintain the stability of the temperature within the store.

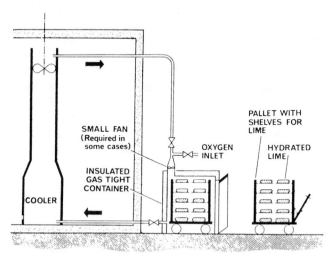

FIG. 16.4. The arrangement of a controlled atmosphere store employing a scrubber using fresh hydrated lime in bags. (From Mechanisation Leaflet for Farmers and Growers 12, by courtesy of the Controller of HMSO.)

Sea fish may be chilled rapidly after being caught by holding in tanks of stirred sea water which are either cooled by mechanical refrigeration or by ice. Sparging air through the tanks aids heat transfer and prevents the build-up of ice agglomerations within the ice/sea water slurry.[23] Poultry is chilled after slaughter and evisceration either in chilled water (prior to freezing) or with cold air (prior to sale chilled). Water chilling involves moving the carcasses continuously counter-current to a flow of chilled water which is chlorinated to a total residual level of 50 ppm to prevent cross contamination with salmonellae. With air chilling there is some dehydration of the carcass. Water sprays may be used to maintain their surfaces moist, the evaporation of this water into the air stream aiding the cooling process. Fruit and vegetables, particularly those of high intrinsic value, may similarly be rapidly chilled by humidified air at or a little above 0°C. The humidification system, however, must be such that no water droplets are entrained in the cooling air, to be deposited on the produce, and which, particularly at contact points, provide sites favouring subsequent mould growth.

Where the initial cooling of produce is to be carried out in the store chamber itself it is sometimes advantageous if the fan and duct systems in forced ventilation stores are so constructed that the direction of air flow can be reversed. Periodic air reversal can reduce the spatial temperature variations during the initial cooling of a room full of, say, fruit to storage temperature.

It has already been noted that fluctuating conditions external to the store can affect storage conditions. Annual (summer to winter) and diurnal (day to night) temperature variations may be taken as examples. Consider a large body with an extended plane surface (strictly speaking a 'semi-infinite solid' extending, in a Cartesian coordinate system, throughout the region $x \geq 0$ with a plane face defined by $x = 0$). If heat transfer within such a body is by conduction and its surface is subjected to a sinusoidal temperature variation of period T, a temperature wave will be propagated into the body with a velocity

$$\left(\frac{4\pi K}{T}\right)^{1/2}$$

where K is the thermal diffusivity of the body. The amplitude of the temperature oscillations at depth x within the body is reduced by a factor

$$\exp\left[-x\left(\frac{\pi}{TK}\right)^{1/2}\right]$$

below that at the surface. Now consider a large silo of bulk wheat $(K \simeq 0.30 \, \text{m}^2 \, \text{month}^{-1})$. From the above expressions it can be seen that 3·4 m from the outer surface the annual thermal oscillations would be reduced to 5% of their initial value, the temperature maxima being propagated into the silo at a velocity of $0.56 \, \text{m} \, \text{month}^{-1}$. Thus not only will annual temperature fluctuations be measurable well within the stack, they will be appreciably out of phase with the seasons. The diurnal fluctuation will be reduced to 5% of its initial value only 18 cm below the surface of the silo and so has little effect on storage. Similarly the diurnal temperature variations within the exposed insulated walls of refrigerated stores are rapidly attenuated and the heat leakage into the store remains fairly constant at an average value corresponding to the climatic season. Again, unrefrigerated underground storage locations insulated only by the mass of the subsoil around and over them will maintain a temperature approximately equal to the local year-round average ambient. This form of storage is known as cellar storage. Underground storage chambers of this type have been used traditionally in many parts of the world—particularly for the storage of grain.

16.3. MAINTENANCE AND CONTROL OF STORAGE CONDITIONS

16.3.1. TEMPERATURE

Refrigerated storage rooms are thermally insulated to reduce heat leakage. The insulation is in the form of a low bulk-density porous or fibrous material, e.g. cork, foamed plastics of various sorts, cellular glass, mineral or glass fibres, etc. In the traditional form of construction a conventional self-supporting and weatherproof building is erected. Then the insulation is applied to the walls and ceiling and faced with a protective sheath with an easily maintainable surface. Such buildings still have their place, particularly where a complex of chambers each operating at a different temperature are required.

However, it is increasingly usual for storage chambers to be built using prefabricated insulating panels. The store is built directly on a concrete floor slab which, if in direct contact with the ground, may require no insulation since, once the subsoil has been cooled, there will be an acceptably low leakage of heat from the ground into the store through the floor slab. If the floor slab is raised above the ground surface, say to be level with the loading bay for insulated road vehicles, floor insulation will be required. On the floor slab a framework, usually of structural steel, supports walls and ceiling, which are formed of large prefabricated insulating panels. These panels are composite units with outer and inner facings bonded to the insulating core. Large units minimise the length of jointing that has to be made along the edges of the panels. Care must be exercised in the design and construction of these joints so that thermal bridges are not established between the inside and the outside of the store and that the joint will not fail as temperature changes and adverse weather conditions cause minor changes to the dimensions and geometry of the panels. An external cladding is usually required to protect the panels and the supporting framework from the weather.

A more recent development is the construction of heavy prefabricated panels in which concrete structural slabs are bonded either side of an insulation layer to form a unit which is load-bearing as well as insulating.

In geographical areas where, for example, previous mineral extraction has left a network of tunnels, and where these are conveniently sited, sized and free from ingress of water, the opportunity has been taken in a number of instances to adapt them for use as low-cost refrigerated storage facilities. No insulation is required since the thickness of the surrounding earth or rock compensates for the comparatively high thermal conductivity of these materials.

Insulation is sometimes desirable in unrefrigerated storage. For instance, root vegetables and potatoes can be stored in clamps or barns using either earth or straw as an insulating material. The purpose of the insulation is to minimise the effects of sudden ambient changes on the produce and prevent frost damage. Canned goods may be transported in insulated vehicles for the same reason if sufficiently low ambient temperatures might be encountered to give a risk of freezing.

While too little insulation will lead to high refrigeration costs, over insulation will be initially more expensive and will reduce the available storage space in a building, cabinet or container. This is a particularly important consideration in food transport. In road or rail transport or in containerised transport by sea, the external height and width of the unit will be either standardised or limited to a maximum value. These containers are not so large that the space within the external volume occupied by the insulation can be ignored in comparison with the volume available for storage and, since the provision of refrigeration presents more problems here than in static storage, an economically satisfactory compromise must be achieved between reducing the heat leakage to restrict refrigeration requirements and reducing the insulation thickness to increase the payload.

The effect of minimising insulation thickness on the risk of condensation on the external surface (see Section 16.3.2) must not be overlooked.

Particularly where journey times are likely to be short and the container may be allowed to re-warm between deliveries, there is an additional heat load which may be of significance when designing the system, namely the heat extracted from the insulation itself as it re-cools at the start of a journey. It would be unwise to assume that the heat entering the chamber from the insulation is simply that expected in steady state conduction through the insulation (see Appendix II.2) or that a brief period of pre-cooling will have brought the insulation to the steady state condition.

While local costs and special requirements determine the insulation installed, recommended thermal resistances for the walls of static refrigerated stores and freezers are available, from which it can be concluded that leakage rates of the order of 7 W m^{-2} are normal. Data and procedures for estimating the heat leakage through different insulated structures are available.[24]

Because it must offer a similar thermal resistance to an equivalent section of insulated wall, the access door to a refrigerated store will be a heavy structure requiring a little effort to open and close manually. As soon as it is opened, air exchange across the threshold will lead to heat gain to the chamber and so door opening times must be minimised or other steps taken to reduce air exchange while the door is open. Mechanical handling of produce into store is almost universal, so the systems must be compatible with the efficient operation of, for example, fork-lift trucks moving palletised loads through the opening. Automatic, pneumatically operated opening and closing systems may be installed. Alternatively, while the door is open, the air within the store may be retained by a curtain of overlapping strips of heavy plastic material. A loaded truck may be driven through these, temporarily brushing them to one side. If the strips are translucent the driver can see through them sufficiently well to identify any hazard on the other side. An alternative system is an 'air curtain' fixed above the lintel of the door. This directs a curtain of air downwards and slightly outwards generating a pressure zone which holds back the store air. However, such a system must be properly designed, installed and maintained, otherwise the air stream can be diverted into the store.

If the refrigeration requirements for a store are to be estimated, heat generation within the store and the cooling of stored produce must be taken into account as well as heat leakage into the store. Indeed, the energy dissipated by the air circulating fans can be a substantial fraction of the total load.

At the time of writing, most refrigerated stores are cooled by vapour compression refrigerators using ammonia or halogenated hydrocarbon refrigerants. There are serious disadvantages to both materials. Ammonia (NH_3, known as 'Refrigerant 717' or 'R717') is toxic; human beings lose consciousness in an atmosphere containing about 2% NH_3. It also forms an explosive mixture with air (explosive limits 15–28% NH_3).[25] Escapes of ammonia into store chambers are serious matters, even if operating personnel are not directly affected. Injection of carbon dioxide, which reacts with ammonia to form ammonium carbonate, can be employed in the decontamination operations after such a leak. The halogenated hydrocarbon refrigerants, when introduced, were welcomed as being safer materials than the earlier refrigerants, such as sulphur dioxide or ammonia. Recent findings regarding the effect on the Earth's ozone layer of their release into the atmosphere has completely changed this. The halogenated hydrocarbon refrigerants that found the greatest application were R12 (dichlorodifluoromethane) and R22 (chlorodifluoromethane). Recently R22 has been favoured for commercial installations. While this material may be less of environmental hazard than R12, the use of such materials in the future will inevitably reduce as more environmentally acceptable alternatives are developed and introduced.

The cooling effect produced by the conventional vapour-compression refrigerator is the result of the liquid refrigerant boiling at low temperature in the pipes of an evaporator. This evaporator may either cool the store air directly (a 'direct expansion' system) or cool a liquid (say a calcium chloride solution, or 'brine') which is in turn fed to a heat exchanger to cool the air (an 'indirect' system). The control of refrigeration in indirect systems is particularly simple. However, such systems are more complex, and therefore more costly, than direct expansion and so are less frequently used.

The gas produced by the boiling of the refrigerant in the evaporator is recompressed before being brought back to the liquid state in the condenser. In large systems it is usual to employ several compressors in parallel for this so that the refrigeration capacity can be better matched to current requirements by operating the appropriate number of compressors. Also, a compressor may be taken out of service for maintenance while the cooling duty is maintained by the operation of the others.

Automatic control systems for refrigeration installations have long been used and the introduction of microprocessor-based controls into this area opens the possibility of more comprehensive control than has been possible in the past. However, the cost of developing dedicated software individually for systems is high and this approach to control will become more attractive as standard, but flexible, software packages are developed for this application.[26]

Other cooling systems are available and are used, particularly, in food transport. Here there are problems in providing, powering and maintaining vapour compression refrigerators under conditions where reliability is essential while the equipment is unattended. Water ice, aqueous eutectic mixtures, solid carbon dioxide and liquid gases (carbon dioxide, nitrogen and air), all of which refrigerate by absorbing latent heat, have found applications in this field, mainly to supply non-mechanical refrigeration throughout the journey.

In recent years the great advance in this field has been the development of container transportation. Sealed box-like containers of standardised dimensions have been built which can transport foods directly from supplier to consumer, whether by lorry, railway flat-car or in a specially designed ship, without the need for any handling of the goods during the whole transport chain. Containers with built-in refrigeration equipment have found greatest application in road transportation, because there is a driver in attendance to ensure that the equipment is operating.

For transportation at sea or when standing at the quay side, containers can be serviced with cold air from a central source via ducts and equipped with clip-on mechanical refrigeration units for distribution from the port of arrival by road.[27] Liquid carbon dioxide has also been used to provide an initial boost to the cooling system at the time of loading. Precooling of the transport container and minimisation of heat gain by produce during loading are essential to reduce refrigeration requirements during the journey. The rapid cooling that results from spraying liquid carbon dioxide into the container after loading can be used to effect this.

16.3.2. MOISTURE AND HUMIDITY

Heat passing though the walls of a refrigerated storage chamber must first be supplied to the outer surface of these walls by transfer from the outside air and by solar radiation. When solar radiation does not predominate, the outer wall surface will be below the temperature of the air outside the store wall. If the dew point of this air is higher than the surface temperature of the wall, water will condense on the wall surface, a circumstance which can result in deterioration of the fabric of the wall. Increasing the thermal insulation of the room will reduce the heat leakage and increase the temperature of the outside wall. The avoidance of surface condensation can be a determining factor in wall insulation when the humidities in the air external to the wall are likely to be high. Even under normal conditions, surface condensation can occur at locations where, due to design faults, the thickness of insulation is reduced by structural members, pipes or fixing bolts.

Whether surface condensation occurs or not, there is often a higher partial pressure of water vapour in the air outside the store than in that inside it. Thus there is a water vapour concentration gradient which will tend to cause diffusional flow of water vapour through the wall into the store. If the water vapour pressure at any point within the store wall equals the saturated vapour pressure of water at the local temperature, water will condense from the vapour phase at that place. Since the low thermal conductivity of insulating materials depends on their porous or cellular nature, water logging seriously affects their efficiency. To prevent condensation within the wall, a barrier to water vapour flow must be provided. Some insulating materials are comparatively resistant to vapour flow—notably 'closed cell' foamed plastics, where the plastic membrane is continuous around the air bubbles in the material. Other materials are formed into boards and provided with a prefabricated barrier, say of aluminium foil, on one side. Alternatively bituminous felt, aluminium foil, galvanised steel or flexible polyethylene sheeting may be interposed between the wall and the insulation. Again, a bituminous adhesive fixing the insulation to the structural wall may provide the barrier. It is essential that any barrier should be on the outer face of the insulation to prevent water vapour reaching this vulnerable material.

It has already been noted (Section 16.3.1) that the insulating effect of the subsoil is considerable for stores built directly on the ground. If no precautions are taken and the store is operated below 0°C, the 0°C isothermal surface under the store may, particularly during the winter, be in the subsoil below the floor. When this occurs, any water in the subsoil will freeze and, owing to the lowered vapour pressure in the region, ice will tend to accumulate due to diffusional water movements. These ice accumulations usually form lens-shaped masses below the store floor and in time damage the structure of the building, giving rise to a condition known as 'frost heave'. Frost heave is a particular danger when the water table in the subsoil is high and when the subsoil contains fine silts and clays. Frost heave of stores built on difficult subsoils can be prevented by installing a heating system—say an electrical heater mat—beneath the floor insulation so that the 0°C isothermal surface does not pass through the subsoil. Alternatively, waste heat from the refrigeration plant can be used to heat a suitable fluid which is then pumped round pipes buried in the sub-soil.

The equilibrium relative humidity of many foods (fruits, vegetables and meat for instance) is greater than the humidity recommended for their storage. There will therefore be some desiccation of the produce by the store air. Moisture will also enter a refrigerated store through air exchange at doors, etc. The relative humidity established in the store air represents a dynamic equilibrium between the take-up of moisture by the air and the dehydrating effect of the air cooler. If the temperature of the cooler surface falls relative to the air temperature, the dehydrating effect of the cooler is increased, and vice versa. Thus in stores designed to operate at a high humidity, extended cooling surfaces and small temperature differences are used. Conversely, where a low relative humidity is desired, a restricted cooling surface at a correspondingly lower temperature is employed. A temporary method of lowering the humidity of an existing storage chamber is to introduce heat into the room to enable a lower cooler temperature to be employed without changing the store air temperature. Steam or atomised water from sprays may be used to increase store humidities.

Vegetables, such as carrots, require a high humidity to prevent loss of moisture. However, if liquid water condenses or is deposited on the surface (say, from improperly adjusted atomisation sprays used to increase humidity) local rotting may occur. A very stable temperature is therefore required at these high humidities to prevent the dew point of the air temporarily rising to a value above the surface temperature of the produce. Stable conditions at 0°C can be achieved by using an ice-bank system. In this the refrigerator evaporator is submerged in a water tank and works to build up a mass of ice by freezing the surrounding water. The remaining water in the tank, cooled to 0°C by the ice present, is then pumped through a specially designed spray tower to both cool and saturate air, which is then circulated through the store.

The moisture removed from the store air by the cooling system will either condense as water on the surface of the cooler or form frost upon it. Sometimes coolers are kept wetted by brine solutions or cooling effected by spraying brine (or water, as above) through the store air. Where brine is used it will become diluted by the condensing water.

Frost formation provides the most difficult problem since the ice crystals stay where they form on the cooler surface. Such is the thermal conductivity of the frost layer and the heat transfer coefficient at the frost–air interface that considerable frost formation may occur on an isolated pipe before heat transfer becomes impaired (see Appendix II). More serious is the effect the frost has on air flow through the cooling equipment. Regular defrosting of the coolers is therefore required. This can be effected by circulating hot brine through indirect units, by discharging hot refrigerant gases through direct expansion coolers or by shutting off the refrigeration and melting the frost with electric heaters.

Fruits and vegetables respire (Section 16.1.4) and in this process heat is generated. If these materials are placed in a store, this heat must be removed by the store air which must be cooler than the produce. If the produce is sealed into closed packages, the package must take up a temperature intermediate between the average temperature of the produce and the temperature of the store air so that this heat flow is maintained. If the package is moisture-proof the air within will humidify and, if the equilibrium relative humidity of the produce is high enough, a situation can be achieved where water evaporates from the produce to condense on the inner face of the package.

For materials which do not generate heat on storage, the situation is simpler. Once they come to temperature equilibrium with the store there is no temperature gradient between the produce and the store air. The air within the package will simply saturate and then there will be no further loss from the produce. This would be the case with frozen foods.

However, if the temperature control system of the store is not of high quality, the store temperature will cycle up and down appreciably. This will cause the package surface to swing first below and then above the mean temperature of the frozen food within. Water may therefore sublime from the produce to condense as ice on the package, only to re-sublime and re-condense variously as ice crystals on the produce. Such ice (cavity ice) can normally be seen to some extent in frozen food packages removed from domestic refrigerators and clearly has caused at least some quality loss through product dehydration.

In the long term storage of palletised stocks of frozen foods, particularly where the pallet load has been shrink-wrapped in plastic film for convenience of handling, the internal temperatures will be much less affected by store temperature fluctuations and so the formation of cavity ice will be correspondingly less than would be found in an isolated consumer pack.

This concept has been taken further in the 'jacketed store'. Here, the refrigeration system within the store is external to a container which virtually fills the volume of the store chamber leaving only a small gap round the outside through which the refrigerated air circulates. Frozen produce is placed within the container, which is then closed. An auxiliary cooling system brings the frozen produce to store temperature before being switched off. The container of produce then holds its temperature under conditions of saturation in the surrounding air, while the cooling system located in the jacket deals with heat leakage through the walls.

An alternative approach to avoiding quality deterioration due to loss of moisture from stored frozen foods is to 'glaze' the surface with ice. This can be effected immediately after the freezing process by quickly treating the material with chilled water either by dipping or spraying. On storage the water loss will then take place from the ice layer and not from the produce. This process may be subject to some legal control as the ice layer adds to the apparent product weight.

16.3.3. STORAGE ATMOSPHERE COMPOSITION
16.3.3.1. Controlled atmosphere stores

The chief concern here, as explained in Section 16.1.4, is the maintenance and control of storage atmospheres containing more carbon dioxide and less oxygen than normal air. In the storage of fruit the required carbon dioxide can be generated, and the surplus oxygen absorbed, by respiration in the stored produce. This method is employed in the controlled atmosphere storage of apples.

Alternatively, the carbon dioxide required for the storage atmosphere may be supplied from outside, either from liquid carbon dioxide held in cylinders or by the evaporation of solid carbon dioxide in food transportation. In the latter instance the solid carbon dioxide both generates the required gas and provides the refrigerant; the carbon dioxide concentration in the store is therefore determined by the dynamic equilibrium between the rate of sublimation (which is controlled by the refrigeration requirements) and leakage of the gas from the chamber. When the first two methods are employed, however, the storage chamber should be as free of gas leaks as possible, either to minimise the time taken for respiration to supply sufficient carbon dioxide to achieve the required storage conditions, or to minimise the requirements for externally supplied gas. The normal water vapour barrier (Section 16.3.2) is insufficient for this purpose, and the required barrier is often provided by metal sheet or foil cladding on the inside of the store walls, or by multi-layer bituminous preparations. Close attention must be paid to the sealing of doorways. Metal gas-tight covers may be fitted across door openings behind a normal insulated refrigerator door.

If fruit is placed in such a gas-tight storage chamber, the oxygen tension in the store atmosphere will fall as this gas is converted by respiratory activity into carbon dioxide. Since one volume of oxygen will convert to one volume of carbon dioxide, the sum of the percentages by volume of these gases in the store will remain constant at its initial value (i.e. the value for normal air—about 21%). When the carbon dioxide concentration reaches a predetermined value (say $x\%$ by volume) a controlled ventilation of the store with air can be used to maintain the atmosphere composition constant throughout subsequent storage. The oxygen concentration will thus be automatically maintained at $(21 - x)\%$. Such conditions have been found satisfactory for some varieties of fruit, but others have been found to require lower oxygen concentrations than are attainable by this method. For such fruit a system such as that shown in Fig. 16.4 is employed. The appropriate concentration of oxygen is maintained by controlled addition of fresh air as shown. The excess carbon dioxide produced by respiration is removed by feeding the storage atmosphere at a controlled rate to a 'scrubber'. This unit may take a variety of forms. The cheapest and most widely used scrubbers are based on passing the store atmosphere over bags of hydrated lime or through sprays of caustic soda solution to absorb the carbon dioxide. These methods have the disadvantage that the absorbent cannot easily be regenerated. Regenerative scrubbers have been constructed using activated carbon. Regeneration is by air-purging, one activated carbon absorber being regenerated while the second is 'on stream'. The system is unsuited to maintaining atmospheres with the lowest concentrations of oxygen since the chamber holding the regenerated absorbant is full of normal air at the end of the regeneration process and this will be swept into the store chamber when the absorber is put 'on stream'.

Storage chambers for controlled atmosphere storage are not large, since it is desirable to fill the stores and close them within 7 days to get the full benefit of the artificial atmospheres. The maintenance of these chambers in such a degree of leak-tightness that the store atmosphere can be rapidly brought to the required composition is a not negligible charge on the process. One alternative to maintaining a highly sealed store is to accept a certain measure of leakage and inject gases to modify the atmosphere rather than rely solely on the respiratory activity of the fruit. Nitrogen gas, generated from liquid nitrogen holding tanks, or the exhaust gases produced from burning hydrocarbon fuels in air can be used. The expense of these systems, of course, increases the less gas-tight the store, but they do offer a way of building up to the desired atmosphere quicker than can be achieved by relying on the fruit alone.

To control the storage atmosphere to the desired levels, routine methods of measuring the concentration of oxygen and carbon dioxide are required. While the traditional methods of volumetric analysis (say, using an Orsat apparatus) are available, they are inconvenient and unsuited to use in control systems. Since the thermal conductivity of CO_2 $(0.015\ W\ m^{-1}\ K^{-1})$ is considerably different from those of N_2 and O_2 $(0.024$ and $0.025\ W\ m^{-1}\ K^{-1}$, respectively) the thermal conductivity of the store atmosphere can be used as a measure of its CO_2 content. Infra-red absorption can also be used to determine carbon dioxide, as can the measurement of the refractive index of the store atmosphere using an interferometer. The paramagnetic properties of oxygen lead to a method of determining the concentration of that component of the atmosphere and other instrumental systems are available. In the past, control was effected manually after analysis of the current store atmosphere but it is now becoming more common to link measurement and control systems using micro-processor technology.

16.3.3.2. Modified atmosphere and controlled atmosphere packaging

Fruit and vegetables packed in perforated or partly closed plastic packages will be protected to a degree from loss of water and will also develop a local atmosphere richer in carbon dioxide and depleted in oxygen compared with normal air. The degree of change will depend on the mass and respiration rate of the contents and the degree of ventilation of the package. Both will vary with time and from package to package. The atmosphere is therefore not susceptible to close control.[28] A radical change of atmosphere cannot be attempted since a fraction of the packages would generate damaging gas mixtures. Closed packages formed from material with high carbon dioxide and low oxygen permeability can also be used. While the problem of variable air exchange is eliminated, the atmospheres generated are still dependent on the rate at which the contents convert oxygen to carbon dioxide and the uniformity of the packaging film.

Non-respiring products (meat, cheese, baked goods, etc.) can be placed in packages of relatively impermeable films, gas flushed with mixtures of gases appropriate to the contents and then sealed. It cannot be expected, however, that the atmosphere composition at the time of sealing will be maintained throughout the storage period even if the film is intact and properly sealed. The film will always have some residual permeability to gases; carbon dioxide can be absorbed by the material packaged, lowering its concentration in the surrounding atmosphere and possibly increasing the acidity of the packaged material. Biochemical activity may also modify the atmosphere. Nevertheless, useful extensions of storage life can be achieved by these methods, which are grouped together under the heading of 'modified atmosphere packaging' (MAP), and they are widely used in retail marketing.

'Controlled atmosphere packaging' (CAP), on the other hand, aims at maintaining a fixed atmosphere in a sealed package throughout the storage period. This is achieved by including within the package chemical agents of various sorts. To prevent product contamination these agents are packed in sachets permeable to the gases being scavenged or produced by the agent. Systems which absorb oxygen, absorb carbon dioxide or absorb ethylene (which catalyses the ripening of fruits), which convert oxygen to carbon dioxide (which may be useful where the contents of the package do not do this naturally) or which generate ethyl alcohol vapour (which can act as a preservative) have been produced. These systems largely originated from Japan, where they have found wide acceptance. With the rapid growth in sales of packaged, chilled foods (i.e. sold under refrigeration, but unfrozen), favoured by the consumer because of their 'fresh' image, and with the concentration in the UK of a substantial fraction of the retail food market into the hands of a small group of technologically advanced supermarket chains, developments in the application of MAP and CAP techniques can be expected.

REFERENCES

1. Winkworth, D., Moving with the times. *Food Processing*, **56**(4) (1987) 27–9.
2. Ryall, A. L., Lipton, W. J. (Vol. 1), Pentzer, W. T. (Vol. 2), *Handling, Transportation and Storage of Fruits and Vegetables*, 2 Vols. AVI, Westport, Conn., USA, 1974.
3. Van Arsdel, W. B., Copley, M. J. and Olson, R. L. (ed.), *Quality and Stability of Frozen Foods*. Wiley-Interscience, New York, 1969.
4. Anon., *Recommendations for the Processing and Handling of Frozen Foods*, 3rd edn. IIF/IIR, Paris, 1986.
5. Jul, M., The intricacies of the freezer chain. In *Refrigeration of Perishable Products for Distant Markets*. IIF/IIR, Paris, 1982, pp. 61–7.
6. Sinha, R. N. and Muir, W. E. (ed.), *Grain Storage. Part of a System*. AVI, Westport, Conn., USA, 1973.
7. Woodroof, J. G., *Peanuts: Production, Processing, Products*. 2nd edn. AVI, Westport, Conn., USA, 1973.
8. Pantastico, B. (ed.), *Postharvest Physiology, Handling and Utilisation of Tropical and Subtropical Fruits and Vegetables*. AVI, Westport, Conn., USA, 1975.
9. McGlasson, W. B., Scott, K. J. and Mendoza, D. B., The refrigerated storage of tropical and subtropical products. *Int. J. Refrig.*, **2**(6) (1979) 199–206.
10. Anon., *Recommendations for Chilled Storage of Perishable Produce*, 3rd edn. IIF/IIR, Paris, 1979.
11. BSI, Methods for sensory analysis of food. Part 1. Introduction and general guide to methodology (BS5929 Part I). British Standards Institution, London, 1986.
12. Anon., *Recommended Conditions for Land Transport of Perishable Foodstuffs*. IIF/IIR, Paris, 1974.
13. Anon., *The Carriage of Refrigerated Cargoes*. IIF/IIR, Paris, 1973.

14. Hugot, E., *Handbook of Cane Sugar Engineering*, 3rd edn. Elsevier, Amsterdam, 1986.
15. McGinnis, R. A. (ed.), *Beet Sugar Technology*, 2nd edn. Beet Sugar Development Foundation, Fort Collins, USA, 1971.
16. Geeson, J. D., The use of controlled and modified atmospheres for the storage and distribution of fruits and vegetables. *IFST Proc.*, **17**(3) (1984) 101–6.
17. Goodburn, K. E. and Halligan, A. C., *Modified-Atmosphere Packaging—A Technology Guide*. British Food Manufacturing Industries Research Association, Leatherhead, Surrey, UK, 1988.
18. Smith, J., Simpson, B. and Lambert, A., Use of modified atmospheres for shelf life extension of food. *Food Sci. Technol. Today*, **2**(4) (1988) 250–5.
19. Anon., *Guide to Refrigerated Storage*, 2nd edn. IIF/IIR, Paris, 1976.
20. Harvey, H. G., *Survey of Odour in Packaging of Foods*. Institute of Packaging, Melton Mowbray, England, 1963.
21. Cromarty, R. W., Contamination by odours from different cargoes carried and procedures for de-contamination. In *Marine Refrigeration*. IIF/IIR, Paris, 1965.
22. Boyes, W. W., Perishable commodities which may be stowed in the same ship spaces or hatches without danger of cross-taint. In *Marine Refrigeration*. IIF/IIR, Paris, 1965.
23. Hansen, P., Containers for chilling, stowage and transport of fresh fish in ice water. In *Advances in the Refrigerated Treatment of Fish*. IIF/IIR, Paris, 1981.
24. Anon., *ASHRAE Guide and Data Book—Fundamentals and Equipment*. American Society of Heating, Refrigerating and Air Conditioning Engineers, Atlanta, Ga., USA, 1981.
25. Anon., *Fire Safety in Cold Stores*. IIF/IIR, Paris, 1987.
26. Doyle, M. M., Practical problems involved in the use of micro-processors in the larger custom built refrigeration plants. In *Advances in Refrigeration and Heat Pump Technology achieved by the Application of Micro-electronics and the Control of Systems by Micro-electronic Devices. Vol. 1.* IIF/IIR, Paris, 1984.
27. Burton, G. A., Developments in containerisation by road and rail. In *Proc. 13th Int. Congress of Refrigeration*. AVI, Westport, Conn., USA, for IIF/IIR, 1973, pp. 361–8.
28. Cowell, N. D. and Scott, K. J., The variability of atmospheres produced by fruit store in polyethylene box liners. *J. Horticultural Sci.*, **37**(2) (1962) 87–93.

PART IV

ANCILLARY TECHNIQUES

CHAPTER 17

PLANT HYGIENE—HYGIENIC DESIGN, CLEANING AND DISINFECTION

17.1. INTRODUCTION

In the past, food processing operations were often carried out as small-scale batch operations, numbers of batches of material being processed during a working day. The duration of the working day often depended on raw material availability or on consumer demand, and items of process plant were cleaned by hand after production ceased, using such cleaning agents as were then available, often no more than soap and water. Contamination and spoilage of food materials by microbiological infection and, more seriously, contamination by pathogenic organisms capable of leading to outbreaks of food poisoning could, and did, occur. More recently, the scale of many food processing operations has greatly increased. Larger batch sizes and, in many cases, continuous operation have replaced the more traditional small-scale batch techniques, in the drive for greater productivity. Round the clock operation is becoming common and 'clean in place' (CIP) systems are increasingly replacing the more traditional methods of cleaning, particularly in continuous, high-capacity plants.

In the tonnage-capacity production plants of today, the problems of microbiological contamination are exactly those of the small-scale operator, but are much magnified. Adulteration and spoilage of large quantities of product, rather than a few kilograms, can occur, and the much larger consumer markets put at risk—should an outbreak of food poisoning arise—a far greater number of people.

Food processors must continuously guard against contamination of their products and, by correct design, operation and maintenance of their processes and equipment, must reduce to a minimum the risk of costly losses and danger to the health of the consumer.

The area of activity concerned with preventing the contamination of food materials during processing and storage is called 'hygiene', but it must be emphasised that hygiene in the food processing plant is not simply concerned with cleaning.

17.2. HYGIENIC DESIGN

Hygienic requirements should be considered in detail when the factory is being designed. Hygienic design embraces the design of the plant, equipment and building, including both construction and layout, the supply of services, such as bacteriologically acceptable water supplies and waste disposal facilities, as well as the design and installation of facilities for the cleaning and sterilising of raw materials, plant and equipment.

Hygienic design factors must be taken into consideration in all stages of factory development, including:

(i)   Site selection,
(ii) In the design of buildings housing process equipment.
(iii) In the design and lay-out of the processing equipment.

17.2.1. SITE SELECTION
Important hygiene requirements at this stage include:

(i)   The availability of a satisfactory water supply suitable for all likely production requirements and of waste-disposal facilities for both liquid and solid wastes. (These aspects are discussed in Chapter 18.)
(ii) The absence of possible centres of pollution from other manufacturers, such as land-fills, streams, etc., used for waste disposal by other producers. These sources of possible contamination are particularly prevalent in industrial areas and can make site selection difficult. Swamp areas and heavily wooded land should be avoided since both harbour rodents and insects and provide breeding grounds for micro-organisms.

17.2.2. DESIGN, CONSTRUCTION AND LAY-OUT OF BUILDINGS[1]
Raw materials commonly arrive at the factory in a contaminated condition, requiring preparation before processing. Vegetables, for example, are contaminated with soil, foreign matter, bacteria, etc. (see Chapter 2). Areas where grossly contaminated materials are handled

should be recognised and segregated from other processing areas. Careful planning of such areas at this early stage will prevent contamination problems later. Buildings of single-storey construction can be used to advantage where hygienic considerations are important. Large roof spans free from supporting pillars become possible, permitting more efficient utilisation of floor space, easier house-keeping and better lighting. Materials handling is often simpler with this type of construction.

17.2.2.1. Walls and ceilings
Interior wall surfaces of processing rooms should be smooth and easy to clean. They should be free from cracks and crevices which shelter insects and aid microbiological growth. Impervious surfacing materials such as glazed tiles are favoured, and other materials such as brick, cement, wood, etc., should be coated with a material capable of withstanding the action of steam, acids, and alkaline solutions commonly encountered in the food industry. Dust, splashes of food material and other unfavourable deposits collect on exposed ledges, window sills and roof trusses. These surfaces should be curved or sloped to discourage such accumulation and to permit easy cleaning and draining after washing. Corners and crevices must be avoided and unavoidable corners, as, for example, those between floors and walls, should have curved, water-tight joints. False ceilings can harbour dust, rodents and insects besides complicating ventilation and lighting arrangements, and should not be permitted.

17.2.2.2. Floors
Like walls, floors should be constructed of impervious materials which can be easily cleaned. They must be capable of carrying the loads imposed on them and of standing up to the wear encountered under all likely working conditions. They should be chemically resistant to all materials likely to come into contact with them. Floors likely to receive large quantities of water during processing and cleaning should be sloped to permit adequate drainage. Stagnant pools of water must be prevented at all costs since these soon become sources of contamination. Pitches of about one in fifty ($\frac{1}{4}$ in per linear foot) are usually adequate.

Drains should be vented to the outside atmosphere and should carry screens to prevent access of rodents to the plant. Smooth floors, when wet, can become very slippery and present a safety hazard to operating personnel, especially when the latter wear protective rubber footwear. Roughened, slip-resistant flooring materials providing continuous surfaces free from crevices are available.

17.2.2.3. Ventilation

The provision of adequate ventilation is important. Poor ventilation leads to condensation which can support the growth of micro-organisms on walls and ceilings. Ventilation of retorts, cooking, and boiling vats, etc., is best carried out by providing hoods over these vessels, trunking carrying vapours away through the roof to the outside atmosphere. The trunking should be designed to avoid dirt collection, a cylindrical cross-section being favoured. Extraction fans can be fitted in the trunking if forced ventilation is considered necessary. Ventilation outlets should be screened to prevent insects and birds entering the system.

Since many food materials readily acquire odours and flavours from the atmosphere in contact with them during processing, areas used for handling a variety of products, including meat and materials containing small quantities of fats—dried milk products, flour and cocoa—are better processed in well-ventilated rooms supplied with clean air under controlled humidity conditions. The whole process area is maintained at a pressure slightly greater than atmospheric. Only treated air enters. The positive pressure ventilation system prevents ingress of insects, dust, etc.

17.2.2.4. Lighting

Adequate lighting of a process area is essential. It affects the health and safety of the operatives as well as the efficiency with which they work. Satisfactory illumination shows up any accumulation of dirt as well as general untidiness and exposes unhygienic working conditions. By encouraging good 'housekeeping', lighting conditions directly influence the overall standard of hygiene within the plant.

17.2.3. EQUIPMENT DESIGN

It is now generally accepted that equipment design and plant layout, based on considerations both of utility and of hygienic design, increases the likelihood of success in food processing operations. This conclusion is recognised by food processors, equipment manufacturers and health authorities, all of whom are now collaborating in the production of 'codes of practice' for hygienic or sanitary design. It is intended that these standards[2-6] be used as a guide for those engaged in the design, installation, operation and maintenance of food processing plants.

Hygienic design requirements vary to some extent, depending on the nature of the food being processed. However, the underlying principles are common to the design of all food processing equipment. In general, the design, materials of construction and methods of installation of a food-processing plant should be chosen so as to facilitate cleaning and disinfection of the plant. For this reason the equipment must be easy to dismantle and reassemble quickly, using simple tools. Alternatively, it must be designed for cleaning-in-place (Section 17.3.3.2). Interest in hygienic design of food processing plant appears to have first arisen in the dairy industry in the USA. In the UK, a Working Party, set up in 1966, by the Joint Technical Committee of the Food Manufacturers' Federation (FMF) and the Food Machinery Association (FMA), considered recommendations of the 3A Sanitary Standards Committee,[2] the US Baking Industry Sanitation Standards Committee[3] and the National Canners Association of USA,[4] a summary of which was published in the journal *Food Processing* in October 1964 and April 1965.[5] The FMF/FMA endorsed the seven 'principles of sanitary design'[5] enunciated and, in 1967, produced a 'guide to good practice' entitled 'Hygienic Design of Food Plant'.[6] The principles are:

1. All surfaces in contact with food must be inert to the food under the conditions of use and must not migrate to or be absorbed by the food.
2. All surfaces in contact with food must be smooth and non-porous so that tiny particles of food, bacteria, or insect eggs are not caught in microscopic surface crevices and become difficult to dislodge, thus becoming a potential source of contamination.
3. All surfaces in contact with the food must be visible for inspection, or the equipment must be readily disassembled for inspection, or it must be demonstrated that routine cleaning procedures eliminate possibility of contamination from bacteria or insects.
4. All surfaces in contact with food must be readily accessible for manual cleaning, or if not readily accessible, then readily disassembled for manual cleaning, or if clean-in-place techniques are used, it must be demonstrated that the results achieved without disassembly are the equivalent of those obtained with disassembly and manual cleaning.
5. All interior surfaces in contact with food must be so arranged that the equipment is self emptying or self draining.
6. Equipment must be so designed as to protect the contents from external contamination.
7. The exterior or non-product contact surfaces should be arranged to prevent harbouring of soils, bacteria or pests in and on the equipment itself as well as in its contact with other equipment, floors, walls or hanging supports.

A slightly revised version of these principles (which has since become an established code of practice for the design of food processing equipment) further recommends that 'equipment should be so designed internally to provide the minimum number of crevices and dead spaces where any particles could collect'.[7]

Inherent in both versions of the 'principles' is an awareness of the important part played by the nature of the equipment surfaces. These are related to the nature of the materials of plant construction and the way they are fabricated and used.

17.2.3.1. Nature and materials of construction of contact surfaces

Toxic substances, likely to endanger health if consumed with the product, must not be used in the construction of food equipment if contact with edible material can occur. Metals commonly placed in this category include copper, iron, zinc, cadmium, antimony and lead. Some standards still permit the inclusion of lead in solder in amounts not exceeding 5%, although the use of welded and cemented-seam cans has virtually replaced soldered-seam cans.

Stainless steel is the material of construction most widely used for food contact surfaces in the fabrication of food processing equipment, piping systems, etc. This metal offers mechanical strength, ease of fabrication, resistance to corrosion (though not recommended for use with salt-brine solutions[8]), abrasion and thermal shock at relatively low cost. The preferred grades are Types 304 and 316.[9] Type 316 is more expensive but offers greater corrosion resistance. Stainless steel can be mechanically polished or electropolished to a high surface finish, giving a smooth surface of good cleanability.

Pits, crevices and other surface defects, which may be present on food contact surfaces, are thought to be capable of acting as 'harbourage sites', trapping micro-organisms which might survive any sterilisation process applied. These organisms could grow, leading to contamination. This reasoning generated a demand for highly polished stainless steel surfaces.

Mechanical polishing (grinding and buffing) to produce a fine surface is expensive and produces a wide variety of finishes. Since surface defects cannot be totally removed complete integrity against this source of contamination cannot be assured so a highly polished surface does not necessarily lead to a higher level of hygiene. Nevertheless, to many food processors a polished, stainless steel surface implies a hygienic and easily cleaned surface and is automatically preferred.

Cleanability, the extent to which soil may be removed from a surface, is affected by the degree of adherence and also by the cleaning regime used (Section 17.3.3). Surface adhesion is a complex phenomenon, many factors playing a part in binding food residues, micro-organisms, etc., to a surface. The roughness of the surface itself is only one of these factors. For this reason the literature on the cleanability of stainless steel surfaces of different degrees of finish is contradictory and there is evidence that high degrees of surface finish do not necessarily produce more easily cleaned surfaces.[10] The 3A standards[2] for food contact surfaces specify stainless steels with a surface finish of 150 grit and this value now finds wide application.

Aluminium and its alloys are also extensively used in food plants but since the metal is attacked by both acids and alkalis, care must be exercised in the selection of suitable cleaning agents. Dissimilar metals, capable of promoting chemical or electrolytic action if in contact in a liquid environment (e.g. cleansing agents, can lead to corrosion problems (e.g. pitting) and must be avoided. Aluminium is prone to this type of attack.

Other materials encountered include Monel metal (a copper–nickel alloy), brass, copper and bronze when suitably tinned and, in smaller capacity plants for higher value products, titanium. In certain cases the high-corrosion resistance, mechanical strength and cleanability outweigh the initial cost of this material.

Plastic materials offer many advantages as materials of construction in the food industry and their use is increasing. If used, they must be abrasion resistant and must be free from constituents which can migrate into the foodstuff.[11]

Glass pipelines and vessel linings find use in specialised areas of the food industry. Corrosion problems are negligible and inspection to ensure cleanliness of pipe runs is easy. With correct installation and handling, breakage, with the attendant risk of glass contaminating the foodstuffs, is minimal.

Wood, due to its absorbent properties and the difficulties associated with its cleaning, is not recommended as a material for food contact surfaces. Its use still persists for cutting surfaces in meat preparation and in the hand slicing of speciality vegetables and fruits. Non-absorbent, toughened rubbers have been developed and are preferred for these applications.

17.2.3.2. Plant construction

In the construction of food plant items much can be done to streamline the flow of materials over internal contact surfaces, thus avoiding those undesirable accumulations of food soils which are a potential source of contamination when trapped in less accessible areas of the equipment. Recesses, seams, ledges, inside threads, rivets, bolts and screws should be avoided as these promote stagnant regions which assist deposition and soiling. Permanent joints in metal parts should preferably be butt-welded, and the weld should be ground flush with adjacent surfaces, taking care to avoid pits and crevices (Fig. 17.1(a)). Lap welds (Fig. 17.1(b)) should be contoured to promote drainage.

All surfaces in contact with food materials must be constructed and installed so as to be self-draining to reduce undesirable build-up of food material. To assist complete emptying, bottoms of vessels can be dished or, if flat-bottomed, pitched (Fig. 17.2). A minimum bottom slope of about one in a hundred ($\frac{1}{8}$ in ft^{-1}) is recommended. When dished bottoms are fitted, drain lines from vessels should be flush fitting and sited at the lowest point to avoid stagnant pools of liquid. Sharp interior corners should be avoided, minimum radii of about 7 mm ($\frac{1}{4}$ in) being preferred.

Shaft seal assemblies and bearings for pumps and agitators used with liquid or semi-liquid products should be located outside the product contact zone. The shaft seals must be readily removable to facilitate cleaning and inspection of both seals and sealing materials. All packing materials must be non-toxic, non-porous and non-absorbent, and must be inert to food materials and cleaning compounds.

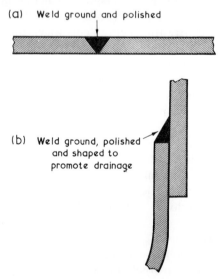

(a) Weld ground and polished

(b) Weld ground, polished and shaped to promote drainage

FIG. 17.1.   (a) Butt weld. (b) Lap weld.

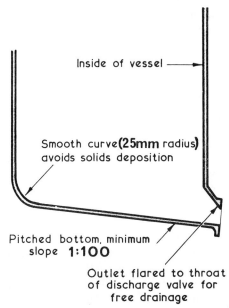

Inside of vessel ⟶

Smooth curve(25mm radius) avoids solids deposition

Pitched bottom, minimum slope **1:100**

Outlet flared to throat of discharge valve for free drainage

FIG. 17.2.   Hygienic design features for tank bottom.[15]

Equipment should be designed to prevent contamination of the contents from external sources. Readily removable covers must be provided for vessels, and all access points must be covered when not in use. These covers should be designed to permit free drainage of any liquid inadvertently coming into contact with them, the pitch of the surface carrying the liquid away from the access point. Lid hinges should also be of a simple take-apart type, permitting easy cleaning. Adequate ventilation and correct design of hoods and trunking will, of course, overcome the nuisance and constant contamination risk caused in so many plants by condensation drips from steam-heated blanchers, retorts, evaporators and boiling pans.

The importance of good house-keeping in maintaining satisfactory hygienic standard cannot be overstressed, and any design leading to a higher standard of cleanliness is highly desirable. For this reason even exterior non-product contact surfaces should be easily cleanable. They should be contoured so as to prevent build-up of soils and other deposits which encourage the growth of micro-organisms and insect pests in and around the equipment. This means that external surfaces should be free from open seams, crevices and other inaccessible recesses. Lagging around heat transfer equipment should be sealed to prevent ingress of insects.

17.2.3.3. Installation of equipment

The design of supporting steelwork and masonry shows a lack of appreciation of hygienic design principles in some plants. Bed-plates and support foundations for food equipment often serve as breeding grounds for insects and bacteria. Food material can become trapped in inaccessible gaps where satisfactory cleaning is not possible. Equipment should be installed on a floor or foundation of non-absorbent, easily cleanable material. Narrow gaps between the undersides of equipment and the floor must be avoided. The clearance must be sufficiently high to permit access for inspection and cleaning. Alternatively, the equipment or supports can be completely sealed into the floor. Joints must, however, be water-tight and flush-fitting or contoured to permit free drainage.

17.2.3.4. Installation of pipework

All pipes and pipe fittings used with food materials should be hygienically designed and be capable of easy dismantling for inspection and cleaning or the system designed for clean-in-place (CIP) operation.

Pipe runs containing foods are usually constructed using longitudinally welded, austenitic stainless steel tubes. The condition of the longitudinal weld depends on the method of fabrication and any subsequent polishing. (See Section 17.2.3.1.)

Product pipes and fittings are connected by couplings but lengths of pipe may be joined by butt welding. In welded systems inspection of product surfaces is not so easy and compatible materials of construction must be chosen to avoid dissimilar metal corrosion under the conditions of use. All types of connection should be designed to hygienic standards.[6] Couplings should carry easily cleanable external threads and be free from crevices in which food residues can collect and micro-organisms grow. Jointing materials—gaskets, etc.—must be suitable for food use and compatible with normal cleaning and sterilising procedures. Gaskets must be properly located and connections correctly tightened to avoid forming paths permitting the ingress of micro-organisms.[12]

Both pipes and fittings must be completely self-draining and adequate pipe supports are necessary to prevent sagging of pipe runs since this could lead to the retention of pockets of food material. 'Dead-ends' should be avoided as far as is possible. The shorter the dead-end the easier it is to clean.[12] The pocket arising from a dead-end should be reduced to a minimum and a recommended rule of thumb is that it must not exceed one pipe diameter.[13] The direction of flow into a blanked Tee-piece should always be towards the dead-end rather than away from it (Fig. 17.3).

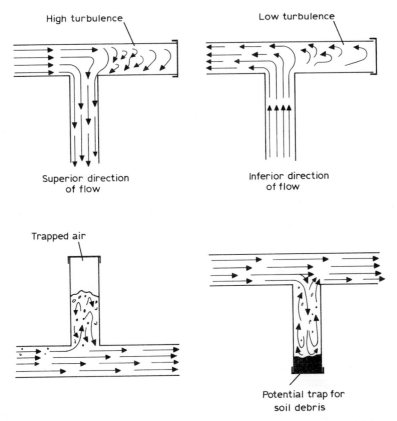

FIG. 17.3. Tee-piece flow directions. In practice pocket shown should be an absolute minimum and no more than 1 pipe diameter. (Adapted from Romney.[13])

To minimise the risk of scale, paint or condensate getting into the food, overhead pipes should not pass directly over vessels or process lines exposed to the atmosphere. Pipes carrying services, such as steam, water or air, to process vessels should pass behind the vessels rather than over them. To assist in hygienic house-keeping, pipes, vessels instrument-consoles, CIP control-panels, etc., should not be fitted too close to walls or floors. Adequate space to permit cleaning of both equipment and the floor area must always be allowed.

With the plant and equipment designed to take advantage of modern hygienic principles an essential step towards hygienic operating conditions in the factory will have been taken. However, acceptable standards of hygiene will only be achieved if correct cleaning and sterilising procedures are followed.

17.3. PLANT CLEANING AND DISINFECTION

17.3.1. INTRODUCTION

Cleaning, disinfection and sterilisation operations are essential in a food processing plant if edible food materials are to be produced under safe, hygienic conditions. These operations may be carried out on the raw material and product streams in certain processes—as in the preparation of canned fruits and vegetables—but must be performed on the plant and equipment in every food factory. Cleaning and disinfection of plant and equipment is considered here. Raw material cleaning is considered in Chapter 2 and sterilisation of foodstuffs by heat and irradiation in Chapters 11 and 15. Cleaning and disinfection of plant and equipment must not be considered as optional extras by plant operatives. They are an integral part of plant operation requiring a certain technology of their own. The performance of these cleansing operations must be co-ordinated with those involving the actual processing of the food material. For efficient performance, in particular with CIP operation, the development of a satisfactory programme of operations will necessitate detailed study. This should show up both bottle-necks and areas where savings in time, wash-water and chemical usage can be realised.

Food equipment must be cleaned and disinfected immediately after use and if left standing for other than short periods of time should be disinfected again before re-use. These two operations are quite distinct, although satisfactory disinfection is much easier to achieve on a clean surface[14] since micro-organisms in the soil cannot be protected from contact with chemical disinfectants.

In cleaning, residual food materials in the plant and soils deposited during processing are physically removed by brushing, by the action of highly turbulent fluids, or by a combination of both these agencies. This removal is usually aided by the addition of detergents and conditioners which assist the wetting of the surface of the soil and its subsequent removal from the equipment surface. This detergent cleaning should be followed by a clean water rinse. Care must be taken that the dislodged soil is not deposited in other parts of the system. Detergent cleaning is best preceded by a clean water rinse which often removes much of the soil.

In removing soils, large numbers of contaminating micro-organisms, if present, will have been removed. Any micro-organisms remaining on the equipment surfaces after cleaning must be destroyed if the risk of contamination is to be avoided. The contact surfaces will require disinfection, using either steam, hot water or a chemical disinfectant.

The development of combined detergent–sterilants has, in certain cases, made possible the combining of cleaning and disinfection into a single operation. This has the advantage of reducing process downtime. However, some chemical disinfectants are less effective when combined with detergents and, although this can be overcome by increasing the concentration of disinfectant, cleaning costs will increase.

17.3.2. CLEANING AND DISINFECTION— TERMINOLOGY AND METHODS FOR CLEANSING

There is an element of ambiguity in the nomenclature associated with food plant cleaning and sterilisation.

Cleaning concerns those processes for the removal of soil from surfaces but not those concerned with destroying all forms of life on food contact surfaces. The term sterilisation refers to a process which will destroy all living organisms, and a sterile surface is one free of all micro-organisms. This condition is approached in 'aseptic' operations but not in general plant cleansing.

The terms 'commercial sterility' and 'near sterility' have both been used to describe conditions where acceptably few micro-organisms have survived sterilisation treatment. In the UK, the term 'disinfection' is now preferred to (commercial) sterilisation for processes concerned with the destruction of micro-organisms to a safe level, but not necessarily bacterial spores, on surfaces and in equipment.

In North America, a chemical agent that reduces the number of microbial contaminants on food contact surfaces to safe levels as regards public health is called a 'sanitiser' and sanitising (sanitation) is used to denote an operation leading to physical and microbiological cleanliness. In the UK, 'cleaning and disinfection' is the preferred term although the term 'cleansing' still finds use.

The standard method for cleansing food plant and equipment involves:

(i)   Cleaning, using water and a detergent suited to the soil, the hardness of the water, the material of construction of the equipment and the cleaning technique used.

(ii) Disinfection, using the heat in steam or hot water or a chemical disinfectant (sterilant, sanitiser).

These two aspects of cleansing will now be discussed in more detail.

17.3.3. CLEANING

The cleaning operation can be performed in one of two different ways, modern food processing plants being designed to permit cleaning by either:

    (i)   dismantling and cleaning, or

    (ii)   in-place cleaning or cleaning-in-place (CIP).

17.3.3.1. Dismantling and cleaning

This older method of cleaning, still widely practised and very efficient when carried out correctly, requires the plant to be constructed so as to permit rapid dismantling. After dismantling, the plant surfaces are cleaned by brushing and flushing with detergent solution. Residual detergent is rinsed away with clean water, the detergent being selected to ensure that food material and released soil film is carried away in solution or suspension. This method of cleaning allows visual inspection of plant contact surfaces to ascertain that cleaning is complete.

A wide variety of cleaning equipment is available. Brooms, mops, buckets, scrapers and 'squeegees' are standard requirements. Manual and mechanical brushes are also useful. Compressed air jets are invaluable for removing powdered soils from machinery surfaces. Vacuum cleaners also find extensive application in solids cleaning. Water jets operating at both low and high pressures are useful, when used with discretion—they can, however, disperse dirt over very wide areas. Two-phase cleaning guns have very wide application in food plant cleaning. These include steam-water jets and steam-detergent jets. Steam guns are also used for cleansing plant surfaces. They should not be used in the vicinity of plant moving parts—gear trains, pulleys, etc.—since they rapidly strip lubricant off bearing surfaces. For small items of equipment, soak-tanks containing detergent solution are convenient. After pre-rinsing in a water stream, items can be left to soak before brushing *in-situ*. A final rinse with hot water at about 82°C (180°F) will ensure natural drying.[15]

For larger items of equipment, such as storage vessels, spraying is preferred to manual cleaning. Manual internal cleaning can be difficult, whereas the use of correctly designed spraying heads can thoroughly clean relatively inaccessible surfaces. A variety of types of head are available (Fig. 17.4). Head and fittings can be temporary or permanent fixtures, but permanent installation is preferred. The head should be designed to hygienic standards, being self-cleaning and self-draining. Leakage of cleaner to the food product during processing operations should not be possible.

The incorporation of permanent cleaning facilities into major items of process plant is a big step towards in-place cleaning.
Foam cleaning and gel-cleaning are finding increasing use where larger areas—walls, working surfaces, etc.—need to be cleaned.
With foam cleaning a foaming agent is added to the detergent solution. This produces a longer-life, thick foam, which clings to the surface being cleaned thus increasing contact time between dirt and detergent. Pressure activated foaming equipment is now available. The use of foam cleaning gives visual evidence of the area actually contacted by the cleaner.

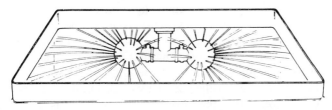

FIG. 17.4.   In-place cleaning sprays operating inside a stainless steel tank. (By courtesy of The APV Co. Ltd, Crawley.)

In gel-cleaning, a gelling agent added to the detergent produces a mixture which sticks to inclined and to vertical surfaces thus giving long contact times for efficient softening of the soil.

With both foam cleaning and gel-cleaning the need for mechanical flushing remains and the cleaning agent must be capable of easy removal with a water rinse.

17.3.3.2. Cleaning-in-place

Food processing plants require frequent cleaning. Dismantling plant for cleaning leads to long periods of downtime and high labour usage. Continual dismantling and reassembly can result in mechanical damage and increased maintenance charges. Manual cleaning of the inside surfaces of larger vessels is arduous and even a conscientious operator can overlook the small pocket of dirt that could lead to spoilage of product.

To obviate the disadvantages inherent in dismantling and cleaning, cleaning-in-place has been developed. CIP techniques are capable of achieving the highest standards of hygiene in process plant, equivalent to that obtained by dismantling and cleaning all the pipework and plant by hand.[8] Better control of hazardous cleaning chemicals also leads to greater safety and more economic use of these materials.

As with dismantling and cleaning, following an initial wash-water rinse to remove gross soil, detergent solutions are used to strip food residues and soiling films from the internal surfaces of the system.

In principle, pipework is cleaned by a turbulent flow of appropriate cleansing solution. Larger plant items in the line which are uneconomic to fill are fitted with stationary spray balls or rotating jets designed to reach every part of the inside surface. Initial water rinsing is recommended since this preliminary cleaning process enables a much reduced and more accurately assessable amount of detergent to be used for removing residual soil. After a final water rinse to remove detergent, the cleaned surfaces are disinfected using chemical disinfectants (Section 17.3.4.2).

The exact arrangement of a CIP system depends on the complexity of the plant layout and the process conditions. Basically, make-up or storage tanks containing detergent/disinfectant solutions are piped into the system. Under normal operating conditions these tanks and associated delivery lines are isolated to prevent the possibility of chemical solutions entering into and contaminating the process stream. This is achieved by incorporating removable 'keypieces' which complete one flow path but not both, or by separating the two different streams by means of two interlocked isolation valves separated by an open drain line during production runs.[14] As soon as possible after production has ceased, raw material and finished product storage tanks are completely isolated, the system drained, and then flushed with cold water to remove gross soil. Appropriate detergent solutions under specified conditions (see below) are then circulated through the equipment. After a further water rinse a disinfectant solution is similarly circulated, to be followed by a final cold water rinse. These operations take place on a sequential basis.

Depending on the degree of soiling, for economy parts of rinses/solutions can be discharged to drain or diverted to recovery tanks for reuse. This has led to the development of 'single-use' systems (for short activity detergents which are used once and discarded, and also for heavily soiled circuits); 're-use' systems with make-up tanks for caustic and acid detergents as well as heating facilities for solution/water rinse temperature variation, permitting repeated use of detergents; and 'multi-use' systems combining elements of both single and re-use systems (see Tamplin[14]). By incorporating automatic valves and a sequential timing system the cleansing process can be made almost fully automatic and independent of human operators thus affording considerable labour savings. With the addition of computer control, fully optimised CIP systems can now be remotely operated to achieve consistently high standards of hygiene.

17.3.3.3. Factors influencing the degree of cleaning achieved

Factors influencing the degree of cleaning, whether by dismantling or CIP, include:

(i) temperature, composition and concentration of detergent solutions,
(ii) contact time between detergent solutions and the soil deposit,
(iii) degree of turbulence promoted, and
(iv) the nature and thickness of the soil film.

Detergent composition governs the ability of the process to remove soil deposits in a given system. The detergent will be selected following laboratory trials with the particular type of solid and expected degree of deposition. Solution concentration and temperature affects the rate of reaction between soil and detergent. Solution temperature can be adjusted by steam injection. With CIP the degree of turbulence promoted and the circulation time will influence the scouring effect produced by the flowing liquid stream. It is this scouring effect which replaces the brushing in manual cleaning, so the piping system should be designed to produce high Reynolds numbers (Appendix I) in the circuit. Flow velocities for pipeline sizes commonly encountered should not be less than $1.5\,\mathrm{m\,s^{-1}}$ ($5\,\mathrm{ft\,s^{-1}}$).[12]

The quality of the water supplied to the plant is also important. If the water is bacteriologically acceptable and has been softened (Chapter 18) only detergent need be added, but if the mineral content of the water is high, water conditioners (sequestering agents such as sodium polyphosphates) must be added to prevent precipitation on pipeline and equipment surfaces (Section 17.3.3.5). Sequestering agents, such as ethylenediamine tetraacetic acid (EDTA), gluconic acid and their salts, are heat stable and find use as conditioners in detergent formulations for use at higher temperatures with harder waters. These agents are expensive and in new CIP installations the use of soft water is preferable.

If the soil deposits are not great, the cleaning and sterilising solutions can be mixed and circulated together.

17.3.3.4. Detergents

Detergents are almost invariably used in the wet cleaning of food contact surfaces. The nature of the soil to be removed and the material of construction of the plant surfaces will dictate the type of detergent required. They should be readily soluble in water so as to avoid the possibility of deposition of unwanted solids. The resulting solution must not attack the contact surfaces, corrosion being avoided by correct selection of detergent for the particular material of construction. With stainless steels, the almost automatic first choice for food plant fabrication, risk of corrosion is slight. It must be remembered, however, that stainless steel is not universally inert to chemical corrosion and, in any case, alternative, cheaper materials of construction might well be used (Section 17.2.3). The detergent solution must be able to emulsify or disperse fats and oils, adequately wet the surface of the soil, and penetrate to the soil-contact surface interface thus dislodging the soil. It should also be able to dissolve or disperse the food materials released and have good rinsing properties. A wide variety of detergents are available. They may be classified as:

(i) Detergents composed principally of inorganic alkalis.
(ii) Inorganic and organic acid detergents.
(iii) Detergents composed principally of surface active agents.
(iv) Alkaline polyphosphates, used for their water conditioning capabilities rather than their alkalinity.

Inorganic alkaline detergents. Alkaline detergents have good emulsifying properties and can dissolve food solids such as protein. They include:

(a) *Sodium hydroxide.* Caustic soda solution is a powerful detergent with excellent emulsifying and dispersing properties. It is an effective bactericide and is widely used in mechanical bottle washing. Solutions of caustic soda are strongly corrosive to certain metals, aluminium and zinc being rapidly attacked. Use of the solution involves a safety hazard, and protection of personnel must be considered.

(b) *Sodium metasilicate.* Another useful detergent having good wetting, emulsifying and deflocculating properties, sodium metasilicate, is much less corrosive than caustic soda and actually inhibits corrosion of aluminium and tin. It is often used with a sodium polyphosphate, the mixture being recommended for use where water hardness exceeds $100\,\mathrm{mg\,litre^{-1}}$ $CaCO_3$.

(c) *Sodium orthosilicate and sodium sesquisilicate.* Both are compounds giving highly alkaline solutions which are powerful saponifiers. They attack greases and protein readily. The sesquisilicate is not as corrosive as the orthosilicate but care is necessary when using either of these solutions.

(d) *Trisodium phosphate.* A solution of trisodium phosphate has excellent emulsifying and dispersing properties. It is a water softening agent and, as such, is used in conjunction with other detergents as a water conditioner in general cleaning compounds.

(e) *Sodium carbonate—soda ash.* Soda ash as well as the bicarbonate and sesquicarbonate of sodium have been used both as water softeners and as cleaners but their main use is as buffering agents in a number of cleaning compounds.

Acid detergents. The employment of acid detergents in food plant cleaning has increased in recent years, although they are by no means as commonly used as alkalis. Inhibited inorganic acids such as hydrochloric, nitric and phosphoric acids have been used in the past to remove hardness scale (Chapter 18) and, in dairies, to remove 'milkstone' (inorganic deposits, consisting mainly of calcium phosphate, which build up on hot surfaces during milk processing). Both deposits are relatively insoluble in alkaline solution but are successfully removed by acids. Plant corrosion and operator safety are major considerations when using these inorganic acids. Such acids are now being replaced in these applications by relatively non-corrosive organic acids such as sulphamic, citric, tartaric and gluconic acids. Gluconic and sulphamic acids are widely used in the descaling of heat transfer equipment such as evaporators and pasteurisers. Acid detergents can be safely used in conjunction with iodophors in formulations for detergent-sterilants (Section 17.3.4.2).

Detergents composed of surface active agents. A wide variety of surface active agents are available and they are added to detergent formulations to reduce the surface tension of the resulting solution. They enhance wetting and penetrating properties and many are excellent emulsifying agents and can disperse oils, fats, greases, etc. They are compounds containing both water-soluble (hydrophilic) groups and oil-soluble (hydrophobic) groups (Chapter 5). In the presence of water–oil systems the hydrophilic part dissolves in the water phase and the hydrophobic part in the oil. A firm bond is established between water and oil. In a turbulent water stream the emulsion is carried away from an oil or fat contaminated surface and cleaning achieved. Surfactants stable under both acid and alkaline conditions are available. They are readily soluble in cold water and are non-corrosive. Many surfactants are prone to foam formation in CIP systems and anti-foaming agents are frequently used in conjunction with them in detergent formulations.

Surface active agents of value in detergent solutions for use in food plant cleaning may be classified as (a) anionic or (b) non-ionic.

(a) *Anionic surfactants.* These surfactants are used solely for their detergent properties. Here the active ion in solution is negatively charged. There are many varieties available and they have excellent wetting, dispersing and emulsifying powers. They are especially useful in the removal of fatty acids or inorganic (polar-type) soils. They are non-corrosive but they do have a tendency to generate foam.

Some anionic surfactants exhibit synergistic effects with other compounds, the detergent capability of the mixture being better than that of the individual components. Mixing anionic and cationic surfactants is not recommended since the detergent capabilities of the resulting mixture may be reduced.

(b) *Non-ionic surfactants.* These surfactants are not dissociated in solution, consequently they are virtually unaffected by water hardness. They are powerful wetting and dispersing agents and are used to emulsify colloidal solids, being inert to the electric charge present on the colloid. Some non-ionic surfactants have a pronounced foaming action but low-foaming varieties are available. Some are less soluble at higher temperatures and come out of solution on heating. Under these conditions foaming is less. On cooling the surfactant redissolves and is readily rinsed away.

Two other types of surfactant may be encountered in plant cleaning.

(i) Certain *'cationic'* surfactants, though poor detergents, are excellent bactericides and are used for their sterilising properties (Section 17.3.4.2) in combined detergent–sterilants.

(ii) *'Amphoteric'* surfactants are mild detergents whose usual application is in hand cleansers and hair shampoos.

It must be remembered that cleaning agents used in food processing are potential contaminants of the food so final rinsing of detergents and disinfectants (sterilants) from plant surfaces after cleansing is vital. Studies of rinsing kinetics using the different surfactants show that ease of removal from piping systems, as measured by the residual amounts of surfactant after different rinsing periods, decreases in the order non-ionic, anionic, cationic, with amphoteric surfactants being the most difficult to remove.[16] For an introduction to rinsing kinetics see Loncin and Merson.[17]

17.3.3.5. Water conditioners (Sequestering/chelating agents)

If hard water is used for cleaning purposes not only is the efficiency of cleaning reduced but, in addition, hardness scale is likely to develop on pipeline and equipment surfaces. Since hardness is due to the presence of salts of calcium and magnesium (Chapter 18), additives capable of preventing the precipitation of these ions from solution will prevent loss in detergent capability as well as possible scale formation. Such additives are known as 'water conditioners' and the restraining action as sequestering or chelation.

Sodium polyphosphates are widely used inorganic sequestering agents. The cheapest of these is tetrasodium pyrophosphate. It is reasonably stable in hot, highly alkaline solutions and is often used in mechanical bottle washers and soak tanks. It is not very soluble and is a poor sequestering agent for calcium. Two other polyphosphates, the tri- and (so-called) tetra-polyphosphates of sodium are effective sequestering agents for both calcium and magnesium. They are readily soluble in warm water but lose their efficiencies at higher temperatures. Sodium hexametaphosphate is widely used with water high in calcium but is less effective with 'magnesium hardness'. Like the tri-and tetra-polyphosphates it decomposes to the less effective pyro- and ortho-phosphates at higher temperatures.

Though more expensive than their inorganic counterparts, because of their stability to heat and their high solubilities, organic sequestering/chelating agents are widely used to prevent hardness constituents depositing on plant surfaces. The hardness constituents and other metal ions are bound in a chelate ring structure and are not precipitated. Ethylene diamine tetra-acetic acid (EDTA) and its sodium or potassium salts are among the most important organic sequestering agents. Sodium gluconate and sodium heptonate are both very powerful sequestering agents in the highly alkaline conditions necessary for removal of difficult deposits of proteins.[1,14] Besides their capacity for preventing the precipitation of hardness salts, sequestering/chelating agents are used to soften existing scale when detergent cleaning. The use of these agents in hard surface cleaning is discussed by Jennings.[18]

17.3.4. DISINFECTION (COMMERCIAL STERILISATION)
The methods selected for plant disinfection must be kept under rigid bacteriological control. Either heat or chemical disinfectants are used.

17.3.4.1. Thermal disinfection
Moisture plays a part in the destruction of micro-organisms by thermal treatment, dry heat being less effective than the heat in steam or hot water. Heat can be supplied in the form of hot air but far higher temperatures and/or longer times are necessary to kill micro-organisms using hot air. According to Hayes,[1] moist heat is a favoured disinfecting or sterilising agent because it is non-corrosive, economical, has excellent penetration powers, leaves no residue and is active against the large majority of micro-organisms.

Saturated steam can be conveniently directed through pipe runs and equipment and steam guns are widely used on interior and exterior surfaces of larger plant items (Section 17.3.3.1). Steam should be used with care on plastics. With steam, recommended 'holding' (temperature/time) conditions to eliminate all but bacterial spores is about 85°C for 1 min but considerable preheating periods may be required to achieve these conditions. An extended discussion of steam sterilisation is given by Chalmers.[19]

Hot water is frequently used on processing equipment, such as plate heat exchangers, when destruction of bacterial spores is not required. Common time/temperature holding combinations employed are 85°C for 15 min or 80°C for 20 min and the volume of water used and its flow rate will influence the warm-up time needed.[14]

17.3.4.2. Chemical disinfection

Hayes[1] gives a comprehensive list of properties desired in a chemical disinfectant for use in food plant. Besides the ability to kill micro-organisms the more important include: stability and safety, both during storage and in use, non-corrosive, readily soluble in water, easily rinsible and cost-effective.

Aqueous solutions of many of these disinfectants are very convenient to use with both CIP and dismantling–cleaning systems although some can foam excessively in highly turbulent flow streams and are not recommended for CIP use. They can be used in cold dilute solution thus reducing the possibility of corrosion, which can arise if material of construction and disinfectant are mis-matched, particularly if post-disinfection rinsing techniques are inadequate.[14]

Provided the plant contact surfaces are clean, the lethality of chemical disinfectants to micro-organisms is no less than that of heat treatment. Chemical disinfectants are thought to kill by either oxidation of vital enzymes in the cell structure of the micro-organisms (hypochlorites, iodophors, peracetic acid), or by disruption of cell membrane transport (quaternary ammonium compounds, amphoterics, biguanides).[20]

Until recently the two most popular groups of chemical disinfectants used in the food industry were chlorine compounds and quaternary ammonium compounds. More expensive and lesser used disinfectants were 'iodophors' and 'amphoteric' bactericides. Because of their toxicity, taint and corrosion risk, as well as potential health hazard through chemical contact, in the UK hypochlorites and iodophors are gradually being replaced by peracetic acid in applications where destruction of all micro-organisms is required.[20] Biguanide is another newer disinfectant finding growing use in the food industry. Like peracetic acid it also has low toxicity and is not corrosive towards stainless steels.

Chlorine compounds. An aqueous solution of sodium hypochlorite (NaOCl) is the most commonly used chlorine compound, a fresh commercial solution containing 9–14% available chlorine. The recommended concentration for use in stainless steel plant is 150–250 mg litre^{-1} of available chlorine with a contact time of 15 min. A method more suitable for larger vessels involves spraying contact surfaces with a solution containing 250 mg litre^{-1} available chlorine for 5 min. For maximum wetting, spraying should start at the lowest point and rise up the surfaces. Stainless steel heat exchangers are very prone to attack by hypochlorite solutions and because of the risk of corrosion, metal equipment should not be kept in contact with sterilising solutions containing chlorine for extended periods prior to rinsing.[14] A concentration of 200 mg litre^{-1} available chlorine should not be exceeded in aluminium plant.

Solutions of calcium hypochlorite (Ca(OCl)$_2$), gaseous chlorine and chloramines (Section 18.3.2) are also used in the food industry. Chloramine compounds are less corrosive and more stable than chlorine and hypochlorites.

At the recommended concentrations chlorine exerts a rapid bactericidal action against both Gram-positive and Gram-negative bacteria leaving non-toxic residues (sodium chloride). A disadvantage of chlorine containing disinfectants is their decrease in bactericidal efficiency in the presence of organic matter. For this reason, contact surfaces should be thoroughly cleaned and rinsed free of organic detergent compounds before disinfection.

Quaternary ammonium compounds (QATs). Although more expensive than hypochlorites, the use of these cationic disinfectants is firmly established in applications where foam formation can be tolerated because of other desirable properties.

QATs are ammonium salts having some or all of the hydrogen atoms in the [NH$_4$]$^+$ radical replaced by alkyl or aryl groups, one of these being a long chain (C$_8$–C$_{18}$) group. The inorganic anion is usually chloride or bromide, as for example in 'alkyl trimethyl ammonium bromide' and 'lauryl dimethyl benzyl ammonium chloride'. These disinfectants kill microorganisms by binding tightly to the cell membrane preventing transport of nutrient into, or waste products from, the cell.[20] They are very effective against Gram-positive bacteria and, to a lesser extent, Gram-negative bacteria if a sequestrant is added. The bactericidal efficiency of some QATs is reduced in the presence of organic matter, but others retain their lethality to micro-organisms under these conditions. Since they are cationic, QATs should not be mixed with anionic detergents and contact surfaces should be free of these surfactants before using them.

QATs are available as powders and pastes but their use in aqueous solution is preferred. They are stable to heat, colourless, odourless and, at concentrations suitable for use, have low toxicity and taint risks. QATs have a pronounced foaming tendency which is accentuated when pumping in CIP systems. Antifoaming agents can be added but these are expensive and not necessarily successful. QATs can be corrosive (particularly when the inorganic anion is 'chloride'), and can attack both aluminium and stainless steels.

For a fuller discussion of quaternary ammonium compounds and their use in the food industry see Hayes[1] and Lawrence.[21]

Iodophors. Iodophors are soluble complexes of surface active agents and iodine. The surfactants are usually non-ionic although anionic and cationic varieties may be used. They can be formulated so as to possess detergent as well as bactericidal properties. They are expensive but have found use as detergent–sterilants, particularly in the dairy industry.

In cold acid solution iodophors have a rapid bactericidal action against a wide range of bacteria. They are usually used with phosphoric acid and they are most active in a pH range of 3–5.[1] Iodophors are unaffected by water hardness. They are stable and, though often regarded as non-toxic, strong solutions have to be labelled as corrosive and should be carefully handled. After rinsing, iodophors do not normally impart stains, objectionable odours or tastes. Some plastic materials and rubbers are said to become discoloured after exposure to iodophors due to absorption of iodine.[1] To avoid the possibility of product becoming tainted, long contact times between these materials and solutions of iodophors should be avoided.

Because iodophors are corrosive towards all the metals used in the food industry, including stainless steel, the dairy industry has moved towards the use of peracetic acid in the last few years.[20]

Amphoteric–ampholitic bactericides. Amphoteric surfactants[22] have detergent properties, with some having excellent wetting and penetrating powers while some are moderate bactericides. They are organic materials—usually substituted amino acids or betaines—containing both acidic and basic groups. Depending on solution pH they can exhibit anionic or cationic behaviour and in the latter state show their bactericidal properties. They are non-corrosive, non-toxic and are little influenced by water hardness but, besides being expensive, they are prone to foaming and so considered unsuitable for CIP cleansing.[14]

17.3.5. BACTERIOLOGICAL CONTROL

Cleaning and disinfection methods selected for plant cleansing operations must be kept under rigid bacteriological control. The modes of action, methods for testing the efficiency of disinfectants (sterilants) and food contact surface tests are discussed by Sykes[23] and the evaluation of disinfectants by Hayes.[1]

REFERENCES

1. Hayes, P. R., *Food Microbiology and Hygiene.* Elsevier Applied Science Publishers, London, 1985.
2. 3A Sanitary Standards. Formulated by International Association of Milk, Food and Environmental Sanitarians, United States Public Health Service and The Dairy Industry Committee.
3. Sanitation Standards, Baking Industry Sanitation Standards Committee, New York, USA.
4. Recommendations for Sanitary Design. National Canners Association, Washington, D.C., USA.
5. Milleville, H. P. and Gelber, P., Sanitary design of food processing equipment. *Food Processing,* **25**(10) (1964) 93–114; **26**(4) (1965) 170–7.
6. Joint Technical Committee, FMF/FMA, Hygiene Design of Food Plant. Food Manufacturers' Federation and Food Machinery Association, 1967.
7. Cook, K., An 'emblem' to denote hygienic standards of food plant design. In *Hygienic Design and Operation of Food Plant,* ed. R. Jowitt. Ellis Horwood, Chichester, England, 1980, pp. 25–33.
8. Charlish, V. R. and Warman, K. G., Solving hygiene problems by process design. In *Hygienic Design and Operation of Food Plant,* ed. R. Jowitt. Ellis Horwood, Chichester, England, 1980, pp. 35–51.
9. Hayes, G. D., *Food Engineering Data Handbook.* Longman, 1987.
10. Milledge, J. J. and Jowitt, R., The cleanability of stainless steel used as a food contact surface. *Inst. Food Sci. Technol. (UK) Proc.,* **13**(1) (1980) 57–62.
11. Tice, P., Food contact plastics. In *Design for Hygiene—The Changing Scene in the Food Industry.* Institution of Mechanical Engineers Seminar, May 1987.
12. Timperley, D. A. and Lawson, G. B., Test rigs for evaluation of hygiene in plant design. In *Hygienic Design and Operation of Food Plant,* ed. R. Jowitt. Ellis Horwood, Chichester, England, 1980, pp. 80–108.
13. Romney, T., Designing for hygiene. *Food Sci. Technol. Today,* **2**(4) (December 1988) 268–71.
14. Tamplin, T. C., CIP technology, detergents, and sanitizers. In *Hygienic Design and Operation of Food Plant,* ed. R. Jowitt. Ellis Horwood, Chichester, England, 1980, pp. 183–225.
15. Graham-Rack, B. and Binstead, R., *Hygiene in Food Manufacturing and Handling,* 2nd edn. Food Trade Press, 1973.
16. Plett, A. A., Rinsing kinetics of fluid food equipment. In *Engineering and Food.*

Vol. 2: Processing Applications, ed. B. M. McKenna. Elsevier Applied Science Publishers, London, 1984, pp. 659-68.

17. Loncin, M. and Merson, L. M., *Food Engineering Principles and Selected Applications*. Academic Press, New York, 1979.

18. Jennings, W. G., In *Advances in Food Research. Vol. 14*, ed. C. O. Chichester and E. M. Mrak. Academic Press, New York, 1965.

19. Chalmers, C. H., The value of steam as a sterilizing agent. *J. Soc. Dairy Technol.*, **14**(2) (1961) 72–5.

20. Lane, A., Disinfection in the food industry. In *Food Technology International Europe 1989*, ed. A. Turner. Sterling, London, 1989, pp. 91–6.

21. Lawrence, C. A., Quaternary ammonium surface-active disinfectants. In *Disinfection, Sterilisation and Preservation*, CL 26, ed. C. A. Lawrence and S. S. Block. Lea and Febiger, 1968, pp. 430–52.

22. Kornfeld, F., Ampholytic surfactants. *Food Manufacture*, **41**(8) (1966) 39–46.

23. Sykes, G., *Disinfection and sterilization*. Spon, London, 1965.

CHAPTER 18

WATER SUPPLIES AND WASTE DISPOSAL

18.1. INTRODUCTION

Two requirements often vital to the successful operation of a modern food processing plant are (a) an adequate supply of water of various qualities, and (b) satisfactory facilities for the disposal of waste materials.

Such is the importance of these two facilities, that failure of the water supply, either in quantity or quality, or an inability to discharge waste materials safely and cheaply, can quickly bring the most efficient process line to a standstill. Their availability influences the choice of a factory site and they are factors which must be fully examined during an initial 'site survey'.

18.2. WATER SUPPLIES

18.2.1. WATER QUALITY REQUIREMENTS

The multiplicity of uses for water in the food industry (cleaning, blanching, sterilisation, cooling and steam generation for power, process heating and direct 'in-process' use) calls for enormous quantities of this commodity.

Water used in the food and beverage industries can be classified as:

(i) General purpose water.
(ii) Process water.
(ii) Cooling water.
(iv) Boiler feed water.

(i) General purpose water for cleaning and preparation of food materials, for the washing of plant and ancillary equipment, etc., is used in the greatest quantities. These waters should be clean and wholesome, that is, potable and clear, colourless, free from tastes, odours and toxic ions and bacteriologically acceptable.[1,2]

(ii) The requirement for a process water depends on the process. In addition to being potable, these waters may require softening to remove soluble salts which can influence the texture of certain vegetables, cause unsightly deposits on equipment surfaces, on bottles during washing, etc., and can lead to scale formation in heat exchange equipment.

(iii) The water quality requirement for a cooling water is less stringent. The water may be non-potable if contamination of food materials can be eliminated. Removal of colours, tastes and odours is not so important. A hard cooling water should be softened to prevent scale formation. Since large quantities of cooling water are required, re-use of this water is recommended whenever possible.

(iv) With boiler feed water,[3-5] the removal of 'hardness' to avoid scale formation may be sufficient treatment. With water for higher pressure boilers a reduction in total solids content is advisable if priming (i.e. the carry-over of large quantities of water with steam) is to be avoided.

18.2.2. NATURAL WATERS—SOURCES AND QUALITY

The source of all water for factory use, excluding those plants using sea water for such specialised applications as cooling and fish freezing, is meteoric water—water precipitated as rain, snow or hail over the land masses of the earth.

The nature of the water collected depends on the atmosphere through which it descends and on the terrain on which it falls. Falling rain water is relatively pure. It contains little dissolved and suspended solids and very little bacterial flora. However, the quality of the water reaching the factory 'intake' or the municipal water plant is very variable. Chemical substances which the water contacts are both dissolved and retained in suspension, organic matter is leached from decaying vegetation and a variety of micro-organisms find such an environment congenial for growth. Whatever the source, natural waters will contain impurities. These impurities will vary in different supplies.

Natural water supplies may be classified as either (a) surface or (b) ground waters.

(a) *Surface waters.* These come from rain falling on open uplands and moorlands. The rain subsequently drains into lakes and man-made reservoirs.

(b) *Ground waters.* These originate from wells or springs and consist of rain water which has percolated into the ground to become trapped in underground pockets.

Surface waters are open to direct contamination with human and animal refuse and industrial wastes. They may contain mineral matter, organic matter and micro-organisms, be turbid, highly coloured and possess unpleasant odours and tastes. These waters require treatment before use. Ground waters possess lower turbidities and bacterial contents but may have high soluble solids contents.

Increased use of deep-well disposal of toxic liquid wastes has given rise to concern for the quality of some ground waters. Contamination risks from this source must be guarded against. With surface waters the composition may vary frequently, changing, for example, after sudden rainfall. With deep wells and large lakes the composition may remain relatively constant over many years. Any likely variation in composition must be considered when drawing up a water treatment flowsheet for a particular process.

18.2.3. CHOICE OF SUPPLY: MUNICIPAL SUPPLY OR FACTORY TREATMENT?

Many factories purchase their water supplies direct from the municipal authorities, the price per unit of volume usually falling with increasing requirement. In general, these municipal supplies will have been screened, clarified, filtered and sterilised, to produce a potable water.

For use in the food industry further treatment may be necessary. The treatment necessary for the production of a water of satisfactory quality for a particular consumer depends on the use for which the water is required. Where large quantities are needed, it is often advantageous for the user to purchase raw, untreated water and purify it to his own specific requirements.

18.3. WATER PURIFICATION—TYPES OF IMPURITIES AND METHODS FOR REMOVAL

The major impurities requiring removal are:

(1) Suspended matter, (2) micro-organisms, (3) organic matter—colours, tastes and odours, (4) dissolved mineral matter, (5) iron and manganese, (6) dissolved gases.

18.3.1. REMOVAL OF SUSPENDED MATTER

Water containing suspended matter is undesirable for most uses. Suspended impurities are of variable character, silt, clay, silica, finely divided vegetable and animal matter all being common.

The size range of the solids may be wide. After preliminary screening (if it is necessary to remove larger floating debris, etc.) coarse solids settle out rapidly on standing. Fine particles, particularly colloidal particles, may remain in suspension imparting turbidity/colour to the waters. Underground water supplies are likely to be free of turbidity, except after periods of heavy rain, owing to the filtration undergone as water percolates through permeable strata.

The method selected for removing suspended matter depends on the volume of water to be treated and on the size and nature of the suspension. Screening (straining), settling, coagulation/flocculation and filtration may all be used, depending on the initial quality of the water.

18.3.1.1. Screening

If raw water contains suspended particles greater than 1 mm size, then preliminary screening may be necessary. If larger size material, floating debris, vegetation, etc., as well as silt, is present then several screens of differing types and screen aperture sizes (Section 4.7) may be required.

Coarse screens are often fixed bar screens having a screen surface consisting of vertical metal bars about 25 mm thick and spaced at 25–100 mm intervals depending on the particular application. For larger capacity water treatment plants these screens are often fitted with automatic cleaning devices. If very little larger size suspended material is present in a surface water then the water may flow directly to an intermediate screen or, in the case of a ground water, even to a fine screen.

Intermediate screens are often travelling band screens. This type of screen has an aperture size of 5–10 mm, the screen surface being a vertical, continuously moving band or belt through which the water stream flows. These screens easily clog and are normally fitted with water-cleaning jets which wash away any debris likely to 'blind' the screen to discharge troughs.

Fine screens are frequently rotary drum screens (Section 4.7.2.3). The screen surface is often woven stainless steel fabric (particularly with smaller screen aperture sizes). The screen surface is easily blinded so again water jets are incorporated to automatically wash away collected debris. The screen aperture selected depends on the size of the particulate material to be removed from the water and falls in the range 20–5000 μm.[6] Drum screens for removing particulate material at the lower end of this size range are known in the water treatment industry as 'micro-strainers'.

18.3.1.2. Sedimentation (settling)

This is for removal of smaller size particulate matter which passes the screens.

If, after screening, the water contains very little suspended solids water may pass straight to filtration units.

More frequently the water contains appreciable amounts of finer suspended matter which would rapidly block the filters. In this case sedimentation is used to remove finer particles. Often the particles may be very small and their settling velocity extremely low. The terminal velocity of a particle settling under the influence of gravity acceleration, g, is given by the Stoke's Law equation

$$u_t = \frac{d^2 g(\rho_s - \rho)}{18\mu} \qquad (18.1)$$

It can be seen that if d, the particle diameter, is small then u_t, the terminal velocity, is small for a particle of density, ρ_s, settling in a liquid of density, ρ, and viscosity, μ. The smaller the terminal velocity the longer it takes the particle to settle.

In circular, up-flow sedimentation basins, which are in wide use, the objective is to produce a clarified overflow, all the suspended solid going to the underflow stream. The 'surface overflow rate', Q, is given by

$$Q = uA \qquad (18.2)$$

where A is the area for flow upwards and u is the upward velocity of liquid in the basin. If this upward velocity is just less than the settling (terminal) velocity of the smallest particles present, then these particles will settle against the upward flow of liquid. If the smallest particles settle then obviously larger particles will settle. Under these conditions, A becomes the minimum area for complete clarification to occur and represents the required area of the sedimentation basin for the surface overflow rate, Q. Similar principles apply to rectangular horizontal flow basins. A more detailed account of settlement is given by Barnes and Wilson.[7]

In real situations complete clarification is not achieved. The smaller the particles the longer the residence time in the settler would need to be for complete separation (with high value products centrifugal separators can be used to reduce the processing time but in water and waste water treatment this approach is not economically viable). Particles smaller than

1 μm are unlikely to settle due to Brownian motion, convection currents, etc. Colloidal particles, which often impart colour to natural waters, come into this small size range (0·001–1·0 μm) and these and other small particles that cause turbidity in water need special treatment before sedimentation.

18.3.1.3. Coagulation and flocculation

A combination of coagulation and flocculation[7,8] is used to agglomerate smaller particles. The size of the agglomerates are larger thus increasing the terminal velocity so as to permit settling in a reasonable time.

Small particles suspended in water (and waste-water in food processing) usually carry negative electrostatic charges. Like charges repel so the particles repel each other. The repulsive forces are greater than those of attraction so the suspension is stable and there is no tendency for particles to agglomerate.

In coagulation, the surface of the particles *and* the chemical environment are modified by the addition of chemicals called 'coagulating agents'. To overcome the repulsion between the charged particles they are neutralised by the addition of ions of opposite charge.

According to the Schultze–Hardy Rules, the effect of monovalent < divalent < trivalent ions.

Widely used coagulating agents in water treatment are salts of aluminium, Al^{3+}, and iron, Fe^{3+}. Aluminium sulphate, sodium aluminate and ferrous sulphate are often used.

A solution of coagulating agent is metered into a zone of intense mixing in a flocculating tank (Fig. 18.1). Here it contacts partially treated water from the screens, or even raw water if the initial content of suspended solids is low and sufficiently small in size (storage in reservoirs and ponds before treatment will often allow sufficient residence time for the removal of much of the larger-sized, suspended matter by gravity sedimentation). After the coagulation stage, gentle mixing brings about flocculation—the growth of coarse, large flocs that are easy to separate in sedimentation vessels.

More recent studies in coagulation and flocculation shows that other mechanisms besides electrostatic repulsion may play a part in the agglomeration and separation of smaller particles, e.g. enmeshing in a precipitate

$$Al_2(SO_4)_3 + 3Ca(OH)_2 = 2Al(OH)_3 \downarrow + 3CaSO_4$$

The gelatinous precipitate of aluminium hydroxide traps the fine colloidal particles and the whole mass settles to the bottom of the vessel, carrying with it suspended matter, micro-organisms, etc. The water then rises

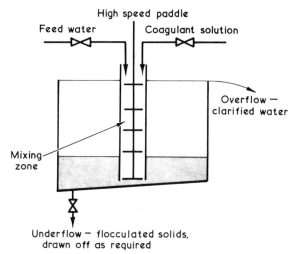

FIG. 18.1. Flocculating tank.

through a 'sludge blanket' of previously deposited floc. The upward velocity of the water is too low to permit carry-over and a reasonably clear water is produced.

Iron salts work in a similar manner. These salts are cheaper than aluminium salts and produce stronger flocs. However, iron salts can create problems—they impart colour to the water, are corrosive and can catalyse undesirable biochemical reactions.

Polyelectrolytes are often used in combination with inorganic agents as 'coagulant aids' but are now important in their own right as coagulants.[8] They are more expensive than inorganic salts but much smaller dosages are required to effect separation and less volume of sludge is produced. Some cationic polyelectrolytes behave like inorganic salts, i.e. similar to Al^{3+} and Fe^{3+}. Others, even though monovalent, are more effective than Al^{3+} and Fe^{3+} in bringing about coagulation and flocculation. This means that yet other mechanisms play a part in destabilisation and floc formation. One such mechanism is polymer-bridging.

After coagulation/flocculation the agglomerates of small particles behave as single, larger particles. These settle rapidly and are removed as a sludge 'underflow' after a relatively short residence time in a correctly designed sedimentation basin/tank. Using a suitable coagulant together with a coagulant aid such as activated silica, colour, turbidity, suspended matter and appreciable quantities of micro-organisms are removed. In sedimentation practice the overflow is never completely clarified and the product water leaving the sedimentation basins passes to filters for final 'polishing'. In water treatment roughly 90% of suspended matter passing the screens should be removed by sedimentation and 10% by filtration.

18.3.1.4. Filtration

Three types of filter are usually used in the filtration of large capacity potable water supplies.[6,9] All three use beds of sand, supported on layers of graded gravel, as the filter medium. These are

(i)   Slow (low rate) sand filter.
(ii) High rate sand filter.
(iii) Pressure sand filter.

(i) *Slow sand filter.* This was pioneered in the UK in 1804 and its application has subsequently spread to many countries. It still finds wide use although fewer new installations are reported since high rate sand filters became popular (see below).

Low rate sand filters consist of a rectangular basin containing up to a 1 m thick bed of silica sand (0·2–0·4 mm diameter) deposited over a layer of graded gravel. The sand bed is submerged beneath a water layer, maintained at a depth of 1–2 m. Water percolates through the sand bed under the influence of gravity, the head of water acting as the driving force.

During a 1–6 month operating period a zoogloeal slime ('Schmützdecke') 2–3 cm thick develops on the top of the sand bed. As well as filtering out suspended particles, a high concentration of micro-organisms, which develop in the bacterial slime, oxidise organic matter, nitrogen compounds, colouring matter and effectively remove 98–99% of bacteria present in the water. A high quality water is produced. Before the advent of terminal disinfection, this 'hidden' biological action protected users of the water from the ravages of cholera that decimated adjacent populations using water from the same source not treated in slow sand filters (N.B. in modern water treatment practice, water from slow sand filters with a 'schmütz-decke' is always terminally disinfected).

Since the voidage of the bed is small, the rate of filtration through these units is low so a large area of land is required. This is expensive in urban areas. In addition, more than one filter will be required since when the flowrate of water becomes sufficiently low (due to increased resistance to flow as void spaces in the bed become blocked with debris), shutdown and cleaning is necessary. Removal and replacement of the upper layers of sand is laborious, labour-intensive and hence costly, though newer units can have automatic cleaning systems installed. Because of the high capital and operating costs of slow sand filters and the inception of terminal disinfection, high rate filtration has largely superseded slow sand filtration.

(ii) *High rate sand filter.* This uses coarser silica sand (0·4–1·2 mm diameter, i.e. large compared to the slow sand filter) and thinner sand beds (0·4–0·7 m).

Since the resistance to flow through the bed is much less, the rate of filtration of water is considerably greater. However, *no 'schmützedecke' (zoogloeal film) forms* so there is *no microbial oxidation*. Removal of bacteria and other micro-organisms is less than 80% so any protection against waterborne infection is much reduced. For this reason high rate sand filtration *must* be followed by 'terminal disinfection' (Section 18.3.2).

High rate sand filters are easy to clean. The sand is fluidised with a back-flow of treated water and air and the trapped particulate material is rapidly swept away. Cleaning time required is measured in minutes rather than days.

High rate filters are frequently used as pre-filters before slow sand filters—this reduces the load of particulate material on the slow sand filter hence its operating life is increased and cleaning down time reduced.

High rate units are also used immediately after coagulation–flocculation

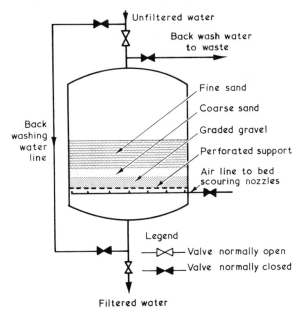

Fig. 18.2. Pressure sand filter.

in some water treatment plants. The flocs formed collect on the sand bed and there is evidence that higher rates of flow are obtained, possibly due to increase in bed voidage.

(iii) *Pressure sand filter.* These high rate sand filters are smaller capacity package units, frequently used in on-site water treatment plants in food factories (Fig. 18.2). Water, under pump pressure, is forced downwards through the sand bed. It is customary to have duplex units, one filtering and one off-stream for cleaning. Again cleaning, by back-washing/air-scouring, is rapid.

18.3.2. REMOVAL OF MICRO-ORGANISMS

Micro-organisms are commonly encountered in surface waters. Their content in waters from deep wells is usually low. Commonly occurring micro-organisms in surface waters[10] include diatoms, fungi, algae, protozoa, rotifera and nematodes together with a variety of non-pathogenic bacteria. Should the supply be contaminated by sewage, pathogenic bacteria may also be present.

If introduced into food processing plant, living micro-organisms and their decomposition products may give rise to off-colours, tastes and odours in food equipment and foodstuffs, while pathogenic bacteria not only cause spoilage of the product but also food poisoning.[11] To minimise such introduction, process waters must be free from micro-organisms.

The final stage in the production of potable (general purpose) water is to render the water bacteriologically safe by means of terminal disinfection.

A number of enteric diseases of man are transmitted by fecal wastes. Transmission can be by direct contact with infected persons, via insect vectors (e.g. flies) or through contaminated food and water. Water-borne pathogenic diseases are most likely in areas where sanitary practices are poor and the disposal of sewage is inadequate.

Testing a water for pathogenic organisms is very uncertain and since these, if present, are invariably associated with non-pathogenic organisms, such as coliform bacteria, the latter are used as indicator organisms. Drinking water standards generally consider a water to be bacteriologically acceptable provided that testing in a specified manner shows one coliform organism or less per 100 ml.[12]

Several methods are available for terminal disinfection. They involve the use of:

(1) Thermal energy.
(2) Radiation methods—e.g. ultra-violet (UV), though little used in the UK until relatively recently, is finding some application in small

scale treatment plants, and Thames Water Authority has installed a totally automatic UV plant with a capacity of 12 million gallons per day ($54\,552\,m^3\,day^{-1}$).

(3) Ultrasonic treatment—cell disruption.

(4) Chemical disinfection.

Chemical methods are normally used for the large scale terminal disinfection of water supplies. With improvements in equipment for the production of ozone, interest in the use of this material for the sterilisation of potable water has been growing in recent years.[13] In France, over 500 installations are employing ozone and its use is spreading to other countries. The advantages claimed for ozone include: superior bactericidal action; elimination of tastes, especially those from phenolic wastes and from algal contamination; and avoidance of residuals other than a high dissolved oxygen content.[6]

The usual method of sterilising water supplies is by treatment with chlorine or chlorine derivatives.[14,15] Liquid chlorine is employed for large-scale treatment; for smaller capacities chlorine dioxide, chloride of lime (bleaching powder, containing about 33% w/w Cl_2) and hypochlorites are used. Sodium hypochlorite ($NaOCl$) and calcium hypochlorite $Ca(OCl)_2$ are used in about 1% solution.

The effectiveness of disinfection depends on chlorine concentration, contact time, temperature, pH, and on the amount of organic matter present.

Chlorine reacts with organic nitrogenous matter in the water. The amount of chlorine required for complete reaction is called the 'chlorine demand'. To ensure complete destruction of all bacteria, 'residual chlorine' must remain in the water after a specified contact time. This contact time increases with water pH and decreases with temperature.

The reaction between chlorine and water is reversible:

$$Cl_2 + H_2O \rightleftharpoons HOCl + HCl$$

The hypochlorous acid reacts with nitrogenous matter to give chloramines

$$HOCl + NH_3 \rightarrow NH_2Cl + H_2O$$
$$2HOCl + NH_3 \rightarrow NHCl_2 + 2H_2O$$

Although less powerful bactericides than chlorine, chloramines are more stable and give a degree of protection after treatment, not afforded by chlorine alone. Holden[16] discusses an ammonia-chlorine treatment which takes advantage of this extra protection.

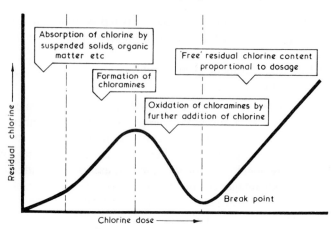

FIG. 18.3. Break point curve.

When dosing with chlorine, the 'residual chlorine' initially rises with chlorine dose. This occurs while chlorine is absorbed by organic matter and chloramines are formed. Further addition of chlorine causes oxidation of the chloramines and the residual chlorine content again starts to increase when oxidation of chloramines is complete. The position of minimum residual chlorine is known as the 'break point' (Fig. 18.3). After the break point the free residual chlorine content becomes proportional to dosage. In the 'break point' method of chlorination the aim is to achieve a small residual of free chlorine sufficient to destroy micro-organisms present in the water without imparting a chlorine taste or odour. Chlorine dosage and contact time must be adequate to ensure sterilisation and must be confirmed by bacteriological examination of the treated waters. In another chlorination method, particularly suited to 'on-site' treatment, a much greater dose of chlorine is added to the water. At these higher concentrations bacteria are rapidly destroyed and contact times are short. Since the residual chlorine content is considerably higher than that desired, this technique is called 'superchlorination'. Knowing the final chlorine content acceptable for the particular application, the excess is removed by dechlorination. This is brought about by contact with suitable chemical agents. Sulphur dioxide is commonly used: alternatively the water can be passed through a bed of activated carbon which absorbs excess chlorine.[16]

18.3.3. REMOVAL OF ORGANIC MATTER, COLOUR, TASTES AND ODOURS

Surface waters usually contain organic material leached from decaying vegetable matter with which it has been in contact. These waters can be both turbid and highly coloured, especially in swampy areas. Peat bogs often give rise to colour in ground waters.

Evidence suggests that a large part of the colouring in water is due to the presence of a colloidal suspension of ultramicroscopic particles, as well as to dissolved impurities in 'true' solution. Colour of natural waters can also be influenced by the presence of iron and manganese (Section 18.3.4).

Tastes and odours are normally confined to surface waters, although some deep well waters contain hydrogen sulphide and may carry a 'metallic' taste due to the presence of iron.

Practically all odours in natural water supplies are associated with the organic matter present. Death and decay of algal growths and other micro-organisms can give rise to undesirable odours and unsightly appearance. Chlorophenols, produced when water contaminated with traces of tar, phenols, etc., is chlorinated, can impart disagreeable tastes to water.

The use of ozone avoids these taste problems but the removal of organic compounds, often only present in trace amounts, e.g. organic pesticides, is an important step in the production of a potable water.

In general, organic matter, colours, tastes and odours are unacceptable in a water to be used for food and beverage products. Several methods are available for their removal from water supplies. A combination of coagulation, settling and filtration is generally employed. With highly coloured waters the use of coagulant aids such as activated silica is recommended. Break-point chlorination has been used with success in the removal of certain colours but only experiment will determine its utility in any particular case. Aeration and super-chlorination are also employed.

The removal of colour, taste and odour producing substances from water by adsorption with activated carbon is, in general, the most efficient method available. Normally a slurry of powdered activated carbon is added to the water in a mixing vessel, the contaminated carbon then being removed by sand filtration. Alternatively filtration through granular beds of activated carbon is used.[6]

18.3.4. REMOVAL OF DISSOLVED MINERAL MATTER

All natural waters contain dissolved mineral matter, sulphates, chlorides and bicarbonates of sodium, magnesium and calcium being common. Other constituents include iron, manganese, silica and nitrates. For water treatment purposes it is convenient to examine the effects of these soluble impurities under three separate headings:

(i)   Alkalinity.
(ii) Hardness.
(iii) Iron and manganese.

18.3.4.1. Alkalinity

Almost all waters contain alkalinity due to the presence of the soluble bicarbonates of calcium, magnesium, sodium and potassium. In some waters soluble carbonates and hydroxides also give rise to 'alkalinity' which can be regarded as the capacity of a water to receive acid without substantially lowering the pH. Alkalinity is determined by titration with a standard acid solution using phenolphthalein and methyl orange as indicators. The titration enables 'bicarbonate alkalinity', 'carbonate alkalinity' and 'caustic alkalinity' to be determined.[6,17] Low alkalinity waters are required for certain mineral waters and beers. Boiler feed water should also have a low alkalinity if 'caustic embrittlement' (a form of 'crack corrosion') caused by caustic soda is to be avoided. Caustic soda is formed by the decomposition of sodium bicarbonate deposited in steam boilers using high alkalinity feed waters. Hydrogen zeolite treatment will remove 'alkalinity' when necessary (see below).

18.3.4.2. Hardness

Effects of hard water. Soluble calcium and magnesium salts dissolved in water give rise to 'hardness'. A water may contain 'temporary hardness' (carbonate hardness) due to the presence of calcium and magnesium bicarbonates, or 'permanent hardness' (non-carbonate hardness), due to sulphates, chlorides and nitrates of these elements.

The use of a hard water can lead to difficulties in food processing. Calcium and magnesium salts in process water produce a marked toughening of the skin of certain vegetables during blanching and canning. Washing operations using soap or other alkaline detergents are more difficult with hard water and softening leads to appreciable savings in detergent. A tough scale of calcium carbonate and sulphate is deposited on the walls of heat exchange equipment—pasteurisers, water heaters, steam boilers, etc.—when the water supply is hard. Besides reducing the flow capacity of equipment, these deposits inhibit heat transfer and, in boilers, can result in the failure of boiler tubes through overheating.[18]

Water softening. Of water softening processes commonly encountered, viz. (a) precipitation, (b) base exchange, and (c) demineralisation, the first two, either in combination or individually, provide the soft water requirements for most of the food industry.

(a) *Precipitation process.*[6] Hydrated lime $Ca(OH)_2$ and sodium carbonate (Na_2CO_3) are added in metered quantities to the hard water. The lime removes temporary hardness precipitating the hardness salts as their insoluble carbonates:

$$Ca(HCO_3)_2 + Ca(OH)_2 = 2CaCO_3 + 2H_2O$$
$$Mg(HCO_3)_2 + Ca(OH)_2 = MgCO_3 + CaCO_3 + 2H_2O$$

Similarly soda ash removes permanent hardness:

e.g.

$$CaSO_4 + Na_2CO_3 = CaCO_3 + Na_2SO_4$$

So bicarbonates, chlorides, sulphates and nitrates of calcium and magnesium are removed.

A coagulant is usually added to flocculate the finely divided precipitate which is then separated by filtration if completely clear water is required. The cold lime-soda process reduces hardness of a water to about $70 \, mg \, litre^{-1}$ ($1.0 \, mg \, litre^{-1}$ as $CaCO_3 \equiv 0.07$ grains per Imperial gallon).

For complete removal of hardness, the precipitation can be followed by a 'base exchange' or 'zeolite' process.

(b) *Zeolite process* (*base exchange*). Zeolites are complex silicates. Natural zeolites can exchange sodium ions for ions of calcium, magnesium, iron and manganese in solution

e.g.

$$Ca(HCO_3)_2 + Na_2Z = 2NaHCO_3 + CaZ$$

Water to be softened is passed downwards, under gravity or pressure, through a bed of granulated zeolite. The cation exchanging properties of the zeolite remove the hardness. Exhausted zeolite is regenerated by backwashing with clean water followed by sodium chloride solution (salting). This removes the Ca and Mg as soluble chlorides leaving the bed in its original condition:

e.g.

$$CaZ + 2NaCl = Na_2Z + CaCl_2$$
$$\text{or} \qquad\qquad\qquad \text{or}$$
$$MgZ \qquad\qquad\qquad MgCl_2$$

Zeolite softeners produce water of zero hardness. Hydrogen cation exchanging, synthetic zeolites have been developed. Ca, Mg and Na ions in water are removed, an equivalent amount of hydrogen being given up as

carbonic acid, sulphuric acid or hydrochloric acid
e.g.

$$CaSO_4 + H_2Z = CaZ + H_2SO_4$$

or   or

$$MgSO_4 \qquad MgZ$$

Hydrogen zeolites are regenerated by treatment with mineral acid, so acid resistant materials of construction are required.

Zeolite exchangers are best operated as 'duplex' units, one section being 'on-stream' while the 'off-stream' section is undergoing regeneration.

(c) *Demineralisation*. Zeolite exchangers are packed columns for bringing about 'ion exchange'—a process capable of absorbing, into an insoluble solid ion exchange medium, a particular kind of ion contained in water and replacing it by an equivalent amount of another ion of the same charge. Replacing calcium and magnesium ions with sodium ions, in water softening, is the oldest application of ion exchange.

Natural or synthetic zeolites were the first ion exchange materials to be used commercially in water treatment and have increasingly replaced the lime-soda precipitation process, particularly in small-scale water softening.

Although aluminosilicates still find use for the removal of total hardness, organic ion exchange materials—polystyrene-based resins, acrylic polymers, macroporous resins (capable of removing organic compounds from water while resisting fouling), for example, and carrying active groups in their polymeric structures—are very widely used for removing dissolved mineral substances and organic matter. These resins have led to cationic, anionic and mixed bed ion exchangers capable of producing demineralised waters of a variety of qualities for specific process purposes, including those where extremely high water purity is required.

Ion exchangers are widely used in the food industry for upgrading general purpose water to process water (Section 18.2.6). It must be remembered that ion exchange resins, particularly when offstream, are subject to microbial contamination. As for other food plant and equipment, facilities for cleaning and disinfection must be incorporated into ion exchange systems producing process water in food plants. A concise account of ion exchange in water treatment is given by Lorch.[19]

18.3.4.3. Iron and manganese

Iron and manganese are found in many water supplies, commonly as bicarbonates. Iron may also be present as a consequence of dissolved oxygen corrosion.

Waters containing organic matter in addition to these metals can give rise to 'iron-bacteria' or 'manganese-bacteria'.[16] The development of iron-bacteria can lead to the deposition of slimes and hard scales on the insides of pipes and vessels. These bacterial growths can rapidly clog pipe lines and fittings, besides producing unpleasant odours.

Staining and discoloration of equipment is also encountered with waters containing these metals.

Aeration, followed by settling and filtration, is a common treatment when iron is present as soluble bicarbonate. The bicarbonate is oxidised to insoluble, higher oxides. Sodium hexametaphosphate may be added as a sequestering agent. Manganese is not oxidised by aeration but insoluble oxides are produced by treatment with chlorine, the insoluble solids being removed by filtration.

Ion exchange is sometimes used to remove iron and manganese from water if the concentrations of these components are low. Some resins can effectively remove both substances in the absence of dissolved oxygen but at concentrations greater than 0.1 mg litre^{-1}, both iron and manganese cause fouling of the resins with consequent decrease in exchange capacity.

In 'manganese–zeolite' treatment, natural 'greensand' coated with manganese dioxide is used to remove trace amounts of iron and manganese. Potassium permanganate solution is used to oxidise iron and manganese bicarbonates in solution, the insoluble oxides being filtered out of the water by a layer of anthracite. Any remaining iron or manganese is then removed by passage through the manganese–zeolite exchange medium which follows the anthracite filter.

18.3:5. REMOVAL OF DISSOLVED GASES

Natural water supplies may contain carbon dioxide, oxygen, nitrogen and hydrogen sulphide, in solution. Most of the carbon dioxide arises from the decay of organic matter. Oxygen and nitrogen come from aeration of the water, although oxygen may also be produced by photosynthesis. The proportion of carbon dioxide and oxygen present depends on algae content, sunlight, water depth, etc., during storage.

The presence of dissolved gases in process water can lead to a variety of difficulties. Incondensable gases, introduced into steam-raising plant and process-heating equipment using steam via boiler feed water, form troublesome films which act as resistances to heat transfer during the condensation of vapours.[18] Free carbon dioxide dissolved in water reacts with iron, a common material of construction, leading to corrosion and iron pick-up. Oxygen, dissolved in water, vigorously attacks iron, galvanised iron, steel and brass, all commonly used in water systems. Oxygen attack is accelerated by increase in temperature and also by the presence of carbon dioxide. Hydrogen sulphide, found in sulphur waters, gives a corrosive solution which rapidly attacks iron pipes. The ferrous sulphide formed is either deposited on the pipe walls, or is carried away in the water stream as a fine, black suspension. Sulphur bacteria may develop in waters containing hydrogen sulphide. *Beggiatoa*, for example, produces thread-like, clogging growths on surfaces in contact with these waters.[16]

Carbon dioxide and dissolved air can be removed by boiling the water and venting off these non-condensable gases. Boiler feed-water is often deaerated in this way.[19] Chemical dosing for removal of oxygen and prevention of dissolved oxygen corrosion is also used, both sodium sulphite and hydrazine solutions being employed as oxygen scavengers. A mixture of sodium silicate and caustic soda solutions is also used to inhibit oxygen corrosion in water systems. For treatment of waters containing small quantities of hydrogen sulphide, chlorination is of value. With higher proportions of the gas, forced draught aeration followed by chlorination is used. With high concentrations, degassing, using carbon dioxide stripping, has been successfully applied.

The method selected for the on-site treatment of waters for use in food processing depends on the quality of the raw water supply and on the quality of the water required. This latter requirement varies with the process. In general, a combination of coagulation, settling, filtration, softening, chlorination and degassing will be required.

In both the selection and maintenance of satisfactory water supplies and waste-water disposal facilities in the food factory, a knowledge of certain important chemical and physical properties of the water is required. Commonly required are: alkalinity; hardness; nitrogen content in various forms; dissolved oxygen; biochemical oxygen demand (BOD); chemical oxygen demand (COD); total solids; suspended solids; and settleable solids. Another frequent requirement is the concentrations of a number of metallic and other ions. Details of laboratory procedures for the analysis of water and waste samples are given in Standard Methods for the Examination of Water and Wastewater.[20]

18.4. WASTE DISPOSAL

18.4.1. INTRODUCTION

Every food processing plant takes in raw materials which are converted to finished products. Besides finished products, waste materials are produced.

Typical wastes, indicating the variety encountered, include: foreign matter, peelings and contaminated water from fruit and vegetable preparation plants; blood, fats and greases from meat and poultry processing; waters contaminated with milk products from the dairy industry; detergent solutions from plant sanitary operations and waste wash water and human sewage from facilities used by plant operatives.

In earlier times many food processors used to lose their wastes down some convenient hole in the ground or in some near-by stream. This cheap but short-sighted solution is no longer possible. With the increasing pollution problems created by our expanding technological society, the disposal of industrial wastes (effluents) becomes a vital economic factor in the efficient operation of any plant.

With liquid wastes, the disposal of untreated effluent to a municipal sewage plant may be possible in urban areas. Much depends on the nature, strength and volume flow rate of the effluent. For municipal disposal a relatively constant strength effluent at a steady flow rate is preferred and the installation of storage balance tanks at the factory site may be all that is necessary.

In country areas municipal disposal facilities may not be available, and in towns the nature of the effluent may be such that the local authority insists on some form of pretreatment before discharge to their sewers. In these circumstances on-site treatment facilities must be provided. In general, municipal sewage treatment is cheaper than factory treatment and is the method recommended whenever possible.[21]

18.4.2. FACTORY TREATMENT

A complete survey of factory operations, including the determination of material balances over individual plants within the site, is an essential prerequisite to the installation of a waste treatment plant. A full knowledge of the various material streams in each part of the factory may show up unexpected losses of finished product, excessive usages of water and contamination of other wastes capable of re-use within the factory. The survey may indicate a need for better control of water in the plants, for the recirculation of 'once-through' water, the re-use of non-potable water streams as cooling media, or the desirability of separating heavily contaminated waters from those capable of re-use. The separation of concentrated and dilute effluent streams is particularly important if the wastes contain materials capable of being profitably recovered. In this case it is important to prevent over-dilution of the effluent since the profitability of a recovery process decreases with increasing initial dilution. An overall survey of factory material flow streams may lead substantial savings on plant operating costs, as well as to a much reduced effluent load and consequent cheaper waste treatment facilities.[22,23]

Some processors give little consideration to their effluent until faced with a pollution problem demanding action. Under these circumstances the first requirement is to stop the offending pollution.

Ideally, the requirements for waste treatment should be fully considered while the factory is at the design stage. The treatment plant then becomes an integral part of the overall factory design embracing:

(i)   Avoidance of waste as far as possible.

(ii) Maximum utilisation of waste products.

(iii) Prevention of pollution at the effluent loading expected under maximum production conditions.

Food processing wastes are generally stronger than domestic sewage. They contain a large proportion of organic matter and have high 'biochemical oxygen demand'. The 'biochemical oxygen demand' (BOD) is a measure of the quantity of oxygen required for the oxidation of organic matter in water by micro-organisms present, in a given time interval at a specified temperature. The time is usually 5 days, the temperature $18\cdot3°C$ ($65°F$) in Britain and $20°C$ ($68°F$) in the US.

Food wastes having high BOD values, when discharged to rivers and streams, give rise to pollution. The high organic content can lead to rapid putrefaction and odour problems, the growth of pathogenic organisms and a diminution in the oxygen content in the water, resulting in damage to aquatic flora and fauna. Pollution can render water unfit for human, animal or industrial use. Waste materials must be pretreated before discharge so that organic material undergoes decomposition to a more stable form harmless to subsequent users of the water. The important quantities determining the strength of a food waste are the BOD and the suspended solids content. These values are normally quoted in parts per 100 000, or in milligrams per litre (parts per million) of the sample. Since the BOD test is time-consuming, another commonly used test for the polluting nature of specific contaminants is the Chemical Oxygen Demand or COD test. Details of the various tests used in waste treatment and pollution control may be found in Standard Methods for the Examination of Water and Wastewater.[20]

18.4.3. WASTE TREATMENT PROCESSES

Food wastes may be subjected to:

(i)   Physical treatment.

(ii)   Chemical treatment.
(iii) Biological treatment.

Examination of a few typical values for the polluting strengths of some food wastes:

Waste	BOD_5 (mg litre^{-1})
Fruit and vegetable preparation	500–2 500
Cannery—baked beans	2 000
peas	4 000
Milk washings	75–1 500
Meat processing	200–3 000

shows them to be considerably stronger than domestic sewage ($BOD_5 = 200$–400 mg litre^{-1}), with which they are often compared. So food waste liquors are likely to require all three treatment stages. Physical and chemical treatments, whether singly or in some combination of the two, are often called 'primary treatments'. Biological treatment is then known as 'secondary treatment'. The BOD of a typical food waste stream is a consequence of (a) suspended solids, and (b) dissolved solids. The removal of suspended solids by physical and/or chemical means considerably reduces the BOD before the biological treatment stage. Material separated by primary treatment may be a possible source of valuable recovery products.[24]

18.4.3.1. Physical treatment

This preliminary treatment affords a separation of suspended solids and other high BOD materials (fats, greases, oils, etc.) from the bulk of the aqueous effluent. The size range of solids is wide and several separation methods are used. A common method involves the separation of coarse material, using screens. Stationary bar screens, vibrating screens and rotary drum screens are all used. Screen apertures range from 25 mm down to micrometre sizes, depending on the application. Since these screens are prone to 'blinding', facilities for 'in-place cleaning', such as mechanical rakes or wash water jets, should be incorporated. Preliminary screening can be followed by passage through a gravity sedimentation tank (Fig. 18.4). Entering the cylindrical vessel, the liquid stream slowly rises to the top of the tank to be removed via an overflow launder as a clarified liquid stream. Denser solids settle to the bottom as a thick sludge underflow. Slow speed scraper blades help compact the sludge and drive it to the centre off-take

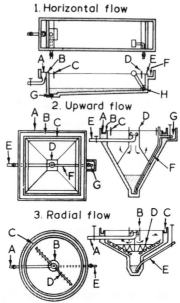

FIG. 18.4. Gravity sedimentation tanks. (1) Horizontal-flow tank. A, inlet channel; B, inlet weir; C, baffle; D, scum-board; E, outlet weir; F, outlet channel; G, sludge draw-off; H, floating arm (or other device) for removing supernatant liquid before desludging. (2) Upward-flow tank. A, effluent channel; B, effluent weir; C, scum-board; D, baffle box; E, inlet pipe; F, sludge pipe; G, sludge well. (3) Radial-flow tank. A, inlet pipe; B, baffle box, C, effluent channel; D, power-driven scraper; E, sludge pipe. (From Southgate, B. A., 'Treatment and Disposal of Industrial Waste Waters', by permission of the Controller of HMSO.)

pipe for continuous removal. Residence times in these units are insufficient for anaerobic decomposition to occur, being of the order of 1–3 h.

If the effluent contains large quantities of inorganic matter, as in the preparation of fruit, vegetables, etc., then a simple gravity settler or grit tank should be installed. Grit tanks consist of long, narrow channels designed to produce a low liquid flow velocity (about $0.3 \, \mathrm{m \, s^{-1}}$). At this order of velocity the more dense inorganic matter settles out. Since some organic material also settles, the resulting sludge should be removed continuously to avoid decomposition.

Certain food wastes (e.g. from meat processing) contain oils and fats in large quantities. Besides giving rise to high BOD values and consequent pollution if discharged untreated, these materials also represent valuable by-products and should be recovered.

These organic materials are immiscible with the aqueous effluent stream and float to the surface after passage through suitably designed residence tanks. Residence times of about an hour are required with flow velocities of about 0.3–$0.6\,\mathrm{m\,s^{-1}}$. The layer of fat can then be mechanically skimmed from the surface of the bulk liquid.

An alternative method of oil and fat removal is by aeration–flotation. Controlled aeration of the effluent stream by injection of air under pressure to the bottom of a flotation tank gives a mass of small bubbles which rise through the liquid, carrying grease and fine solids to the surface. The addition of certain surface active agents can assist this process. The separated surface layer is then removed. Lash and Kominek give a concise account of available physical treatment methods for waste treatment.[25]

18.4.3.2. Chemical treatment

In principle, chemical treatment for removal of solid matter in food wastes is identical to that used for the removal of suspended solids in natural waters (Section 18.3.1). A coagulant solution (often lime and ferrous sulphate) is added to the effluent. The floc formed carries down suspended solids. The coagulant dose depends on effluent pH, alkalinity and solids content. In batch operation the coagulant solution is added to the effluent in a mixing tank. The floc formed is allowed to settle. Underflow and overflow can then be separated. The process can also be carried out continuously.

With both physical and chemical methods for separating solid materials, large volumes of wet sludge and clarified liquors are produced. The sludge passes to sludge drying beds which can occupy large areas. If space is not available, dewatering centrifuges (Chapter 7) may be required to reduce the volume of sludge handled. The disposal of sludge from both primary and secondary treatment plants poses a major problem to food processors and is currently the subject of much investigation (Section 18.4.4).

In some applications a combination of physical and chemical treatments is sufficient to lower the solids content and BOD to acceptable values for discharge to rivers and lakes. With very many food wastes the BOD of the clarified liquors would still be unacceptably high. Biological treatment then becomes necessary.

18.4.3.3. Biological treatment (secondary treatment)

This treatment involves the use of micro-organisms to reduce high BOD wastewater streams leaving the food factory, to BOD levels acceptable for discharge to water-courses, without the risk of pollution arising. The microbial reactions, which would cause problems if allowed to take place in a stream or river after uncontrolled waste discharge, are carried out under controlled conditions either at the factory site or (the preferred method when possible) with the food waste mixed with sewage at a municipal waste treatment plant.

The pollutory constituents in the waste-water arriving at the secondary treatment plant (normally dissolved and finely-divided suspended organic matter in the case of food processing wastes) act as nutrients for the growth of micro-organisms (biomass) which is then removed from the aqueous stream by secondary sedimentation. After secondary treatment the final effluent should be sufficiently low in dissolved and suspended pollutory material to satisfy the discharge standards set by the regulatory agencies overseeing the quality of the receiving stream.

The microbial action can be:

(i) Aerobic.
(ii) Anaerobic.

(i) *Aerobic biological treatment.* Several biological treatment processes of this type are used including (a) trickling or percolating filters, (b) activated sludge systems, (c) lagoons and (d) spray irrigation. The bioreactors involved in these processes are normally of the attached-growth or suspended-growth type.[26] Newer 'hybrids' of these two basic types of reactor now being developed incorporate microbial films which are attached to surfaces on inert carrier particles made of plastic or metal. These are suspended in, and in some types of reactor are fluidised by, the waste liquid. Increased rates of BOD removal are claimed in pilot-plant trials with these newer units.[26]

(a) *Attached-growth microbial reactors*
Trickling filters (Fig. 18.5). This misnamed but long-established stationary film attached-growth microbial reactor, widely used for on-site food waste treatment, frequently consists of a cylindrical concrete tank, 2–3 m in depth and 7·5–15 m in diameter, packed with broken rock, stones, or other solid media offering a high specific surface (S_0) and voidage (x) (see Appendix 1). The bed is underlaid with drains. Clarified waste liquor is fed on to the upper surface of the bed by spray nozzles or rotating distributor arms. The waste liquid, after primary treatment to remove suspended solids, trickles through the bed and a slime of biologically active micro-organisms (zoogloeal growth) forms on the surface of the packing. The large surface area of the bed facilitates intimate contact between air, waste

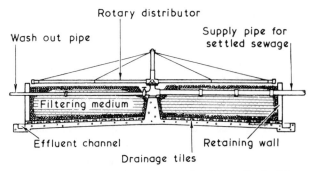

FIG. 18.5. Section of a trickling filter. (From Southgate, B. A., 'Treatment and Disposal of Industrial Waste Waters', by permission of the Controller of HMSO.)

liquor passing through the bed and the attached active growth which contains heterotrophic micro-organisms. The organisms use the pollutory materials in the effluent liquor as a source of food, thus removing them.

The organisms present in the film include bacteria, protozoa and fungi and also worms, fly larvae and rotifers, depending on the nature of the feed and the depth in the bed. Algal growth may develop on the upper surface of the bed if sunlight, temperature and nutrient composition are favourable and this can lead to problems (see below). The predominant bacteria present in the film is *zoogloea ramigera*, a polysaccharide producer which causes the zoogloeal growth to attach to the surface of the packing. Organic matter and oxygen are absorbed into the film to be utilised in the growth of more micro-organisms and the production of carbon dioxide and water, the stable end-products of the desired aerobic reaction. The major removal of BOD occurs in the upper levels of the bed where incoming fresh waste liquor ensures that the nutrient supply is high. At lower levels where nutrient availability is less, autotrophic nitrifying bacteria oxidise ammonia to nitrates.

The treated liquors leaving the bed possess a much reduced content of dissolved organic pollutory matter but will contain suspended biomass (humus) sloughed off the zoogloeal film during passage of the liquid. These solids are removed by passing the liquors through a secondary sedimentation tank. A relatively clear overflow, suitable for discharge to a river can be produced. The secondary sludge underflow produced is frequently mixed with sludge from the primary treatment stage and anaerobically digested.

'Low-rate', percolating filter beds contain a randomly packed medium about 30–50 mm in size. This gives a voidage of some 45–55% and specific surface of 80–110 m^2 m^{-3}. This 'conventional' form of percolating filter is also employed for the partial purification of waste liquor before discharge to a sewer for subsequent municipal treatment. In this case a somewhat coarser packing medium (75–125 mm) is often used. This permits higher rates of treatment but yields an effluent with a higher BOD.

The zoogloeal growth on the medium takes time to develop and it can be poisoned by the addition of toxic chemical substances. Over-loading the reactor with strong wastes can lead to rapid development of thicker growths which may block the interstitial spaces in the bed. A pool of water may then develop on the surface of the filter, a symptom of mal-operation known as 'ponding'. Algal growth can also give rise to ponding.

Macro-invertebrate organisms such as fly larvae and worms burrowing in the microbial film play an important part in preventing blockage in low-rate trickling filters and there is evidence to suggest that they improve the settling characteristics of suspended biomass in the treated liquid.

The thickness and nature of the bio-growth range from tenuous bacterial slimes around 0·25–1 mm thick (with aqueous wastes low in organic content) to dense masses of fungal mycelium which may be several millimetres thick, with some strong food wastes.

Alternating double filtration (ADF) is used in the treatment of some food wastes, particularly dairy wastes. In ADF, two filters are used in series. Settled waste liquor is passed to the primary 'ripe' unit which performs the major part of the BOD removal. Biomass formed is removed by sedimentation while the clarified, treated liquid leaving the sedimentation tank, low in both dissolved and suspended solids, is used to 'regenerate' the loaded, second trickling filter. The passage of treated effluent 'sloughs' off the heavy growth, thinning the zoogloeal film and increasing the rate of transport of nutrients and oxygen into it. Periodically the sequence of filtration is reversed. Up to 95% removal of BOD is reported with conventional trickling filters working on dilute food wastes.

High rate trickling filters containing specially designed wood or plastic packing media are now widely used. Plastic packing modules are available in a variety of types. They are designed to give high specific surfaces of up to 300 m^2 m^{-3} and voidages of over 90% so these units can handle both high hydraulic and BOD loadings without flooding or blocking. The high liquid flowrates keep the zoogloeal film thin so the influence of macro-invertebrates on the sloughing of the biomass is less important than with low rate-filters. Plastic media possess low bulk densities and are normally arranged in ordered stacks in packed towers which can be over six metres high. In some bio-towers, 50–100 mm size rings or tubes, of various surface configurations to enhance surface area, are randomly dumped. Specific surfaces and voidages are similar to those for stacked beds. In both cases, because of the low density packing, the retaining wall need only be of lightweight construction. A much reduced ground-area requirement is a major advantage offered by these units. They are used for both new installations and in up-dating older waste treatment plants. They are popular as 'roughing filters' for the partial treatment of liquors before passage to a municipal sewer or to a further 'on-site' biological oxidation stage, frequently a conventional trickling filter or a variation of the activated sludge process.

Moving film, attached growth microbial reactors are finding increasing use in food waste treatment. In the rotating biological contactor (RBC), the zoogloeal film builds up on a number of thin, circular discs, 3–4 m in diameter and 10–20 mm thick, carried on a horizontal shaft which slowly rotates in an open tank through which waste-water passes. Some 40–50% of the disc surface is immersed and as the discs rotate at about 5 rpm the slime film is alternately exposed to both nutrients and air. The discs, which can be fabricated in plastic or expanded metal, are often ribbed to increase the available surface area. Larger units may have several concrete compartments containing the disc modules. Smaller capacity package units in which the bio-disc modules come fitted in metal tanks are also available. The units are easy to operate and BOD removal is said to be high.[12,26]

(b) *Activated sludge systems*, also called suspended growth microbial reactors. These alternative aerobic oxidation systems are used instead of (or sometimes in conjunction with) trickling filtration for the treatment of a variety of food wastes.

In the 'conventional' activated sludge process (Fig. 18.6) a mixed population of micro-organisms, in the form of a floc, is maintained in suspension in a stream of partially treated waste-liquor resulting from

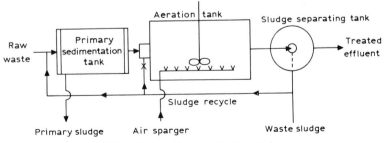

FIG. 18.6. Conventional activated sludge process.

primary treatment. Suspension is normally brought about by a combination of aeration and mechanical agitation. During a 6–8 h residence time in the reactor, small suspended particles and colloidal matter, not removed in the primary treatment stage, agglomerate on the microbial flocs. The range of participating micro-organisms can be wide but depending on the nature of the waste one species of organism may predominate. With food wastes *zoogloea ramigera* and protozoa are often present. As well as particulate matter, dissolved organic matter is also adsorbed and then utilised by the aerobic micro-organisms, part being oxidised to carbon dioxide and water and part assimilated into new biomass. In consequence the BOD of the waste is much reduced. The 'mixed liquor' leaving the reactor passes to a settling tank where, with correct operating conditions, low BOD supernatant liquor, virtually free of suspended solids and low in dissolved pollutory matter, and a thick sludge 'underflow' are produced. Part of the settled sludge, which contains viable micro-organisms conditioned to exposure to the waste liquor as well as non-viable organisms which biochemically reduce the nutrient load, is recycled to maintain the active microbial suspension in the aeration stage. It is necessary to produce a flocculant, active suspension so as to achieve rapid adsorption and assimilation of organic material while producing a rapidly settling sludge possessing good separation characteristics and with the ability to dewater easily, hence dispose of cheaply. To realise these objectives suitable nutrient and microbial solids concentrations are required. This makes the activated sludge process somewhat sensitive to changes in both waste–liquor composition and concentration. For this reason activated sludge processes are sometimes regarded as less reliable than trickling filters.

Alternative activated sludge processes. Varying the ratio of food, F, to recycled micro-organisms (mixed liquor volatile suspended solids, MLVSS), M, leads to changes in the nature of the microbial population. This results in several variations of the activated sludge process. In the 'conventional' process, originally developed for treating domestic sewage, moderate organic loadings (0·5–1·0 kg BOD per kg MLVSS per day) maintain a maximum population of bacteria and protozoa. When readily degradable food wastes are mixed and treated with domestic sewage, F/M values may be as high as 1·0 but with less degradable material the ratio is nearer 0·1 kg BOD per kg MLVSS per day. With 'conventional' operation, BOD reductions of up to 95% can be obtained with aeration times of 6–10 h and sludge residence times of 4–5 days.

In the *high rate* process, high organic loads can be handled and F/M values may reach 5·0 kg BOD per kg MLVSS per day. The rate of BOD removal is high. However, with more food available, cell growth is favoured so much sludge is produced. This can result in a sludge which is more difficult to separate.

Besides the ability to treat high organic loads advantages of the high rate activated sludge process are the short aeration times (2–3 h) and sludge residence times (12 h or less). This means that the reactor size is reduced. However, although the rate of BOD removal is high, overall reduction in BOD is only 60–70%, so further treatment, e.g. percolating filtration, will usually be necessary.

Although the 'high rate' modification of the activated sludge process will not produce a final effluent suitable for discharge to inland water-courses it finds extensive use for:

(a) Rapid pre-treatment of strong wastes before further on-site processing or disposal to a municipal authority waste treatment plant.

(b) Treatment before discharge to estuary or coastal waters where discharge requirements are less demanding.

Extended aeration process. Operating at very low F/M ratios (less than 0·1 kg BOD per kg MLVSS per day) gives another variation of the activated sludge process—the extended aeration process. Interest in this particular mode of operation centres on the very low production of sludge requiring costly further treatment and ultimate disposal (Section 18.4.4) as compared to the alternative suspended growth processes in common use. Since nutrient availability is low, so cell growth is slow. Endogenous respiration results in further inactivation of microbial cells. The little sludge solids produced by this reaction are reported to be inert and suitable for direct land disposal. Aeration times are long (1–2 days) as are sludge residence times, being 24–28 days. However BOD reductions of 95% or more are achievable. Since detention times are long, reactor volumes are large so the method is usually used with smaller installations.

Biological design features, kinetcs, etc., for the various modifications of suspended growth microbial reactors are discussed by Winkler[26] and Benefield and Randall.[27]

(c) *Lagoons (stabilisation ponds) and oxidation ditches.* If a sufficient area of flat land is available lagoons—water-tight embankments enclosing a lake of waste-liquor—offer a simple method for the treatment of some food waste streams when correctly designed and operated. This is particularly the case where operations are seasonal and capital expenditure on expensive equipment is difficult to justify. Lagoons are frequently used for the treatment of cannery and other food waste discharges from factories sited in rural areas. The simplest lagoons involve both aerobic and anaerobic decomposition in the break-down of organic matter. Aerobic conditions normally predominate in the bulk of the liquid and anaerobic activity is confined to the layer of sludge deposited on the bottom. For efficient operation, lagoons depend on natural surface aeration although under certain conditions (favourable nutrient availability, sunlight and temperature), algal growth may also play a part in making oxygen available. For optimum aeration, lagoon depths of 0·9–1·5 m are recommended. At greater depths odour problems may arise due to increased anaerobic decomposition at lower levels in the lagoon. Odours can also develop if the lagoon is overloaded; aeration becomes inadequate and the oxygen content of the liquid falls allowing anaerobic conditions to become established. If odours arise sodium nitrate is sometimes added to produce additional oxygen to encourage aerobic oxidation.

Lagoons often act as sedimentation basins and flow equalisation tanks and can be useful in this capacity in simple waste treatment plants.

With larger lagoons the inclusion of mechanical aeration facilities has now become popular. The system behaves rather like an activated sludge system; floating mechanical surface aerators introduce air into the system as well as keeping the microbial floc that develops in suspension. Aeration time is measured in days rather than hours, depending on the BOD reduction required and a further treatment stage in a naturally aerated lagoon may follow. Waste stabilisation pond design and use are discussed by Gloyna.[28]

The *oxidation ditch* is another simple and relatively cheap aerobic oxidation system developed for treating agricultural and food waste streams from farms and small factories. Primary sedimentation is usually omitted and simple *Pasveer ditch* systems consist of little more than a parallel-sided, continuously looped trough (rather like the running track at a sports stadium) some 1–2 m deep, excavated in the ground and suitably lined to render the containment surface impervious to water.[26] Waste liquor is circulated round the ditch at a flow velocity of about 0·3 m s^{-1} by means of one or more surface agitators which aerates the liquid and also keeps the microbial flocs formed in suspension. Part of the waste stream is passed to a secondary sedimentation basin for sludge separation, part of the separated sludge being returned to the ditch to maintain the desired F/M ratio. Simple oxidation ditches are usually operated as extended aeration activated sludge systems with hydraulic residence times in the range 1–4 days and sludge retention times of 20–30 days or longer. BOD removal is very efficient and final sludge production is low.

(d) *Spray irrigation.* This method is popular where land with a reasonably porous soil is available within economic pumping distance of the source of the waste liquors. Screened liquor is pumped to the irrigation site (fields carrying a variety of grass crops are often used but wooded areas can also be used) and distributed over the area by sprinklers. The method is cheap, avoids pollution of water-courses if carried out under controlled conditions, and can be used to irrigate edible crops. Spray irrigation is used satisfactorily on both milk and cannery wastes.[23,29]

Anaerobic biological treatment. The anaerobic stabilisation of organic matter is finding increasing application in food waste treatment. Anaerobic micro-organisms break down organic matter in the waste in the absence of molecular oxygen and, via a series of reactions, methane and carbon dioxide are produced as the main products. Compared to aerobic treatment the advantages of anaerobic stabilisation are the avoidance of expensive aeration facilities and the low production of stable, humus-like solids. However, odorous, unstable liquids are also produced and these may require further treatment. In addition, anaerobic processes are slow so long residence times in large reactors are necessary.

There are two main areas of application for anaerobic processes in food waste treatment.

(1) Food waste liquors with high contents of less degradable solids— meat-processing wastes, starches, etc.—are more amenable to anaerobic than aerobic oxidation and are often treated directly in anaerobic reactors.

(2) Anaerobic digestion of primary and secondary sludges associated with aerobic waste treatment is common in municipal plants treating food factory wastes mixed with sewage. The process can also be used for on-site treatment of wastes from larger capacity food plants. Anaerobic sludge digestion produces a reduced volume of relatively inert material having little unpleasant odour and which can be dewatered relatively easily.

As with aerobic waste treatment processes, reactors for anaerobic treatment range from simple lagoons to sophisticated plants incorporating advanced biochemical engineering features.

Anaerobic lagoons find wide use with high strength food wastes, e.g. meat-processing wastes. These lagoons are deeper than the aerobic type,

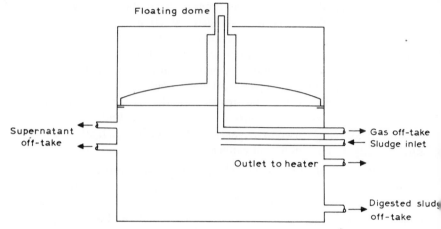

Floating dome

Supernatant off-take

Gas off-take
Sludge inlet

Outlet to heater

Digested sludge off-take

FIG. 18.7. Conventional floating dome anaerobic digester.

the layer of active anaerobic sludge being at the bottom of the lagoon. In meat-processing waste treatment using anaerobic lagoons a layer of grease, several centimetres thick, is allowed to accumulate to form a cover for suppressing odours, retaining heat and maintaining anaerobic conditions.[12]

Anaerobic digesters (reactors), though costly, are more commonly used than anaerobic lagoons.

Single-stage digesters (Fig. 18.7) are usually large tanks equipped with external heat exchangers to maintain the desired temperature for microbial growth. A variety of temperatures are used but those for mesophilic growth (30–35°C) are frequently recommended.[26] Facilities for gas collection and removal are also incorporated. Recirculation of digesting sludge through the heat exchanger gives mild agitation which aids the digestion which occurs in the middle third of the tank volume. The vessel also acts as a sedimentation tank, the lower third storing compacting stabilised solids after sedimentation and the upper third supernatant liquid. The digested inert sludge is drawn off from the bottom of the unit for dewatering and ultimate disposal. Supernatant, which often requires further treatment, is withdrawn from higher levels. Residence times can be 10–30 days or even longer and up to 95% BOD removal can be achieved. The main components of digester gas are methane (50–70%) and carbon dioxide (50–30%). This mixture can be used in waste-heat boilers.

In the high-rate anaerobic digestion process two reactors are used, the first being agitated by gas recirculation or by mechanical impeller. Since this system is completely mixed, and is also maintained at optimum temperatures for microbial growth, the rate of digestion of high strength waste (fed almost continuously to the first vessel) is significantly increased. Final digestion occurs in the second vessel which is also used for separation and storage. Waste retention times are reduced to 10–20 days. Since anaerobic fermentation is accompanied by the formation of hydrogen sulphide unpleasant odours can arise. To minimise odour problems, as well as permit the collection of combustible gas in larger plants, digesters are usually covered.

Three stages of digestion have been identified:

(i) Liquefaction—High molecular weight insoluble organic materials, e.g. proteins, polysaccharides, etc. are hydrolysed by extra-cellular enzymes produced by micro-organisms, being broken down into soluble, low molecular weight substances, e.g. amino-acids, sugars, alcohols, etc.

(ii) Acid fermentation—The soluble organic material formed during hydrolysis is metabolised by facultative and anaerobic organisms, being converted into volatile lower fatty acids, alcohols carbon dioxide and hydrogen (N.B., the formation of acids lowers the pH).

(iii) Methane fermentation (methanogenic phase). Under favourable conditions organic acids are converted into methane, carbon dioxide and small amounts of hydrogen by several species of strictly anaerobic bacteria, and new cells develop. However, the balance between acid production and methane production is critical. Methanogenic organisms are very sensitive to temperature and to low pH. If pH falls below 6·2 methane production ceases. Under these conditions organic acids accumulate and unpleasant, sour-smelling sludges develop.

Sensitivity to pH gives the anaerobic digestion process a reputation for instability. Methanogenic micro-organisms, as well as being susceptible to pH, only grow slowly and they are easily inhibited by a large number of substances commonly occurring in wastes. Even under favourable growth conditions the residence time in the digester will be long so washing-out (removing from the system) those viable micro-organisms which are present must be avoided.

After digestion and settling, the reduced volume of sludge solids is usually dewatered further before ultimate disposal. The separated liquid is likely to have a high BOD and normally requires aerobic treatment before discharge to a water-course.

18.4.4. DISPOSAL OF WASTE SLUDGES AND SOLIDS

The disposal of solid wastes and sludge solids from food industry waste-treatment plants poses special problems. The possibility of profitable recovery of materials from the waste stream must always be considered.[24] If the residues are valueless then it is necessary to arrange for their 'ultimate disposal' in a manner which cannot cause offence due to contamination or pollution of the environment.

Sludges arise from primary separations using screens, settling tanks, filters, etc., and from secondary treatment—as biomass from trickling filters and activated sludge plants, also as inert sludge solids from anaerobic digesters. Primary sludges are likely to contain fats, carbohydrates, proteins, siliceous matter and anything else introduced into the factory drainage system and it is these that offer the best recovery prospects. In recent years, however, the use of biomass produced in suspended growth reactors using food waste liquors as a substrate for growth, has received considerable attention as a possible source of valuable protein for animal feed.

Though seemingly quite dense, a typical sludge consists mainly of water so a major factor in sludge disposal is dewatering. As a first step, before attempting costly mechanical separations, 'sludge-conditioning' using chemical or thermal methods should be considered.

After chemical or thermal conditioning the separation of water from sludges using mechanical methods—gravity thickeners, flotation cells, belt filters, etc.—frequently becomes easier.

Chemical conditioning. Chemical treatment can produce significant improvements in the settling rates and in the filterability of some sludges. Common agents used are:

(i) The polyvalent inorganic ions, Fe^{3+} and Al^{3+}. These are cheap and often very effective in aiding sludge thickening.
(ii) Organic polyelectrolytes are now being used. These are considerably more expensive than inorganic salts but required dosages are at much lower concentrations.

Thermal conditioning. This method can produce 'remarkable' improvements in filterability. It was first used in some sewage works over forty years ago but has become more popular in recent years. In outline, treatment at high temperatures and pressures (up to 200°C and 10–20 atm) breaks down the colloidal structure found with food and other biological sludges, releasing intracellular water.

In the Zimpo Process, which is a wet oxidation process, air is introduced into the sludge which is contained in a pressurised heating vessel (cooker). This thermal conditioning oxidises part of the organic matter. A similar process is the Porteous Process. Both processes are said to be good for the treatment of activated sludges but give strong supernatant liquors which are 'fairly resistant to biological oxidation'. An advantage with thermal conditioning is that the sludge is sterilised.

Mechanical separation.

(i) *Gravity thickening*—carried out in sedimentation vessels carrying slow speed stirrers. Gentle compression exerted by the slow speed stirrer on the settled sludge removes more water from the underflow. The supernatant is returned to the waste treatment process.

(ii) *Flotation*—(a) using dissolved air injected into the sludge at 3–10 atm, (b) using electro-flotation, i.e. electrolytically generated gas bubbles.

The sludge underflow from gravity thickeners and floating solids scraped from the surface of flotation cells can be further concentrated using belt filters. The use of centrifuges for dewatering secondary sludges is unlikely to be economic. Primary sludges, in the case of food wastes, often find use (possibly after drying) as animal feed.

Stabilised sludges from anaerobic digestion processes are often mixed with sand or straw and left to dry in sludge drying beds. Water is lost by a combination of drainage, evaporation and sludge compression. Sludges treated in this way may find use as compost on farmland.

Ultimate sludge disposal. Whatever the treatment used for the stabilisation and reduction in volume of sludges produced in food waste treatment, considerable amounts of treated biological sludge solids still have to be disposed of, safely, without affecting the environment.

Methods used for the ultimate disposal of these sludges and other valueless food wastes include:

(a) *Dumping.* The waste material is transported to a suitable site and disposed of by 'land-filling' under controlled, hygienic conditions. The nuisance caused by odours, rodents, insects, etc., can be a major problem. Although still widely used this method continues to be viewed with suspicion in these pollution-conscious times. Recent experiences with methane fires, resulting from long term anaerobic decomposition of organic matter in 'recovered' land-fill sites, throws further doubt on the future for this disposal method.

(b) *Incineration.* Incineration of solid wastes, at sufficiently high temperatures, results in complete destruction of all organic matter liable to cause pollution. In such a system the generation of smoke and odours, which may arise with inadequate design or mal-operation, must be carefully controlled. Some incinerators are able to handle low-calorific value organic materials having very high water contents.

Incinerators have not achieved the early success predicted for them in waste disposal. Besides high capital cost, a major reason for their relatively poor acceptance is the development of too low an operating temperature in some units. To help achieve energy conservation, hence economy in operation, heat exchangers, for heat recovery, are frequently incorporated into the incinerator system. These can lead to a drop in temperature which adversely affects combustion.[30] Complete decomposition of the wastes giving inert, harmless products is essential. This is unlikely to be achieved unless the unit is capable of providing controlled temperatures, often exceeding 1300°C. Complete destruction must be assured of any pesticide/herbicide or similar residues (and any of their reaction products) that may have entered the food chain and are present in the feed stream to the incinerator.

(c) *Composting.* Composting of waste materials under controlled conditions can produce a humus suitable for agricultural purposes.

REFERENCES

1. WHO, *International Standards for Drinking Water*, 3rd edn. World Health Organisation. Geneva, 1971.
2. Official Journal of the European Community, Directive 80/778EEC, Annex I, Council Directive of 15 July 1980 relating to the quality of water intended for human consumption.
3. Hamer, P., Jackson, J. and Thurston, E. F., *Industrial Water Treatment Practice.* Butterworths, London, 1961.
4. Sendelbach, M. G., Boiler water treatment, *Chemical Engng*, **95**(11) (15 August 1988) 127–32.
5. Blake, R. T., *Water Treatment for HVAC and Potable Water Systems.* McGraw-Hill, New York, 1980.
6. Tebbutt, T. H. Y., *Principles of Water Quality Control*, 3rd edn. Pergamon Oxford, England, 1983.
7. Barnes, D. and Wilson, F., *Chemistry and Unit Operations in Water Treatment.* Applied Science Publishers, London, 1983.
8. Schwoyer, L. K. (ed.), *Polyelectrolytes for Water and Waste Water Treatment.* CRC Press, Boca Raton, Fla., USA, 1981.

9. Smethurst, G., *Basic Water Treatment.* Thomas Telford Ltd, London, 1979.
10. Curds, C. R. and Hawkes, H. A., *Ecological Aspects of Used-Water Treatment. Vol. 1. The Organisms and Their Ecology.* Academic Press, New York, 1975.
11. Jay, J. M., *Modern Food Microbiology,* 3rd edn. Van Nostrand Reinhold, New York, 1986.
12. Hammer, M. J., *Water and Waste Water Technology.* John Wiley, New York, 1975.
13. Banner, J. C., Industrial uses of ozone. *Process and Control Engng* (February 1988) 30.
13. Banner, J. C., Industrial uses of ozone. *Process and Control Engng,* **2**(4) (February 1988) 30.
14. Cheng, I. Wei., Cook, D. L. and Kirk, J. R., Use of chlorine compounds in the food industry. *Food Technol.,* **39**(1) (1985) 107–15.
15. Johnson, J. D., *Disinfection—Water and Wastewater.* Ann Arbor Science, Woburn, Mass., USA, 1975.
16. Holden, W. S. (ed.), *Water Treatment and Examination. A Successor to 'The Examination of Waters and Water Supplies', by Thresh, Beale and Suckling.* Churchill, London, 1970.
17. Nordell, E., *Water Treatment for Industrial and Other Uses,* 2nd edn. Van Nostrand Reinhold, New York, 1961.
18. Goodhall, P. M., *Efficient Use of Steam.* IPC Science and Technology Press, 1979.
19. Lorch, W., *Handbook of Water Purification.* McGraw-Hill (UK), London, 1981.
20. Franson, M. A. (ed.), *Standard Methods for the Examination of Water and Waste Water,* 15th edn. American Public Health Association, American Water Works Association and the Water Pollution Control Federation, 1980.
21. Bates, A. J., Reducing charges on effluent discharges to sewers. In *Food Industry Wastes: Disposal and Recovery,* ed. A. Herzka and R. G. Booth. Applied Science Publishers, London, 1981, pp. 51–67.
22. Anon., *A Guide for Waste Management in the Food Processing Industries.* National Canners Association, 1969.
23. Green, J. H. and Kramer, A., *Food Processing Waste Management.* AVI, Westport, Conn., USA, 1979.
24. Birch, G. G., Parker, K. J. and Worgan, J. T., (ed.), *Food from Waste.* Applied Science Publishers, London, 1976.
25. Lash, L. D. and Kominek, E. C., Primary waste treatment methods. *Chemical Engng (Desk Book Issue),* **82**(21) (1975).
26. Winkler, M. A., *Biological Treatment of Waste-Water.* Ellis Horwood, Chichester, England, 1981.
27. Benefield, L. D. and Randall, C. W., *Biological Process Design for Wastewater Treatment.* Prentice-Hall, Englewood Cliffs, N.J., USA, 1980.
28. Gloyna, M. J., *Waste Stabilization Ponds.* Monograph Series No. 60, World Health Organization, Geneva, 1971.
29. Keith, L. W. and Leham, W. D., Land treatment of food processing wastewater. In *Utilisation, Treatment and Disposal of Waste on Land.* Soil Science Society of America, Inc., 1986, pp. 171–83.
30. Rendell, J. Waste incineration. *Process Engng,* **69**(3) (March 1988) 71–3.

CHAPTER 19

MATERIALS HANDLING

19.1. GENERAL CONSIDERATIONS

19.1.1. SCOPE AND IMPORTANCE OF MATERIALS HANDLING

Materials handling is concerned with the five elements: Movement—Time—Place—Quantity—Space.[1] Efficient materials handling is Movement in the most efficient manner at the right Time, to and from the correct Place, in the required Quantity with the maximum economy of Space. Handling adds nothing to the value of the product. It is vital, therefore, to ensure maximum handling efficiency during all the following movements of the material:

(i) *As a raw material* from supply point to store or process.

(ii) *As a material in process* between stages during processing.

(iii) *As a finished product* to packing, storage and despatch.

Any reduction in this defined scope will result in a restricted outlook with corresponding loss of effectiveness.

Case studies indicate that substantial savings can be effected by changing from manual to mechanised handling. Savings of the order of 50% of the labour bill are not uncommon. A typical example of this is given in Fig. 19.1 which shows reductions in labour charges of 40–90%. These savings are partially offset by increased capital charges but the overall effect is a large reduction in operating costs.

In addition to direct savings, good handling techniques confer other advantages, such as:

(i) Improved utilisation of men, machines and storage space.

(ii) Reduced material wastage.

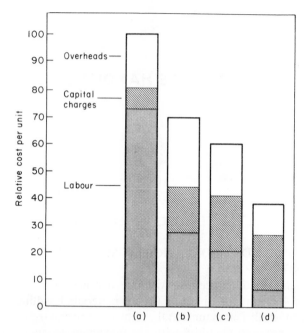

Fig. 19.1. Comparison of costs of handling flour in a mill producing at a rate of $75 \, t \, 24 \, h^{-1}$. (a) Flour bagged from mill and handled manually in bags. (b) Flour bagged from mill and handled mechanically in bags. (c) 50% as for (b) and 50% bulk handled pneumatically. (d) 100% bulk handled pneumatically.

(iii) Improved control and rotation of stock.

(iv) Improved working conditions and reduced operator fatigue.

These result in increased productivity, improved product quality and reduced absenteeism.[2]

19.1.2. THE RULES OF EFFICIENT MATERIALS HANDLING

Materials handling technique has improved rapidly over the last few decades, and during this time practitioners have accumulated a set of generally applicable rules which provide valuable guides to action. These rules are not fundamental in any scientific sense. They have been changed and will continue to be changed, from time to time, as new techniques develop. Good handling practice is exemplified by the list of rules reproduced in Table 19.1 which fall conveniently into three groups: planning rules; selection rules; and operating rules.

TABLE 19.1
The rules of efficient materials handling

1. Planning rules.
   (a) Plan to use method study to optimise material flow.
   (b) Plan handling and storage activities to give maximum overall operating efficiency.
   (c) Plan to maximise use of the building cube.
   (d) Plan to integrate handling activities into a co-ordinated system covering supplier, receiving, storage, production, inspection, packaging, warehousing and despatch.
   (e) Plan to maximise utilisation of handling equipment and manpower.
   (f) Plan to review systems regularly.

2. Equipment selection rules.
   (a) Standardize handling methods and equipment throughout the factory.
   (b) Match equipment size to planned factory capacity.
   (c) Reduce ratio of dead weight of mobile handling equipment to the load carried.
   (d) Select equipment which maximises safety and reduces product damage.
   (e) Select equipment which gives lowest handling cost per unit of material moved.

3. Operating rules.
   (a) Use gravity to move goods, wherever practicable.
   (b) Move materials as unit loads.
   (c) Eliminate inefficient handling procedures and practices.
   (d) Establish preventative maintenance schedules for equipment.
   (e) Establish rigid safety procedures for handling operations.

19.1.3. PLANNING AN IMPROVED SYSTEM

In order to design an improved handling system, answers to the following questions are required:

(i)   What is the present system of handling?
(ii)   What is the present handling cost per unit of production?
(iii) How can the present system be improved?
(iv)   What will the new system cost?
(v)   What savings can be expected from the new system?

Answers to questions (i) and (iii) can be obtained using established planning techniques[1] in conjunction with the rules discussed in Section 19.1.2. Questions (ii) and (v) are, generally, much more difficult to answer accurately. Some cost systems, because of the widespread nature of the handling activity, are unable to provide the required data. In such circumstances a special cost study has to be made.

19.1.4. THE NEED FOR HANDLING KNOWLEDGE

Responsibility for materials handling is, properly, vested in specialist handling engineers, and many food manufacturers adopt this procedure. Almost invariably these specialists take decisions in conference with production executives. Where a specialist handling department is not provided, the responsibility for efficient movement of materials falls on the production manager and his staff. Therefore, in either of these situations, it is important for production executives to have a sound knowledge of the fundamentals of good handling practice.

19.1.5. SAFETY CONSIDERATIONS

Every year about 20 000 accidents are reported as occurring in the UK food and allied industries.[3] Of these, handling and lifting materials accounts for about 20% of the total and represents the single largest group of accidents. A similar situation exists in the USA where handling accounts for 27% of all plant accidents. The mechanisation of handling has not reduced the accident rate; it has merely altered the types of handling hazards. The safety provisions embodied in the Factories Act 1961 have been reinforced by the Health and Safety at Work Act 1974 which applies severe penalties to both employers and employees who permit or engage in practices which endanger health or safety. The safety aspects of materials handling and movement, therefore, warrant the most careful attention.

Handling accidents fall into two groups:

(i)　Unsafe conditions including:

Insufficient working space.
Inadequate aisle space.
Inadequate guarding of running machinery.
Defective equipment.
Inadequate lighting and ventilation.
Unsafe design or construction of equipment.
Bad floor surfaces.

(ii)　Unsafe acts such as:

Unsafe loading and stacking.
Disregard of traffic signals.
Carrying out repairs and adjustments on the run.
Operating without authority.
Working at unsafe speeds.

Using incorrect equipment.
Exceeding the capacity of equipment.
Failing to use protective clothing.
Practical joking.

19.1.6. SELECTION OF HANDLING METHOD

The rules set out in Table 19.1 represent commonsense guides to action which, properly applied, assure effective and economical movement of materials. Selection of a particular method from the alternative procedures which satisfy compliance with these rules depends on a number' of considerations. These include: the nature of the materials; whether they are to be handled as packages or as bulk; the movement distances and frequency; the capacity required of the movement system and local conditions such as temperature and humidity of the premises, the state of roadways, etc.

The properties of the materials, such as their fragility, corrosive or combustible or dust generating properties and their susceptibility to contamination or tainting, are obvious considerations. Again, hot, sticky or abrasive materials pose specific movement problems. Changes in the properties of the materials as they proceed through the process also affect selection considerations.

Of particular concern to the food and allied industries is the fact that manufacturing (and hence handling) activities are, in many cases, seasonal in nature both in the supply of raw materials and the demand for finished products. This imposes special constraints in the selection and operation of handling procedures. The factors determining method selection have been reviewed by Bates.[5]

From the foregoing it will be clear that in most materials handling situations there is no such thing as an ideal system, the best compromise is the most which can be hoped for. In this case, regular monitoring and reviewing of handling costs and methods is obligatory if efficiency is to be achieved.

19.1.7. CATEGORISATION OF MATERIALS HANDLING EQUIPMENT

The many types of handling equipment may be classified conveniently into five main groups as set out in Table 19.2. This grouping is used in this chapter as a basis for considering the application of handling equipment in the food industry.

TABLE 19.2
Categorisation of materials handling equipment

Classification	Direction					Frequency			Location served				Service nature			Movement height				Material state			
	Vert. up	Vert. down	Incline up	Incline down	Horizontal	Continuous	Intermittent	Occasional	Point	Path	Limited area	Unlimited area	Permanent	Temporary	Non-fixed	Overhead	Working height	Floor level	Underfloor	Packaged	Bulk	Solid	Liquid
(1) Conveyors			×	×	×	×			×	×			×				×	×	×	×	×	×	
(2) Elevators	×	×				×			×				×			×				×	×	×	
(3) Cranes and hoists	×	×						×			×	×	×	×			×	×		×	×	×	
(4) Trucks								×	×						×			×		×	×	×	
(5) Pneumatic equipment	×	×	×	×	×	×				×			×			×	×				×	×	×

× = applicable.

19.2. CONVEYORS

Conveyors may be described as equipment for inclined or horizontal continuous movement serving a point or path. The service is generally fixed, and conveying takes place at working height, floor level or underfloor. Packaged or bulk solid materials may be transported.

Motion of the material may be imparted either (a) by gravity or manually, or (b) by power. The method of motivation provides a convenient basis for subdividing the many types of conveyor into two main groups as follows:

(i)   Gravity or manually powered: chute, roller, or skate-wheel conveyors.

(ii) Powered: roller, belt, slat, chain, vibratory, magnetic, screw, flight and pneumatic conveyors.

These and other types of conveyor are described in BS 3810.[4]

19.2.1. GRAVITY CONVEYORS
19.2.1.1. Chutes

Chutes are smooth-surfaced inclined troughs used to convey from high to low levels under the force of gravity. The factors to be considered in their design and use are as follows:

(a) *Friction.* An average value for the coefficient of friction of wooden cases on a wood surfaced chute is about 0·5 and for wooden cases on a metal surface is about 0·3. Coulomb's classical laws of friction, although useful, do not explain many observed events and it has become necessary to modify these laws.[6,7] Thus friction force is now considered to be dependent on the sliding velocity since this affects the temperatures and hence the natures of the sliding surfaces. Again, the friction force is regarded as supplying energy to overcome adhesion between the surfaces and to deform or shear asperities, *i.e.* irregularities, of these surfaces. Sliding surfaces are supported on peaks of the highest of these asperities and the friction force is therefore dependent on this, very small, contact area which will vary with the applied load. With bulk materials, it is necessary to consider both the friction between the material and the chute and the interparticulate friction within the material. The latter determines whether the material slides down the chute or whether it pours down.

(b) *Moisture.* Atmospheric humidity and the moisture content of the conveyed material affect both sliding and interparticulate friction, and this variable must be allowed for in designing chutes.

(c) *Chute inclination.* Steep chutes give high acceleration rates, consequently the risk of product damage is increased.

(d) *Chute length.* The longer the chute the greater the package terminal velocity. Since the kinetic energy of the conveyed unit is proportional to the square of its velocity, conveying on long or steep chutes can result in considerable damage to packages.

(e) *Uniformity of package weight.* Chute conveying of units of mixed weights may lead to excessive damaging of the lighter packages by bumping. Light and heavy units should, therefore, be conveyed separately.

(f) *Position of centre of gravity of package.* A vertical line through the centre of gravity of the package must pass through the surface of the package in contact with the conveyor, otherwise tumbling will result. Similarly, unevenly balanced packages must be conveyed heavy-end down.

These remarks are applicable to conveyance on many other types of inclined conveyors and must be borne in mind if product damage and accident rates are to be minimised.

Chutes may be of wood or metal: they may be straight; they may be curved to effect change of direction or they may be spiralled to effect space economy. Bulk food materials are best conveyed on metal chutes enclosed to restrict product contamination.

19.2.1.2. Gravity and manpowered roller or skate-wheel conveyors
A roller conveyor comprises free running rollers mounted horizontally in a frame so as to form a table on which the packages or containers may be conveyed either at an inclination (by gravity) or horizontally (by manual effort). Skate-wheel conveyors function similarly but consist of sets of wheels mounted in groups of three or more on axles (Fig. 19.2).

These conveyors are used for the handling of: cases, cartons, drums, barrels, trays, and similar units having firm, flat bases. Sacks and similar loose packages can be conveyed only if they are supported on boards or trays. With roller conveyors at least three rollers and with skate-wheel conveyors at least six wheels (two across and three along the conveyor) must be in contact with the package base at all times.

Although these two types are similar in application, the following differences are noteworthy:

(i) Wheels are better than rollers on curved conveyors since there is less friction between package and conveyor when wheels are used.
(ii) Rollers are better load bearers than wheels.
(iii) Rollers weigh about three times as much as an equivalent skate-wheel assembly. Hence rollers have higher inertia and are more difficult to start and to stop compared with skate-wheels.
(iv) Rollers are more robust than skate-wheels.

Both types are free-running, so they may be used for horizontal or near-horizontal movement; a down-grade of 3% (2°) is adequate for gravity transportation of most packages. Gravity, assisted by air (Section 19.6) may also be used for package handling. Special care must be exercised to minimise bumping damage when using these conveyors.

FIG. 19.2. A skate-wheel conveyor.

19.2.2. POWERED CONVEYORS

19.2.2.1. Roller conveyors

These may be belt driven (the rollers being mounted above and in friction contact with driven belts) or chain driven (the rollers being fitted with end sprockets which engage with driven endless chains).

Powered rollers are used for packages similar to those carried by gravity rollers (Section 19.2.1.2). They may be used for movement both upwards and downwards at shallow angles (10–12°). Belt-driven rollers are used for low-speed conveying (0.2–$0.3 \, m \, s^{-1}$). Chain-driven rollers are used for heavy duty, high-speed conveying (up to $2.5 \, m \, s^{-1}$). Both types are reversible and may be fitted with switch points and intermediate discharging devices, thus serving a limited path.

19.2.2.2. Belt conveyor

This comprises an endless belt, friction driven at one end and carried on an idling drum at the other end. Belts may be of a wide variety of materials such as: plain or coated canvas, woven wire or stainless steel ribbon. They may be flat (for package conveying) or troughed, using idling rollers or slides (for bulk transfer). Hence they are suitable for moving almost any type of material—wet, dry or packaged. Correct tensioning and tracking of the belt must be ensured at all times. This may be effected by automatic spring-tensioners or by manual adjusters. Plain belts may be used on inclines up to 22° while belts fitted with non-slip devices such as cleats or cross-bars may be used up to 45° of inclination. Belts range in width from a few centimetres up to several metres and belt conveyors from a few metres to several kilometres long are used. Information is available for calculating power requirements, maximum belt speeds and capacities of belt conveyors.[8]

Discharge arrangements warrant careful consideration. Belts are costly items and are easily damaged at both loading and discharge points. Again, carry-over of food products, causing fouling of the area beneath the conveyor, can be a problem. Simple arrangements, like belt brushes, are frequently satisfactory with bulk dry materials. Sticky materials can be removed by spring-loaded scraper blades but these often cause excessive belt wear if improperly adjusted.

Apart from their wide applications in transfer operations, belt conveyors find extensive use as in-process conveyors during sorting, cleaning and heat-processing. They may be fitted with load cells or lever systems which measure the deflection of a unit length of belt, thus providing a continuous weighing system which can be used for monitoring, proportioning, feeding and other process operations.[9]

19.2.2.3. Slat conveyors

These comprise wooden or metal slats carried on endless driven chains. This provides a rigid flat surface with excellent load-bearing characteristics which is much less susceptible to damage and more easily repaired than is a belt. They are used for transporting packaged goods and small bulky items like fish and large fruits. In these latter cases careful attention to cleaning is obligatory.

19.2.2.4. Chain conveyors

Milk churns, barrels, crates and trays are conveniently handled by loading directly on to driven chains. Floor level or overhead chains may also be used to transport wheeled trolleys along a fixed, programmed path using hook couplings. Overhead or monorail conveyors using trays or hooks slung from a driven chain find applications in the poultry and meat industry. Bulk conveying by chains is dealt with in Section 19.2.2.8.

19.2.2.5. Vibratory conveyors

These use the inertia of material, conveyed by a relatively slow forward movement of the conveyor surface, to maintain product flow during a rapid backward movement of the conveyor surface. This motion (called 'throws and catches') is repeated at high frequency and may be produced electromagnetically or mechanically. Vibratory conveyors commonly take the form of a trough or vertical spiral. By suitable control of the vibration, the material may be caused to flow forward at a variable rate, to remain stationary or to flow backwards. Thus a spiral unit will convey either upwards or downwards. The accuracy with which the flow of material can be controlled enables these conveyors to be used as feeders for equipment like mills and mixers. Their gentle handling makes them suitable for friable foods (e.g. potato crisps) whilst wet, stringy, hot, or abrasive materials are conveyed without difficulty. Vibratory conveying is substantially dustless and is becoming increasingly popular in the food industry.[10]

19.2.2.6. Magnetic conveyors

Electromagnetic and permanent-magnetic belts and rollers are used to convey, hold and orientate ferromagnetic materials. In the food industry, they are used to convey food cans and to hold them inverted for rinsing and drying. Magnetic rollers may be used to discriminate between the open and closed ends of cans. Such conveyors are positive in action and are silent, in distinct contrast with the usual railed conveyors used for can handling.

19.2.2.7. Screw conveyors

These operate on the principle of a rotating helical screw advancing material in a trough or casing. Bulk dry materials (e.g. sugar, flour and grain) and semi-liquid non-abrasive materials (e.g. sugar-beet pulp and comminuted meat) may be conveyed horizontally, at an inclination, or vertically.

The discharge rate and power consumption are considerably affected by the inclination and conveying distance and for these reasons screw conveyors are best used at or near the horizontal. Screw conveyors are characterised by their uniform discharge rate and, hence, find applications as feeders for mills and other process equipment. Many patterns of screw conveyor are available, and, in addition to functioning as conveyors, may be used as mixers or, when fitted with heat exchangers, as continuous heaters, e.g. screw blanchers (Section 10.5) or continuous coolers or chillers.

19.2.2.8. Flight conveyors

These conveyors function on the basis of the material being dragged along an enclosed channel by an endless chain. The chain may be a simple link chain (drag-link conveyor) or the links may have ears or flights attached to them (flight conveyors) (Fig. 19.3). The duct is kept filled with material which is conveyed because the interparticulate friction is greater than the wall friction. Flour, grain and similar materials are effectively conveyed at high capacity. Ring systems with intermediate charge and discharge points are common. Alternatively, the return leg may run in the same casing. Chain speeds are relatively low, 0.1–$0.15 \, \text{m s}^{-1}$ being typical. Inclination is limited by the tendency of the material to slip back, and with most types a maximum angle of $30°$ is permissible.

19.2.2.9. Uses of conveyors

Conveyors represent the largest group of handling devices, accounting for over 50% of all handling equipment sales. They are available for movement of any type of solid or semi-solid material and in a wide range of capacities. Fitted with an appropriate heating surface, conveyors may be used for in-transit processing such as: heating; cooling; baking; blanching; mixing; sorting; sieving; coating; etc. They may be used to pace and time operations.

As with any other type of moving machinery, stringent safety precautions must be taken when operating conveyors. These include side-

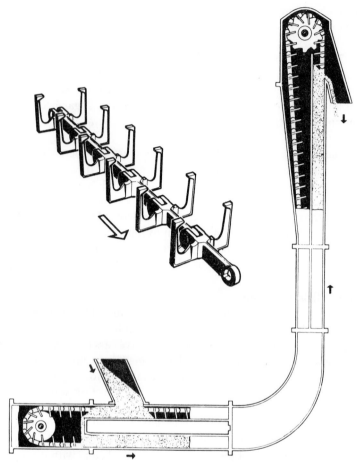

FIG. 19.3.   The Redler 'En Masse' conveyor used as a flight elevator. The inset shows the elevator chain in more detail. (By courtesy of Redler Conveyors Ltd, Stroud, Glos., England.)

guards on belt and roller conveyors and anti-nip shields on driven rollers. Additionally, conveyors may need to be enclosed to protect the product and to restrict the spread of food dusts, many of which represent health or explosion hazards or both.

Conveying surfaces must be non-contaminating, easily cleaned and resistant to fraying, chipping, excessive wearing, abrasion or other damage which might represent a contamination hazard. Finally, conveyors should be designed to minimise impact, abrasion or puncturing damage of the conveyed material.

19.3. ELEVATORS

Elevators are conveniently considered as equipment for continuous movement of material in a vertical path (see Table 19.2). Elevation equipment is described in BS 3810.[4]

19.3.1. PACKAGE ELEVATORS

Packages are carried vertically on free-swinging trays suspended between a pair of endless chains. Loads are charged on the upgoing side, pass around the top of the conveyor and are discharged on the downgoing side. Travel speeds of 0.1–$0.2\,\mathrm{m\,s^{-1}}$ are common (Fig. 19.4). These elevators are useful in multi-storey buildings where access is restricted. Strict safety precautions are necessary with open conveyors of this type.

19.3.2. BULK ELEVATORS

The four types of bulk elevator most commonly encountered are: screw, pneumatic, flight and bucket.[11] Screw conveying (Section 19.2.2.7) is used for elevation but owing to the friction involved, power consumption becomes unduly high at lifts above about 5 m. Pneumatic elevation is discussed in Section 19.6.

19.3.2.1. Flight elevators

Vertical elevation using flight conveyors (Section 19.2.2.8) requires the use of specially designed flights and casings such as those used in the 'en masse' system. The flight elevator combined with the flight conveyor in a ring circuit provides a flexible, totally enclosed system (Fig. 19.3) suitable for high-capacity multilevel movement of a wide range of particulate foods.

19.3.2.2. Bucket elevators

These are high-capacity units primarily for bulk elevation of relatively free-flowing materials such as sugar, beans, salt and cereals. Light, fluffy, sticky or wet materials can be dealt with but require special equipment.

The bucket elevator consists of steel or malleable iron buckets carried on an endless belt or on single or double endless chains. The more important considerations affecting the design and operation of these elevators are:

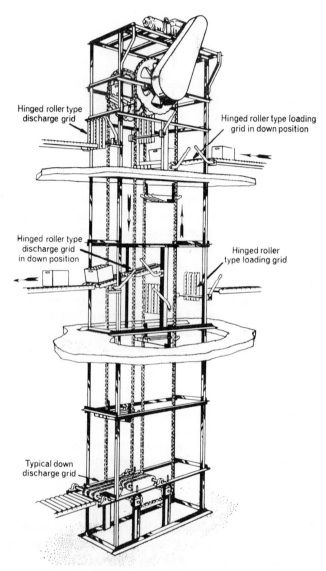

Fig. 19.4. A vertical swinging tray elevator. (By courtesy of W. & C. Pantin Ltd, Epping, Essex, England.)

(i)   The physical properties of the conveyed material (its moisture content, angle of repose, flow properties and crystal form).

(ii) The shape and pitch (i.e. spacing) of the buckets.

(iii) The speed at which the elevator is driven.

(iv) The method of feeding the elevator.

(v)   The method of discharging the elevator.

Drive speed, although dependent on the type of material, is controlled mainly by the method of discharge. There are four main types of discharge—gravity, centrifugal, positive and continuous (Fig. 19.5).

Gravity discharge buckets are carried pivoted on two chains and are tipped mechanically. Large capacity buckets are carried at about $0.25 \, \mathrm{m \, s^{-1}}$, usually at an inclination, providing a slow-speed high-capacity elevation system.

Centrifugal discharge types dredge up the material at the feed point (elevator 'boot') and discharge centrifugally into a chute. Commonly, discharge is arranged to take place when the line produced from the bucket centre to the sprocket centre makes an angle of approximately 45° to the vertical. With this method of discharge the linear speed of the drive chains is critical if the product is to be thrown cleanly into the outlet chute with minimal fall into the down-leg. In general it is found that linear velocities of around $1.5 \, \mathrm{m \, s^{-1}}$ are necessary. At these high speeds, belt carriers are used and considerable wear and tear of the running equipment is encountered. Additionally, stringent anti-explosion precautions are necessary. Centrifugal discharge systems are characterised by high capacity.

Positive discharge may be produced by tipping the buckets by means of a change-of-direction sprocket located on the down-side of the conveyor. This facilitates the dicharge of sticky and lumpy materials. This is a slower

(i)   (ii)   (iii)

FIG. 19.5.   Bucket elevator discharge systems. (i) Centrifugal discharge—the solid is thrown from the bucket to the discharge chute; (ii) positive discharge—the carrying chains are snubbed back to discharge wet or sticky material; (iii) continuous discharge—closely spaced buckets discharge onto the backs of the preceding buckets.

type, running at about $0.25\,\mathrm{m\,s^{-1}}$, with corresponding reduction in wear and tear and spark risk compared with centrifugal discharge systems.

Continuous discharge is a slow-speed system ($0.5\,\mathrm{m\,s^{-1}}$ approx.) which overcomes the disadvantage of spillage into the down-leg by discharging into the outlet using the backs of preceding buckets as chutes. The spacing between the buckets is small so that discharge is virtually continuous.

The feeding of bucket elevators must be carefully controlled (e.g. by using a screw feeder—Section 19.2.2.7), since the accumulation of material in the elevator boot places considerable strain on the belt or chains carrying the buckets.

Improved feeding is effected in the Econ-O-Lift (Gough Econ Mechanisation, Stoke-on-Trent, Staffs, England) bucket conveyor/elevator by the use of interlocking buckets which are carried pivoted on a pair of driven chains. The conveyor stops automatically at the feeding points, the chains are telescoped, and the buckets interlock to permit non-spill feeding. The conveyor re-starts automatically at the end of feeding and the chains resume a linear form, the buckets being tipped mechanically at the discharge points.[12]

19.4. CRANES AND HOISTS

These are used for intermittent movement of materials in a vertical direction with associated horizontal movement, a path or limited area being served (Table 19.2). The many types of cranes and hoists and their associated lifting tackle are described in BS 3810.[12]

19.4.1. CRANES

The main constructional features of a typical crane are shown in Fig. 19.6. The boom pivots on the mast which may be supported by fixed legs or guyed by ropes or cables. 'Derricking' is the act of winching the boom (or jib) up or down so as to alter the elevation of the boom and, hence, the area served by it. The lifting capacity and stability of cranes are considerably affected by the boom inclination. Failure to appreciate this causes many accidents.

Derrick cranes find wide application in handling from holds of barges or ships, from railway trucks and in similar situations where their unique lift and swing motion can be used to maximum advantage. Fixed-elevation jib cranes find many applications in the food industry (e.g. the charging of large vertical canning retorts and the handling of heavy packages). Jib-

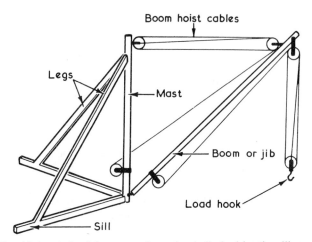

FIG. 19.6. A derrick crane—the swing is limited by the sills and legs.

crane attachments are obtainable for fork-lift trucks, providing a mobile unit of wide flexibility.

The overhead travelling crane (Fig. 19.7) is capable of vertical movement serving a large area and finds application in warehousing operations. Cranes of this type give excellent building cube utilisation since aisle requirements are minimal and stacking to within a foot or so of the crane beams is practicable.

19.4.2. HOISTS

The act of hoisting is, primarily, a vertical lifting or lowering movement, so that a crane is a hoisting mechanism motivated by a source of power remote

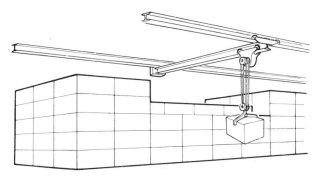

FIG. 19.7.   An overhead crane system.

from the load carrier. Hoists referred to in this section are lifting and lowering mechanisms in which the load is carried suspended from the motivator.

Hoists generally employ some type of gear arranagement in order to increase the mechanical advantage of the system (i.e. the ratio: weight lifted/effort applied). The types of gearing most frequently encountered in the food industry are:

(i) Lever hoists which work on the principle of the wheel and axle. The effort is applied by a ratchet lever, and lever hoists handling $\frac{1}{2}$–5 tonnes are common. They have low mechanical efficiency (35%) and are self-braking.

(ii) Differential hoists which employ a fixed double sheave in conjunction with a movable sheave block and fall system. They are operated by pulling on an endless chain which runs round the pulley wheels. They have low efficiencies (30–40%), are self-braking and may be used in intermittent, slow movements where accurate positioning is necessary (e.g. machinery installation and truck battery handling).

(iii) Worm geared hoists in which a driven worm turns a spur gear which lifts the load. They are capable of producing high mechanical advantage and have corresponding high capacity (up to 20 tonnes).

(iv) Spur geared hoists which use either compound gear trains or epicyclic (i.e. planetary) gears. These hoists have high efficiency (up to 85%).

Types (iii) and (iv) are compact and powerful and are well suited to high-speed electrically powered hoisting. When attached to an overhead runway they provide an inexpensive and flexible system for handling packaged materials. Large hoists of this type are used in port-handling of containerised loads up to 70 tonnes in weight. In one application, self-propelled cars, each with its own operator, winch and lifting beam, run on an overhead track circuit supported by masts travelling on railed tracks.[13]

Air operated hoists have certain advantages over electric hoists: they are spark proof and therefore safe in dusty conditions; they are smooth in operation; they permit accurate positioning of the load and they cannot be overloaded. With a minimum of moving parts, air hoists are cheap to maintain and are resistant to corrosive, hot or wet conditions. Disadvantageously, air hoists require a supply of compressed air at about $800 \, \text{kN} \, \text{m}^{-2}$ and lifts are restricted to the stroke of the piston unless some sort of multiplier is used.

19.5. TRUCKS

19.5.1. GENERAL CONSIDERATIONS
This group includes all handling equipment which is capable of movement in a horizontal non-fixed path. It is convenient to categorise trucks on the basis of their vertical lifting characteristics giving three main groups as follows:

(i) Trucks with no vertical lift (hand trucks, platform trucks and tractors).
(ii) Trucks with low vertical lift (pallet and stillage trucks).
(iii) Trucks with high vertical lift (fork-lift trucks and stackers).

Hand trucks, powered trucks and their ancillary equipment, such as pallets and truck attachments, are described in BS 3810.[13]

19.5.1.1. Loads for trucks
Although trucks can handle any load which can be accommodated on the carriers, proper observation of the rules of material handling (Section 19.1.2) requires materials to be handled as *unit loads*.[14] A unit load is a group of items or a mass of bulk material which is handled as a single entity. It is standardised on the basis of weight, number or size. The movement of unit loads instead of single items results in: faster and cheaper handling and stocktaking, reduced product damage, improved stock rotation and better building-cube utilisation. Common forms of unit loads are:

(i) Assemblies of items on platforms, skids, pallets and flat sheets.
(ii) Groups of small items or masses of bulk material in containers such as bins, crates, trays or tanks.
(iii) Strapped, taped, baled, shrink-wrapped or bundled assemblies.
(iv) Loose loads which are handled as assemblies, by baling clamps, shovels, etc.

19.5.1.2. Drive systems for trucks
Drive resistance considerations affect the size and type of motivator selected. This is an important matter: a drive unit which is too small causes delay and disorganisation; one which is too large contravenes the dead-weight rule (Section 19.1.2). When selecting a drive system, three types of resistance must be considered. These are:

(i) *Tractive resistance* (TR) which is the force required to overcome rolling friction when a specified gross weight (truck and load) moves over a given surface. The magnitude of TR is dependent on the nature of the surface, varying from $150\,\text{N tonne}^{-1}$ ($\sim 35\,\text{lbf ton}^{-1}$) for a smooth concrete surface, to $1500\,\text{N tonne}^{-1}$ ($\sim 350\,\text{lbf ton}^{-1}$) for clay. For design purposes a value of $200\,\text{N tonne}^{-1}$ ($45\,\text{lbf ton}^{-1}$) is assumed for well maintained floors.

(ii)   *Acceleration resistance* (AR) which is the force required to overcome inertia to acceleration. Trucks usually accelerate at around $0{\cdot}2\,\text{m s}^{-2}$ ($\sim 0{\cdot}6\,\text{ft s}^{-2}$) and at this rate, AR has a value of $200\,\text{N tonne}^{-1}$ ($\sim 45\,\text{lbf ton}^{-1}$).

(iii) *Grade resistance* (GR) which is the force additional to TR required to surmount a specified incline. Inclination is conveniently referred to as 'percentage grade' which is:

$$\frac{\text{vertical travel}}{\text{horizontal travel along the plane}} \times 100$$

Using this concept, for a gross weight of 1 tonne, GR has a value of $98\,\text{N}$ per 1% grade ($22{\cdot}4\,\text{lbf}$ per ton per 1% of grade).

Total tractive effort (TE) is calculated by summing these three resistances, hence:

$$\text{TE} = \text{TR} + \text{AR} + \text{GR}$$

Thus a man can conveniently move a load of 1 tonne on a hard, smooth, horizontal surface ($\text{TE} = 200 + 200 + 0 = 400\,\text{N}$ or $90\,\text{lbf}$) but if a shallow incline (say 2% grade) intervenes then TE increases to $400 + 2 \times 98 = 596\,\text{N}$ or $134\,\text{lbf}$ and fatigue rapidly sets in. The considerable effect of ascending gradients on the magnitude of TE and, hence, on the size of drive-system is noteworthy.

In addition to TE, allowance must be made for other energy consuming activities such as: loss of efficiency between motor and drive wheels; energy consumed in load lifting and lowering; and power used for steering and manoeuvring.

Manpowered drives despite their obvious limitations find use in confined areas and when intermittent working at low speed is acceptable. Power-assisted manpower is also of value, high and low lift facilities being added to the manoeuvrability and low capital costs of manpowered equipment.

Battery powered drives have the general characteristics shown in Table 19.3. Trucks driven by this method have a high dead-weight to capacity ratio and are limited by the storage capacity of their batteries. They are best suited to movement over short distance (100 m continuously) and on smooth level surfaces (maximum 10% grade).

TABLE 19.3
Characteristics of truck engines

Characteristic \ Drive System	Electric	Petrol	LPG	Diesel
Risk of product contamination by fuel and exhaust	none	high	moderate	v. high
Type of haul (continuous)	short	long	long	long
Gradient surmountability	poor ($<10\%$)	good	good	good
Noise level	very low	high	high	high
Starting (cold)	easy	mod. difficult	mod. difficult	mod. difficult
Fire and explosion risk in dusty conditions	very low or none[a]	high	moderate	low
Engine wear	low	high	moderate	high

[a] When flashproofed.

Internal combustion (*IC*) *drives*, using petrol or diesel fuel or liquefied petroleum gas (LPG), find application where long travel distances and steep gradients are involved (Table 19.3).

IC engines should not be used in conditions where fire risk, product contamination risk or poor ventilation exist. LPG engines are similar in design to petrol engines, differing only in using a gaseous fuel which is said to cause less engine wear than occurs with liquid fuels. The exhaust is cleaner and the fuel less odorous than in petrol and diesel systems. LPG engines are sometimes used inside well-ventilated warehouses.

19.5.1.3. Wheels for trucks
The type of wheel selected should: handle the food gently, not cause floor damage, be easy to start and keep rolling (i.e. low AR and TR), and result in the lowest operating cost. The more important characteristics of truck wheels are indicated in Table 19.4.

19.5.1.4. Stillages and pallets
These are the subject of various standard specifications.[15,16] Pallets and stillages (or skids) must be loaded in patterns which ensure stability during transit and storage.

Stillages (or skids) are platforms mounted on pairs of parallel runners at each side or on legs at each corner (Fig. 19.8). Stillages may be 'live' (i.e. with four wheeled legs), 'semi-live' (with two wheeled and two fixed legs), or 'dead' (with fixed runners or legs). They may be made of wood or metal and are primarily intended for in-use movement or single-layer storage.

Table 19.4
Wheels for trucks

Wheel type Characteristic	Iron and steel	Aluminium	Polyurethane and phenolic	Rubber cushion	Rubber pneumatic
Load bearing	*****	**	***	****	***
Floor protection	*	**	***	****	*****
Impact resistance	*****	*	**	***	****
Wear resistance	*****	**	**	***	**
Non-spark properties	*	*****	*****	*****	*****
Oil resistance	*****	*****	****	*	*
Type of ride	*	**	**	***	*****
Noise rating	*	**	****	****	*****
Manoeuvrability	*****	*****	****	***	*

*****—very good;   *—very poor.

Stillages should not be used for stacking unless load boards are interposed between layers, otherwise the heavy loading at the runners causes damage to underlying layers.

Pallets are load boards with two decks supported by bearers or, alternatively, with a single deck supported by at least three bearers. Pallets may be two-way or four-way entry. In the former type the decks are separated by solid stringers and in the latter by stringers and block bearers (Fig. 19.9).

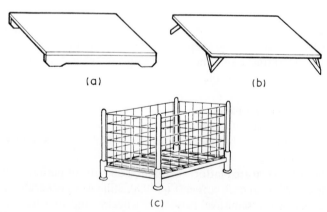

Fig. 19.8.   Types of stillage. (a) Two-way entry. (b) Four-way entry. (c) Collapsible box stillage.

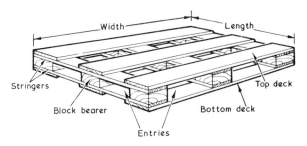

FIG. 19.9. Pallet components.

In the UK, pallets are restricted to a few standard sizes, the $1000 \times 1200 \, mm^2$ pallet being the most common. In Europe, the so-called Europallet ($800 \times 1200 \, mm^2$) is widely used. Pallet handling equipment and racking and pallet transportation vehicles work most efficiently with standard pallet sizes. Standardisation of pallet sizes and types within industry, although far from complete, has permitted a considerable amount of pallet-sharing between customer and supplier with corresponding cost savings. In spite of this, pallet costs due to losses, pilferage, etc., are still substantial. Many attempts have been made to reduce these costs by using 'one-trip' or metal or plastic pallets to replace the traditional wooden pallet, but wood remains the most cost-effective material for pallet construction.

The establishment of nationally-based pallet exchange, recovery and management organisations, who supply, retrieve, repair and return pallets, is claimed to alleviate many of the problems involved in pallet use.[17]

19.5.2. TRUCKS WITH NO VERTICAL LIFT

19.5.2.1. Hand trucks

Despite the emphasis on mechanisation, these are available in wide variety. Truck manufacturers are able to offer trucks designed for specialised handling applications at low prices. In special circumstances (e.g. in confined areas) hand trucks are valuable handling adjuncts. Their main disadvantage is the tendency to use them in disregard of the performance effectiveness (Section 19.1.2) and in this circumstance inefficiency results.

19.5.2.2. Platform trucks

Manpowered platform trucks, although still used, are being rapidly replaced by powered burden-carriers. Powered trucks with capacities ranging from 1 to 3 tonnes are common. They are used as fork-lift truck economisers, where their lightness, manoeuvrability and relative cheapness may be fully exploited. Both operator-led and operator-carrying types are available. Unpowered platform trucks are used in 'tractor trains' (Section 19.5.2.3).

19.5.2.3. Tractors

A powered tractor towing a train of platform trucks (i.e. a 'tractor train') provides an inexpensive high-capacity handling system for unit loads. The trucks are loaded by hoist, crane or by a stacker (Section 19.5.4) and function as an efficient transportation system for serving distant points. In some instances this enables a fork-lift truck to be replaced by a cheaper stacking truck.

The capacities of tractors are indicated in terms of drawbar pull. Tractors capable of moving loads of up to 40 tonnes are common. The capacity is substantially reduced on inclines where grade resistance (GR) must be allowed for. The stated maximum drawbar pull should be scrupulously observed since some types of tractor, if overloaded, are likely to rear up on the back wheels and cause accidents by toppling.

Driverless tractor trains, electronically controlled and running on programmed paths, are becoming increasingly popular (Section 19.5.5.4).

19.5.3. TRUCKS WITH LOW VERTICAL LIFT

A low-lift truck is a self-loading machine which carries its load on a skid or pallet. The forks or platform are engaged with the load which is lifted sufficiently to allow free movement, the procedure being reversed at the discharge point. These trucks may be manpowered, power assisted, or fully powered and lifts varying from 5 to 10 cm may be produced mechanically or hydraulically. Unit loads up to 1 tonne may be handled conveniently, rapidly and cheaply. Low-lift trucks are very manoevrable, requiring only half the aisle space of a fork-lift truck, and they may be moved from floor to floor by elevator since they are relatively light in weight. However, these trucks generally have small-diameter wheels giving high floor loading. Particular care must be exercised in the choice of wheels in this case (Section 19.5.1.3).

Pallet trucks are equipped with forks which are fed, with the help of the booster wheels (Fig. 19.10), into the pallet entry. On actuating the lift mechanism, the load wheels (which are normally carried housed in the forks) swivel down and lift the load clear of the ground for transit.

Stillage (or skid) trucks carry their loads on stillages. The lowered platform of the truck is slid beneath the stillage, the platform is then raised and held locked for transit.

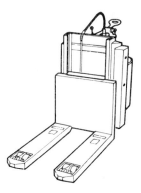

Fig. 19.10.   A twin-fork low-lift pallet truck. (By courtesy of Matling Engineering (1962) Ltd, Wednesbury, Staffs.)

19.5.4. TRUCKS WITH HIGH VERTICAL LIFT

Trucks with high vertical lift are primarily intended for stacking activities. Their use for movement over long distances is inefficient and expensive. High-lift trucks range from manpowered stackers to powered lift-trucks handling 10 tonnes and equipped with a large array of ancillaries. Typical examples are shown in Fig. 19.11, the stacking truck being specifically for working in narrow aisles, and for relieving or replacing the more expensive and more space-consuming fork-lift truck. The use of this type of equipment is well known and calls for no description. The general characteristics which are operative in selecting and operating high-lift equipment are discussed below.

Load distribution methods may be of different types as follows:

(i)   Counterbalanced trucks which use the rear mounted battery or motor to balance the load, the front wheels acting as a fulcrum.

(ii)   Outrigger trucks which carry their loads within the wheel-base, the front wheels being carried on extended legs. Non-straddle trucks have the legs inside the forks whilst straddle trucks have the legs outside the forks so as to clear the base of the load.

(iii)   Reach trucks which are characterised by the ability of the forks, the fork carriage, or the whole mast, to move forward horizontally to facilitate manoeuvring of the load.

(iv)   Sideloading trucks which carry their loads at right angles to the direction of travel and are used for handling lengthy loads, such as timber and girders.

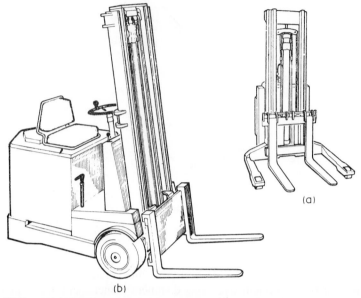

FIG. 19.11. High-lift free moving equipment. (a) Straddle type pallet truck. (b) Driver controlled counterbalanced type fork lift truck. (By courtesy of Matling Engineering (1962) Ltd, Wednesbury, Staffs.)

Masts are usually telescopic and lifts of 3 m are general. The 'free lift' is the maximum lift attainable before the mast starts to telescope out. Lift speeds of $0.2 \, \text{m s}^{-1}$ and lowering speeds of around $0.25 \, \text{m s}^{-1}$ are common. Masts may be fixed, or forward moving as in reach trucks, or swivelling so as to turn the forks at an angle to the direction of movement. It is usual to provide a backward tilt of 10–12° for safe carriage and a forward tilt of 2–3° to permit easy positioning and pick-up of loads.

Load capacity is generally rated as 'W kg at X cm load centres'. This means that the truck is rated to carry a load of W kg with its centre of gravity at a horizontal distance of X cm from the heels of the forks when these are in the lowered position. Other rating systems are described by Apple.[1] Mast tilt, and lifting or tilting the load, considerably affect load capacity and stability.

Gradient surmountability and underclearance are specified by manufacturers. The presence of ramps and other floor-level projections must be considered when selecting equipment.

Manoeuvrability specifications indicate the minimum aisle widths required for travelling, turning and stacking. Unfortunately, fork-lift trucks, in particular, require wide aisles which reduce maximum utilisation of floor area.

Speeds for battery driven trucks are 8–$10\,km\,h^{-1}$ whilst internal combustion types run at 15–$20\,km\,h^{-1}$. In the interests of safety, speed limits must be rigidly enforced.

Attachments for trucks include: extension forks, drum and bale clamps, squeeze clamps and crane attachments. The use of these devices should be carefully considered having regard to the rules given in Section 19.1.2.

19.5.5. ANCILLARY TRUCKING EQUIPMENT

Equipment manufacturers offer a wide range of ancillary equipment designed to extend the applications of truck handling or to improve its effectiveness.

Such ancillaries include: automatic pallet loading and unloading machines; pallet racking and devices for automatic truck dispatching; and guidance.

19.5.5.1. Automatic pallet loaders and unloaders

These find extensive application in modern automatic handling. Automatic palletisers are widely used for forming palletised unit loads from sub-units such as cartons, boxes and sacks. These are conveyed into the palletiser and are formed into tiered layers by means of powered rams controlled by a programming device. Loaders handling 5–15 sub-units min^{-1} are common and high-speed units are capable of dealing with 35 sub-units min^{-1}.[18] Automatic de-palletisers are also available.[19]

19.5.5.2. Pallet racking

Stacking pallet loads, one on top of another, leads inevitably to damage of the product by crushing and to inefficient handling. This is alleviated by the use of pallet racking which is a skeleton framework designed to support individual pallet loads. Racking may be of the fixed or flow type. In the former, the pallets are supported on fixed rails which are, usually, adjustable. The flow type racking incorporates pallet supports using either inclined rails fitted with gravity rollers or skate wheels (Section 19.2.1.2) or horizontal rails fitted with driven rollers or chains (Section 19.2.2).

Flow type racking or 'live storage', as it is termed, confers many handling advantages such as:

(i) Reduced product damage.
(ii) Better rotation and easier selection of stored materials.

(iii)   Improved height utilisation.
(iv)   Reduced handling costs.
(v)   Suitability for computer controlled operation.

Pallet loads may be loaded on to racking in the conventional manner using fork lift trucks but stacker cranes are increasingly used for this duty.[20] A stacker crane is an overhead travelling crane (Section 19.4.1) equipped with an inverted mast which can be rotated about its vertical axis. The pallet load is carried on forks which are arranged to travel up and down the mast. Movement of the pallet on the forks may be assisted by driven chains or rollers built into the bearing surface of the forks. Stacker cranes are fast, flexible and precise in operation, amenable to automatic control and work in much narrower aisles and to a greater height than is the case with fork lift trucks.

Pallet racking, especially the flow-type, is expensive to install and careful study should be undertaken before investing in an installation.

19.5.5.3. Truck routing
Inefficient truck routing leads to increased warehousing expenditure which, in itself, is a non-productive on-cost. Computer-controlled truck routing systems, of which the Lex Logisticon Dispatcher System (Lex Logisticon Ltd, High Wycombe, Buckinghamshire, England) is typical, can effect substantial cost reduction in handling. The system uses a computer which stores information about stock, warehouse layout and equipment and operator availability. This computer is linked to the mainframe computer enabling two-way transfer of data about order movements and stock and dispatch status. The dispatcher computer is also linked to two-way radio data terminals which travel with the trucks. All truck movement tasks are assigned to the truck via the dispatcher computer which organises tasks into an integrated work schedule for each truck and operator. Immediately a task is completed the operator keys in 'job done' and the next task appears on the display on the truck terminal.

19.5.5.4. Automated truck guidance
Automated guided vehicles ('AGVs') are driverless vehicles, automatically controlled, which are capable of carrying loads, or towing trailers or trains of vehicles.[13,21] Guidance is either of the wire or optical guidance type. In the former, the motor of the AGV is inductively coupled to the guide wire which is buried in the floor, while optical systems involve the use of coloured guide lines attached to or painted on the floor; photoelectric

sensors on the vehicle track these coloured lines. Both systems restrict AGV movement to predetermined routes and are subject to interference of the guidelines by dirt, grease, etc.

A recent development, permitting free-path AGV movement, uses a computer to signal the vehicle route as $X-Y$ coordinates. The computer selects the best route for an assigned task and also provides slow, stop and traffic control of the vehicle. Passage of the AGV is electronically mapped and precise location may be achieved by using a wheel odometer supplemented by a rotating laser mounted on the truck. The laser beam scans bar codes mounted along the route and is claimed to estimate position to an accuracy of ± 6 cm (GEC Electronic Projects, Rugby, England).[22]

AGVs are available with a wide range of attachments, such as forks equipped with motorised load transfer devices, proximity alarms, infra-red and radio communications, etc. Capacities range from 500 kg to 6 tonnes.

AGVs may be programmed to dispatch or pick up loads on predetermined routes. They may be set to stop at or by-pass locations or wait for set times at specified places, returning to stores to stack loads and then to reload with fresh materials. Finally, the AGV may be signalled to return to base, to plug itself in to recharge its batteries and to signal readiness for further duty when fully charged.

19.6. PNEUMATIC EQUIPMENT

Pneumatic handling utilises a flow of air to reduce or eliminate solid–solid friction in a system. Three classes of handling may be distinguished:

(i) Package conveying using the 'air-cushion' principle.
(ii) Conveying of particulate solids fluidised by air.
(iii) Conveying of particulate solids suspended in air.

19.6.1. 'AIR CUSHION' CONVEYING OF PACKAGED MATERIALS

In one example of this method of handling, packages are conveyed by gravity on an inclined chute. A package placed on the chute depresses patented valves set in the chute surface. These admit air beneath the package to form an 'air cushion'. Another type of air-cushion conveyor which is suitable for conveying both packages and bulk food materials uses a flow of low-pressure air, issuing from louvres punched in the conveying surface, to lift and propel the load. Air-floated pallets using the Hovercraft principle may be used to handle heavy loads (~ 7 tonnes) over uneven surfaces in confined conditions.[23]

19.6.2. FLUIDISED CONVEYING

Fluidisation is concerned with persuading a mass of particles to behave as a fluid by using a flow of air to separate the particles so that they no longer interact with one another. Clearly, the properties of both the fluid and the particles are operative in determining the magnitude of the pressure drop which it is necessary to establish to produce flow of the fluid through the particle bed. The interaction of these properties is reflected in the general equations (I.6 and I.7) given in Appendix I.

At the so-called 'point of fluidisation', where particle interaction is just overcome, the pressure drop is referred to as the 'minimum fluidising pressure' (Δp_{mf}) and no further bed expansion occurs when pressure is increased.

Particulate solids, contained in silos or bulk transportation vehicles, may be fluidised to assist discharge (Fig. 19.12). Air is introduced in sufficient quantity and at sufficient pressure to produce gravity flow of the material. This is sometimes called 'dense phase' conveying[24] and is characterised by a high solids to air ratio. The beds used in fluidised handling consist of porous ceramic tiles, sintered metal or plastic, fine wire-mesh and similar materials.[25]

Fluidised solids may be forced through pipe-lines by air under pressure as in the 'powder pump' shown diagrammatically in Fig. 19.13. Specially

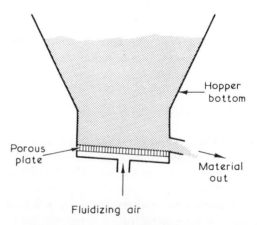

FIG. 19.12.   Fluidised bed discharge.

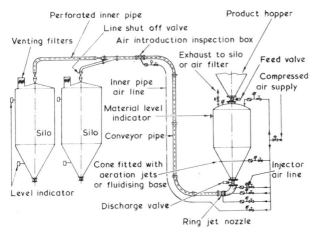

FIG. 19.13.   The Pennsalt-Gattys dense phase pneumatic conveying system. (By courtesy of Pennsalt Ltd, Camberley, Surrey, England.)

designed road and rail vehicles which discharge bulk loads of flour, salt, sugar, etc., using this principle are commonly encountered.

Solids contained in a pipe-line may be fluidised by passing air through a perforated flexible inner-tube running the length of the pipe-line. The fluidised material is then conveyed by establishing a pressure drop along the pipe-line (Fig. 19.13).

19.6.3.   CONVEYING OF SOLIDS SUSPENDED IN AIR

Considering further the flow situation described in Section 19.6.2, as Δp_{mf} is exceeded, particles will increasingly become entrained in the flowing air stream. At some value of Δp all the particles will be in suspension and, providing the pressure drop is maintained, will remain so. System changes, such as sudden direction changes or pressure drop due to a leak or an increase in solids to air ratio, result in instability, settling of the particles (saltation) and rapid blockage of the system.

In practice, air flowing axially along a pipe-line is used in sufficient quantity and at sufficient pressure to suspend particulate materials and to convey them through the pipe-line. This method of handling, characterised by a low solids to air ratio, is called 'dilute phase' or 'dispersed phase' conveying.[24]

19.6.3.1.   Types of dilute phase conveyor

Figure 19.14 shows the three main types of dilute phase conveyor. The 'positive pressure' or 'push' system operates at super-atmospheric pressure

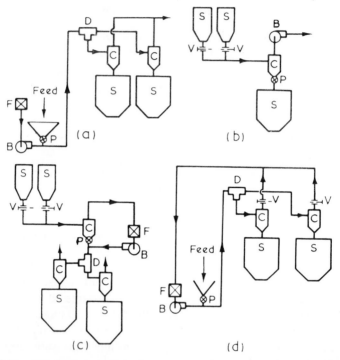

FIG. 19.14.   Dilute phase pneumatic conveyor types. (a) Open push type. (b) Open pull type. (c) Open push–pull type. (d) Closed push type. B, blower; C, disengager; D, diverter; F, air filter; P, feeder; S, silo; V, slide valve.

and is used for delivery to several outlets from one inlet. The 'negative pressure' or 'pull' system works at sub-atmospheric pressure and is used for delivery to one outlet from several inlets. The combination or 'push–pull' system is used for delivery to several outlets from multiple inlets.

Recirculation of the conveying air, as in the 'closed' system, reduces contamination of the product by the air and limits product dehydration. However, such systems are often difficult to control and an intercooler may be required to prevent the pump overheating the recirculated air.

19.6.3.2. Factors affecting dilute phase conveying

Air velocity. Most food materials may be conveyed satisfactorily at air speeds within the range of 15–$25\,\mathrm{m\,s^{-1}}$. Above this, abrasion of tube bends and product damage may become troublesome. At speeds which are too low, solids tend to settle out (saltate) and block horizontal pipe runs.

Air pressure. This is required to provide energy to:

(i)   Accelerate the conveying air.
(ii) Lift the particles.
(iii) Overcome resistances due to interparticulate and particle-wall collisions.
(iv) Overcome fluid friction in ducting and beds.
(v)   Overcome resistance due to disengagement of the solid at the discharge point.

Thus there will be a pressure drop along the conveyor as the energy in the air is expended. If air at high pressure is used, its correspondingly high initial energy will enable more conveying to be accomplished, per kilogram of air, than if low-pressure air is used. However, high-pressure systems are proportionately more expensive and the maximum pressure used for general purpose dilute phase conveying is about $170 \, kN \, m^{-2}$.

Solid-air ratio. Obviously, for maximum efficiency this ratio should be as high as possible. For flour and salt this ratio may be up to $80 \, kg$ solid m^{-3} air while wheat is limited to $30 \, kg$ solid m^{-3}. There is an upper limit for this ratio for each material, which if exceeded will cause blockage of the system as a result of saltation.

Material properties. The size, shape, density and surface properties of the particles comprising a material control its behaviour during pneumatic transfer (Appendix I). Other properties such as friability, hygroscopicity and susceptibility to impact and abrasion damage or oxidation must be considered.

19.6.3.3. Components of dilute phase conveyors

Air movers. High-speed, single-stage, centrifugal fans deliver air at about $120 \, kN \, m^{-2}$ and must be supplied with cleaned air if excessive abrasion of the light impellers is to be avoided. The slower-running, multi-stage, heavy-duty centrifugal fan can deliver up to $140 \, k \, N \, m^{-2}$ and, being slower running, is relatively resistant to particle abrasion. The discharge from centrifugal fans falls markedly as the discharge pressure rises, so solids blockage may occur. Centrifugal fans are used in low-pressure conveyors ($105–125 \, k \, N \, m^{-2}$).

Positive displacement blowers, of the Root's type, pump through driven, intermeshing lobes. The clearance between the lobes is small so that an inlet air cleaner is required to reduce wear. Blowers of this type are less affected by downstream pressure than fans, and produce lubricant-free air. Single-stage blowers generate up to $200 \, kN \, m^{-2}$ and double-stage blowers

FIG. 19.15. The sonic valve. (By courtesy of the patentees—Henry Simon Ltd, Stockport, England.)

generate up to about $270 \, kN \, m^{-2}$. Blowers are, therefore, used extensively in medium pressure systems $(120–200 \, kN \, m^{-2})$.

Compressors deliver air at high pressures but require lubrication. This contaminates the air with oil vapour which is difficult to remove. Nevertheless, compressors find applications in high-pressure systems $(200–800 \, kN \, m^{-2})$ and in dense phase conveying.

Stabilisers. If one air mover supplies several conveyor pipes, each must be unaffected by changes in the others. Figure 19.15 shows an air stabilising valve designed to satisfy this requirement. The valve works on the principle that once the pressure drop across an air nozzle exceeds a certain minimum value, the velocity at the throat equals that of sound and no further reduction in the downstream pressure affects the mass-flow rate through the nozzle. Thus, a constant rate of supply may be maintained against a fluctuating pressure in the conveyor.

Feeders. Figure 19.16 shows two types of feeder. The venturi feeder is

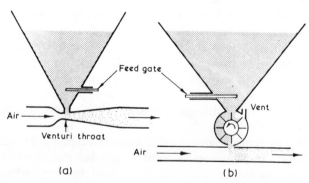

FIG. 19.16. Feeding devices for pneumatic conveyors. (a) Venturi feeder. (b) Rotary feeder.

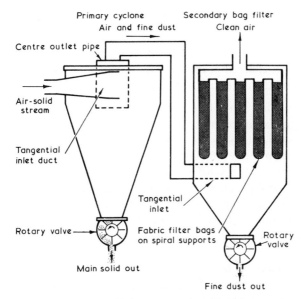

FIG. 19.17.   Separation system for a pneumatic conveyor.

only suitable for low-pressure systems. The rotary valve is widely used for
feeding medium-pressure conveyors and, although simple in principle, calls
for careful design in order to minimise air leakage. Excessive air loss from
feeders wastes power, causes dust and leads to system instability. Rotary
valves work well on free-flowing non-abrasive powders and special types
are available for more difficult materials.

Separators. Preliminary disengagement of the conveyed material from
the conveying air at the discharge point may be affected by discharging into
a receiver of sufficient size. The efficiency of this method is improved by
fitting an impingement plate in the air path. It is more general, however, to
bring about separation by means of a cyclone followed by a bag filter
(Fig. 19.17).

19.6.3.4. Safety precautions. Product charging
Static charges of considerable potential can be developed during the
pneumatic conveying of many food materials (e.g. sugar, flour and grain).
Both product–wall and product–product charges can be produced. These
may initiate dust explosions or cause shocks to operators. Charging of the
product can also cause wall adhesion, agglomeration and blocking.

Ducting should be effectively earthed taking particular care to install bridging plates on ducting joints. Product charging can be reduced by:

(i) Controlling the product moisture content.
(ii) Inserting charged probes into the product-air stream.
(iii) Ionising the air by radio-active materials.

Dust generation. Dust is a health hazard and, when combustible, represents an explosion risk. For a dust explosion to occur, three simultaneous contributions are necessary: a combustible dust in appropriate concentration; air in sufficient quantity; an ignition source. Frequently, these requirements are satisfied during food processing operations, in particular, during pneumatic conveying. Consequently, most stringent precautions are necessary during pneumatic conveying. Precautions are outlined in Section 2.3.1 but reference should be made to the large and expanding literature on dust hazards.[26]

19.6.3.5. Advantages of the method

A well designed system is self-cleaning, dustless and sanitary. Is has high capacity for installation and running costs which compare favourably with other conveying systems and makes good use of the building cube.

19.7. HYDRAULIC CONVEYING

The transport of solids suspended in water is not new. Coal (10 cm pieces) was pipelined in a stream of water, at 50 tonnes per hour, from Thames Wharf in London, 600 m to Hammersmith Power Station during the years 1913–24. Many other large installations exist, e.g. the 46 cm Black Mesa pipeline transports 6 million tonnes of coal a year 450 miles across North Arizona, USA.

If a free-draining material is unaffected by water (e.g. peas) then it may be transported cheaply and conveniently as a two phase suspension (pipelining). Other materials may need dewatering or drying which is costly. Alternatively, such material may be conveyed sealed in metal or plastic containers (capsule conveying).

19.7.1. PIPELINING
19.7.1.1. General considerations

Hydraulic and pneumatic systems exhibit many points of similarity, e.g. both systems display: bed expansion; fluidisation; formation of a horizontal surface and flow when there is a pressure drop along the conveyor. However, the following important differences are evident:

(1) Gases are compressible whereas liquids are not.
(2) The rheological properties of liquid–solid slurries, particularly divergence from Newtonian behaviour, exert much larger effects than is the case in gas–solid suspensions.

These facts complicate mathematical analysis of hydraulic systems and, although equations exist enabling the calculation of system parameters, such equations are too generalised to indicate firm design information.

In general, turbulent flow of a settling slurry takes place. At low liquid velocity the slurry moves by saltation over a stationary bed, particles being picked up, carried a short distance before being dropped and the process repeating itself. As fluid velocity increases, sliding-bed transfer accompanies saltation, this effect increasing with liquid velocity until homogeneous suspension is achieved.[27]

Liquid–solid systems, as distinct from pneumatic systems, show smooth, progressive bed expansion with increasing liquid velocity. Furthermore, at velocities in excess of U_{mf} (minimum fluidizing velocity) no bubbling takes place and particulate fluidisation occurs. With gas–solid systems bubbling and slugging take place giving rise to aggregative fluidisation (see Appendix I).

19.7.1.2. Pipelining equipment

The equipment used for hydraulic transfer depends on the following system properties:

(i) For the solid phase; particle size, shape and density.
(ii) For the liquid phase; velocity, density and viscosity.
(iii) For the slurry; velocity, ratio of solid to liquid and rheological properties.
(iv) For the pipeline; length, diameter and geometry, such as bends, elevation and fall.

Slurry preparation may involve simply stirring the solid at a measured rate into the liquid. Some materials, such as coal and abattoir waste, may require grinding, kibbling or wet milling.

Pumping of the suspensions is usually effected by means of centrifugal pumps for in-plant, short distance transfer. These will handle solids up to $0.5 \times$ smallest impeller gap without damage. Alternatively, ejector or venturi pumps may be used (see Fig. 19.16(a)). For long distance, high lifts and high density particles, positive displacement pumps, operating at over 40 bar (4 MN m^{-2}), are used.

Disengagement of the solid at the delivery point may be simply effected using a settling tank or cyclone separator. More difficult materials may require filtration, centrifugation or even drying.

Abrasion is frequently a serious problem. The life of some pump parts and pipeline components may be quite short (weeks). Abrasion resistant materials, such as PTFE and synthetic rubber, are often used to combat abrasion. The fitting of easily replaceable wear-plates at vulnerable points in pipelines is also common.

The advantages of pipeline systems include: high capacity for low capital investment and running costs; continuous operation; simple installation and environmental acceptability since underground transportation is practicable.

19.7.2. CAPSULE CONVEYING

19.7.2.1. General considerations

In cases when the material which is to be conveyed reacts with or is affected by the fluid or the pipeline, then it may be conveyed hydraulically as a capsulated mass. Capsulation may be effected by a number of different procedures, such as:

(i)   Enclosing water-reactive materials, such as slaughterhouse waste, in metal or plastic capsules.
(ii) Compressing water-reactive, coherent materials, such as waste paper or garbage, into capsules which are then coated with a water resistant film.
(iii) Water-insoluble powders, such as spent filter aid, may be mixed to a paste with a gelling agent and the paste then compressed into capsules.

The preformed capsules are then fed into a pipeline and are conveyed by a pumped flow of liquid, usually water. Conveying may take place as single capsules or as trains of capsules up to 30 m in length linked to each other by chains or cables. Alternatively, capsules may be kept together by using a leading capsule of slightly higher density than those following.

19.7.2.2. System parameters

Capsule shapes vary from spheres to cylinders or bullet-like shapes, the latter being preferred since they maintain their orientation during flow and negotiate bends satisfactorily.

Capsule size determines the speed at which the capsules travel in the pipeline. It is not necessary for the capsules to fit the pipeline snugly. Thus, capsules (diameter d) flowing in a pipeline (diameter D) will flow at liquid velocity if the ratio (d/D) approaches about 0·95 whereas a diameter ratio (d/D) of about 0·8 gives slow accelerating capsules which reach only about 65% of the liquid velocity. At diameter ratios of 0·5 and below capsules may settle and block the pipeline.[28] Capsule length is only of importance in ensuring that pipeline bends may be negotiated easily.

Pressure gradient (Δp) between the system inlet and outlet is a function of a number of system properties, such as: length; diameter; inclination; and geometry of the pipeline; fluid density and viscosity (hence its temperature); and capsule density, shape and surface smoothness. In general, relatively low pressure gradients usually suffice to achieve acceptable capsule flow rates.

Capsule conveying equipment is essentially similar to that described for pipelining applications in Section 19.7.1.2 with the exception that disengaging the flowing capsules requires simpler devices.

Advantages of capsuling are those of environmental acceptability, low labour and equipment costs as for slurry pipelining but, additionally, corrosive, water sensitive and contaminating materials may be transported over long distances with little or no pipeline or pump abrasion. Small diameter pipelines of around 10 cm are used and these may be buried easily below the frost line, minimising temperature (hence viscosity) variations, freeze-ups, etc. Finally, pipelines not in use for capsule conveying may be used to transport other liquids, such as oil, thus ensuring a high degree of utilisation. Much of the pioneering experimental work leading to the development of this materials handling procedure was carried out by H. S. Ellis in the early 1960s.[31]

19.8. AUTOMATION IN MATERIALS HANDLING

19.8.1. AUTOMATED EQUIPMENT CONTROL
Automatic controllers comprise three elements: sensors which detect and signal changes in process variables; analysers which compare the sensor signals with preset standards and determine a corrective strategy; and controllers which carry out the adjustments to the system variables.

Sensors are available for in-line measurement of most common physical, and some chemical, properties which are of importance in food processing. Physical measurements include flow, temperature, fluid and solid level, pressure, humidity, colour, density, viscosity, pH, conductivity and refractive index (and hence, soluble solids content or concentration). Sensors capable of measuring electromagnetic radiation properties are used for recognition, inspection and sorting using visible and infra-red radiation whilst near-infra-red spectra are employed for in-line analysis for moisture, fat, protein, etc.[29] In-line sensors are used for detecting changes in weight, volume and number and for positioning or orienting units. The output signals from sensors are usually either electrical in the range 0–10 V at 4–20 mA or pneumatic in the pressure range 30–100 kN m^{-2}.

Analysers receive and interpret signals generated by a sensor. They range in complexity from an amplifier connected to a relay, to a sophisticated, programmable logic controller (PLC). PLCs employ a microprocessor to analyse the sensor signal and use the information to carry out automatic sequence control of processes ranging from simple tasks, such as packaging or pallet loading, to complex operations, such as automation of a complete production process.[9]

Controllers adjust the process on receipt of a signal from the analyser. These take the form of a switch, valve, pump or motor which is electrically, pneumatically or hydraulically operated.

The employment of automation in palletisation and depalletisation and in truck routing and guidance are outlined in Section 19.5.5. Other important applications of automation in handling include auto-weighing and automatic warehousing (Sections 19.8.2 and 19.8.3).

19.8.2. AUTOMATIC WEIGHING

Many manual weighing procedures have now been replaced by automatic systems which are integral with handling equipment. Such automatic systems commonly comprise a load cell linked to a microprocessor linked to recording and control equipment.

Load cells used in auto-weighers use strain gauges (usually assembled in a Wheatstone Bridge) bonded to a short metal beam rigidly clamped at one end. The load is applied to the free end. Flexing of the beam by the load generates a voltage change which is passed to the analyser. An alternative load cell system is the shear type in which the strain gauges are attached to the inner web of a short hollow beam. Devices of these types are fast in response, cheap and easy to maintain, resistant to adverse environments and capable of high accurracy (1 part in 20 000).[9] However, load cells are sensitive to vibration and should be fitted with properly designed filtering and damping systems.

Reject gear may be used simply to stop a conveyor or process, or to sound an alarm but, more usually, the out-of-specification units are rejected by means of dropping flaps, horizontal ploughs, pusher arms fitted to the conveyor or, in high speed systems, by the use of an air jet.

19.8.2.1. Checkweighers

Individual units appropriately spaced are presented at speeds up to 200 per min to a weighing head comprising a load cell linked to a microprocessor which may be programmed to:

(i) Record totals of acceptable, overweight and underweight units.
(ii) Display mean weights.
(iii) Indicate weight change trends.
(iv) Reject units outside predetermined ranges.
(v) Produce a permanent one-hour average record and a half-hour warning of out-of-range performance.

19.8.2.2. Automatic batch weighers

The material to be weighed is charged (via a screw or vibrating conveyor) to a weighing vessel fitted with a load cell which automatically tares the empty vessel. As the target weight is approached the feed rate is reduced so that overrun is minimised. For solids which are self-levelling the weigh vessel is supported on three load cells, the analyser computing the mean weight and signalling for discharge when the target weight has been reached.

19.8.2.3. Continuous automatic weighers

These are of two main types. The first type measures the rate of loss of weight from a weigh vessel suspended from a load cell. The vessel discharges material continuously to process at a uniform rate. A microprocessor integrates weight and time and regulates the discharge rate and also controls the feed to the weigh vessel to maintain a constant head of feed which is essential in loss-of-weight systems of this type.

The second type of continuous weigher is the belt-weigher in which material is fed at controlled, uniform rate to a short, specially mounted conveyor belt. The belt passes over a low displacement weigh platform fitted with a load cell. The weight signals are used to adjust the feed rate or belt speed and, hence, provide a continuous weighing system. Computer-controlled belt weighers are integral parts of continuous dry-blending processes. In one such process up to 13 components may be measured simultaneously and changes in formulation can be made at rates up to seven times a second.[30]

19.8.2.4. Computer weighers

In this relatively recent development, the material is fed to the pans of a multihead weigher. The contents-weight of each filled pan is signalled to a microprocessor which computes the weight combinations at high speed (2500 per s), selects the pan combination giving the total weight closest to the target weight and signals discharge of the selected combination. Selectivity of weight pans is possible so that feeding of the weigher with different amounts permits ingredient control of a blend (Driver Southall Ltd, Walsall, England).

19.8.3. AUTOMATIC WAREHOUSING

Warehousing, the interface between production and distribution, is a costly and non-productive activity which should be kept to a minimum. However, due to the difficulty of matching production exactly to demand, some storage is necessary but, in this case, maximum efficiency in utilising space and labour is vital.

Because of high land costs, warehouses up to 30 m high are encountered calling for automated handling. In a typical system, goods are palletised automatically (Section 19.5.5.1), each case and pallet being coded individually using bar codes or ink markers operated by a microprocessor. The coded assemblies are then conveyed, e.g. by chain conveyor, through a code reader where they are registered by a computer which directs them to predetermined storage locations, the coordinates of which are registered by the computer. The loaded pallets are stored on pallet racking of various types (Section 19.5.5.2). Stacking and retrieval is usually effected by automatic stacker cranes or by man-rider aisle cranes when extensive order-picking is required. The whole operation (which is capable of handling two pallet loads per minute, typically) is computer optimised taking into account such factors as stock rotation and equipment and space utilisation.[20] With high speed, complex handling systems of this type, equipment reliability and rapid fault diagnosis and rectification are vital considerations.

REFERENCES

1. Apple, J. M., *Plant Layout and Materials Handling*, 3rd edn. John Wiley, New York, 1977.
2. Anon., *Materials Handling Costs. A New Look at Manufacture.* Dept of Industry Committee for Materials Handling, London, 1976.
3. Anon., *Food and Packaging; Health and Safety.* HMSO, London, 1984.

4. Anon., Glossary of terms used in materials handling. BS 3810 Part 2. British Standards Institution, London, 1965.
5. Bates, J., Review of bulk conveying systems. *Processing* (March 1982) 22–3.
6. Bowden, E. P. and Tabor, D., *Friction and Lubrication of Solids.* Oxford University Press, Oxford, 1964.
7. Roscoe, B., Friction fact and fiction. *Chemy. Ind.*, **14** (July 1982) 467–74.
8. Anon., *Cereal Millers Handbook. Vol. 1.* Burgess, Minn., USA, 1963.
9. McFarlane, I., *Automatic Control of Food Manufacturing Processes.* Applied Science Publishers, London, 1983.
10. Anon., The value of vibes. *Food Manuf.*, **55**(12) (1980) 39, 43.
11. Redmond, R., Elevators should come tailor made. *Materials Handling News*, **320** (1984) 19, 20.
12. Anon., Glossary of terms used in materials handling. BS 3810 Part 4. British Standards Institution, London, 1968.
13. Anon., Glossary of terms used in materials handling. BS 3819 Part 1. British Standards Institution, London, 1964.
14. Loeffler, F. J. and Proctor, C. R. (ed.), *Unit and Bulk Materials Handling.* American Society of Mechanical Engineers, New York, USA, 1980.
15. Anon., Specifications for pallets for materials handling. BS 2629. British Standards Institution, London, 1967.
16. Anon., Specifications for pallets for through transit. BS 2629 Part 2. British Standards Institution, London, 1970.
17. Anon., Building blocks on sound foundations. *Materials Handling News*, **333** (1985) 23–5.
18. Anon., Handing over to a robot. *Materials Handling News*, **319** (1984) 38–40.
19. Anon., Push–pull not only for forklifts. *Materials Handling News*, **331** (1958) 48.
20. Lacy, K., High tech bay bought as package. *Materials Handling News*, **331** (1985) 59–61.
21. Anon., It's all change on the ghost train. *Materials Handling News*, **327** (1985) 23–36.
22. Anon., New AGV plots its own path. *Materials Handling News*, **324** (1986) 20.
23. Anon., Hoverpallets aboard ship. *Mechanical Handling*, **52**(11) (1965) 513–21.
24. Anon., Glossary of terms used in materials handling. BS 3810 Part 3. British Standards Institution, London, 1967.
25. Kraus, M. N., *Pneumatic Conveying of Bulk Materials*, 2nd edn. McGraw Hill, New York, 1980.
26. Anon., Dust as deadly as dynamite. *Materials Handling News*, **318** (1984) 57–9.
27. Vocadlo, J. J. and Sagoo, M. S., Slurry flow in pipes and pumps. *J. Engng. Ind.*, **95**(3) (1973) 65–71.
28. Boulden, L. L., Moving solids like liquids. *Machine Design*, **43**(2) (1972) 87–91.
29. Mohsenin, N. N., *Electromagnetic Radiation Properties of Foods and Agricultural Products.* Gordon and Breach, New York, 1984.
30. Hope, V. E., Information system boosts biscuit production. *Food Engng. Int.*, **3**(3) (1978) 28–31, 43.
31. Ellis, H. S., The pipeline flow of capsules. *Can. J. Engng*, **42**(2) (1964) 1–8; **42**(8) (1964) 155–61.

CHAPTER 20

PUMPING IN THE FOOD INDUSTRY

20.1. INTRODUCTION

The transport of low viscosity liquids, solid–liquid suspensions (slurries), high consistency pastes, etc., from one place to another in a process plant is one of the commonest operations encountered in the food processing industries. The transfer is usually accomplished by pumping the materials through pipeline systems.

Pumps are mechanical devices for supplying energy to a liquid to promote its flow at the specified flowrate and under the desired conditions of transfer. These requirements are dependent on both the operating conditions for the process and the design of the transfer pipeline. The pump must be carefully selected to suit these conditions.

20.2. GENERAL COMMENTS ON PIPELINE SELECTION

The design of the piping system can influence the ease and cost of pumping very considerably. The piping arrangement should be designed so as to minimise the energy required for pumping. The liquid flowrate, any vertical lift (increase in potential energy of the liquid) or increase in downstream pressure (increase in pressure energy) to be overcome are normally fixed by the process. However, energy losses which arise due to friction and shock losses as process fluids flow through the equipment, pipes and ancillary fittings—valves, bends, tee-pieces, etc.—are very much influenced by piping system design and can be minimised by careful selection of components fabricated so as to minimise these losses.

Other important points to bear in mind in pipe system design in order to minimise energy losses include:

(a)   keeping the total length of the pipe-run as short as possible;
(b)   maintaining the same pipe diameter throughout the length of the pipe-run whenever possible (if changes are unavoidable reducing or expanding unions should be incorporated;
(c)   using the correct type of fitting for a specific duty, e.g. avoid using gate valves (on–off valves) as flow control valves;
(d)   keeping the number of pipe-fittings to a minimum.

Having finalised the piping system design a suitable pump 'matched' to suit the system must be selected.

20.3.   FACTORS INFLUENCING THE CHOICE OF A PUMP

The pump is the 'heart' of the fluid transfer process and an incorrectly matched pump can lead to inefficient pump operation and even damage and expensive downtime.

Factors which need to be taken into account when selecting a pump for a particular duty include:

(1) *The volumetric flowrate of liquid to be transferred.* This influences the type and size of the pump used. For larger capacities more than one pump may be required.

(2) *The total system head against which the liquid is to be pumped.* This is determined by a combination of several factors, including:

(a)   the velocity of the liquid in the piping system at the required volumetric flow rate;
(b)   the vertical lift required;
(c)   the system pressure;
(d)   energy losses due to friction and shock losses.

The pump head, ΔH_p, needed to transfer unit mass of fluid, density ρ, at an average velocity, u, through the system under the required operating conditions is given by

$$\Delta H_p = \frac{\Delta u^2}{2g} + \Delta z + \frac{\Delta p}{\rho g} + h_f \tag{20.1}$$

where g is the acceleration due to gravity, $\Delta u^2/2g$ is the velocity head, Δz is the potential head, $\Delta p/\rho g$ is the pressure head and h_f is the total head loss due to friction. Each of these terms must be evaluated and the system head determined. In practice the velocity head is small and is usually neglected.

The head loss due to friction, h_f, may be determined by substituting the 'total equivalent length', Σl, for the pipe system, together with the appropriate 'friction factor', f, taken from a 'pipe friction chart', in an equation such as the Fanning equation for friction loss in pipe systems. For a fuller account of the principles underlying pumping calculations see Holland.[1]

For a given flowrate the velocity of the liquid in the pipe depends on the pipe diameter selected. Larger diameter pipes are more expensive but the lower velocities generated result in reduced friction losses and, hence, cheaper pumping. Smaller diameter pipes are cheaper but pumping costs greater. The aim is to achieve the 'optimum pipe diameter' so as to minimise pumping costs.[2]

(3) *Fluid properties.* With food products, ranging from low viscosity homogeneous liquids to two phase froths, pulps and pastes of widely differing pH and temperature,[3] properties of importance in pump selection include:

(a) Consistency (viscosity or non-Newtonian flow behaviour).
(b) Density.
(c) Temperature, which, in association with the corresponding vapour pressure of the liquid, influences the possibility of cavitation. This undesirable phenomenon can arise with low boiling liquids when bubbles of vapour—which form on the suction side of the pump if the pressure is low—collapse as the pressure increases inside the pump casing. Vibration and noise result, leading to inefficient operation and possible damage to the pump. Positioning of the pump is critical. To avoid the possibility of cavitation a 'nett positive suction head' (NPSH) must be applied on the suction side of pumps.
(d) Corrosive and/or erosive nature of the liquid. As well as any corrosive effect due to chemical reaction between the food liquid and any mismatched materials of construction (which could also lead to contamination of the process stream), the size and shape of suspended particles in a slurry can influence wear, particularly of close-clearance surfaces. These factors affect the choice of materials used for the manufacture of pump components.
(e) Shear deformation. Certain speciality food product streams can undergo undesirable changes in their flow characteristics, crystal habit, etc., if subjected to excessive shearing forces when passing

through pumps. Internal gear pumps,[4] or peristaltic pumps,[5,6] for example, afford gentler handling of products than external gear pumps and are recommended with these products.

(f) Lubricating properties. This may influence pump selection since some pumps are able to handle non-lubricating liquids while some all-metal rotary pumps require the liquid being pumped to act as a lubricant.

(4) *Type of prime mover.* Though most pumps are coupled to electric motors, either directly or via pulleys and V-belts, reciprocating pumps can also be actuated by steam or compressed air.

(5) *Hygienic requirements.* In the food industry contamination must be guarded against at all times. As with product contact surfaces for all food equipment, the internal surfaces of pumps must be readily accessible to the action of cleaning and sterilising agents[3] (see also Section 17.2.3).

20.4. TYPES OF PUMPS

In the food industry, liquids of widely differing physical and chemical properties have to be pumped under various process operating conditions. A number of different types of pump have been developed to satisfy these requirements.

Pumps are commonly classified as either (1) positive displacement pumps (reciprocating and rotary types) or (2) centrifugal pumps.

20.4.1. POSITIVE DISPLACEMENT (PD) PUMPS
All PD pumps operate by trapping a certain volume of fluid within the body of the pump and forcing it from the suction (inlet) side to the discharge (outlet) side at higher pressure. Positive displacement pumps are self-priming.

20.4.1.1. Reciprocating Positive Displacement Pumps
Piston pump. In this pump the internal volume is changed by means of a piston moving inside a close-fitting cylinder. Suction and discharge valves control the flow of liquid drawn into the cylinder on the suction stroke and discharged at a higher pressure on the delivery stroke. Simple, single-cylinder, single-acting piston pumps give a pulsating delivery which is frequently unacceptable. With a double-acting cylinder, liquid is discharged in both directions of the piston movement giving a smoother

discharge flow. More expensive multi-cylinder, double-acting piston pumps give an even smoother flow (see Section 5.2.2.2). The amount of liquid delivered depends on the piston area, the length of the stroke and the operating speed of the pump. They can handle viscous liquids and develop high pressures. Since with a well-maintained piston pump the volume delivered is accurately known these pumps find use as metering pumps. A problem which may arise with reciprocating piston pumps is leakage between the piston and the cylinder which reduces pump efficiency. Because of the risk of scoring cylinder linings and valves these pumps are not normally recommended for use with liquids which contain abrasive solids unless reusable linings are fitted. Well-maintained reciprocating pumps can have efficiencies greater than 95%.[7]

Diaphragm pump. This simple, inexpensive type of reciprocating pump is able to handle viscous liquids and slurries as well as corrosive liquids and suspensions containing abrasive solids. It can be run dry.[8] A corrosion-resistant flexible diaphragm of resilient material separates the actuating side from the product contact side of the pump. Movement of the replaceable, resilient diaphragm causes transport of liquid. The diaphragm allows the passage of abrasive particles with minimal abrasion damage besides reducing the amount of surface in contact with the corrosive/erosive environment. As with normal piston pumps, inlet and outlet valves are required with these units.

In common with all positive displacement pumps, reciprocating pumps can deliver liquids at high pressures, i.e. they will work against very high heads. With this type of pump the head the pump is working against does not appreciably affect the amount of liquid delivered. This makes them particularly useful as metering pumps. High-capacity reciprocating pumps are quite expensive but smaller units for lower flowrates[8] are frequently used.

20.4.1.2. Rotary positive displacement pumps

Pumps of this type include helical screw pumps, gear pumps, lobe pumps and peristaltic pumps. They are used to a far greater extent than the reciprocating type of PD pump since, while offering similar advantages, they do not need inlet and outlet valves, neither is there the mechanical problem of converting rotary to reciprocating motion.

Helical screw pump. This has a screw revolving in a close-fitting barrel. Liquid is carried along the length of the barrel in the space between the screw and the wall of the barrel. In another type of screw pump a specially-shaped worm rotating in a resilient rubber or similar elastomer stator

causes the creation of transfer cavities. In either type liquid is carried from
the inlet to the delivery side of the pump to be discharged at higher pressure.
The helical screw pump can handle viscous liquids and abrasive,
solid–liquid suspensions since the resilient material of the stator allows the
passage of solids with little damage. The head developed can be very high
and depends on the pitch and length of the rotor. These pumps should not
be run dry.

Gear pumps. In the external gear pump (Fig. 20.1), the most widely used
positive displacement rotary pump, two gear wheels with external teeth
enmesh inside a close-clearance casing. Liquid is carried round in the spaces
between the teeth and the casing. In the internal gear pump, which has
gentler liquid handling characteristics,[4] an internally geared wheel meshes
with one externally geared wheel. The pumps are normally directly coupled
to electric motors and give an even flow against high discharge pressures.
They are available in a wide range of materials of construction to suit

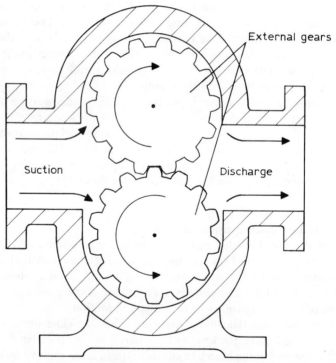

Fig. 20.1.   External gear pump.

different environments but are not recommended for use with abrasive suspensions since wear of the teeth causes leakage and consequent reduction in efficiency.

Lobe pump. This is similar in principle to the gear pump but two shaped rotors move so that the tips of one or other of the rotors contacts the other rotor and the surrounding casing (Fig. 20.2). Liquid is transported in the free space generated, to be discharged at an increased pressure. These pumps are easy to clean and handle shear sensitive products well.[3] They are about the most widely-used PD type pump for food applications.

Peristaltic pump. This simple device (Fig. 20.3), used for many years as a small capacity, low head pump in the laboratory and pilot-plant, is now finding wider application for larger scale pumping duties in the food industries. The liquid being pumped is contained in a flexible tube or hose. The fluid is positively displaced by a combined rolling and squeezing action generated by a series of moving cams or rollers acting along a section of the tube. The inside of the tube is the only surface contacting the liquid and as

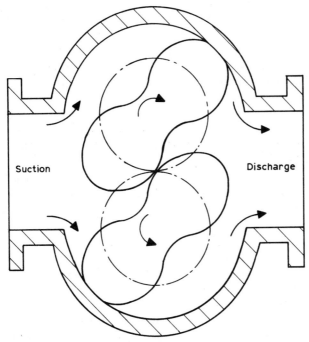

FIG. 20.2. Lobe pump.

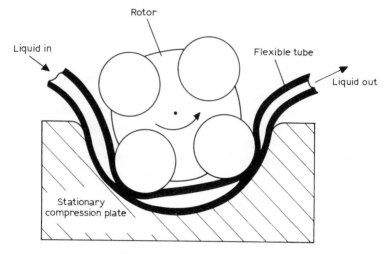

FIG. 20.3.   Peristaltic pump.

no glands are required to carry internal moving parts a peristaltic pump with a hose compatible with the chemical nature of the product is one of the most hygienic pumps available. Thick-walled tubes of reinforced elastomers offering high chemical resistance at temperatures in excess of 100°C are available for more stringent applications.[5] The pumping action is gentle and quite large pieces of solids such as mandarin orange segments, walnuts, Stilton cheese and chicken pieces in products sensitive to shear damage can be transferred without damage.[6]

In general, positive displacement pumps are widely used for pumping more viscous liquids. They are self-priming and are capable of delivering high heads. They must not be allowed to pump against a closed delivery line since over-pressure can develop. A pressure relief valve should be incorporated in the discharge line to allow the controlled release of any excess pressure arising through mal-operation.

20.4.2. CENTRIFUGAL PUMPS

The most widely used liquid transfer pump in the general process industries is the centrifugal (rotodynamic) pump and this relatively cheap and simple pump also finds much use in the food industry.

Basically, a centrifugal pump consists of an impeller rotating in a casing having inlet (suction) and exit (discharge) ports (Fig. 20.4). Fluid normally enters axially into the eye of the impeller which rotates at a constant speed.

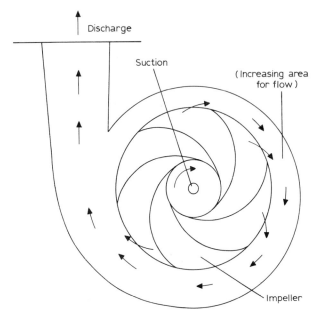

Fig. 20.4. Principal features of a centrifugal pump.

The fluid is accelerated and thrown from the tips of the impeller blades at high velocity, passing into an increasing area for flow where the velocity (kinetic) energy is converted into pressure energy. The fluid leaving the pump flows through the pipe system by virtue of the pressure or head imparted by the pump.

When running at constant speed, the head developed by a centrifugal pump varies with the flowrate. At zero flow the pump head is a maximum and as the rate of flow increases the head developed falls. This relationship for a particular pump is shown by the manufacturer on a head versus capacity curve which is characteristic for the pump. (Fig. 20.5). The pump must be chosen (matched) to suit the head requirements of a particular system. Since system heads vary with the flowrate they must be calculated for different flowrates. These system head requirements can also be shown on a head versus capacity curve. In practice the discharge flowrate is regulated by a control valve situated in the delivery line. The actual capacity delivered by the pump when operating in the system depends on the design of both the pump and the system and can be found by combining the head-capacity curve for the pump with that for the system. The actual

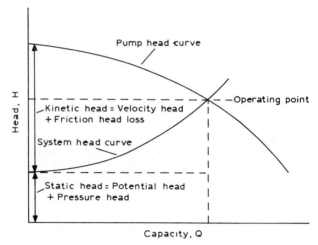

FIG. 20.5. Pump head curve, system head curve and operating point for a centrifugal pump system.

flowrate is given by the 'operating point', the intersection of the two curves (Fig. 20.5).

As mentioned previously, a centrifugal pump will only operate effectively if a nett positive suction head is available. These pumps require a minimum NPSH, which increases with flowrate, if cavitation is to be avoided. The pump manufacturer will provide this data on another 'characteristic curve' showing required NPSH versus capacity. To avoid cavitation the system must be designed so that the available NPSH exceeds the required value at the operating conditions.

The available NPSH is given by the equation:

$$\text{NPSH} = z_s + \frac{(p_s - p_{vp})}{\rho g} - h_{fs} \tag{20.2}$$

where z_s is the potential head on the suction side of the pump, p_s is the pressure of the atmosphere on the suction side, p_{vp} is the vapour pressure of the liquid, h_{fs} is the head loss due to friction on the suction side, ρ is the density of the liquid and g is the acceleration due to gravity. Since h_{fs} increases at higher flowrate the available NPSH falls as the flow is increased.[1]

Particular care is necessary if the liquid to be transferred is contained in a vessel situated below the level of the inlet to the pump. With this configuration a suction lift is required and, unless the feed tank is pressurised, the suction head is negative. If the feed and delivery tanks are at atmospheric pressure the pump attempts to run on air but since the density of air is very low the head is small and normal centrifugal pumps will not prime under these conditions. If the vapour pressure of the liquid approaches that of the atmosphere above it, then no suction lift is possible and cavitation is likely, particularly at higher flowrates.

It must be stressed that the more volatile the liquid and the higher its temperature the greater the available NPSH must be for effective operation. Submerged pumps should be considered if suction lifts cannot be avoided.

Centrifugal pumps are usually directly coupled to electric motors, although slurry pumps often have pulley drives to permit variable speed operation. The efficiency of the energy conversion depends on the design of the pump impeller and pump casing and also on the viscosity of the liquid. For a particular type and diameter of impeller, varying the speed of rotation changes the head developed and the capacity of the pump.

For a particular impeller/pump casing:

Flowrate is proportional to speed.
Developed head is proportional to $(speed)^2$.
Power requirement is proportional to $(speed)^3$.

For varying impeller diameters at constant speed:

Flowrate is proportional to $(diameter)^3$.
Developed head is proportional to $(diameter)^2$.
Power requirement is proportional to $(diameter)^5$.

The above relationships show the variations in centrifugal pump performance with changes in impeller speed and diameter.

Single stage centrifugal pumps are the most commonly used pumps for the conveyance of slurries. They are particularly useful for handling lower viscosity slurries. They are usually the cheapest of pumps and have the lowest maintenance costs, but only moderate efficiency at the 'best efficiency point'. Small centrifugal pumps (less than $12 \, m^3 \, h^{-1}$) tend to be very inefficient.[7] Efficiencies of all centrifugal pumps fall rapidly when pumping higher viscosity liquids and they are unsuitable for these duties.

When pumping liquids containing suspended solids care must be taken in the design of the impeller to minimise wear by reducing abrupt changes in flow direction and by providing large passages to prevent blockages. Parts subjected to high wear should have increased thicknesses. Localised turbulence increases wear so closed impellers with high efficiencies are preferred. Elastomer-lined pumps resist impact wear from suspended particles and offer the longest life. They can also be used with relatively large solids that are soft and not too sharp. Hard-metal pumps are also recommended for use with fine, sharp-edged particles.[9] The economic life of pump components can also be lengthened by reducing the pump speed.[10]

Conventional centrifugal pumps are very useful for high capacity/low head applications. If higher pressures are required with this type of pump, multi-stage pumps, in which the liquid passes sequentially through a series of impellers, may be considered although these have so far found little application.[9] An increase in either head or capacity can be obtained by running two centrifugal pumps together. When operating two identical pumps in series at a volumetric flow rate, Q, a total pump head, $2H_p$, is developed. Parallel operation leads to a flow rate, $2Q$, at a total pump head, H_p.[1] In both modes of operation efficiency remains about the same as for a single pump.

REFERENCES

1. Holland, F. A., *Fluid Flow for Chemical Engineers*. Edward Arnold, London, 1973.
2. Coulson, J. M. and Richardson, J. F., *Chemical Engineering. Vol. I*, 3rd edn. Pergamon Press, Oxford, England, 1977.
3. Fuggle, T., Pumps, valves and seals for hygienic applications. In *Design for Hygiene—The Changing Scene in the Food Industry*. Seminar, Institution of Mechanical Engineers, May 1987.
4. Harvest, J., Recent developments in gear pumps. *The Chemical Engineer*, **403** (May 1984) 28–9.
5. Anon., Peristaltic pumps tough enough for industry. *Processing*, (April 1983) 13.
6. Anon., Pump is gentle with delicate foods. *Food Processing*, (September 1985), 24.
7. Odrowaz-Pieniazek, S., Solids handling pumps—A guide to selection. *The Chemical Engineer*, **341** (February 1979) 94–101.
8. Marshall, P., Positive displacement pumps—A brief survey. *The Chemical Engineer*, **418** (October 1985) 52–5.
9. Odrowaz-Pieniazek, S. and Steele, K., Advances in slurry pumps. Part I. *The Chemical Engineer*, **422** (February 1986) 34–7.
10. Lambert, D. J., The use of pumps in food processing. In *Food Technology International Europe 1989*, ed. A. Turner. Sterling, London, 1989, pp. 112–13.

CHAPTER 21

PACKAGING

21.1. GENERAL PRINCIPLES

Packaging should be regarded as an integral part of food processing and preservation. The success of most preservation methods depends on appropriate packaging, e.g. to prevent microbiological contamination of heat-processed foods or moisture pick-up by dried foods. Packaging also plays an important role in maintaining the quality and extending the shelf-life of fresh produce, fruit, vegetables, eggs, meat and fish and manufactured foods, such as bakery, sugar confectionery and dairy products and alcoholic and non-alcoholic beverages.

The main functions of a package are to contain the product and protect it against a variety of hazards which might adversely affect its quality during handling, distribution and storage. The package also plays an important role in selling the product but that aspect of the subject is outside the scope of this chapter. The following are some important considerations to be taken into account when selecting a packaging material or container for a particular duty.

Mechanical damage. Both fresh and processed foods are susceptible to mechanical damage. The cracking of egg shells, the bruising of fruit and the breaking of biscuits are examples. Such damage may result from: sudden impacts or shocks during handling and transport; vibration during transport by road, rail or air; and compression loads imposed while packages are stacked in warehouses or ships' holds. Appropriate packaging can reduce the incidence and extent of mechanical injury. The selection of strong, rigid packaging material, e.g. metal, glass, wood and fibreboard, can reduce damage due to compression loads. The inclusion of a cushioning material as a component in the package can protect against shocks and

617

vibration. Examples of such cushioning materials are tissue paper, corrugated papers and boards, pulpboard and foamed plastics. Restricting movement of the product within the package can also help. This may be done by tight wrapping or shrink wrapping and by the use of shaped containers such as egg trays.

Permeability characteristics. The degree of permeability of the package to water vapour, gases and volatile odour compounds is another important consideration.

Foods with high equilibrium relative humidities will tend to lose moisture to the atmosphere and this can result in a loss in weight and a deterioration in appearance and texture. Meat and cheese are typical examples of such foods. Products with low equilibrium relative humidities tend to absorb moisture, particularly in high humidity atmospheres, and this can also cause a loss in quality. Dry powders, such as cake mixes and custard powder, may cake, biscuits and snack foods may lose their crispness and dehydrated products may spoil if their water activity rises above the level which permits microbiological and/or chemical activity. On the other hand, in the case of fresh products with high respiration rates, i.e. some fruits and vegetables, it may be necessary to allow for the passage of water vapour out of the package, otherwise a high humidity will develop in the package and fogging may occur when the temperature fluctuates.

The shelf-life of many foods may be extended by creating an atmosphere inside the package which has a low oxygen content. This is achieved by maintaining a partial vacuum in the container (vacuum packaging) or by displacing air with nitrogen or carbon dioxide gas (gas packaging). Cheese, cooked and cured meat products, dried meats, egg and coffee are examples of such foods. The shelf life of fresh meat and fish and some manufactured products may be extended by packaging them in an atmosphere containing different ratios of oxygen, carbon dioxide and nitrogen. This technique is known as modified atmosphere packaging (MAP) (see Section 16.3.3.2).[1] In these and other, similar, cases it is necessary that the packaging material used should be a good barrier to gases and the package effectively sealed so that the composition of the in-pack atmosphere does not change significantly during the storage and distribution of the product.

However, if fresh produce is sealed in a gas tight container, the oxygen within the pack will be used up and replaced with carbon dioxide as a result of respiration. Thus over a period of time an anaerobic atmosphere will develop inside the package. If the oxygen level falls below 2% off-flavours may develop and discolouration occur in certain fruit and vegetables. To prevent such changes it is necessary to use a packaging material that permits movement of oxygen into and carbon dioxide out of the package.

To retain the pleasant odour associated with many foods, e.g. coffee, it is necessary to use a packaging material which has a low permeability to the volatile compounds which give rise to these odours. Such materials may also be used to prevent the contents from being contaminated with foreign odours.

In those cases where vapour and gas movement into or out of the package is to be minimised, metal and glass containers, suitably sealed, may be used. Many flexible film materials, either singly or in laminate form, are also good vapour and gas barriers. Where some vapour and gas movement is desirable then films which are semi-permeable to vapours and gases are available and if necessary the packaging material may be perforated.

Greases and oils. Fatty foods require a greaseproof package to prevent egress of grease or oil to the outside spoiling the appearance of the pack and possibly damaging the printing and decoration. Greaseproof and vegetable parchment papers and hydrophilic films provide varying degrees of greaseproofness for different applications.

Temperature changes. The package must be able to withstand the changes in temperature which it is likely to encounter without any loss of performance or appearance. This is of particular importance when foods are to be heated or cooled in their packages. The rate of change of temperature and the type of heat may influence the choice of packaging material. For example glass containers must be heated and cooled slowly to avoid breakage and specially formulated paperboards are required for microwave heating to avoid off-flavours developing.

Light transmission. Many food components are sensitive to light, particularly in the visible blue and ultra-violet parts of the spectrum. Exposure to light can lead to destruction of vitamins, fading of colours and accelerate the development of rancidity of fats. To prevent such changes a packaging material which is opaque to light may be used or, where sight of the product is desirable, the packaging material may be coloured to exclude short-length light waves. Amber glass, commonly used for beer bottles, is an example of the latter.

Chemical and biochemical considerations. The packaging material must be chemically compatible with the food with which it is in contact so that (i) no health hazard arises from that contact and (ii) no adverse change in the quality of the food or the integrity of the package occurs as a result of chemical reaction between them. A health hazard could arise in a packaged food as a result of toxic substances present in the packaging material (including base material, coatings, adhesives, inks, etc.) leaching into the product. Examples of such potential hazards are the leaching of lead from solder in 3-piece tinplate cans, now seldom used, and vinyl monomer from polyvinylchloride film. Thus great care should be taken when selecting packaging materials for particular duties to avoid those containing toxic components. Many countries have legislation controlling the composition of food packaging materials. A much more detailed treatment of this aspect of food packaging can be found elsewhere.[2,3]

An example of an undesirable chemical reaction between the package and its contents is that between acid foods and tinplate cans. Acid corrosion of the tinplate, resulting in the solution of tin and the production of hydrogen gas can lead to bleaching of coloured foods, in extreme cases swelling of the cans (hydrogen swelling) and even perforation. Thus packaging materials which are likely to react adversely with the food should be avoided or some other barrier substance should be interposed between the food and the packaging material. In the example of acid corrosion cited above the application of a lacquer to the inside of the can solves the problem.

Microbiological and biological considerations. One function of a package may be to prevent or reduce microbiological contamination of the contents. This is most important in the case of sterilised food where post-process contamination must be prevented. In the case of pasteurised products or foods preserved by drying, freezing, curing, etc., this role of the package is not quite so vital although it should still provide a high level of protection against contamination. Metal and glass containers, effectively sealed, provide the best barriers to microbiological contamination. Laminates or flexible films, some incorporating foil, are also available for use with sterilised foods. Single films, papers and paperboards vary in their ability to prevent contamination and a careful selection must be made for each application. In all cases where a high measure of protection is required the sealing of the package must be effective.

The influence of packaging on the in-pack microflora is another important consideration. Packaging foods in materials highly permeable to gases is unlikely to bring about any significant change in the in-pack microflora. However, if an anaerobic atmosphere is created in the package by vacuum or gas packaging or as a result of respiration of the product, this may influence the number and type of micro-organisms that grow and the spoilage pattern of the product, provided it is not sterilised, dried or frozen. Thus with fresh products and those which have received only mild heat or curing treatments, there is a possibility that pathogenic micro-organisms could flourish under these anaerobic conditions and result in food poisoning. Such packaging procedures should not be adopted without a detailed study of the microbiological implications taking into account the nature of the food, the treatment it receives prior to packaging, the hygienic conditions under which it is packaged and the temperature at which the packaged product is to be stored.

Packaging can also play a role in protecting food against insect infestation. Metal and glass containers, effectively sealed, will provide complete protection. The resistance of films, papers and paperboards to insects covers a range from high to low. In addition to the resistance of the material itself the design of the container is important. Good design to eliminate, as far as possible, cracks, crevices and pinholes at corners and seals of cartons and cases, taping over the stitching, holes in sacks and other similar precautions all help. Apart from the use of metal and glass containers, packaging is not an effective barrier against rodent infestation.

In addition to the above considerations a good package has a size and shape which makes it convenient to handle and store. Equipment must be available to form, fill and seal the package at an acceptable speed and an adequately low failure rate. The package must be aesthetically compatible with its contents. The decoration must be attractive. The labelling must be clear without detracting from the good appearance of the package and must comply with relevant regulations.[2,4-7]

21.2. MATERIALS AND CONTAINERS

21.2.1. PAPER AND BOARD MATERIALS AND CONTAINERS

Most papers and boards used for food packaging are made from wood. There are also some uses for board made from repulped waste paper but not in direct contact with foods. Paper pulp is produced from wood by a mechanical process (groundwood pulp) and by digestion in an alkaline solution (sulphate pulp) or acid solution (sulphite pulp). Groundwood pulp produces paper of comparatively low strength and brightness. It is seldom used on its own but may be added to chemical pulp for paper manufacture but not usually for direct contact with foods. In the papermaking process itself the first step is the beating of the pulp, i.e. subjecting a suspension of pulp in water to a controlled mechanical treatment to obtain the correct sized fibres. Sizing materials and other additives to impart particular properties to the paper are added at this stage. The suspension is then put through a series of refining operations before being fed to the papermaking machine. In the Fourdrinier machine[8] a layer of fibres is deposited on a moving, vibrating wire mesh belt and, by a sequence of vacuum filtration, pressing and drying, converted into paper. In the cylinder machine six or more wire mesh cylinders deposit layers of pulp onto a moving felt blanket. This method is used for board manufacture where combinations of different pulps are used.

The most common types of *packaging papers* are:

Kraft paper made from sulphate pulp. This is a general purpose wrapping paper with good mechanical strength.

Sulphite paper made from pulp produced by acid digestion. Again it is a general purpose paper, not as strong as kraft.

Greaseproof paper made from sulphite pulp and given a severe mechanical treating at the beating stage to produce a close-textured paper with greaseproof characteristics under dry conditions.

Vegetable parchment made by passing a web of chemical pulp through a bath of sulphuric acid a number of times. It is then washed, neutralised and dried. This treatment results in the surface layers being dissolved reducing the porosity and increasing the grease resistance of the paper. It has better wet-strength than greaseproof paper.

Tissue paper is an open-structured paper used to protect delicate products and provide some cushioning protection.

Wet-strength papers are obtained by the addition of resins to the pulp. These retain more of their strength when wet as compared with untreated papers.

Coated papers. Papers of various types may be coated with a variety of substances to improve their protective properties. Wax-coated papers are heat sealable and offer a moderate resistance to water and water-vapour transfer. Plastic coated papers are available which feature various characteristics, i.e. barriers to water vapour, gases, volatiles, greases and oils, depending on the type of plastic coating used.

These various types of paper are used as wraps for individual portions, e.g. butter and margarine, or for parcelling several items together. They may be fabricated into bags of various sizes, e.g. for sugar, flour or small quantities of fruits and vegetables. Multiwall paper sacks are used for larger quantities of fresh produce and also salt, sugar, grains and similar products.

Paperboard (folding boxboard) is made from similar raw materials as paper on the cylinder machine and in thicknesses in excess of 0·30 mm. There are three main types available *Chipboard* is made from repulped waste. It is dull grey in colour and mechanically weak. It is available lined on one side with unbleached, semi or fully bleached chemical pulp. Replacement of the outer ply with better quality pulps provides a range of cream-lined and white-lined chipboards. Chipboards are seldom used in direct contact with foods but may be used where the product is already wrapped or contained in a bag or pouch, e.g. breakfast cereals. *Duplex board* is made from a mixture of semi-bleached chemical and mechanical pulp lined on both sides with chemical pulp and is used for some frozen foods, biscuits, cakes and similar products. *Solid white board* is made entirely from fully bleached chemical pulp and is used for some frozen foods and other products requiring special protection. Paperboard is also available coated with wax, polyethylene, polyvinylidene chloride and polyamides. Such coated boards are used for wet or fatty foods and other products requiring special protection. The most common form of paperboard container is the carton. Cartons are supplied to the user in a flat or collapsed form and erected at the packaging point.

Paperboard is also used in the form of rigid or set-up boxes which are erected by the manufacturer and filled and sealed by the user. These provide more mechanical protection compared with cartons.

Moulded pulp containers are manufactured by moulding a water-borne suspension of pulp into shape either under pressure (pressure injection) or vacuum (suction moulding) and drying the resulting container. These containers have good cushioning characteristics and minimise in-pack movement. Egg trays, trays and boxes for fruit and sleeves for glass containers are typical examples.

Fibreboard is of two types. Solid fibreboard consists of paperboard, usually chipboard, lined on one or both sides with kraft paper. Corrugated fibreboard consists of one or more layers of a corrugated (fluted) material sandwiched between flat sheets of paperboard. The corrugated component may be chipboard, strawboard or board made from semi-chemical pulp. Single-, double- and triple-wall boards are used in the construction of cases (Fig. 21.1). Commercial corrugated fibreboard has four fluting ranges as shown in Table 21.1. Coated fibreboards are also available. The most common form of container made from fibreboard is the case. The type of

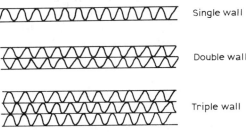

FIG. 21.1.   Types of corrugated fibreboard.

TABLE 21.1
Fluting specifications for corrugated fibreboard

Flute	No. of flutes per metre	Flute height (mm)
A (coarse)	104–125	4·50–4·70
B (fine)	150–184	2·10–2·90
C (medium)	120–145	3·50–3·70
E (very fine)	275–310	1·15–1·65

fibreboard used depends on the degree of rigidity and/or cushioning required. Inserts may be included in such cases to reduce in-pack movement. Fibreboard cases are used for already packaged goods, e.g. canned, bottled or cartoned products, or for unpackaged products such as butter, fruits, vegetables and eggs.

Composite containers are constructed from more than one type of packaging material. Most commonly they have a cylindrical body made of paperboard or fibreboard and ends made of metal or plastic. Depending on the requirements of the package the body may be made from coated or laminated boards. Smaller containers, up to 200 mm diameter, are referred to as fibre tubes or cans. Applications for these include spices, pepper, salt, chocolate beverages, cream and fruit juice. Larger versions are known as fibreboard drums. These can be used as alternatives to paper and plastic sacks or metal drums for cooking fats and shortenings, powders, such as milk powder, and emulsifying and stabilising agents.[2,8–17]

21.2.2. WOOD AND TEXTILES

Wooden containers are mainly used where a high degree of mechanical protection is required. Good quality wood, free from knots, cross-grain and splits, and well cured to not more than 15% moisture should be used. Some varieties of wood, such as pine, larch, cedar, cypress and fir, should not be used in close-boarded form for foods because of the danger of tainting. Wooden containers take the form of crates, cases, drums or barrels.

Applications include: open crates or cases for fish, fruits and vegetables; plywood drums for powders and fats; casks, kegs and barrels for beer, wines and spirits.

Jute and cotton cloths are woven materials used in the form of sacks or bags. Jute sacks are used for fresh fruit and vegetables, grains and dried legumes. Cotton bags hold smaller quantities of flour, sugar, salt and similar products.[2,9,17–20]

21.2.3. FLEXIBLE FILMS

Non-fibrous materials in continuous sheet form up to 0·25 mm thick are termed packaging films. They are flexible, usually transparent, unless deliberately pigmented, and, with the exception of regenerated cellulose, they are all thermoplastic to some extent. This last property enables many of them to be heat sealed. Such materials consist of a basic polymer or mixture of polymers to which a variety of substances are added to give them particular functional properties, improve their appearance and/or handling characteristics. Such additives may include plasticisers, stabilisers, colouring materials, antioxidants, anti-blocking and slip agents. Films are made by one of three general methods:

(i) *Extrusion*. The mixture of polymer and additives is fed through an extruder, consisting of a revolving screw or screws in a heating barrel, which forces the melted mixture through an orifice in the form of a slit or annular opening. The extrudate is stretched to control the thickness of the film and then cooled.

(ii) *Calendering*. The heated mixture of polymer and additives is fed through a series of heated rollers with a progressively decreasing clearance.

(iii) *Casting*. The polymer and additives are dissolved in a solvent and the solution fed onto a moving belt. Heat is applied to remove the solvent. The film is removed from the belt and further dried in an oven. Many films may be oriented. This operation involves heating the film to a certain critical temperature and applying tension to it in one (uniaxial) or two directions at right angles to each other (biaxial). This has the effect of producing a more ordered arrangement of polymer molecules and alters the mechanical physical and thermal properties of the film.

In Table 21.2 some of the properties and applications of films commonly used for food packaging are summarised. They may be used in the form of wrappers, e.g. for sweets, butter and bread, preformed bags, e.g. for fruit and vegetables; pouches or sachets made by form–fill–seal techniques (see Section 21.3) for a wide range of solid and liquid products.[2,17,21,22]

21.2.4. LAMINATES

A laminate consists of two or more webs of flexible material combined together. The materials involved may include papers or paperboards, films and foil. The paper or paperboard provides stiffness, protects the soft foil and has a suitable surface for printing. The film(s) usually contributes to the

TABLE 21.2

General properties and applications of films commonly used for food packaging

Flexible film	Permeability to:				Resistance to high temp.	Resistance to low temp.	Heat sealable
	Water vapour	Gases	Volatiles	Oils			
Regenerated cellulose							
—Plain (P)	H	L—dry H—wet	L	L	L	H	−
—Waxed coated (MS)	L	L	L	L	L	H	+
—Waxed coated (DMS)[a]	L	L—dry H—wet	L	L	L	H	+
—Waxed coated (QMS)	H	L—dry H—wet	L	L	L	H	+
—Copolymer coated (MXXT)	L	L	L	L	L	H	+
Cellulose acetate	H	M/H	H	L	M	L	+[a]
Polyethylene (PE)							
—Low density	L	H	M	M	L	H	+
—High density	L	M	M	M	M	H	+
—Irradiated	M	M	M	M	M	H	+
Polyvinyl chloride (PVC)	V[a]	V[a]	H	L	L	H	+
Polyvinylidene chloride copolymer (PVDC)	L	L	L	L	L	M	+
Polypropylene							
—Cast	L	L	L	L	H	L	+
—Oriented	L	L	L	L	H	H	+[a]
Polyester—Oriented	L	L	L	L	H	H	+[a]
Polystyrene—Oriented	H	M	M	L	L	H	−
Rubber hydrochloride (pliofilm)	V[a]	V[a]	H	M[b]	L	V[a]	+
Polyamides (nylons)	V	L	L	L	H	H	+[a]
Polycarbonate	H	H	H	L	M	H	+[a]
Fluorethylenes	L	L	L	L	H	H	+
Ionomers	M	H	L	L	L	H	+
Ethylene-vinyl acetate copolymers (EVA)	M	H	M	M	L	H	+

H, high/good; L, low/poor; V, variable; M, moderate; +, yes; −, no.

Heat shrinkable	Chemically compatible	Notes	Applications
−	H		Fresh fruits & vegetables; some sugar and flour confectionery products.
−	H		Cheese, butter, some dried foods.
−	H	[a] Coated one side only.	Fresh red meat.
−	H		As for plain but heat sealable.
−	H		Biscuits, snack foods, dried foods.
−	H[b]	[a] Sealing difficult. [b] For food grades.	Fresh fruits and vegetables, window cartons, chocolate products.
−	H		Frozen foods, dried foods, fresh vegetables (ventilated).
−	H		Dried foods, cook-in-pack products.
+	H		
+	H[b]	[a] Depending on plasticiser. [b] For food grades.	Fruits and vegetables, fresh meat (highly plasticised), processed meats (low plasticiser).
+	H		Cheese, cooked and cured meats, poultry.
−	H		Fruits, vegetables, bread.
+/−[b]	H	[a] Temperature critical. [b] Both types available.	Biscuits, snack foods, dried foods, cheese, coffee.
+/−[b]	H	[a] Temperature critical. [b] Both types available.	Cheese, cooked and cured meat, cook-in-pack products.
−	H	[a] Very difficult to heat seal	Fruit, vegetables, cream, yoghurt, preserves.
+	H[c]	[a] Depends on plasticiser content. [b] Some essential oils penetrate. [c] For food grades.	Fruit and vegetables (highly plasticised), cheese, dried foods, coffee (low plasticiser).
−	H	[a] High temperature.	Cheese, cooked and cured meats, cook-in-pack products.
−	H[b]	[a] High temperature. [b] Food grades.	Limited by cost: frozen foods, cook-in-pack products.
−	H		Limited by cost: dried and freeze dried foods, sterilisable packs.
−	H		Fatty foods.
−	H		Mainly as laminate components.

barrier properties of the laminate, provides a heat sealable surface and strengthens the laminate. The foil acts as a barrier material and has an attractive appearance. Laminates may be formed from paper–paper, paper–film, film–film, paper–foil, film–foil or paper–film–foil combinations. The web of a laminate may be bound together by aqueous or non-aqueous adhesives as appropriate. If one or more of the webs is thermoplastic it may be bonded to the other web by passing them between heated rollers. A freshly extruded thermoplastic web, still in the molten state, may be applied directly to another web and thus bonded to it. Co-extruded or structured film combinations result when two or more thermoplastic materials are simultaneously extruded and bonded together. Examples of laminates and their uses include: vegetable-parchment–aluminium-foil for butter; paper–polyvinylidene chloride for margarine and milk powder; regenerated-cellulose(MXXT)–polyethylene for vacuum packed cheese, cooked and cured meats; polyester–polyethylene for coffee; cellulose acetate–foil–paper–foil–polyethylene for dried soup mixes. The retortable pouch (flexible can) is made from a laminate. This may be 2-ply, polyamide or polyester–polyolefin; 3-ply, polyester–foil–polyolefin or 4-ply, polyester–foil–polyester–polyolefin. The polyolefin in these laminates could be polypropylene, high density polyethylene or an ethylene–propylene copolymer. Such pouches can withstand the rigours of retorting and can be used as an alternative to rigid metal or glass containers for some heat processed foods.[2,17,21–24]

21.2.5. RIGID AND SEMI-RIGID PLASTIC CONTAINERS

Many of the thermo-plastic materials listed in Table 21.2 can be formed into rigid or semi-rigid containers, the most common being low and high density polyethylene, polyvinyl chloride (PVC), polypropylene, polyester (polyethylene terephthalate (PET)) and polystyrene. Acrylic plastics are also used for this purpose. These include polyacrylonitrile, a copolymer of acrylonitrile and methyl acrylate, and a terpolymer acrylonitrile–butadiene–styrene (ABS). A thermosetting plastic, urea-formaldehyde, is used to make screw-cap closures for glass and plastic containers. The methods used to form containers include:

Thermoforming, in which a plastic sheet is clamped in position above a mould, heated until pliable and then brought into contact with the mould so that it follows its contours. It cools through contact with the mould, sets and is ejected from the mould. The shaping of the soft plastic is achieved by applying a superatmospheric pressure above the plastic sheet (pressure moulding), a vacuum beneath the sheet (vacuum forming) or by sandwiching the sheet between male and female moulds.

Blow moulding, in which compressed air is introduced into a sealed mass of molten plastic located in a mould. The air pressure causes the soft plastic to expand taking up the shape of the mould. The plastic cools, sets, the mould is opened and the container ejected.

Injection moulding in which plastic powder granules are softened in a cylinder containing a rotating screw. The molten material is forced under pressure into a mould, taking up its shape. After cooling the mould is opened and the container ejected.

Compression moulding is used for thermosetting plastics. Plastic powder is placed between male and female moulds held together by hydraulic pressure. The moulds are heated and the plastic melts taking up the shape of the cavity. The moulds are cooled, opened and the container ejected.

Examples of thermoformed containers for food include cups and tubs for margarine, cottage cheese and yoghurt, trays for frozen foods and ice cream, trays for eggs and fresh fruit. Blow moulded bottles are used for oils, fruit juices, milk, beer and other carbonated beverages. Injection moulding may also be used to produce tubs for yoghurt, cream and soft cheese, as well as phials, jars and boxes for a variety of uses.[2,17,23,25,26]

21.2.6. METAL MATERIALS AND CONTAINERS

Aluminium foil is produced from aluminium ingots by a series of rolling operations. The end product has a thickness in the range 0·15–0·008 mm. Most foil used in packaging contains not less than 99% pure aluminium with traces of iron, silicon and other elements. Foil containing 1·25% manganese is used to form semi-rigid containers. After the rolling, foil is annealed in an oven to control its ductility. Thus foils of different tempers can be produced from a full annealed (dead-folding) to a fully hard, rigid material. Foil is a bright attractive material, odourless, tasteless and safe for use with foods. For contact with acid or salty products it needs to be coated with nitrocellulose or some other protective material. It is mechanically weak, easily punctured, torn and abraded. Its strength can be improved by coating or laminating with other materials. Foil in thicknesses below 0·03 mm will contain perforations and so is not totally impermeable to vapours and gases. Coating with a plastic material will reduce its permeability so that it is a very good barrier material. It is stable over a wide temperature range. Flexible, fully annealed foil, suitably coated, is used for wrapping chocolate and processed cheese. Foil laminated to parchment paper is used to wrap butter and margarine. Foil coated with or laminated to suitable other plastics or paper is used in the form of sachets or pouches for a variety of products such as dried soup mixes, sauce mixes, instant pudding mixes, salad dressing and jams. Such pouches may be vacuum or gas packed where necessary. Foil may also be a component in the laminate used for retortable pouches. Thicker grades of foil are used for capping glass containers. Heavy gauge foil containing manganese is used to form plates, trays and dishes for frozen pies, desserts and complete meals.

Tinplate consists of mild steel sheet or strip, 0·50–0·15 mm thick, coated on both sides with a layer of tin. The coating seldom exceeds 1% of the total thickness of the tinplate. The structure of tinplate is more complex than would appear from this simple description and several detectable layers exist, as shown in Fig. 21.2. The mechanical strength and fabrication characteristics of tinplate depend on the type of steel and its thickness. The appearance and corrosion resistance depend on the tin coating. The stages of manufacture of tinplate are shown in Fig. 21.3. These result in three types of tinplate, namely: *single (or cold) reduced electroplate* (CR), *single reduced, hot-dipped tinplate* and *double reduced electroplate* (DR). Only a relatively small amount of hot-dipped tinplate is used for packaging some very corrosive food products. Double reduced electroplate is stronger in one direction than its single reduced counterpart and can be used in thinner gauges than the latter for certain applications. Tinplate used for food-can fabrication has a thickness near the lower end of the thickness range and can be as low as 0·17 mm for CR plate and 0·15 mm for DR plate. The amount of tin coating is usually expressed as weight per unit area, in $g\,m^{-2}$. In the case of hot dipped plate the coating weights are the same on both sides of the plate. However, when the tin is applied electrolytically, a different coating weight can be applied to each side of the plate. Such plate is said to be differentially coated. In general the more corrosive the product the higher the coating weights used. Coating weights for hot dipped tinplate

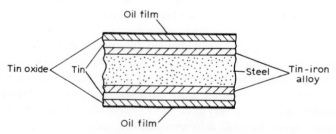

FIG. 21.2.   Structure of tinplate.

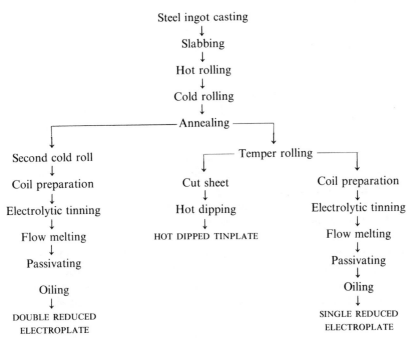

FIG. 21.3. Stages in the manufacture of tinplate (from Malin[30]).

range from 11 to $22\,\mathrm{g\,m^{-2}}$ (written H 11/11 to H 22/22). Electroplate has coating weights in the range 1·4 to $11·2\,\mathrm{g\,m^{-2}}$ (written E 1·4/1·4 to E 11·2/11·2). Differentially coated plate is identified by the letter D together with the coating weights on each side of the plate, e.g. D 5·6/2·8 has $5·6\,\mathrm{g\,m^{-2}}$ of tin on one side and 2·8 on the other. Lacquer may be applied to tinplate to prevent undesirable container–product interaction. Such interactions arise with: acid foods where fruit acid may interact with tin or exposed steel; some highly-coloured products where anthocyanin colour compounds react with tin, causing a loss of colour; sulphur-containing products where tin sulphide is formed, staining the can; products sensitive to small traces of tin, such as beer, or to provide certain functional properties, e.g. a non-stick surface. A range of lacquers is available including natural oleo-resinous materials and synthetic materials comprising phenolic, vinyl, epoxy, butadiene and acrylic based compounds. Cans may be fabricated from prelacquered plate or lacquer may be applied to the made-up can.

Tin-free steel (TFS). The only commercially successful alternative to tin for coating steel for food packaging purposes is chromium. Hi-Top is CR or DR steel electrolytically coated with metallic chromium and then further treated to produce a chromic oxide layer on the surface. The total thickness of the coating is about 0.025μm. This material has approximately the same corrosion resistance as E $5.6/5.6$ tinplate. It needs to be lacquered for most applications. It is finding increasing application in food packaging.

Aluminium is also used to fabricate food cans, usually as an alloy containing 1–3% magnesium. These alloys are less resistant to corrosion than tinplate and lacquering is necessary for most applications. A range of lacquers for aluminium is available and the metal may receive special surface treatment to improve lacquer adhesion. Aluminium may be used in combination with other metals, e.g. aluminium ends have been used with tinplate bodies in cans for beer and soft drinks.

Rigid metal containers may be manufactured in different ways. In the case of the traditional *three-piece* (*open top or sanitary*) can, the cylindrical can body and two ends are made separately from sheet metal. One end is applied to the body by the canmaker, the other by the food processor after the can has been filled. The ends are applied by double seaming (see Section 21.3). Early tinplate can bodies had an interlocked side seam, sealed by solder. These are being phased out in many countries and replaced by a lapped seam, welded or sealed by nylon cement (see Fig. 21.4). The *drawn* (DR) can is a two-piece container, made from tinplate, TFS or aluminium. The base and body are formed in one operation from a sheet of metal by being pressed out with a suitable die. The top or 'canners end' is applied by double seaming. Because of the straining of the metal such cans are shallow with a maximum height:diameter ratio of 1:2. The bodies are often oval or rectangular in shape and have been traditionally used for fish products, e.g. sardines and herrings (see Fig. 21.4). The *drawn and re-drawn* can (DRD) is made by drawing a cup to a smaller diameter in a series of stages to produce a deeper container as compared with the drawn can. They are usually cylindrical and the height:diameter ratio can be 1.2:1. This technique is used for tinplate or TFS cans (see Fig. 21.4). The *drawn and wall-ironed* can (DWI) is made from a disc of metal 0.3–0.42 mm thick. This is drawn into a shallow cup and is forced through a series of ironing rings of reducing internal diameter so that the wall of the cup gets thinner and higher. Aluminium or tinplate may be used in this way (see Fig. 21.4). The dimensions of cylindrical food cans are usually specified in diameter and height in that order. In the UK and USA the units of dimensions are inches and sixteenths of an inch. Thus a 401/411 can has a diameter of $4\frac{1}{16}$ in and a height of $4\frac{11}{16}$ in. In other countries the units of length used are millimetres.

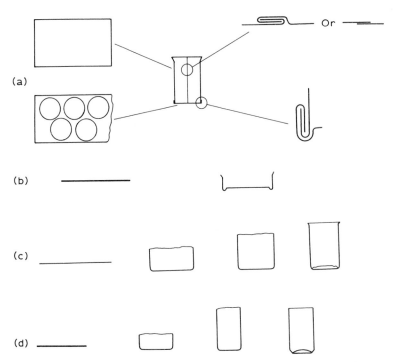

FIG. 21.4. Schematic representation of the manufacture of (a) three-piece can, (b) drawn can, (c) drawn and redrawn can, (d) drawn and wall-ironed can.

In Table 21.3 the dimensions and capacities of some common cans used for heat processed foods in the UK are presented.[2,17,23,24,27–32]

21.2.7. GLASS

Glass is a useful food packaging material. It is inert with respect to foods, impermeable to gases, vapours and oils, and transparent. The smooth internal surface of glass containers enables them to be washed and sterilised, thus permitting multi-trip usage. On the other hand, glass is heavy, susceptible to mechanical damage and cannot tolerate sudden changes in temperature. Broken glass in a food area is an obvious hazard. The composition of a typical UK glass is shown in Table 21.4. The ingredients, which can include up to 30% of recycled glass, are melted in a furnace at temperatures in the range 1350–1600°C. The treacle-like mass thus produced moves into another chamber which acts as a reservoir for the forming machines. Glass containers are formed by a number of methods,

TABLE 21.3

Some common can sizes used for heat processed foods in the UK (by courtesy of CMB Food Cans and Components, Woodside, Worcester, England)

Three piece cans

Metric size (mm)	Imperial size	Capacity (to nearest 5 ml)
52 × 72	202 × 213½	140
65 × 54	211 × 202	155
65 × 78	211 × 301 (Picnic)	235
65 × 102	211 × 400 (A1)	315
65 × 124	211 × 414	385
73 × 51	300 × 200	180
73 × 62	300 × 207 (U8)	230
73 × 105	300 × 402 (14Z)	400
73 × 110	73 × 110 (ET)	425
73 × 115	300 × 408¼ (UT)	445
73 × 120	—	468
73 × 128	—	500
73 × 159	300 × 604	630
83 × 114	307 × 408 (A2)	580
99 × 70	401 × 212	475
99 × 102	401 × 400	720
99 × 119	401 × 411 (A2½)	850
99 × 167	401 × 609	1 215
99 × 175	99 × 175	1 275
99 × 195	401 × 711	1 430
127 × 195	502 × 711	2 330
153 × 83	603 × 304	1 335
153 × 105	603 × 402	1 755
153 × 152	603 × 600 (A6)	2 630
153 × 178	603 × 700 (A10)	3 110
153 × 203	603 × 800	3 580
153 × 235	603 × 904	4 150
159 × 141	606 × 509	2 570

Two piece cans

Metric size (mm)	Imperial size	Capacity (to nearest 5 ml)
Round		
52 × 70	202 × 212	140
73 × 37	300 × 107	125
73 × 57	73 × 56½	210
73 × 110	73 × 110 (ET)	425
73 × 115	300 × 408¼ (UT)	445
83 × 44	307 × 112	210
99 × 48	401 × 114	325
99 × 60	401 × 206	430
153 × 38	603 × 108	600
Taper		
105 × 35	404 × 106	225
153 × 32	603 × 104	450
Oval		
174 × 95 × 25	MB15	240
Bowl		
83 × 60	307 × 206	240
105 × 71	404 × 213	495
Tray		
256 × 156 × 47	256 × 156 × 47	1 500

See Section 20.2.6 for units.

TABLE 21.4
Composition of a typical British glass

	Percentage
Silica (SiO_2)	72·0
Lime (CaO)	11·0
Soda (Na_2O)	14·0
Alumina (Al_2O_3)	1·7
Potash (K_2O)	0·3

the most common of which are (i) suction process, (ii) flow process—blow and blow—and (iii) flow process—press and blow. The principles of these three methods are shown in Fig. 21.5. After forming the containers are cooled under controlled conditions in an annealing lehr to minimise the production of undesirable stresses in the glass which would weaken the containers. Containers are inspected for faults as they leave the lehr. Because of the method of forming glass containers, variations can occur in their dimensions and capacities. Hence it is important for the user to take samples for his supplies of glass containers on a statistical basis and to check the important dimensions and capacities. This will reduce breakages and hold-ups in the plant and customer complaints. The mechanical strength of glass containers increases with increase in the thickness of the glass in the bodies and bases. However the design of the container also influences its strength, e.g. simple cylindrical shapes are more durable than complex shapes with sharp corners. Glass containers become weaker with use due to abrasion of the surface arising from bottle-to-bottle contact or contact with other surfaces. This damage can be reduced by good design, the use of protective plastic sleeves or special surface treatments. The latter include treatment with compounds of titanium, zirconium, aluminium or tin and replacement of the sodium ions in the glass surface with potassium ions. Such procedures permit the use of lighter containers. The resistance of glass containers to sudden changes in temperature, known as thermal shock resistance, is reduced as glass thickness increases. Thus when selecting glass containers which are to be subjected to heating or cooling, e.g. when the product is to be pasteurised or sterilised in its bottle or jar, a compromise must be achieved between their mechanical strength and their thermal shock resistance. Heating and cooling should be carried out relatively slowly to minimise thermal damage to containers.

The method of closing glass containers involves compressing a resilient disc (or ring or plug) against the rigid glass sealing surface and maintaining

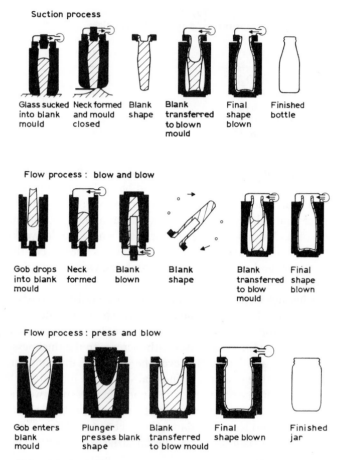

Suction process

Glass sucked into blank mould | Neck formed and mould closed | Blank shape | Blank transferred to blown mould | Final shape blown | Finished bottle

Flow process : blow and blow

Gob drops into blank mould | Neck formed | Blank blown | Blank shape | Blank transferred to blow mould | Final shape blown

Flow process : press and blow

Gob enters blank mould | Plunger presses blank shape | Blank transferred to blow mould | Final shape blown | Finished jar

FIG. 21.5. Methods of forming glass containers (adapted from Moody[35]).

it in the compressed condition by a retaining cap. The resilient component may be made from cork, rubber, pulpboard or plastic. The cap is made of metal or plastic. The cap may be screwed on, crimped on or pushed in or on the glass container. It is important that a closure be selected which will be effective under the conditions of use, i.e. when the pressure in the container is close to atmospheric pressure (normal seal), when there is a partial vacuum in the container (vacuum seal) or when the container is pressurised (pressure seal). Some typical closures are shown in Fig. 21.6. Applications for multi-trip glass containers include milk, beer and soft drinks. Products

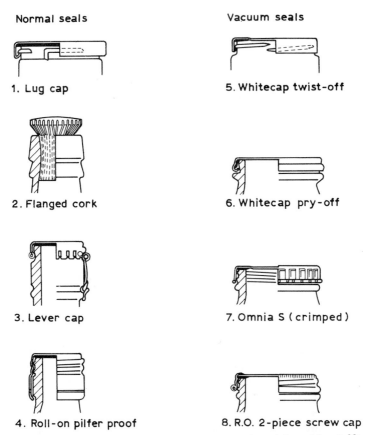

FIG. 21.6. Some closures for glass containers (adapted from Moody[35]).

packed in single-trip glass containers include some beer and soft drinks, wine, sauces, salad dressings, pickles, vinegar, coffee powders, milk powder and spices. Products heated in glass containers include sterilised milk, beer, some fruit-juices and pickled products.[2,17,23,33-35]

21.3. FILLING, CLOSING AND SEALING EQUIPMENT

21.3.1. FILLING EQUIPMENT

Filling equipment for liquids, viscous products and dry solids is discussed below. However, this classification is by no means clear cut and some fillers

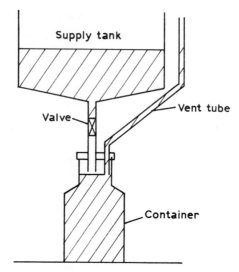

Supply tank

Valve

Vent tube

Container

FIG. 21.7.   Principle of a simple gravity filler.

can handle two or more of these categories of materials, e.g. piston fillers can handle some liquids, pastes and solids.

Filling liquids. A *simple gravity filler* is shown in Fig. 21.7. When the container is in position, forming an airtight seal with the filling head, the valve is opened and liquid flows into the container. Flow will cease almost as soon as the bottom of the vent tube is submerged. The valve then closes, the container is removed and the cycle recommences. In a *vacuum-gravity filler* the supply tank is closed and a pressure slightly below atmosphere is maintained in the headspace. When the container is in position the pressure in it falls to that in the supply tank and the liquid flows under gravity into the container. Filling stops soon after the end of the vent tube is submerged (Fig. 21.8). Both these types of fillers are suitable for filling low viscosity liquids such as wines, spirits and vinegar. They may be designed to fill from the bottom of the container up which reduces foaming. *Vacuum fillers*, such as that shown in Fig. 21.9, are also used for such liquids. As the container is raised a vacuum is created in it, the valve to the supply tank is opened and liquid flows into the container. When the valve closes any excess liquid is drawn into the overflow vessel. Vacuum fillers may also be adapted for bottom filling. They are suitable for low and medium viscosity liquids that do not foam excessively. They will not fill leaky containers. *Pressure–vacuum fillers* have a superatmospheric pressure imposed on the

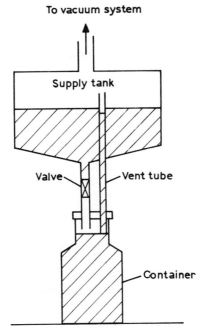

FIG. 21.8. Principle of a vacuum-gravity filler.

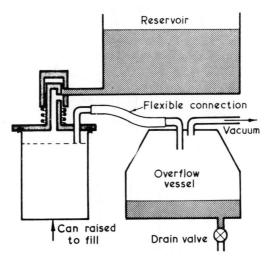

FIG. 21.9. Principle of a vacuum filler.

liquid in the supply tank. This increases rate of fill, particularly for viscous products. The *direct counter-pressure* filler is used for carbonated beverages to prevent loss of dissolved carbon dioxide during filling (Fig. 21.10). When the container is in position the pressure valve is opened first and when the full pressure is established in the container the liquid valve is opened and filling proceeds. Usually a 'snift valve' is provided in the filling head to release the pressure before the container is removed. In the *differential counter-pressure* filler the initial pressure in the container is somewhat higher than in the supply tank and is controlled during filling. Thus the liquid flows more quietly into the container and the whole system is at a lower pressure than in the direct counter-pressure filler.

Filling viscous products. The most common type of filler for viscous products is the *piston filler* (Fig. 21.11). As the piston rises (A), it charges a measuring cylinder and when it falls (B), it fills the container with the appropriate volume of product. Such fillers may be designed for bottom filling to prevent excessive aeration. Provision may be made for packing the product down into the container or a vacuum may be applied to the

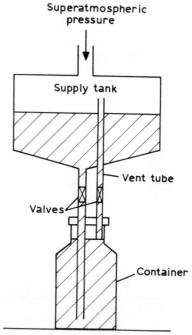

FIG. 21.10. Principle of a direct counter-pressure filler.

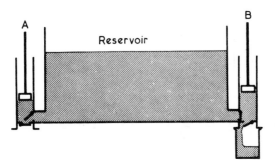

FIG. 21.11.   Principle of a piston filler.

container to reduce the amount of air in the product. Ketchups, sauces, salad dressings are typical of the products filled in this way. Piston fillers can also be used for filling particulate solids such as peas.

Filling dry solids. Large particulate solids, e.g. lozenges and tablets, can be filled by *counting.* A rotating disc or moving belt passes beneath a container of the solid items. The disc or belt contains a fixed number of holes or recesses designed to take individual items. Excess items are wiped off and the required number are delivered to the package. The solid items may be fed into channels in which counting wheels are located. The number of pockets in and the number of revolutions made by each wheel determine the number of items delivered to the package. In a column counter the solid items are fed into columns in single rows. The count is preset by a hold-back pin in the column. While part of the column is held back the preceding section passes in the package. The items may be passed in a single stream between a light source and a photocell which operates a counter and a mechanism for diverting the items when the desired number is fed to the package. *Volumetric filling* may be used for granular solids and some powders. One type of volumetric filler consists of a rotating plate containing a number of cups or pockets. As each cup passes beneath a chute from the supply hopper it receives a charge of solid. Excess solid is removed by a scraper. As each cup lines up with the discharge port in the stationary plate beneath the solid is dropped into the package (Fig. 21.12). Augers can also be used for volumetric filling of solids. These are mounted vertically beneath a supply hopper and the container is located accurately beneath the outlet from the auger. The auger motion is controlled by a clutch and brake so that it can be started and stopped quickly. The volume delivered is determined by the number of turns made by the auger which is controlled by a timer. Products may be loose filled or packed into the container.

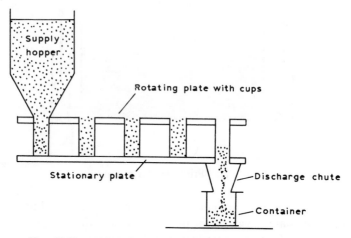

FIG. 21.12.　Principle of a volumetric cup filler for solids.

Powders may also be vacuum filled as can liquids (Fig. 21.9). The outlet pipes are protected by a gauze filter to prevent clogging. There may be a stage of vacuum release or blow-back to clear the gauze before removing the container. An auger may be used to assist the flow of solid into the container. *Filling by weight* is very commonly employed for solids. In net weighing the product is first weighed and then filled into the package. In gross weighing the product is weighed in the package. The former method is best suited to free-flowing solids and for containers that vary in tare weight or are difficult to support on a balance. The supply of product is divided into a main or bulk feed and a fine or dribble feed. Initially both feeds deliver about 90% of the desired weight of product quickly. Then the bulk feed is stopped and the fine feed continues until the desired weight is delivered. The fine feed is then stopped and the product is tipped into the package (net weighing) or the filled package passes on to the closing stage (gross weighing). Beam balances, heads operated by compressed air, electronic and microprocessor controlled systems may be used for weighing. There is increasing need to control the weight accurately and to maintain statistical records of the weight of the packaged products. Control systems with various levels of sophistication are available. A fully automated control system is shown in Fig. 21.13. First the container is tare weighed. It then passes on to be bulk filled with product at high speed. This partly filled container is again weighed, the controller calculates the amount of product required to attain the target weight and instructs the

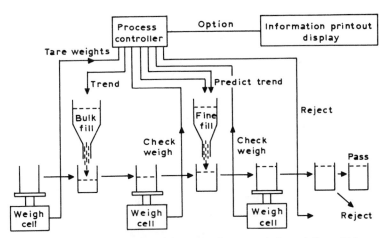

FIG. 21.13. Fully automated weight control system (adapted from Paine and Paine[2]).

fine-filling head accordingly. The filled container is finally check-weighed and any under- or over-filled packages rejected.[2,17,23,35]

21.3.2. CLOSING EQUIPMENT

The ends are attached to cans by means of *double seaming*, a two-stage operation (see Fig. 21.14). The can body and end are clamped tightly between a chuck and baseplate. They rotate with the chuck. The first seaming roller moves in and engages with the chuck forming mating hooks on the can body and end. The second seaming roller tightens these hooks to complete the seam. In high speed seaming machines, and those used for non-cylindrical cans, the can body, end, chuck and base plate remain stationary and the seaming rollers rotate on a carriage around them. Can seams must conform to narrow dimensional tolerances and must be checked frequently. The general method of closing glass containers is described in Section 21.2.7.[31,36] Screw caps are normally applied by a rubber-linked chuck fitted with a clutch which operates at a predetermined torque. Some plastic caps are gripped by a pneumatic ring or doughnut to avoid damage and a pneumatic clutch controls the torque. In the case of crimped closures, e.g. crown corks, pressure is applied to the crown to compress the resilient disc and a clinching head crimps the corrugated skirt under a protrusion on the neck of the container. Push-on or snap-on caps are usually applied by a belt which exerts pressure on the top of the caps pushing the rim over a protrusion on the neck of the container (Fig. 21.15).

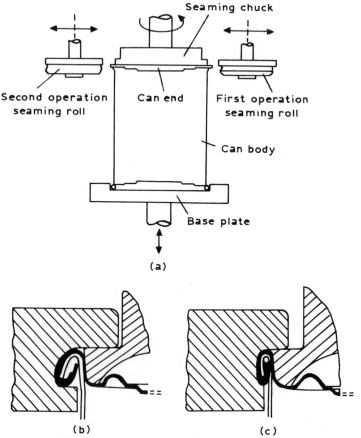

FIG. 21.14. Double seaming of cans. (a) View of seamer. (b) A seam after completion of the first operation. (c) After completion of the second operation.

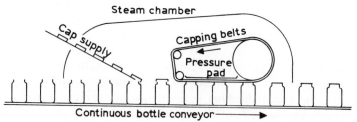

FIG. 21.15. Application of push-on caps to glass containers (adapted from Moody[35]).

Push-in closures, corks or plugs are applied by non-rotating chucks which push the closure in with one or more downward thrusts.[2,17,23,35]

21.3.3. HEAT SEALING EQUIPMENT

Heat sealing equipment must be chosen to suit the characteristics of the film or laminate being sealed. For non-thermoplastic materials (regenerated cellulose, paper, foil) coated with a heat sealable layer the *hot bar or resistance sealer* is appropriate (Fig. 21.16). The material to be sealed is clamped between two electrically heated metal bars to effect the sealing. The temperature of the bars, the pressure exerted by them and the contact time have to be controlled. Metal jaws with matching serrations are often used for coated cellulose films. The serrations stretch out wrinkles and improve the seal. When sealing laminates, smooth jaws meeting uniformly along their length are used. Alternatively one of the jaws is made of unheated, resilient material, often silicone elastomer, to ensure good contact. The resilient surface may have a round contour which helps to expel air or liquids from between the sealing surfaces. For continuous heat sealing of coated material, heated rollers or wheels may be used. Heated metal plates are used to seal wrapped items, e.g. portions of cheese. Unsupported, thermoplastic films, such as polyethylene, are usually sealed by *impulse sealing* (Fig. 21.17). The layers of film are clamped between jaws of resilient material one or both of which has a narrow metal (nichrome) strip running the length of the jaw. An accurately timed pulse of low voltage electricity is passed through the strip, heating it and fusing the two layers of packaging material together. The jaws are held apart by unmelted material each side of the strip thus no appreciable thinning of the sealed area occurs. The jaws remain closed until the melted packaging materials solidify. Both jaws and melted strip may be covered with Teflon to prevent the packaging film from sticking to the latter. In production models the jaws may be cooled by air or water to promote rapid solidification of the melted films. The *band sealer* is suited to continuous sealing of unsupported

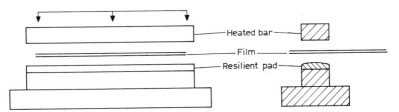

FIG. 21.16.   A hot bar sealer.

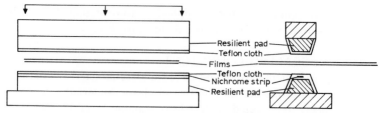

FIG. 21.17.   An impulse sealer.

thermoplastic film (Fig. 21.18). A pair of moving, endless metal belts or bands are heated by stationary, heated shoes. These shoes are so shaped that they touch the bands only near their centres, leaving the band edges relatively cool. Thus, as with the impulse sealer, there is little thinning of the sealed area. The bands may be Teflon coated. After passing between the heated shoes the layers of packaging film pass between pressure rollers and then between cooled shoes to solidify the melted film. A *heated wire* may be used to simultaneously cut and seal unsupported thermoplastic film. If two films are clamped together with their edges protruding a heated rod, wire or flame may be applied to form a *bead seal*. Application of a *hot air blast* can be used to weld overlapped edges of film together. *Electronic sealing* may be used with certain films, notably vinyls. The films are placed between shaped electrodes and subjected to a high frequency electric field. This causes the layers of film to weld together. This method is best used for thick layers of material with suitable electrical properties. *Ultrasonic sealing* or welding may be used to seal layers of film or foil together. This is particularly suited for use with uncoated, oriented films which are difficult to seal by more conventional means. *Hot melt sealing* is used mainly for paperboards. A bead of molten thermoplastic material is extruded onto one board surface. The other board surface is pressed against the molten bead and cooled to form a seal.[2,17,23]

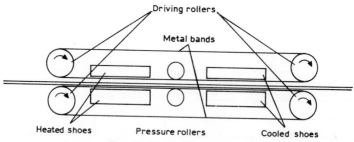

FIG. 21.18.   A band sealer.

21.3.4. FORM, FILL AND SEAL SYSTEMS (FFS)

Coated papers, films and laminates may be fabricated into pillow packs or sachets by a sequential operation in which the pack is formed, filled with product and sealed. Form–fill–seal machines may operate vertically or horizontally. The principle of the vertical form–fill–seal machine for making pillow-packs is shown in Fig. 21.19. In an alternative design the horizontal sealing jaws do not move up and down but simply open and close at timed intervals. The tube of packaging material is moved down the

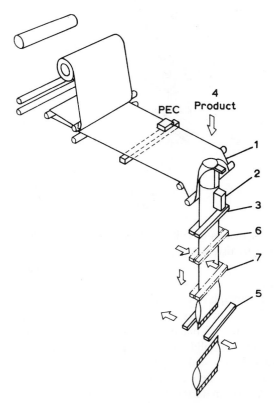

FIG. 21.19. Vertical form–fill–seal machine. (1) Film from reel made into a tube over forming shoulder. (2) Longitudinal seal made. (3) Bottom of tube closed by heat crimped jaws which move downwards drawing film from reel. (4) Pre-determined quantity of product falls through collar into pouch. (5) Jaws open and return on top of stroke. (6) Jaws partially close and 'scrape' product into pouch out of seal area. (7) Jaws close, crimp heat seal top of previous pouch and bottom of new one. Crimp sealed container cut off with knife. (Adapted from Paine and Paine.[2])

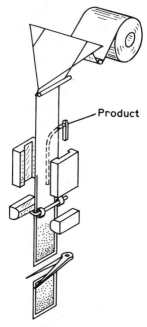

Product

FIG. 21.20.   Vertical form–fill–seal machine for sachets (adapted from Paine and Paine[2]).

forming tube by means of rollers which press against the latter. Vertical FFS machines can also make sachets (see Fig. 21.20). These can be formed from a single web of packaging material as shown in this figure, or from two webs. Vertically formed pillow and sachet packs may be used for liquids and solids. The principle of the horizontal FFS machine for pillow packs is shown in Fig. 21.21. Such a system is used for solid items, e.g. candy bars or biscuits. Horizontal FFS machines can also produce sachets (Fig. 21.22). These can be used for solid and liquid products. Containers may also be produced on a form–fill–seal basis by thermoforming. Cups or trays may be thermoformed into a web of material, filled with product and lidded by another web of material heat sealed to the flanges of the trays (Fig. 21.23).[2,17,21–23]

21.3.5. ASEPTIC FILLING

As discussed in Section 11.4, there are advantages in terms of product quality to be gained by heat processing foods in bulk prior to packaging as compared with heating the packaged product. The sterile product thus

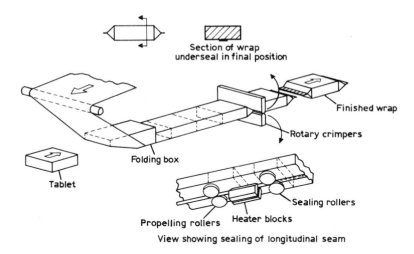

Fig. 21.21. Horizontal form–fill–seal machine. (1) Film drawn from reel, formed into horizontal tube around product with continuous seal underneath formed by heater blocks and crimping rollers. (2) Rotary heaters make the crimped end seals and a cut-off produces individual packs. (Adapted from Paine and Paine.[2])

produced must then be filled into sterile containers under conditions which prevent microbiological contamination of the product, i.e. under aseptic conditions. In the case of rigid metal and glass containers the Dole Process described in Section 11.4.2 is used. However in the case of other packaging materials, i.e. film laminates and laminates containing paper, paperboard or foil, steam cannot be used to sterilise the packaging material and alternative ways have to be found. Treatments with ethylene oxide, hot and cold hydrogen peroxide, ionising radiation, infra-red radiation, ultra-violet

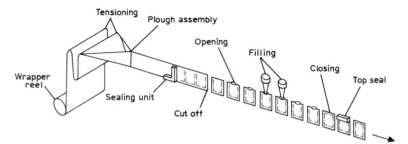

Fig. 21.22. Horizontal form–fill–seal machine for sachets (adapted from Paine and Paine[2]).

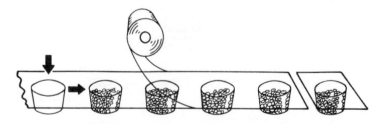

FIG. 21.23. A thermoforming, filling and sealing system (adapted from Paine and Paine[2]).

light and sterile air have all been attempted. Hydrogen peroxide on its own or in combination with one or more of the other agents mentioned above is most commonly employed commercially to date. The Tetra Brik system, offered by Tetra Pak Ltd, Kingston upon Thames, Surrey, England, is a typical example (Fig. 21.24). The packaging material, a polyethylene–paper–polyethylene–foil–polyethylene laminate first has a plastic strip attached to it which will eventually overlap the internal longitudinal seal in the carton. It then passes through a deep bath of hot hydrogen peroxide which wets the laminate. The sterilisation fluid is removed in two stages. First, the laminate passes between squeeze rollers which express fluid which is returned to the bath. Secondly, a high speed jet of hot air is directed onto both sides of the laminate removing residual hydrogen peroxide. The laminate, which is now sterile and dry, is formed into a tube with a longitudinal seal in an enclosed section which is maintained sterile by means of a supply of sterile air under pressure. The product filling tube is located down the centre of the laminate tube. The pre-sterilised product is fed into the sterile zone near the bottom of the tube which is heat sealed through the liquid. The air containing the vaporised hydrogen peroxide is collected in a cover, directed to a compressor where it is mixed with water which washes away residual hydrogen peroxide, sterilised by heat and returned to the filling zone.

Preformed laminate cartons may also be sterilised by a combintion of hydrogen peroxide spray and hot air or ultra-violet light. Preformed plastic cups can be treated with hot, damp, sterile air, impregnated with hydrogen peroxide followed by hot sterile air. The lids are sterilised by infra-red radiation. Filling takes place in a chamber supplied with sterile air under pressure. In the thermoform–fill–seal system the web of plastic passes through a bath of hot hydrogen peroxide which is subjected to hot sterile air to activate the sterilisation process. The covering web is sterilised by a

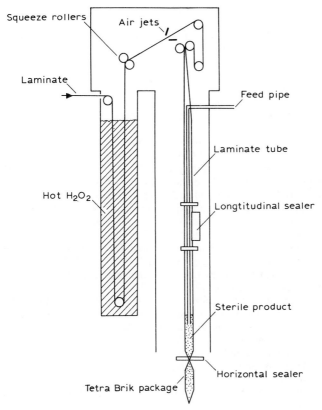

Squeeze rollers

Air jets

Laminate

Feed pipe

Laminate tube

Hot H$_2$O$_2$

Longtitudinal sealer

Sterile product

Horizontal sealer

Tetra Brik package

FIG. 21.24.   Principle of the Tetra Brik aseptic packaging system.

combination of hydrogen peroxide and infra-red radiation. The containers are thermoformed, filled with sterile product and sealed in a zone fed with sterile air under pressure. In all the above systems it is necessary to ensure that residual levels of hydrogen peroxide in the packed product should be low enough to comply with legislative requirements.[2,17,23,31,37–41]

REFERENCES

1. Goodburn, K. E. and Halligan, A. C., *Modified-Atmosphere Packaging—A Technology Guide*. The British Food Manufacturing Industries Research Association, Leatherhead, Surrey, England, 1988.

2. Paine, F. A. and Paine, H. Y., *A Handbook of Food Packaging*. Leonard Hill, Glasgow, Scotland, 1983.
3. Crosby, N. T., *Food Packaging Materials—Aspects of Analysis and Migration of Contaminants*. Applied Science Publishers, London, 1981.
4. Brennan, J. G., Packaging biological materials. *Process Biochemistry*, 6(5) (1971) 47–50.
5. Brennan, J. G., Food packaging principles—Mechanical and physical aspects. *Process. Chem. Engng*, 30(5) (1977) 20–21, 24–26.
6. Highland, H. A., Insect resistance of food packages—A review. *J. Food Proc. and Pres.*, 2 (1978) 123.
7. Wohlgemoth, R., Protection of stored foodstuffs against insect infestation by packaging, *Chem. and Ind.*, (19 May 1979) 330–4.
8. Paine, F. A., Paper and board-making. In *The Packaging Media*, ed. F. A. Paine. Blackie & Son, Glasgow, Scotland, 1977, pp. 1.3–19.
9. Goddard, R. R., Wrapping and packaging papers. In *The Packaging Media*, ed. F. A. Paine. Blackie & Son, Glasgow, Scotland, 1977, pp. 1.20–39.
10. Paine, F. A., Multiwall paper sacks. In *The Packaging Media*, ed. F. A. Paine. Blackie & Son, Glasgow, Scotland, 1977, pp. 1.40–53.
11. Hine, D. J., Folding box-board cartons. In *The Packaging Media*, ed. F. A. Paine. Blackie & Son, Glasgow, Scotland, 1977, pp. 54–75.
12. Robinson, P. B., Rigid boxes. In *The Packaging Media*, ed. F. A. Paine. Blackie & Son, Glasgow, Scotland, 1977, pp. 1.77–87.
13. Lott, A. R., Solid and corrugated fibreboard cases. In *The Packaging Media*, ed. F. A. Paine. Blackie & Son, Glasgow, Scotland, 1977, pp. 1.88–105.
14. Anon., Fibre drums. In *The Packaging Media*, ed. F. A. Paine. Blackie & Son, Glasgow, Scotland, 1977, pp. 1.106–15.
15. Porteous, G. J. P., Moulded pulp containers. In *The Packaging Media*, ed. F. A. Paine. Blackie & Son, Glasgow, Scotland, 1977, pp. 116–19.
16. Jones, W. A., Paper and board developments. In *Developments in Food Packaging*, ed. S. J. Palling. Applied Science Publishers, London, 1980, pp. 117–33.
17. Bakker, M., *The Wiley Encyclopedia of Packaging Technology*. John Wiley, New York, 1986.
18. Rawson, M., Timber and plywood cases and crates. In *The Packaging Media*, ed. F. A. Paine. Blackie & Son, Glasgow, Scotland, 1977, pp. 4.11–19.
19. Paine, F. A., Wooden casks and plywood kegs. In *The Packaging Media*, ed. F. A. Paine. Blackie & Son, Glasgow, Scotland, 1977, pp. 4.20–4.
20. Atkins, W. G., Textile sacks and bags. In *The Packaging Media*, ed. F. A. Paine. Blackie & Son, Glasgow, Scotland, 1977, pp. 4.64–74.
21. Oswin, C. R., Packaging with flexible barriers. In *The Packaging Media*, ed. F. A. Paine. Blackie & Son, Glasgow, Scotland, 1977, pp. 3.44–73.
22. Goddard, R. R., Flexible plastics packaging. In *Developments in Food Packaging*, ed. S. J. Palling. Applied Science Publishers, London, 1980, pp. 55–79.
23. Griffin, R. C., Sacharow, S. and Brody, A. L., *Principles of Package Development*. AVI, Westpoint, Conn., USA, 1985.
24. Norman, G. F., Heat processed foods—Their packaging prospects in the next decade. *Food Process. Ind.*, 48(10) (1979) 39, 41, 45.

25. Briston, J. H., Moulded plastic containers. In *The Packaging Media*, ed. F. A. Paine. Blackie & Son, Glasgow, Scotland, 1977, pp. 3.25–43.
26. Briston, J. H., Rigid plastics packaging. In *Developments in Food Packaging*, ed. S. J. Palling. Applied Science Publishers, London, 1980, pp. 27–53.
27. Paine, F. A., Metal packaging—The basic materials. In *The Packaging Media*, ed. F. A. Paine. Blackie & Son, Glasgow, Scotland, 1977, pp. 2.3–12.
28. Price, D. W., Metal cans. In *The Packaging Media*, ed. F. A. Paine. Blackie & Son, Glasgow, Scotland, 1977, pp. 2.13–51.
29. Green, J. R., Metal foil packaging. In *The Packaging Media*, ed. F. A. Paine, Blackie & Son, Glasgow, Scotland, 1977, pp. 2.102–12.
30. Malin, J. D., Metal containers and closures. In *Developments in Food Packaging*, ed. S. J. Palling. Applied Science Publishers, London, 1980, pp. 1–26.
31. Hersom, A. C. and Hulland, E. D., Canned Foods, 7th edn. Livingstone, Edinburgh Scotland, 1980.
32. Byrne, M., Cutting the cost of packaging. *Food Man.*, **58**(2) (1983) 49–51.
33. Weeden, C., Glass containers. In *The Packaging Media*, ed. F. A. Paine. Blackie & Son, Glasgow, Scotland, 1977, pp. 3.3–24.
34. Osbourne, D. G., Glass. In *Developments in Food Packaging*, ed. S. J. Palling. Applied Science Publishers, London, 1980, pp. 81–115.
35. Moody, B. E., *Packaging in Glass*. Hutchinson, 1970.
36. Anon., *Double Seaming Manual*. The Metal Box Company, England, 1973.
37. Philip, M. C., Food technology in the year 2000. In *Developments in Food Packaging*, ed. S. J. Palling. Applied Science Publishers, London, 1980, pp. 135–56.
38. Fisher, P., Development of aseptic packaging. *Food Man.*, **56**(8), (1981) 25–7.
39. Guise, W., Aseptics set to clean up the market. *Food Process.*, **54**(7) (1985) 33–6.
40. Burton, H., *Ultra-high Temperature Processing of Milk and Milk Products*. Elsevier Applied Science Publishers, London, 1988, pp. 181–227.
41. Herbert, D. A. and Bettison, J., Packaging for thermally processed foods. In *Developments in Food Preservation—4*, ed. S. Thorne. Elsevier Applied Science Publishers, London, 1987, pp. 87–121.

APPENDICES

FLUID FLOW FORMULAE

I.1. FLOW THROUGH EQUIPMENT

For fluids flowing in pipes and ducts or past solid bodies the 'Reynolds Number' is defined by:

$$Re = \frac{Dv\rho}{\eta} \tag{I.1}$$

where D = a characteristic dimension of the system; v = the mean linear velocity of the fluid; ρ = the density of the fluid; η = the viscosity of the fluid, and the 'Friction Factor' is defined by:

$$f = \frac{D}{2v^2} \frac{dF}{dx} \tag{I.2}$$

where dF is the energy used in overcoming friction when unit mass of the fluid flows from a surface at x to $x + dx$.

For incompressible fluids (i.e. liquids) flowing in ducts or channels of uniform cross-section:

$$f = \frac{D(-\Delta p)}{2L\rho v^2}$$

where $(-\Delta p)$ = pressure drop due to frictional losses (in, say, Newtons/(metre)^2); L = length of duct or channel (in, say, metres); and the other quantities are as defined in equations (I.1) and (I.2) and are measured in units consistent with those above.

For flow of incompressible fluids in circular ducts at Reynolds Numbers below 2000 (streamline flow):

$$Re \cdot f = 16 \tag{I.3}$$

At higher Reynolds Numbers, where the flow is turbulent, a number of correlations between Reynolds Number, friction factor and the roughness of the pipe wall have been proposed. For smooth pipes an equation of the form:

$$\frac{1}{(f)^{1/2}} = k_1 \log [Re.(f)^{1/2}] - k_2 \tag{I.4}$$

is often used. A number of different values have been produced for k_1 and k_2, but Nikuradse's proposals ($k_1 = 4.0$, $k_2 = 0.40$) are commonly employed.[1]

For turbulent flow in ducts and channels of non-circular section it is usually assumed that the above formula may be used, provided the characteristic dimension, D, is taken to be $4R$, where R is the 'hydraulic radius' defined by:

$$\frac{\text{cross-sectional area of duct}}{\text{length of the wetted perimeter}} \tag{I.5}$$

For flow through a bed of granular material the following equation has been proposed:[3]

$$\frac{(-\Delta p)x^3}{LS_0 u(1-x)} = k_1 S_0 (1-x)\eta + k_2 \rho u \tag{I.6}$$

where x = the porosity of the bed (i.e. the fraction filled with fluid); L = the length of the bed; S_0 = the specific surface of the granules (surface area of unit volume of the *granules*); and u = the superficial velocity, given by:

$$u = \frac{V}{A}$$

where V = rate of volume flow through the bed; A = cross-sectional area of the *bed*.

The constant k_1 in equation (I.6) takes values between about 4 and 5, depending on the geometry of the granule bed[2] and k_2 has a value of about 0.3.[3] For streamline flow (i.e. at comparatively low flow rates) the second term on the right-hand side of equation (I.6) can be neglected.

I.2. FLUIDISATION

If flow takes place vertically upwards through a granular bed, equation (I.6) will apply until the pressure drop across the bed balances the weight of the bed. If the flow is increased above this level, the bed expands and the granules forming it are no longer all in static contact; the bed is then said to be fluidised and the pressure drop across it is given by:

$$-\Delta p = g(1 - x)(\rho_s - \rho)L \tag{I.7}$$

where ρ_s = the density of the granules; g = the acceleration due to gravity.

If the flow is further increased so that the viscous drag on the granules exceeds their weight, the granules will be carried along in the fluid stream (fluid-solid conveying). This case is discussed by Foust et al.[3]

An important parameter of a fluidised bed is the Froude Number (*Fr*), given by:

$$Fr = \frac{u^2}{gD}$$

where D = the average diameter of the granule.

At Froude numbers below unity 'particulate' fluidisation occurs, the bed being essentially uniform in nature. At Froude numbers above unity the bed takes on a 'boiling' appearance with 'bubbles' of a dilute suspension rising through the bed ('aggregative' fluidisation).

REFERENCES

1. McCabe, W. L., Smith, J. C. and Harriott, P., *Unit Operations of Chemical Engineering*, 4th edn. McGraw-Hill, New York, 1985.
2. Coulson, J. M., Richardson, J. F. with Backhurst, J. R. and Harker, J. H., *Chemical Engineering. Vol. 2*, 3rd edn. Pergamon Press, Oxford, England, 1978.
3. Foust, A. S., Wenzel, L. A., Clump, C. W., Maus, L. and Bryce Anderson, L., *Principles of Unit Operations*, 2nd edn. John Wiley, New York, 1980.

HEAT TRANSFER FORMULAE

II.1 THERMAL CONVECTION

This occurs in fluids when heat is transferred by the motion of the fluid. Two types of convection are distinguished: 'forced' convection, in which the motion of the fluid is caused by external agencies and there is a net fluid velocity in the system, and 'natural' convection, in which movement occurs by virtue of density gradients generated by differential thermal expansion of the fluid.

II.1.1. HEAT TRANSFER COEFFICIENTS

The rate of heat transfer by convection from an area dA of a solid surface (temperature θ_1) to a fluid (temperature θ_2) under steady conditions

$$= h\,dA(\theta_1 - \theta_2) \tag{II.1}$$

where h is the local heat transfer coefficient at the fluid–solid interface.

This heat transfer coefficient is expressed in dimensionless form in the Nusselt Number (Nu):

$$Nu = \frac{hD}{k} \tag{II.2}$$

where D is a characteristic dimension of the system and k is the thermal conductivity of the fluid.

In a heat exchanger where two fluids (a and b) flow on opposite sides of a barrier, the overall heat transfer coefficient between them (U—Section II.2.1) being constant over the heat exchange surface (area A), the rate of heat exchange between them

$$= UA\Delta\theta_m \tag{II.3}$$

TABLE II.1
Values of the constants a, b and c in equation (II.5)[1]

System	a	b	c
Fluid flowing inside a circular tube:			
(i) fluid heated	0·023	0·8	0·4
(ii) fluid cooled	0·023	0·8	0·3
Fluid flowing at right-angles to a circular cylinder	0·26	0·6	0·3
Fluid flowing over tube banks	See reference 1		

where

$$\Delta\theta_m = \frac{(\theta_a - \theta_b) - (\theta_a' - \theta_b')}{\ln(\theta_a - \theta_b) - \ln(\theta_a' - \theta_b')} \tag{II.4}$$

and θ_a, θ_b, θ_a', θ_b' are the temperatures of the fluids a and b at one end and the other end of the heat exchanger respectively.

II.1.2. FORCED CONVECTION

For fluid flowing turbulently, the Nusselt number may be expressed approximately as a function of the Reynolds and Prandtl Numbers by:

$$Nu = a(Re)^b(Pr)^c \tag{II.5}$$

where the Prandtl Number, Pr, is given by

$$Pr = \frac{C_p \eta}{k} \tag{II.6}$$

η = viscosity of the fluid; C_p = its specific heat at constant pressure; and the Reynolds Number is defined in Appendix I.1.

Values of the constants a, b and c suitable for use with liquids of low viscosity are given in Table II.1.

For convective heat transfer to or from a sphere from a fluid in turbulent flow the following expression has been recommended:[2]

$$Nu = 2 + 0·6 Re^{0·5} Pr^{0·33} \tag{II.7}$$

II.1.3. NATURAL CONVECTION

Here the Nusselt Number can be expressed approximately as a function of the Prandtl and Grashof Numbers:[1]

$$Nu = a(Pr . Gr)^b \tag{II.8}$$

TABLE II.2
Values of the constants a and b in equation (II.7)

System	D	Value of $Pr.Gr$	a	b
Horizontal or vertical cylinders	diameter	10^3-10^8	0·47	0·25
		$>10^9$	0·10	0·33
Vertical planes	height	10^3-10^8	0·56	0·25
		$>10^9$	0·12	0·33
Horizontal square planes facing upwards	side	10^3-10^8	0·54	0·25
		$>10^9$	0·14	0·33
Fluid between parallel vertical planes	gap width	$<10^3$	1	0
		10^4-10^6	0·15	0·25
		$>10^6$	heat transfer takes place independently at each face	

where the Grashof Number, Gr, is given by

$$Gr = \frac{D^3 \rho^2 g \beta (\theta_1 - \theta_2)}{\eta^2} \tag{II.9}$$

ρ = density of the fluid; g = acceleration due to gravity; β = coefficient of volumetric expansion of fluid.

Suitable values of the constants a and b for fluid of low viscosity and the appropriate dimension D to be used in Nu and Gr are given in Table II.2.

Natural convective heat transfer at the surface of a sphere, provided that the value of $Gr^{0.25} Pr^{0.33}$ is less than 200, can be calculated from:[2]

$$Nu = 2 + 0·6 Gr^{0.25} Pr^{0.33} \tag{II.10}$$

II.2. THERMAL CONDUCTION

II.2.1. THE STEADY STATE

If heat is transferred by conduction between the parallel faces of an infinitely large slab of thickness d, one face being held at temperature θ_1 and the other at θ_2, the rate of heat transfer per unit area of the slab

$$= \frac{k}{d}(\theta_1 - \theta_2) \tag{II.11}$$

where k is the thermal conductivity of the material of the slab.

In the case of a complex thermal barrier composed of a series of such infinite slabs (thickness d_1, d_2,... and thermal conductivities k_1, k_2,...) either in contact or separated by parallel-sided fluid-filled spaces (there existing convective resistances at fluid–solid boundaries defined by a series of heat transfer coefficients h_1, h_2,...) an overall heat transfer coefficient (U) may be defined by:

$$\frac{1}{U} = \frac{d_1}{k_1} + \frac{d_2}{k_2} + \cdots + \frac{1}{h_1} + \frac{1}{h_2} + \cdots \tag{II.12}$$

and the rate of heat flow per unit area across the barrier

$$= U(\theta_1 - \theta_2) \tag{II.13}$$

If a hollow cylinder (inside radius r_1, outside radius r_2) of material of thermal conductivity k is immersed in a fluid at temperature θ_2, the heat transfer coefficient at the solid–fluid interface being h, and if the inside face of the cylinder is maintained at temperature θ_1, then the rate of heat flow per unit length of cylinder

$$= \frac{2\pi(\theta_1 - \theta_2)}{\dfrac{1}{k}\ln\left(\dfrac{r_2}{r_1}\right) + \dfrac{1}{r_2 h}} \tag{II.14}$$

N.B. The rate of heat transfer increases with r_2 when $r_2 < k/h$; thus lagging pipes with poor insulation may increase the heat loss from them.

II.2.2. THE UNSTEADY STATE

It is frequently necessary to determine the way in which food bodies change in temperature due to outside influences. The discussion that follows will be limited to a consideration of temperature changes in bodies in which internal heat exchange is purely by conduction, where the physical properties of the system do not change with temperature and where the body is initially at a uniform temperature, θ_1, and is subjected to a medium at a constant temperature, θ_2, for time $t > 0$, to which temperature it equilibrates. It is convenient to express the temperature, θ, of a point within such a body at time, t, during the change in terms of the 'dimensionless temperature', V, given by

$$V = \frac{\theta - \theta_2}{\theta_1 - \theta_2} \tag{II.15}$$

Clearly V will have an initial value of 1 and will tend to zero as the change progresses. Formulae for V are conveniently expressed in terms of the Biot (Bi) and Fourier (Fo) Numbers:

$$Bi = \frac{hl}{k} \tag{II.16}$$

$$Fo = \frac{kt}{\rho c l^2} = \frac{\kappa_t}{l^2} \tag{II.17}$$

where h = heat transfer coefficient at the surface of the body; ρ = density of the body; c = specific heat of the body; $\kappa = k/\rho c$ is known as the thermal diffusivity of the body; and l = characteristic dimension of the body—this is taken to be the shortest distance between the surface of the body and the thermal centre (i.e. the location that heats or cools slowest). For a sphere or infinite cylinder, this distance is the radius. For an infinite slab it is half the thickness.

Expressions giving V as a function of Bi and Fo are available in a number of instances,[3] though they are rarely simple in form. Among the most useful for the present purposes are those which give the centre temperature and average temperature of the three bodies mentioned above (the infinite slab, the infinitely long circular cylinder and the sphere). These formulae are given below:

Infinite slab. The temperature, V_1, at the central plane of an infinite slab of material of uniform thickness is given by:

$$V_1 = \sum_{n=1}^{\infty} \frac{2Bi}{(Bi^2 + Bi + \alpha_n^2)\cos(\alpha_n)} \exp(-\alpha_n^2 Fo) \tag{II.18}$$

The average temperature, V_1', of an infinite slab is given by:

$$V_1' = \sum_{n=1}^{\infty} \frac{2Bi^2}{\alpha_n^2(Bi^2 + Bi + \alpha_n^2)} \exp(-\alpha_n^2 Fo) \tag{II.19}$$

where α_n is the nth real positive root of $\alpha \tan \alpha = Bi$.

Infinite cylinder. The temperature, V_2, along the axis of an infinitely long circular cylinder of material is given by:

$$V_2 = \sum_{n=1}^{\infty} \frac{2Bi}{(\beta_n^2 + Bi^2)J_0(\beta_n)} \exp(-\beta_n^2 Fo) \tag{II.20}$$

The average temperature V_2' of an infinite cylinder is given by:

$$V_2' = \sum_{n=1}^{\infty} \frac{4Bi^2}{\beta_n^2(\beta_n^2 + Bi^2)} \exp(-\beta_n Fo) \tag{II.21}$$

where β_n is the nth real positive root of $\beta J_1(\beta) - Bi J_0(\beta) = 0$ and $J_0(x)$, $J_1(x)$ are the zero- and first-order Bessel Functions of the first kind.

Sphere. The temperature, V_3, at the centre of a sphere of material is given by:

$$V_3 = \sum_{n=1}^{\infty} \frac{2Bi\gamma_n}{(\gamma_n^2 + Bi^2 - Bi)\sin(\gamma_n)} \exp\left(-\gamma_n^2 Fo\right) \qquad (\text{II.22})$$

The average temperature, V_3', of a sphere is given by:

$$V_3' = \sum_{n=1}^{\infty} \frac{6Bi^2}{\gamma_n^2(\gamma_n^2 + Bi^2 - Bi)} \exp\left(-\gamma_n^2 Fo\right) \qquad (\text{II.23})$$

where γ_n is the nth real positive root of $\gamma \cot(\gamma) + Bi = 1$.

Tables of the roots of the controlling transcendental equations are available.[2]

The terms in the summations on the right hand side of equations (II.18) to (II.23) reduce in size and for a wide range of problems of practical importance only the first term needs to be taken into account, all others being negligible. Such an approximation is reasonable providing that either the dimensionless temperature is below 0·4 or, for dimensionless temperatures above 0·4, the Fourier Number is greater than 0·4.

If all terms except the first may be neglected, equations (II.18) to (II.23) all reduce to the common form:

$$V = A \exp(-BFo) \qquad (\text{II.24})$$

where A and B are appropriate constants for each equation and are dependent on the Biot Number. Values of these constants for the three bodies under consideration are given in Tables II.3, II.4 and II.5, respectively. It will be noted that as the Biot number reduces, so that the principal resistance to heat transfer is located at the surface of the body, the temperature throughout the body tends to uniformity ($A_{centre} \rightarrow A_{mean} \rightarrow 1$) and $B \rightarrow Bi$ for the infinite slab, $B \rightarrow 2Bi$ for the infinite cylinder and $B \rightarrow 3Bi$ for the sphere.

Equations (II.18)–(II.24) have an additional useful property which enables them to be used to determine the centre temperature and mean temperatures of right circular cylinders of finite length, infinitely long rods of rectangular section and brick shaped bodies (rectangular parallelepipeds). All these bodies have surfaces which can be regarded as being formed by the intersection of infinite cylinders and infinite slabs.

For instance, a right circular cylinder of length $2l$ and radius a has surfaces which may be regarded as being defined by the intersection of an

TABLE II.3
Constants A and B for the heating or cooling of an
infinite slab

Bi	A_{centre}	A_{mean}	B
0·04	1·01	1·00	0·039 5
0·06	1·01	1·00	0·058 8
0·08	1·01	1·00	0·079 0
0·1	1·02	1·00	0·096 8
0·2	1·03	0·999	0·187
0·3	1·05	0·998	0·272
0·4	1·06	0·997	0·352
0·5	1·07	0·996	0·427
0·6	1·08	0·994	0·497
0·7	1·09	0·992	0·563
0·8	1·10	0·990	0·626
0·9	1·11	0·988	0·685
1	1·12	0·986	0·740
1·5	1·15	0·975	0·977
2	1·18	0·963	1·16
3	1·21	0·943	1·42
4	1·23	0·926	1·60
5	1·24	0·913	1·73
6	1·25	0·902	1·82
7	1·25	0·893	1·90
8	1·26	0·886	1·95
9	1·26	0·880	2·00
10	1·26	0·874	2·04
15	1·27	0·857	2·17
20	1·27	0·846	2·24
30	1·27	0·835	2·31
40	1·27	0·830	2·35
50	1·27	0·826	2·37
60	1·27	0·823	2·39
80	1·27	0·820	2·41
100	1·27	0·819	2·42
∞	1·27	0·811	2·47

infinite cylinder of radius a and an infinite slab of thickness $2l$, the plane faces of which are perpendicular to the axis of the infinite cylinder. If, for the particular conditions, the dimensionless temperature, V_2, is found for the axis of the rod from equation (II.20) and the dimensionless temperature, V_1 is correspondingly found for the central plane of the infinite slab from (II.18), then the dimensionless temperature at the geometric centre of the finite cylinder will be the product of these

TABLE II.4
Constants A and B for the heating or cooling of an
infinite circular cylinder

Bi	A_{centre}	A_{mean}	B
0·04	1·01	1·00	0·079 2
0·06	1·02	1·00	0·118
0·08	1·02	1·00	0·157
0·10	1·02	1·00	0·195
0·15	1·04	1·00	0·289
0·2	1·05	0·999	0·381
0·3	1·07	0·998	0·557
0·4	1·09	0·997	0·725
0·5	1·11	0·995	0·885
0·6	1·13	0·993	1·04
0·7	1·15	0·991	1·18
0·8	1·15	0·989	1·32
0·9	1·19	0·987	1·45
1	1·21	0·984	1·58
1·5	1·28	0·970	2·12
2	1·34	0·954	2·56
3	1·42	0·922	3·20
4	1·47	0·895	3·64
5	1·50	0·872	3·96
6	1·53	0·853	4·20
7	1·54	0·838	4·38
8	1·55	0·824	4·53
9	1·56	0·813	4·65
10	1·57	0·804	4·75
15	1·59	0·772	5·07
20	1·59	0·754	5·23
30	1·60	0·735	5·41
40	1·60	0·725	5·50
50	1·60	0·718	5·56
60	1·60	0·714	5·59
80	1·60	0·709	5·64
100	1·60	0·705	5·67
∞	1·60	0·692	5·78

temperatures $(V_1 . V_2)$. The average temperature of the finite cylinder may be correspondingly found from $V'_1 . V'_2$ using equations (II.19) and (II.21).

Similarly, an infinite rod of rectangular section can be regarded as defined by two perpendicular infinite slabs and a brick by three mutually perpendicular infinite slabs. The temperature of the central axis of the rectangular rod and the central point of the brick (as also the average

TABLE II.5
Constants A and B for the heating or cooling of a sphere

Bi	A_{centre}	A_{mean}	B
0·04	1·01	1·00	0·119
0·05	1·01	1·00	0·149
0·06	1·02	1·00	0·178
0·07	1·02	1·00	0·207
0·08	1·02	1·00	0·236
0·09	1·03	1·00	0·265
0·1	1·03	1·00	0·294
0·15	1·04	0·999	0·437
0·2	1·06	0·999	0·577
0·3	1·09	0·998	0·848
0·4	1·12	0·997	1·11
0·5	1·14	0·996	1·36
0·6	1·17	0·994	1·60
0·7	1·20	0·993	1·83
0·8	1·22	0·990	2·05
0·9	1·25	0·988	2·37
1	1·27	0·986	2·47
1·2	1·32	0·980	2·85
1·4	1·36	0·974	3·21
1·6	1·41	0·967	3·53
1·8	1·44	0·960	3·84
2	1·48	0·953	4·12
2·5	1·56	0·935	4·73
3	1·62	0·917	5·24
4	1·72	0·883	6·03
5	1·79	0·853	6·61
6	1·83	0·828	7·04
7	1·87	0·807	7·38
8	1·89	0·789	7·65
9	1·91	0·774	7·86
10	1·92	0·761	8·04
15	1·96	0·719	8·62
20	1·98	0·693	8·91
30	1·99	0·666	9·23
40	1·99	0·652	9·38
50	2·00	0·644	9·48
60	2·00	0·638	9·54
80	2·00	0·630	9·62
100	2·00	0·626	9·67
∞	2·00	0·608	9·87

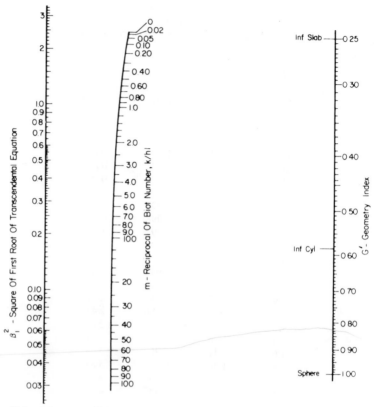

FIG. II.1. Nomograph for the evaluation of temperature distributions in bodies of arbitrary shape. (From Smith *et al.*[5] by permission.)

temperatures of these two bodies) can then be obtained from the product of two and three V-values respectively by following an analogous procedure to that above.

These procedures are detailed by Dalgleish and Ede,[4] who also present charts for the determination of V as a function of Bi and Fo for a number of circumstances.

Where the body being heated or cooled approximates in shape to an ellipsoid with semi-axes l, $B_1 l$ and $B_2 l$ ($B_1, B_2 \gg 1$) Smith *et al.*[5] suggest an approximate method for determining V. First a Geometry Index, G', is calculated from the equation:

$$G' = \frac{1}{4} + \frac{3}{8B_1^2} + \frac{3}{8B_2^2} \qquad (II.25)$$

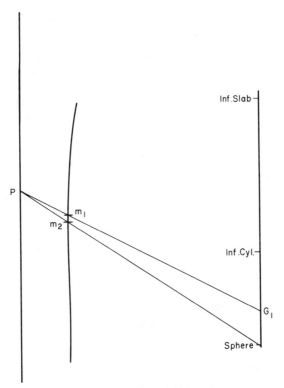

FIG. II.2. Example of the use of Fig. II.1 (for explanation, see text).

Then, referring to the nomograph in Fig. II.1 and the explanatory example in Fig. II.2, knowing the Biot Number $(Bi)_1$ for the ellipsoid a value m_1 is calculated where:

$$m_1 = \frac{1}{(Bi)_1} \tag{II.26}$$

and a line is drawn from the point indicating the Geometry Index of the ellipsoid (G') through the point corresponding to m_1 to cut the left hand line at the point P as shown. Taking the nearest regular solid to the point G' (in the example, this is the sphere) a line is drawn to P, cutting the m-line at m_2. Then, for $Fo > 0.2$, the relationship between Fo and V at the centre of the ellipsoid will be approximately the same as that at the centre of the regular body chosen (in the example, the sphere) when the Biot number for the regular body is $1/m_2$, which can be found using the equations given earlier.

II.3. RADIATION TRANSFER

Matter, as a consequence of its temperature, emits radiation at wavelengths and with intensities that depend on the nature of the radiator. Radiation can also be absorbed in part or whole by bodies and thus its interchange provides a method of heat exchange. The radiating surfaces may be characterised as 'black body', 'grey body' or 'selective emitters'.

II.3.1. BLACK BODY RADIATORS

Black body radiators are conceived to be perfect radiators. They emit the greatest amount of thermal radiation possible at any given temperature. They absorb all energy incident upon them, reflecting nothing. Dark dull surfaces approximate to black body radiators.

The total energy emitted per unit area from a black body at *absolute* temperature T in unit time is:

$$\sigma T^4 \tag{II.27}$$

where $\sigma = 5 \cdot 775 \times 10^{-8} \, \mathrm{W \, m^{-2} \, K^{-4}}$.

If two black body radiators at absolute temperatures T_1 and T_2 $(T_1 > T_2)$ radiate to each other, the net rate of exchange of heat

$$= E = C\sigma(T_1^4 - T_2^4) \tag{II.28}$$

where C is a constant depending on the geometry of the system.

If $T_1 - T_2$ $(= \Delta T)$ is small compared with T_1 equation (II.28) can be re-written:

$$E \simeq 4C\sigma T_1^3 \Delta T \tag{II.29}$$

thus the energy transfer in this case is approximately proportional to the temperature difference (cf. convective transfer).

The thermal energy radiated by a black body is not uniformly distributed over the whole spectrum but has a maximum intensity at wavelength λ given by

$$\lambda T = 0 \cdot 2896 \, \mathrm{cm \, K} \tag{II.30}$$

II.3.2. GREY BODY RADIATORS

The radiation from grey bodies is spectrally distributed in a manner similar to that from a black body, but with the intensity at any wavelength reduced by a factor ε (the 'emissivity' of the body) which is constant over the whole spectrum. Thus equation (II.27) holds for grey bodies if its right-hand side is multiplied by ε, equations (II.28) and (II.29) hold without modification, though C is now also a function of the emissivities of the surfaces, and equation (II.30) stands unchanged.

Most electrical insulators and semi-conductors can, in practice, be regarded as grey bodies. The emissivity of unpolished surfaces of such materials is usually of the order of 0·9.

II.3.3. SELECTIVE EMITTERS

Some materials, particularly metals, metal oxides and certain gases and vapours, show an irregular distribution of radiant intensity, the emissivity of their surface varying over the spectrum.

Since the emissivity of a body is equal to its absorptivity, a body which reflects much radiation radiates little. Thus the emissivity of clean metal surfaces is low. Moreover if a body is perfectly transparent, neither absorbing nor reflecting radiation, it will not emit radiation (i.e. $\varepsilon = 0$). This behaviour is approximated by certain gases such as hydrogen, oxygen and nitrogen. Gases and vapours consisting of polar molecules (e.g. steam and carbon dioxide) are selective emitters with a complex emission spectrum.

REFERENCES

1. Fishenden, M. and Saunders, O. A., *An Introduction to Heat Transfer*. Oxford University Press, Oxford, England, 1950.
2. Hallström, B., Skjöldebrand, C. and Trägårdh, C., *Heat Transfer and Food Products*. Elsevier Applied Science Publishers, London, 1988.
3. Carslaw, H. S. and Jaeger, J. C., *Conduction of Heat in Solids*, 2nd edn. Oxford, University Press, Oxford, England, 1958.
4. Dalgleish, N. and Ede, A. J., Charts for determining centre surface and mean temperatures in regular geometric solids during heating or cooling. NEL Report No. 192, National Engineering Laboratory, Ministry of Technology, East Kilbride, Glasgow, Scotland, 1965.
5. Smith, R. E., Nelson, G. L. and Henrickson, R. L., *Trans. Amer. Soc. of Agric. Engineers*, **10** (1967) 236.

PSYCHROMETRICS

Psychrometrics is the study of the properties of gas–vapour mixtures. The mixture most commonly encountered in food processing is air–water vapour and this appendix is restricted to that system.

III.1. DEFINITIONS

The 'absolute' (or specific) humidity, H, is the weight of water present in the mixture, per unit weight of dry air. Assuming 'perfect gas' behaviour:

$$H = \frac{M_w p_v}{M_A(P - p_v)} \tag{III.1}$$

where M_w = the molecular weight of water; M_A = the molecular weight of air; P = the total pressure of the system; p_v = the partial pressure of water vapour in the system.

The saturation humidity, H_s, is the absolute humidity of saturated air. In saturated air the water vapour pressure equals the vapour pressure of water at air temperature.

$$H_s = \frac{M_w p_w}{M_A(P - p_w)} \tag{III.2}$$

where p_w = the vapour pressure of water at air temperature.

The percentage absolute humidity, H_p, is the ratio of the absolute humidity of a mixture at a given temperature to the saturation humidity at the same temperature (expressed as a percentage)

$$H_p = 100 \frac{H}{H_s} = 100 \frac{p_v (P - p_w)}{p_w (P - p_v)} \tag{III.3}$$

675

The percentage relative humidity, H_R, is the ratio of the partial pressure of water vapour in a mixture at a given temperature to the vapour pressure of water at that temperature (expressed as a percentage)

$$H_R = 100 \frac{p_v}{p_w} \tag{III.4}$$

The dewpoint (or saturation temperature) is the temperature at which a given air–water vapour mixture becomes saturated, if cooled at constant humidity.

The humid heat, C_H, is the heat necessary to raise the temperature of a mass of mixture containing unit mass of dry air, by unit amount.

$$C_H = C_A + C_v H \tag{III.5}$$

where C_A = the specific heat of dry air; C_v = the specific heat of water vapour.

The humid volume, V_H, is the volume of a mass of mixture containing unit mass of dry air, at one atmosphere pressure and a given temperature. Assuming the perfect gas law applies, in SI units:

$$V_H = \frac{22 \cdot 4}{273} (\theta + 273) \left(\frac{1}{M_A} + \frac{H}{M_w} \right) \tag{III.6}$$

where θ = the temperature of the mixture, °C; when $H = 0$, V_H = the specific volume of dry air; when $H = H_s$, V_H = the specific volume of saturated air.

Adiabatic saturation temperature: If a stream of moist air passes co-currently through water sprays at temperature θ_s, under adiabatic conditions, so that the air leaves the system in equilibrium with the water (saturated) and at temperature θ_s, the temperature θ_s is known as the adiabatic saturation temperature. The line relating the temperature and humidity of the air during the adiabatic cooling is known as the adiabatic cooling (or saturation) line. The equation to this line is

$$H_s - H = \frac{C_H}{L_s} (\theta - \theta_s) \tag{III.7}$$

where L_s = the latent heat of vaporisation of water at θ_s.

The wet-bulb temperature, θ_w, is the steady state (dynamic equilibrium) temperature attained by a small quantity of water evaporating under adiabatic conditions in an air stream. Wet-bulb temperature is measured by means of a temperature-sensing element covered by a wick which is maintained saturated with water. The conditions are such that changes in the properties of the moist air mass passing the wick are negligible. The rate of heat transfer from the air exactly balances the rate of evaporation, therefore:

$$H_w - H = \frac{h_c}{L_w k}(\theta - \theta_w) \tag{III.8}$$

where H_w = the saturation humidity at θ_w; L_w = the latent heat of vaporisation at θ_w; h_c = heat transfer coefficient; k = mass transfer coefficient.

Relationship between wet-bulb and adiabatic saturation temperature: It has been shown experimentally that for air–water vapour mixtures θ_w and θ_s are approximately equal and may be used interchangeably for most engineering calculations.

III.2. THE PSYCHROMETRIC (OR HUMIDITY) CHART

The properties of air–water vapour mixtures may be displayed on a diagram, or chart, such as that shown in Fig. III.1. This chart is for air–water vapour mixtures at one atmosphere pressure.

The use of the humidity chart is illustrated in Fig. III.2. The point 'b' on

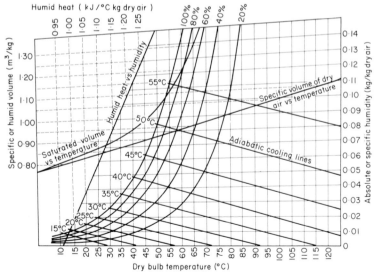

FIG. III.1. Humidity chart.

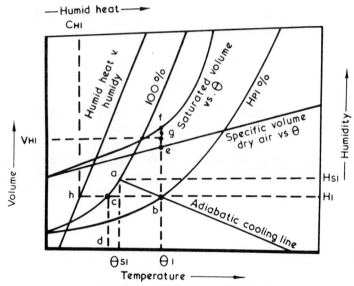

FIG. III.2.   Use of humidity chart.

the chart represents a sample of moist air at a temperature θ_1 and absolute humidity H_1. The percentage absolute humidity of this air, $H_{p1}\%$ is obtained from the curve of constant percentage absolute humidity passing through point 'b'. Interpolation between such lines may be necessary. The abscissa 'd' of point 'c' on the 100% absolute humidity line represents the dewpoint of the air sample. The line a–b represents the locus of points denoting air samples with the same adiabatic saturation temperature. Since the adiabatic saturation temperature of saturated air is equal to the temperature of that air, the abscissa of the point 'a' (where the line a–b cuts the 100% absolute humidity line) indicates the value, θ_{s1}, of the adiabatic saturation temperature for which the line a–b is drawn. The saturation humidity H_{s1} corresponding to this adiabatic saturation temperature is given by the ordinate of the point 'a'. The humid heat and humid volume of the moist air represented by point 'b' can be obtained from auxiliary curves on the chart. The humid heat C_{H1} is the abscissa of the point 'h' on the humid heat v, humidity line having an ordinate H_1. The ordinates of points 'e' and 'f' are the specific volumes of dry and saturated air at θ_1 respectively. The humid volume is the ordinate of the point 'g' which is located so that:[1,2]

$$\frac{eg}{ef} = \frac{H_{p1}}{100}$$

REFERENCES

1. McCabe, W. L., Smith, J. C. and Harriott, P., *Unit Operations of Chemical Engineering*, 4th edn. McGraw-Hill, New York, 1985.
2. Green, D. W. (ed.), *Perry's Chemical Engineer's Handbook*, 6th edn. McGraw-Hill, New York, 1984.

INTERNATIONAL (SI) SYSTEM OF UNITS

This system is based on the following seven *fundamental units:* metre (m); kilogram (kg); second (s); ampere (A); kelvin (K); candela (cd); mole (mol).

In addition the following *derived units* are relevant to this text: newton $(N) = kg\,m\,s^{-2}$; joule $(J) = Nm$; watt $(W) = J\,s^{-1}$.

The following *multiples* and *submultiples* of each unit are also relevant: 10^9, giga (G); 10^6, mega (M); 10^3, kilo (k); 10^2, hecto (h); 10, deca (da); 10^{-1}, deci (d); 10^{-2}, centi (c); 10^{-3}, milli (m); 10^{-6}, micro (μ); 10^{-9}, nano (n).

USEFUL CONVERSION FACTORS

Quantity	Non-SI Unit	Conversion Factor	SI Unit
Length	1 foot (ft)	$= 0{\cdot}304\,8$	m
Mass	1 pound (lb)	$\simeq 0{\cdot}454$	kg
	1 ton (ton)	$\simeq 1{\cdot}02 \times 10^3$	kg
Temperature	1 degree Fahrenheit ($^\circ$F)	$\simeq 0{\cdot}556$	K (or $^\circ$C)
	[492R $\simeq 32^\circ$F	$= 0^\circ$C $\simeq 273$K]	
Volume	1 ft^3	$\simeq 2{\cdot}83 \times 10^{-2}$	m^3
	1 UK gallon (gall)	$\simeq 4{\cdot}46 \times 10^{-3}$	m^3
Specific volume	1 ft^3 lb^{-1}	$\simeq 6{\cdot}24 \times 10^{-2}$	m^3 kg^{-1}
Force	1 pound force (lb force)	$\simeq 4{\cdot}45$	N
Pressure, stress	1 lb force in^{-2} (psi)	$\simeq 6{\cdot}90$	kN m^{-2}
	1 in Hg	$\simeq 3{\cdot}39$	kN m^{-2}
	1 mm Hg ($\simeq 1{\cdot}00$ torr)	$\simeq 0{\cdot}133$	kN m^{-2}
	1 ft H20	$\simeq 2{\cdot}99$	kN m^{-2}
	1 bar (bar)	$= 1 \times 10^2$	kN m^{-2}

(continued)

USEFUL CONVERSION FACTORS—*contd.*

Quantity	Non-SI Unit	Conversion Factor	SI Unit
Dynamic viscosity	$1 \, \mathrm{lb \, ft^{-1} \, s^{-1}}$	$\simeq 1\cdot49$	$\mathrm{kg \, m^{-1} \, s^{-1}}$
	1 poise (P)	$= 0\cdot1$	$\mathrm{kg \, m^{-1} \, s^{-1}}$
Energy	1 British thermal unit (Btu)	$\simeq 1\cdot06$	kJ
	1 kWh	$= 3\cdot6$	MJ
	1 erg (erg)	$= 0\cdot1$	J
Specific energy	$1 \, \mathrm{Btu \, lb^{-1}}$	$\simeq 2\cdot33$	$\mathrm{kJ \, kg^{-1}}$
Specific heat capacity	$1 \, \mathrm{Btu \, lb^{-1} \, {}^\circ F^{-1}}$	$\simeq 4\cdot19$	$\mathrm{kJ \, kg^{-1} \, K^{-1}}$
Thermal conductivity	$1 \, \mathrm{Btu \, h^{-1} \, ft^{-1} \, {}^\circ F^{-1}}$	$\simeq 1\cdot73$	$\mathrm{W \, m^{-1} \, K^{-1}}$
Heat transfer coefficient	$1 \, \mathrm{Btu \, h^{-1} \, ft^{-2} \, {}^\circ F^{-1}}$	$\simeq 5\cdot68$	$\mathrm{W \, m^{-2} \, K^{-1}}$

INDEX